MIDWIFERY AND THE MEDICALIZATION OF CHILDBIRTH: COMPARATIVE PERSPECTIVES

MIDWIFERY AND THE MEDICALIZATION OF CHILDBIRTH: COMPARATIVE PERSPECTIVES

EDWIN R. VAN TEIJLINGEN,
GEORGE W. LOWIS, PETER G. MCCAFFERY,
MAUREEN PORTER
(EDITORS)

Nova Science Publishers, Inc.
Huntington, New York

Editorial Production:	Susan Boriotti
Office Manager:	Annette Hellinger
Graphics:	Frank Grucci, Drew Kane and Jennifer Lucas
Information Editor:	Tatiana Shohov
Book Production:	LaToya Clay, Patrick Davin, Donna Dennis, Cathy DeGregory and Lynette Van Helden
Circulation:	Anna Cruz, Ave Maria Gonzalez, Ron Hedges, Andre Tillman and Evelyn Woodberry

Library of Congress Cataloging-in-Publication Data
Midwifery and the medicalization of childbirth: comparative perspectives / Edwin van Teijlingen ... [et al.] editors.
        p.   cm.
       Includes bibliographical references and index.
       ISBN 1-56072-680-6
       1. Midwifery--Social aspects. 2. Women--Health and hygiene--Sociological aspects. 3. Maternal health services-- Social aspects. I. van Teijlingen, Edwin.
RG950.M5245   1999
618.2--dc21   CIP

Copyright 2000 by Nova Science Publishers, Inc.
     227 Main Street, Suite 100
     Huntington, New York 11743
     Tele. 631-424-6682   Fax 631-424-4666
     e-mail: Novascience@earthlink.net
     e-mail: Novascil@aol.com
     Web Site: http://www.nexusworld.com/nova

Printed in the United States of America

CONTENTS

ACKNOWLEDGEMENTS

We want to thank all the publishers and the authors for their kind permission to reproduce copyright material. All possible care has been taken to trace ownership of the sections included and to make full acknowledgement for their use. We particularly wish to thank those who agreed to write original papers for this volume.

A number of people have assisted us with different aspects of the planning, composing, writing and producing this reader. Our special thanks go to: Teresa McCaffery, Catherine Lowis, Jilly Ireland, Ian McLennan, Sally Macintyre, Anne Ball, Fiona Harris, Vanora Hundley, Cathy Todd, Karen Lucie, Bryce Macgregor, Annette Ross, Julie Bruce, Kathryn Ross, Anna Mackenzie and Rosel Tallach. Furthermore, in the Department of Public Health at the University of Aberdeen: Annie Sergeant and Flora Buthlay for their help (often at very short notice) in producing the typescript and Margaret Beveridge in tracing publishers and copyright holders.

We would also like to thank those subscribers to who replied to our request for maternity/midwifery terms which differ between UK and American English on *ONLINE BIRTH CENTER NEWS*, a publication of the Online Birth Center (available on web address: **http://www.efn.org/~djz/birth/birthindex.html**

Last, but not least, thanks are due to our publishers NOVA Science, for being so patient with us.

ABOUT THE EDITORS

George W. Lowis, Ph.D. (The Pennsylvania State University), is currently an Adjunct Professor of Epidemiology in the Department of Epidemiology and Public Health, School of Medicine, at the University of Miami, Florida. Prior to that he was Project Director of Home Accidents, Pennsylvania Dept. of Health, and most recently, Professor of Sociology at Skidmore College, Saratoga Springs, New York. Books and chapters in books have been published on the epidemiology of multiple sclerosis, aids, and tropical spastic paraparesis (YTLV-I). His publications have also appeared in journals such as International Journal of Epidemiology, Sociological Quarterly, Medical History, Indian Journal of Sociology, and Neuroepidemiology.

Peter G. McCaffery, D.Phil. (Oxon), lectured in the University of Aberdeen's Sociology Department during the 1970s and 1980s, and during the 1990s has contributed to the teaching of Cultural History there. His main interest is in the exercise of professional and expert authority, and in lay attitudes of skepticism toward claims to authoritative knowledge which can be depicted as resting on abstract theory rather than on first-hand experience. His publications have focused on the topic of his doctoral research in the sociology of religion, concerning changes in Catholicism in Britain and the Netherlands during the second half of the twentieth century.

Maureen Porter, Ph.D. (University of Aberdeen), is a medical sociologist who was formerly employed as a research fellow in the Department of Obstetrics and Gynaecology at Aberdeen University, Scotland. She carried out research projects and published papers on women's views of infertility, antenatal care, family planning, abnormal cervical smears and the menopause. She is co-author (with Marion Hall and Sally Mcintyre) of *Antenatal care assessed: a case study of an innovation in Aberdeen*, Aberdeen University Press, 1985. She has also been a breastfeeding counsellor and tutor for the National Childbirth Trust for many years. She is now pursuing other interests but does some teaching in community medicine and breastfeeding counselling.

Edwin R. van Teijlingen, Ph.D. (University of Aberdeen), is a medical sociologist, currently employed as a lecturer in the Department of Public Health, University of Aberdeen, Scotland. Prior to that he worked as a researcher on several evaluation projects whilst employed at the Centre for HIV/AIDS & Drugs Studies, Edinburgh, Scotland. He has published on Dutch maternity care, HIV/AIDS, and health promotion research. In 1994 he completed his Ph.D. thesis *A social or medical model of childbirth? Comparing the arguments in Grampian (Scotland) and the Netherlands*. Furthermore, he has also been joint editor (with Rose Barbour) of the seventh (1994) and eighth edition (1998) of *Medical Sociology in Britain: A Register of Research and Teaching*.

ABBREVIATIONS

ABC	Alternative Birth Center
ACNM	American College of Nurse-Midwives
ACOG	American College of Obstetricians-Gynecologists
AIDS	Acquired Immuno-Deficiency Syndrome
AIMS	Association for the Improvement in the Maternity Services (UK)
AMA	American Medical Association
ANM	Assistant Nurse-Midwife
ARM	Association of Radical Midwives (UK)
BC	British Columbia (Canada)
BMA	British Medical Association
BMJ	British Medical Journal
CHP	Cottage Hospital Plan (Canada)
CNM	Certified Nurse Midwife (USA)
DGH	District General Hospital (Regional UK hospital not an academic teaching center)
DoH	Department of Health (UK)
DMM	District Midwife Manager (UK)
DMPC	District Midwifery Planning Committee (UK)
FIGO	Fédération Internationale de Gynécologie et d'Obstétrique
FTC	Federal Trade Commission (USA)
GP	General practitioner (family doctor UK)
GPO	General Practitioner Obstetrician
HIV	Human Immunodeficiency Virus
HMO	Health Maintenance Organizations (USA)
HMSO	Her Majesty's Stationary Office (UK Government publishing house)
HV	Health visitor (UK)
ICM	International Confederation of Midwives
IFGO	International Federation of Gynecologists & Obstetricians (see also FIGO)
ITU	Intensive Therapy Unit
IVI	Intra-venous infusion
LBW	Low birth weight
LDR	Combined Labor, Delivery, and Recovery rooms (USA)
MANA	Midwives Alliance of North America
MCAP	Midwifery Communication & Accountability Project (USA)
MCH	Maternal Child Health
MCH clinics	Maternal Child Health Clinics (Sweden)
MD	Medical Doctor
MHCA	Maternity Home Care Assistant (the Netherlands)
MIDIRS	Midwives Information & Resource Centre (UK)
MIRIAD	Midwifery Research Database (UK)
MP	Member of Parliament (UK)
NAHAT	National Association of Health Authorities and Trusts
NAPSAC	National Association of Professionals for Safe Alternatives in Childbirth (USA)
NARM	North American Registry of Midwives

NCT	National Childbirth Trust (UK)
n.d.	no date (in publications / references)
NGV	Nederlandse Gynaecologische Vereniging (Dutch Association Gynae./Obstericians)
NHS	National Health Service (UK)
NHSME	National Health Service Management Executive (UK)
N&L	Newfoundland and Labrador (Canada)
OPCS	Office of Population Censuses & Surveys (UK)
PHC	Primary Health Care
PNMR	perinatal mortality rate; the number of stillbirth plus deaths in the first seven days of life per thousand total births
RCM	Royal College of Midwives (UK)
RCOG	Royal College of Obstetricians & Gynaecologists (UK)
RGN	Registered General Nurse (UK)
RMM	Regional Midwife Manager (UK)
SHO	Senior House Officer (junior doctors in the UK)
TBA	Traditional Birth Attendant
TMW or TM	Trained Midwife
UKCC	United Kingdom Central Council (midwifery governing body)
UMM	Unit Midwife Manager (UK)
VBAC	Vaginal Birth after Cesarean (USA)
VMW	Village Midwife (in Papua New Guinea)
WHO	World Health Organization
WICP	Women's Institute for Childbearing Policy (USA)

TERMS USED:
"YOU SAY TOMATO, I SAY TOMATO"

In the field of maternity care and midwifery there are a number of occasions where the UK English term differs from the North American English term. Since this book is aimed at an international readership we have listed the most common of these terms as used in this volume. We have omitted the obvious spelling variations, such as, for example, 'labour' and 'labor' or 'Caesarean section' and 'Cesarean section', from of this list. We have also excluded those terms, which are used interchangeably at both sides of the Atlantic, such as 'to nurse a baby' instead of 'to breastfeed'; or terms which relate to specific occupations which have no direct equivalent, hence no precise translation is possible. Example of the latter are: auxiliary nurse (UK); labor and delivery nurse (USA) and maternity nurse (USA).

UK English	North American Expression
Antenatal or prenatal care	Antepartum or prepartum or prenatal care
Postnatal care	Postpartum care
Labour and delivery (Intrapartum care)	Intrapartum care
Domino Delivery	Short-stay hospital birth
Nappy	Diapers
Dummy	Pacifier

General Introduction to Midwifery and the Medicalization of Childbirth: Comparative Perspectives

Edwin van Teijlingen, George Lowis, Peter McCaffery, Maureen Porter

Introduction

This book provides an introduction to the sociological study of midwifery. The readings have been selected to highlight the interplay between midwifery and medicine, reflecting the medicalization of childbirth. It highlights the major themes in both a historical and a current context, as well as western and non-western societies. This reader is intended for any student who wants to become acquainted with the sociological study of midwifery. It offers social science students an insight into the sociology, organization, politics and history of midwifery and maternity care, whilst it offers students of midwifery, medicine and professions allied to medicine a sociological perspective on their own area of study and practice.

Two major themes underlie the organization of this book: that the conception of midwifery must be broadened to encompass a sociological perspective; and that the ongoing trend toward the medicalization of midwifery is crucial to an understanding of the historical, current, and future status of midwifery. By medicalization of childbirth and midwifery is meant[1] the increasing tendency for women to prefer a hospital delivery to a home delivery, the increasing trend toward the use of technology and clinical intervention in childbirth, and the determination of medical practitioners to confine the role played by midwives in pregnancy and childbirth, if any, to a purely subordinate one.

Toward a Sociology of Midwifery

In many countries, the profession of midwifery is currently in a state of flux. The most obvious manifestations of this are changing work-practices and revised training programs; but these things are merely symptomatic of fundamental changes in the profession. The underlying issue they raise is the question of what it means to be a midwife. In other words, the profession's collective sense of its members' shared identity is at stake. "The midwife challenge", as Kitzinger (1979) calls it, has far reaching implications. It affects the way midwives relate to their clients, to the medical profession, to those who administer health services, and to those who pass the laws which govern professional practice in the sphere of maternity care.

To simplify, one might say that two contrasting views of a midwife's status are in conflict. On one view, childbirth is dangerous, doctors know best how to assess and manage the risks involved, and therefore midwives are essentially doctors' assistants. On the other view, the birth of a child is the start of a lifelong relationship between that child and its mother; what is normally of chief importance, unless a medical emergency arises, is that the experience should enable the woman to feel at a deep emotional level that she herself has delivered this child. A midwife is an expert who comes equipped to provide both the practical help and the emotional support that a woman needs at this important time—preferably on the basis of a bond of empathy already built up over a series of encounters for ante-natal care.

One purpose of this book, reflected in the selection of readings, is to show how a focus on the sociological perspective may illustrate the contrasting views of a midwife's role mentioned above. On the one hand, our conception of midwifery must be broadened to encompass the explanatory power of sociology, whilst on the other hand, we must use the insight which can be gained into issues relating to midwifery by using a sociological approach, in the sense of: (a) adopting the widest possible historical and comparative framework; (b) giving salience to themes such as the division of labor and the impact of gender relationships on occupational status; (c) attending to the ways in which people define situations and engage in a social construction of reality; and (d) looking at some of the more significant sociological concepts that have particular utility in understanding social aspects of midwifery including culture and subculture, group, institution, status and role, power and authority, and social control.

Both the status of midwife and the childbirth process are related to the structure of society. The social organization of different societies accounts to a significant degree for the sheer diversity of human practices at the time of childbirth and their responsiveness to historically changing influences. It affects the work midwives do and how they interact with clients and doctors; and it sheds light on the politics of midwifery and maternal care who, for example, will dominate in the ongoing struggle for control over childbirth the doctor or the midwife; the state or the individual?

MEDICALIZATION OF CHILDBIRTH AND MIDWIFERY

A second theme is that there is a long-term worldwide evolutionary trend towards the medicalization of both childbirth and midwifery, and this collection of readings is geared towards critically examining this theme. One consequence of this trend in the United States is that midwives have almost been eliminated as viable childbirth competitors with medical doctors (Wertz & Wertz, 1977, 1990). The community midwife, for example, had virtually disappeared by the 1930's (DeVries, 1982; Litoff, 1978) only to reappear in a new form in the early 1980's (Declercq, 1992). In most western industrialized countries, on the other hand, midwifery continues to be practiced, although the general attitude toward pregnancy and childbirth has been medicalized. Every pregnancy is considered to be at risk unless proven normal, an attitude which justifies the use of medical technology and intervention (Robinson, 1985; Wagner, 1986; Walker, 1976; WHO, 1985).

Not all writers, however, agree with the thesis that we are still witnessing a "long-term trend towards medicalization". Some argue, instead, that a process of cultural demedicalization appears to be currently taking place in the industrialized societies of North America and Western Europe whereby shifts in emphasis are occurring from illness to health, from therapeutic to preventative medicine, from the dominance and autonomy of the doctor in the birthing experience to patients' rights (Fox, 1990), and from the relatively submissive role played by the midwife to one of renewed importance. Anisef and Basson (1979), for example, contend that the long-term prospects at least for Britain and the US are favourable for promoting norms which view the midwife as economical, efficient, and necessary in cases of normal labor. More recently, Twaddle and Young (1999: 132) conclude that total care by midwives in the UK was equally safe and as efficacious as care shared between midwives and doctors and that midwifery care was preferred by women. Whilst Fox (1990) contends that a substantial demedicalization has already occurred in American society especially as regards doctor/patient relationships. The midwife is especially making a comeback in the United States a process begun during the 1960s, such resurgence occurring on two levels. Traditional or 'lay' midwifery is gaining in popular appeal, while the certified nurse-midwife is slowly gaining medical recognition and acceptance (DeVries, 1982: 82) witness the small rise in home births in several regions during this period (see DeVries, 1996; Reid, 1989). The renaissance of midwifery has called into question some important reproductive values and encouraged a revival of traditional birth patterns including home births, challenging the cultural understanding of normal birth as a medical event, denying the necessity of physicians as primary attendants at normal births, and providing the mother with greater social and emotional support during labor and birth (Peterson, 1983). Partly responsible for this renaissance is the rise of massive social movements such as those in feminism, consumer health, ecology and civil rights (see DeVries, 1993, 1996; Reid 1989; Romalis, 1981: 63-91). Moreover, with the increasing influence of administrators and politicians who are concerned to see a reduction in health expenditures associated with childbirth, an alliance can be expected to grow up between the profession of midwifery, medicine and health economics.

In African countries such as Zimbabwe (Sparks, 1990) and Liberia (Etzel, 1976; 1977), and in Asian countries such as Malaysia (Laderman, 1983) and India (Jeffery *et al.* 1989), a dual system of health care exists. One system is represented by the formally trained doctors and nurses who practice in clinics and hospitals. The other system, represented by traditional health practices and beliefs and encompassing both traditional healers and birth attendants is more prevalent, for the present at least, although the number of midwives being trained according to the western model is increasing, as is the incidence of hospital births. This is further support for our contention that the medicalization of childbirth is occurring as a world-wide trend.

It appears inevitable, however, that, in all these countries traditional midwives will eventually be phased out, either through incorporation of traditional midwives in a health care system based on a western model or as such midwives are replaced by government-trained midwives according to the western model. This is presently occurring in Malaysia where the replacement technique is one where legislation has required additional midwives to be hired and trained according to modern medical techniques and procedures (Laderman, 1983). Government midwives are instructed in general anatomy and physiology, in the normal management of labor and the puerperium, and in the recognition of symptoms deviating from the normal. A two-year training period is required, eighteen months of which are spent in the hospital attending a minimum of 30 women in labor and witnessing more than twenty deliveries. Consequently, in many parts of the country where government midwives have been available for decades traditional midwives have been stripped of their obstetric role and are no longer performing deliveries; their duties are limited to laundry, cleaning and bathing the baby, massaging and otherwise comforting the mother (Laderman, 1983: 104-6).

REFERENCES

Anisef, P. & Basson, P. (1979), 'The institutionalization of a profession,' *Sociology of Work and Occupations* **6** (30): August, 353-372.

Declercq, E. R. (1992), The transformation of American midwifery, 1975-1988,' *American Journal of Public Health* **82** (5): May, 680-684.

DeVries, R. G. (1982), 'Midwifery and the problem of licensure,' *Research in the Sociology of Health Care* **2**: 77-120.

DeVries, R. G. (1996), *Making Midwives Legal*, Ohio State University Press

DeVries, R. G. (1993), 'A cross national view of the status of midwives,' 131-146 in *Gender, Work and Medicine: Women and the Medical Division of Labor*, Riska, E. & Wegar, K. (Eds), Newbury Park, California, Sage Publications.

Etzel, R. A. (1976), 'The birth and development of midwifery, Liberian obstetrics,' Part 1 *Journal of Nurse Midwifery*, **21** (4): Winter, 24-37.

Etzel, R. A., (1977) 'The birth and development of midwifery, Liberian obstetrics,' Part 2 *Journal of Nurse Midwifery*, **22** (1): Spring, 18-30.

Fox, R. C. (1990), 'The medicalization and demedicalization of American society,' 409-413 in *The Sociology of Health & Illness*, Conrad, P. & Kern, R. (Eds), New York: St. Martin's Press, (3rd Edn.).

Freidson, E. (1970), *Profession of Medicine*. New York: Dodd, Mead Co.

Freidson, E. (1990) 'The centrality of professionalism to health care', *Jurimetrics Journal*, **30**: 431-45.

Jeffery, P., Jeffery, R. and Lyon, A. (1989), *Labour Pains and Labour Power: Women and Childbearing in India*. London: Zed Books.

Kitzinger, S. (1979), *Birth at Home*. New York: Oxford University Press.

Laderman, C. (1983), *Wives and Midwives: Childbirth and Nutrition in Rural Malaysia*. Berkeley: University of California Press.

Litoff, J. B. (1978), *American Midwives-1860 to the Present*. Westport, Connecticut: Greenwood Press.

Peterson, K. J. (1983), 'Technology as a last resort in home birth: The work of lay midwives,' *Social Problems*, **30** (3): 272-283.

Reid, M. (1989), 'Sisterhood and professionalization: A case study of the American lay midwife,' 219-238 in *Women as Healers: Cross Cultural Perspectives*. McClain, C. S (Ed.), New Brunswick, New Jersey: Rutgers University Press.

Robinson, S. (1985), 'Midwives, obstetricians and general practitioners: The need for role clarification' *Midwifery*, **1**: 102-113.

Romalis, S. (Ed.) (1981), *Childbirth: Alternatives to Medical Control*. Austin, Texas: University of Texas Press.

Sparks, B. (1990), 'A descriptive study of changing roles and practices of traditional birth attendants in Zimbabwe,' *Journal of Nurse Midwifery*, **35** (3) May-June, 150-161.

Twaddle, S. and Young, D.S. (1999), 'The economics of maternity care, ' 119-136, in *Community-based Maternity Care*, Marsh, G. & Renfrew, M. (eds.), Oxford: Oxford University Press

Wagner, M. G. (1986), 'Birth and Power,' in *Perinatal Health Services in Europe—Searching for Better Childbirth*. Phaff, J. M. L. (Ed), WHO Regional Office for Europe.

Walker, J. F. (1976), 'Midwife or obstetric nurse? Some perceptions of midwives and obstetricians of the role of the midwife,' *Journal of Advanced Nursing*. **1**: 129-138.

Wertz, R and Wertz, D. (1977), *Lying In: A History of Childbirth in America*. New York: Free Press.

Wertz, R. and Wertz D. (1990), 'Notes on the decline of midwives and the rise of medical obstetricians,' 148-60 in *The Sociology of Health & Illness*, Conrad, P. & Kern, R. (Eds), New York St Martin's Press, (3rd Edn.).

WHO (1985), *Having a Baby in Europe—Report on a Study* (Public Health in Europe series no. 26), Copenhagen.

Zola, I. (1972),'Medicine as an Instrument of Social Control,' *Sociological Review*, **20**: 487-504.

---

[1] A much broader formulation of the medicalization concept is offered by Eliot Freidson (1970; 1990) and Irving Zola (1972) who view the medicalization of society in terms of the ability of medicine to become a major institution of social control. This, they suggest, has already been accomplished by medicalizing much of the daily living such as making medicine and the labels "healthy" and "ill" relevant to an ever increasing part of human existence (Zola, 1972: 487); and by the ability of the medical profession to extend their jurisdiction "over the label of illness and anything to which it may be attached, irrespective of its capacity to deal with it effectively" (Freidson, 1970: 251).

SOCIOLOGICAL FACTORS AFFECTING THE MEDICALIZATION OF MIDWIFERY

George W. Lowis & Peter G. McCaffery

INTRODUCTION

In an elaboration of the two organizing themes of the book, we discuss and evaluate a particular conceptual perspective in midwifery: (1) that the conception of midwifery must be broadened to encompass the explanatory power of sociology; and (2) that the midwife's status can best be understood when an examination of the medicalization process of this occupation is undertaken.

This chapter is divided into six subsections which give an indication of its focus: (1) comparative method; (2) socio-cultural context of birth and midwifery; (3) assessing the competence of non-western practitioners; (4) midwifery and sociological analysis; (5) brief socio-historical overview of the medicalization of midwifery in Britain, United States, and the Netherlands; and (6) the process and consequences of the medicalization of midwifery.

PART ONE: TOWARD A SOCIOLOGY OF MIDWIFERY

Nature of the Comparative Method

In order to acquire a more objective, less ethnocentric [1] view of birthing practices, and the role played by its principal participants, it is advantageous to adopt a comparative perspective (inclusive of historical and cross-cultural dimensions). The management of reproduction in modern industrialized societies presents a strong contrast to that of traditional, developing societies. The modern medical system tends to treat childbirth as a formal, depersonalized event dominated by a technological orientation which is concerned with gaining control over natural processes, eliminating pain and reducing mortality (Kitzinger, 1982: 181). A biomedical model of birth persists, where this event is viewed as a potentially dangerous medical condition [2] which can be managed only by hospitalization and by the appliance of science and technology (McClain, 1982; Jordan, 1987a; Davis-Floyd, 1987; 1992; Butter, 1993), and the "authoritarian benevolence of professionalized medicine" (Oakley, 1976: 18).

Advantages of the Comparative Method

A true comparative sociology must see our own culture of childbirth in historical and cross cultural terms, and this can occur only if we have sufficient knowledge of a different birthing system, namely the traditional system (Oakley, 1977; Stanton, 1977; Kitzinger, 1982; Jordan, 1978). The traditional system tends to be family and community centered (Jordan, 1978; 1987a) with the midwife and woman's kinfolk providing strong emotional and physical support (Scheepers, 1991: 961; Recio, 1986: 66; Peng, 1979: 108), while still allowing the woman to remain relatively speaking in control of her labor. Birth is seen, consequently, not only as a biological process but also as a social, emotional and spiritual one [3] (Cosminsky, 1986: 84). On the other hand, childbirth in Western Society tends to be viewed as a clinical phenomenon, governed by biological laws, and virtually unaffected by social processes and events (Illsley, 1967). Also, contrary to the modern medical system which views childbirth as a sickness or illness [4] this system sees it as a function of health and societal rituals [5]. Ceremonies typically celebrate the successful birth and status arrival of the new member of society and congratulate the newly designated parental statuses (Oakley, 1977).

In addition to reducing bias and creating a broader conceptual perspective on childbirth, the comparative method is also capable of providing insight on the gender-based difference in the structure of control. Whereas in traditional society, control is ultimately vested in the lay woman, control in industrialized society is tied principally to the male professional who has ultimate control over her parturition (Oakley, 1976: 20-1). Contraception, abortion and birth are subject matter which are part of a male dominated medical technology. Even when hospitalization for childbirth occurs (which in modern society is almost always), and even though the majority of hospital medical personnel tend to be females, the pregnant woman enters a structure of control where male authority reigns supreme (Oakley, 1976: 18). A cross-cultural view of the role played by women universally, in their wider domestic role, would reveal them as caretakers of health and life, responsible for the application of home remedies, and assessing the need for expert advice or self care during pregnancy and childbirth. They remain invisible, however, in the medical model, and are rarely acknowledged or incorporated in plans to promote health and improve health services (Pearson, 1987: 117; Jordan, 1987a).

Adoption of the comparative method also has potential scientific value. In many parts of the underdeveloped world, where high infant mortality exists, modern medical personnel have introduced health care and midwifery training programs in an attempt to change existing childbirth practices. Often, this has been done without concern for understanding the cultural rationale of the existing practices, and without knowledge of their possible relationship to other institutional aspects of culture such as economic, religious, and familial values and beliefs (Cosminsky, 1982a: 233; 1986: 84; Jordan, 1987a). Such ignorance of indigenous culture has often resulted in health care and training programs which are not as effective as they otherwise might be (Cosminsky, 1982a: 233), and probably have little effect on infant mortality. Often, also, when pressure is exerted on the local population to adopt hospitalization procedures—which run counter to their deeply help cultural belief system about privacy, modesty and diet—failure to cooperate with adopting such procedures will occur (McCormack, 1982a; Cosminsky, 1978: 116-26; Recio, 1986: 66). Jordan (1978), in her Yucatan study, found that Mayan women would go to the hospital only as a last resort—resisting certain known consequences such as separation from midwife and family—because such hospitalization violated traditional norms relating to the management of childbirth (Jordan, 1987a: 312).

One additional illustration is in order. In a particular program designed to train young female assistant nurse-midwives (ANM) to provide maternal and health care in rural areas in Nepal, officials ignored relevant cultural information regarding traditional expectations about Nepalese women; specifically that it was socially unacceptable for girls and women to travel and live alone as ANM were expected to do. Consequently, most ANM never reached the remote rural areas to which they had been assigned, and those who had, rarely remained long—thus impairing the program's effectiveness (Justice, 1984: 193-4).

Sociocultural Context of Birth and Midwifery

One consequence of the rise of the women's movement in the late 1960's was to impart fresh vigor to the conduct of research on cross-cultural diversity in childbirth and midwifery practices. With a few notable exceptions, such as Margaret Mead, the early fieldworkers in anthropology were men. Mead's classic writings such as *Coming of Age in Samoa* (Mead 1928) and *Growing up in New Guinea* (Mead 1930), while not entirely neglecting the subject, tell us very little about the midwife's role in these societies. True, in one of his best know studies, the French anthropologist Claude Lévi-Strauss (1963) analyzed the words of a shaman's incantation used to assist a woman experiencing a difficult birth—but what mainly interested him was the symbolism of this Cuna text from Panama. Not until 1967, in collaboration with Niles Newton, did Mead produce a thorough survey of the available ethnographic evidence on pre-industrial people's childbirth customs found in different places (Mead & Newton, 1967). In the discussion that follows, emphasis is on the variable nature of childbirth and midwifery and their socio-cultural bases.

Childbirth and Midwifery as a Cultural Process

Culture refers, in a general sense, to the way of life of a people or society. People carry on their ways of life within social contexts, not within social vacuums. And when they are behaving according to their ways, they develop preferences, notions of expected behavior, beliefs, knowledge and symbols (that is, patterned behavior). In the sociological perspective people are viewed as social beings who have learned to function according to the patterned behavior in their particular groups and society.

All known human societies pattern the behavior of human beings in the process of reproduction. No society permits the individual to act subjectively, without cultural influence and restraint; there is always a system of patterned beliefs, values and norms, which inform, instruct, and coerce. Cultural patterning regulates such major issues as nutrition in pregnancy, type of help given to childbearing women from conception to delivery, whether birth is a private affair inaccessible to anyone but the woman and a helper, or what particular methods are used to cut the umbilical cord and what is done with the placenta (Newton, 1967: 147). Childbirth specifically may be seen as a cultural system for which every society provides a means of management, including a system of beliefs and practices concerning pregnancy, labor and delivery (Cosminsky, 1986: 75); in short childbirth is a "cultural artifact" (Kitzinger 1989: 99).

Just as childbirth is a cultural system for which every society provides a means of management, so too is midwifery, which is also subjected to social constrains and norms. Midwives are smaller groups (subgroups) within a society who have developed different patterns or ways of behaving that differentiates them from the larger society. Subculture is the term sociologists use to describe these distinctive preferences, beliefs and behaviors which characterize subgroups such as social classes, occupations and ethnic groups. The system of midwifery that develops in a given society may be viewed as a subculture system in that the values, beliefs and practices that characterize the system are common to and shared by the midwives practicing within that subculture. Although midwifery techniques and practices tend to vary from one type of midwife to another (such as from traditional birth attendant to lay midwife to nurse-midwife) they tend not to vary from individual midwife to midwife within each of these types of midwife [6]. Sargent (1982), in her study of factors influencing women's choices of obstetrical care in a community in Benin, West Africa, found that Bariba midwives shared a common set of beliefs and practices [7] in such important matters as diagnosing intrauterine death, accelerating a delivery as in causing the fetus to be expelled, and treatment for a retained placenta.

Childbirth and Midwifery as a Social Process

Earlier our discussion of culture focused on people as being socio-cultural beings who have learned to function according to the expectations held in particular groups. Accordingly, a group may be viewed as a collection of people engaged in social interaction or relations. These relations occur within a social context in that they are reciprocally based and regulated by rules and procedures which define the expected behavior of participants. The social context of childbirth and midwifery will be explored briefly in the next three topics.

Who May be Present at Birth?

In most traditional societies there are rules about who may attend the birth; members of the community other than midwives or female relatives and friends are commonly excluded (Newton, 1967; Ford, 1945). While unattended birth does occur in a few societies [8], by far the most usual pattern is for the woman to have two or more attendants for labor and delivery (Mead & Newton, 1967: 193-5; Stanton, 1979: 26; Macintyre, 1977: 18), and for an elderly woman to be the principal attendant at a normal labor (Ford, 1945). In industrialized societies, however, the situation is almost the opposite where skilled men attend the delivery and relatives and friends may even be excluded.

Occasionally, the father may attend the birth, although in traditional societies this is the exception and not the rule (Macintyre, 1977: 18; Oakley 1977: 23). This pattern also persists in some industrialized societies, although this custom is rapidly changing especially as a result of the successful introduction of what has come to be known as "family centered maternity care." (Stanton, 1979: 26-7). For example, an official UK report recommended that a hospital delivery unit should: "enable refreshments to be available for the woman and her partner or companions" (House of Commons Health Committee 1992: lxix).

Degree of Privacy Accorded the Woman in Labor

In all societies the private versus public approach to childbirth is one of cultural choice. Childbirth, in industrialized societies, is typically private. It is a formal process appropriate only for medical personnel and close relatives. In non-industrialized societies, however, there is variability in the amount of secrecy surrounding parturition. On one end of the privacy continuum, childbirth is regarded as a social event openly accepted by the community. Among the Jarara of South America (Stanton, 1979: 26) and the American Navajo (Lockett, 1939; Stanton 1979: 26) the woman gives birth in full view of members of the community. On the other end of the continuum, the Cuna of Panama surround birth with complete secrecy keeping their young in complete ignorance of this event, as well as the sex act, until the marriage ceremony. In between we find the Ebrie of Africa who carry out the birthing process in relative privacy. The woman goes to the home of her mother to give birth and only maternal relatives and the midwife are permitted to join her (Stanton, 1979: 26).

Social Construction of Birth

One theoretical perspective in sociology views all reality and knowledge as being socially constructed, and that the behavior and relationships of people as dependent on, and influenced by, their interpretation or construction of reality (e.g. Jones 1994: 77-9; Nettleton 1995: 14-35).

As applied to childbirth, this perspective views the biological event differently from that of obstetricians. It does not focus on the physiological process but on the interpretations that people have of this event—how it is experienced, defined and explained by all participants—inclusive of the pregnant woman or the woman in childbirth, birth attendant, community and relevant others. "Birth is everywhere socially marked and shaped" (Jordan 1993: 1). This perspective emphasizes the ways in which the birth experience is socially constructed or defined by all participants from the acknowledgement of pregnancy and labor to the birth and care of the newborn. Thus in the "processes and events of pregnancy and labor we witness the shaping of nature to social purposes" (Kitzinger 1989: 99).

In regard to the current situation in industrialized society, where most births are occurring in the hospital, this perspective emphasized that prior to hospitalization it is the birthing woman who defines what is happening and what it means, whereas upon hospitalization it is the hospital that structures the birthing experience inasmuch as it defines for the women what is happening and what it means (Rothman 1977; 1983). A clarification of the importance of this perspective was noted by Rothman (1983), who, in a study of nurse midwives in New York City, found that those who had begun to do home births, as opposed to hospital births, reconceptualized the previously defined "medical stages" involved in labor and came to the conclusion that the medical model was inappropriate; namely that the medically managed hospital setting structures the birth process in social and ideological terms that are often unrelated to the process itself.

Another factor, relevant to this perspective, and based on technological considerations, must also be considered. As the degree of technological sophistication in childbirth increases, the mother's familiarity with the material culture objects affecting her experience of birth diminishes, as does her control over the birthing process. In traditional societies—where low technology birth prevails—women typically go through labor and give birth in upright or semi-upright positions. Oxygenation is better, and contractions tend to be shorter and more efficient. Most important, the woman is free to move and change her position according to the pain and difficulties encountered during labor, such as changes in fetal heart rate. Consequently, she will experience shorter and less painful labor. The hospital delivery table in industrial societies, on the other hand, discourages such physiologically beneficial adjustments (Jordan, 1987a: 314-25), and restricts and predetermines movement.

Material culture objects also affect the nature of communication and social interaction between the woman and her birth attendants and significant others around the time of the birth. In traditional societies, childbirth involves an active reciprocal physical and social interaction between the woman and her attendant helpers. Advice about positions and movements of the body is constantly being offered with appropriate use of ropes, chairs, stools, hammocks and beanbags. Physical support is extended as is emotional comfort as the occasion arises. In some high technology societies the woman in childbirth remains a passive physical and social participant. In the USA, she may be placed on a hospital delivery table with her legs and arms rendered immobile by respectively stirrups and wrist straps. Little or no interaction, except physical, occurs with the medical staff assuming absolute control over the woman's body and absolute monopoly over the social dialogue—which is usually instructional and one sided—and which may or may not occur (Jordan, 1987a: 315-6). Some of these practices are being challenged in this reader, see, for example, 'The midwife in Contemporary Industrialized Society'.

Universality and Variation in the Birthing Experience

There are cultural rules and regulations governing pregnancy and birth in traditional and industrialized societies centered around such matters as where the birth will occur, which birth positions are preferred or acceptable for the woman to use, and what the attitudes are toward use of interventionist procedures during and before labor. All societies have adopted rules and regulations associated with these cultural universals. However, how they have been defined and used varies enormously. Societies differ, for example, in the extent to which they: will speed up or intervene in the labor process; choose a particular location to have childbirth occur; isolate or prohibit the woman from engaging in certain activities during her pregnancy; or even whether a positive or negative value is attached on the preferred position for the woman during delivery (Oakley, 1977: 21; Romalis, 1981: 910; Ford, 1945: 45-50). These attitudinal and behavioral preferences can be explained only in the context of the particular society's cultural system of beliefs, values, and ideology about the human and natural worlds (Oakley, 1977: 31; Romalis, 1981: 6), and by the supply of available skills and technological resources in the society (Oakley, 1977: 28).

Birthing Position

That women who are giving birth must adopt a particular position for delivery is a universal biological requirement. Which position is adopted as the preferred position, however, is variable. In the majority of non-industrialized societies an upright (vertical) position is preferred [9] (Ford, 1945: 58; Oakley, 1977: 26-27; Arms, 1975: 84; Barns, 1980: McCormack, 1982: Galba-Arauja, 1980; Stanton, 1979: 27; Englemann, 1884) with the kneeling position, and sitting, squatting, and standing positions represented in that order of frequency (Newton, 1967: 210). The kneeling position was favored by the ancient Romans and Arabs and is currently the favored position of several African tribes. Sitting reclining against something or someone or simply sitting upon stumps of trees, stones, or the ground is a favorite position among many tribal groups in South America, Africa and Australia (Barns, 1980; McCormack, 1982b; 1986; Galba-Arauja, 1980).

Up until recently, most hospitals in industrialized societies require that the birthing mother during labor and delivery take up the lithotomy position—the medical term for the lying supine. In this position the woman must lie flat on her back, with her legs spread far apart and sometimes even strapped onto metal stirrups of the delivery table (Arms, 1975: 84). The reclining position has apparently been adopted since it facilitates antiseptic treatment (Oakley 1977: 26-7), and permits the desired optimum control of obstetricians over the movements of women (Arms, 1975: 84). However, gradual changes have taken place over the past decades, for example, the 1992 Parliamentary report on UK maternity services recommended that "all hospitals make it their policy to make full provision whenever possible for women to choose the prositon which they prefer for labour and birth." (House of Commons Health Committee 1992: lxix).

Location of Birth

In most societies cultural meanings are conferred upon where the birth may occur. In traditional societies most deliveries occur in the couple's own home or those of their parents. Occasionally, however, provision is made for the birth to occur in a special shelter set aside for this purpose such as a special room in the house or a menstrual hut outside the home—or simply in a secluded place or bush (Oakley, 1977: 25). In industrialized societies, prior to the early twentieth century, it was rare for a "respectable woman" to have her baby in a hospital. Currently, however, most births occur in hospital (Oakley, 1977: 25-6; Macintyre, 1977: 18; also Van Teijlingen in this volume pages 43-51).

Intervention

Although the act of giving birth is a physiological act, its performance is defined by and enacted within a cultural context—which tends to be variable. Mead and Newton (1967), in their review of the literature on preliterate societies, noted that some have a passive attitude toward labor, allowing it to take its own course, while others take the view that as soon as labor has begun everything must be done to deliver the babies as quickly as possible (Oakley, 1977: 28).

A variable attitude has also been recorded historically for the more industrialized, economically complex societies. Shorter presents evidence that before the eighteenth century Europe a tradition of interference in normal labor existed in both academic medicine and popular midwifery (Shorter, 1985: 371-3). In the mid-eighteenth century, however, a revolution occurred whereby a policy of non-intervention began in which the best wisdom insisted that normal labor be left strictly alone and that nature should be permitted to take its course. This policy applied to all three major stages of labor inclusive of the vaginal examination, and expulsion and delivery of the child (Shorter, 1985: 371-8). According to Shorter (1985: 383) the 1920s saw a second revolution begin, equally massive, in the conduct of normal labor—which, from this period to the present, represents a substantial intervention—the guiding principle being one of protection of the fetus and not the mother.

Shorter's conceptual framework, however, cannot be applied unqualifiedly to the American experience. Childbirth in nineteenth century America was strongly marked by middle and upper class Victorian women's concern for avoidance of, or relief from pain. This was in fact, a prominent feature of medicine during this period. In describing childbirth in the American south during this period, McMillen (1990) states that doctors employed heroic therapies, botanic medicines, or water cures—usually without success since morbidity and mortality resulted—to prove themselves indispensable in the birthing room. Physician response was to apply the new anesthetics, chloroform and ether, to the relief of pain in delivery beginning in the 1840's (Wertz & Wertz, 1989: 109-16). Among blacks, immigrants, and lower class women, however, the perspective of non-intervention or "let nature take its course" prevailed (Litoff, 1978; McMillen, 1990).

Intervention in Traditional Societies

Patterns in traditional societies regarding the management of normal labor range from minimal efforts to speed labor to vigorous attempts to assist the labor. Some of the means used by different groups to stimulate and ease childbirth (Newton 1967; Stanton, 1979) are vaginal lubrication (Fang of Africa); vaginal distension during pregnancy in preparation for delivery; abdominal manipulation or massage (Malaysia and New Guinea); breast stimulation and/or sexual intercourse (Siriono of Bolivia); use of herbs (Ebrie of Africa); use of bracing devices for pushing and pulling such as specifically designed birthing chairs or stools; use of poles or stakes (Wallace & Hoebel, 1952) and ropes used for grasping during delivery. Groups who have used the latter technique are found in Asia (Gorer, 1938), North Africa (Blanguernon 1955); North America (Beals, 1946) and South America (Holmberg, 1950; Hilger, 1957). What is done with the umbilical cord is also a variable matter. In most societies it is the mother or birth attendant who cuts the cord with an implement (Stanton, 1979: 28). In Yucatan, Mexico, the cord is severed with a freshly cut bamboo sliver or other sharp implement (Jordan, 1987b: 39) whereas in Marquesan society the mother bites and separates it with her fingernails (Linton, 1939).

Traditional societies have also developed techniques and procedures to cope with circumstances of difficult labor. These include use of oxytocic drugs (Van Patten, 1932; Beals, 1946; Newton, 1967), and medications such as herbs and powdered bark to speed labor and cause contractions so that the fetus could be expelled (Newton, 1967: 218-9); gagging the woman to cause spasmodic convulsions and force out the fetus (Stanton, 1979: 27); cesarean sections (Wright, 1921; Newton, 1967); and operations to enlarge the birth passages (Newton, 1967) such as deliberate stretching of the vagina or tearing of the perineum, even up to the anus, as sometimes occurs with the Khoi ("Hottentots") of Southern Africa (Stanton, 1979: 27). In circumstances where the placenta is not expelled spontaneously, delivery is facilitated among the Ebrie tribe of Africa who manually remove the placenta, among the Jordanians who induce sneezing and coughing by having the woman blow into a bottle or use snuff (Stanton, 1979: 27), and among the Apache who apply strong pressure on the abdomen (Newton 1967: 218-9)

Intervention in Industrialized Societies

Current patterns of obstetrical management in industrial societies tend to reflect certain beliefs, most of which interestingly have already been recorded in the ethnographic literature (Oakley, 1977: 28; 1993). Two such beliefs are discussed below.

(1) *The widespread use of labor speeding devices and procedures to shorten the labor.* During the first stage of labor, labor is often stimulated with the administration of oxytocin and or surgical rupture of the membranes. In the second stage, conscious women are urged to push hard and bear down so that maximum

force is exerted during contractions. Also routinely used in some hospitals for speeding up labor are forceps and episiotomies. In the final stage, injections of syntometrine and controlled cord traction are frequent practices; or the rapid delivery of the placenta is often accomplished by manipulation of the fundus, with the cord being cut immediately after the birth of the baby and before expulsion of the placenta (Newton, 1967: 221-2; Stanton, 1979: 25-6; Oakley, 1977: 28).

(2) *Delivery is conceived of as a surgical procedure.* The supine position of the woman illustrates this. As is customary on operating tables, the woman's body is flat and her head is without a pillow. Her arms are hold sideways and her legs spread wide apart allow the physician an unobstructed view of the perineum (Newton, 1967: 210-1). The wearing of masks in delivery wards adds to the image of a sterile surgical procedure (Kitzinger 1989: 107). In addition, routine fetal monitoring conveys to women that their bodies are defective machines dependent on high-technology medicine (Davis-Floyd 1992: 104-11).

Summary: Intervention as an Almost Universal Feature of the most Diverse Societies

Even though a variable viewpoint toward cultural intervention characterizes the birth process in both traditional and modern societies, by far the most common approach adopted by groups in these societies has been that of active intervention in all stages of labor. They have apparently concluded that biologically natural childbirth does not for all practical purposes exist but that nevertheless there is a desire for an easy labor to occur, and that birth it too important and dangerous an event to be left to the whims of nature (Stanton, 1979: 26-7; Macintyre, 1977: 17; Arms, 1975; Haire, 1972; Illich, 1975). Fear and pain are also factors, which must be incorporated into this interventionist equation. In traditional societies the pattern of fear probably started with the constant threat of death (Freedman & Ferguson, 1950) which was always linked with birth, until modern times (Stanton, 1979: 27). Even in modern societies, however, there is an element of fear present, and a need to hasten and ease childbirth by various means indicating that they too are anxious to complete a dangerous and uncomfortable process. The demand for assisted deliveries—including, for example, dilating the introitus, vagina and cervix, lubricating the birth canal, and manually detaching the placenta—reflect the cultural attitudes toward and the necessity and desirability of aided childbirth (Oakley, 1977: 28).

Groups in all societies [10] have devised interventionist rules and regulation to guide and control the behavior of their women in childbirth. These are matters which are almost never left to the discretion of birthing women or to Nature. And although these cultural prescriptions may differ between societies, all are guided by some rules and regulations (Macintyre, 1977: 17-8; Stanton, 1979: 25-6). The crucial point is, of course, that—whether traditional or modern—all childbirth behavior is culturally patterned.

Assessing the Competence of Non-Western Practitioners

In her study of the Bariba of Benin, Sargent (1982) did something very unusual for anthropologists conducting fieldwork on non-western childbirth practices. She explicitly addressed the topic of maternal mortality rates, and asked local women what were the complications in labor that they most feared. Their responses indicated that the danger of retention of the placenta worried them more that of postpartum hemorrhage. Again, the distinctiveness of different cultures emerges: Bariba concepts of physiology regard bleeding as, in general, beneficial. Hence it would seem that even where a maternal death would have been explained by a western midwife in terms of hemorrhage, more importance will be attached by the Bariba to some other cause. Sargent's own hypothesis (1982: 151-3) is that the traditional local practice of rolling the woman's abdomen with a broom immediately following delivery of the child may actually provoke complications instead of facilitating expulsion of the placenta.

Sargent's efforts at estimating how frequently rural Bariba women died in childbirth came up against their cultural reluctance to speak about the matter. Nevertheless, she was able to calculate using indirect evidence that the rate probably fell within a range of between twenty and thirty per thousand. It would, of course, be inappropriate to compare this rate with those achieved by modern western maternity care in a developed country, which are of the order of one maternal death in 10,000 births (Loudon, 1992a: 545). What Sargent does compare it with is the rate in the Western-style clinic in the local administrative center, which was about fifteen per thousand. The reality in rural Benin is that sophisticated obstetrics are unavailable; and the care provided by traditional birth attendants (TBAs) may not on balance be significantly inferior to the services of inadequately trained clinic staff.

Discussion of Sargent's findings leads us on to consider a broader question: what are the appropriate criteria for assessing the competence of non-western practitioners? Given the absence, by and large, of accurate statistical data regarding death rates for mothers and babies or subsequent maternal and child health, what assumptions is it reasonable to make about the typical outcome of major complications in labor? On the one hand, there is the danger in relying primarily on what Sargent calls "the emic perspective" (the perspective of the society's own members), since this may systematically divert attention away from detrimental outcomes. It is for this reason that Sargent also adopts "the etic perspective" (the outsider's viewpoint). On the other hand, a cynically-minded anthropologists might describe the reliance on statistical evidence in western society as a ritual especially where it is combined with an uncritical attitude towards the adequacy of already-existing data collection procedures as a basis for definite conclusions.

Another researcher wishing to combine both perspectives is Itavyar (1984); his study of Hausa birth attendants in Sokota, Nigeria, draws attention to the incidence of vaginal fistulae with consequent chronic incontinence, in the wake of prolonged obstructed labor (Shorter, 1982: 268-71). He suggests that this may in some cases result from incisions made by the *ungwanzoma*—a term which it would definitely be misleading to translate as "midwives", because the skills of these practitioners traditionally include surgery.

There may indeed be too few hard data. Nevertheless, it is hard to escape the conclusion that while traditionally maternity care can benefit the great majority of women, it may also have unsatisfactory consequences for the unlucky minority. At its best, it holds many benefits for childbearing women. It takes account of their need for the support of people whom they know and trust, and it allows for the presence of female kin who may not have access to a western-style maternity clinic. It does more than provide emotional support, however, it incorporates a cosmological dimension, an awareness of the presence of unseen forces, whereas for good or ill this has been entirely removed from modern western obstetrics. Nor are the advantages merely psychological. The various standing and squatting positions considered normal in traditional midwifery are now being found by systematic research to reduce the length of labor by comparison with the supine lithotomy position associated with scientific obstetrics (Sleep *et al.*, 1989). Moreover, traditional midwives in several cultures are reported to practice a skill that is relatively little used in Western antenatal care, the art of manipulating the child in the womb to avert a difficult presentation (Jordan, 1978: 21-2). On the other hand, great as these benefits are when birth proceeds with major complications, there is an element of romantic illusion in any account of non-western birth practices which overlooks maternal deaths and injuries.

In reply to this comment, it might be argued that the complications are less likely to occur when a woman is giving birth in familiar surroundings and receives strong social support wherein the deeper meaning of the event is celebrated. This argument gains in resonance from the fact that it mirrors the charge often made against Western hospital obstetrics, of inducing anxiety and alienation in childbearing women, thereby prolonging labor and increasing the incidence of complications (Tew, 1998); and it accords with findings from research on the correlation between stress and birth complications in other species of mammals (Naaktgeboren 1989). But though the anthropological evidence may be read as indicating that TBAs relatively seldom encounter major complications, it can scarcely be claimed to support the view that complications are altogether absent.

Midwifery and Sociological Analysis

Division of Labor

It is helpful to consider midwifery in the context of the sociology of occupations/professions and the division of labor in general. If one does this, the effect is to encourage a focus on group-identities, and thus on the resources available to members of relevant occupational groups to define themselves in the eyes of their potential clientele from rivals. The ethnographic and historical materials derive their value partly from this consideration. With a simpler division of labor, there can sometimes be fewer vested interests in the creation and maintenance of an occupational group identity centered on the birth process. It may not even be seen as a process requiring specialized skills at all (Browner, 1989); it may be seen as one which any older woman who is minded to, can help with; or it may be seen as a chore which demeans those who become involved in it (Jeffery *et al.*, 1989: 108-9).

On the other hand, as the division of labor became more complex, in ancient Greece and again in medieval Europe particularly from the thirteenth century onwards with the foundation of the universities, prestige became attached to any group that could acquire the reputation of having conceptual leverage on the birth-process as a specialized set of problems. It is said of Jaime II of Aragon/Catalonia (reigned 1291-1327) that the furtherance of medicine was one of his chief interests, and he not only founded the University of Lerida in 1300 but insisted that a doctor should be available to the Queen when she was giving birth (McVaugh, 1986, cited by Green, 1989). This early instance of medicalization suggests we should be sceptical about the claim often made e.g. by Litoff (1978), that the invention of the forceps was crucial in bringing about the displacement of midwives by obstetricians—even though it is of course true that forceps and anesthesia were technologies that lent themselves to being used by the male obstetrician in their campaigns to differentiate themselves in the public eye from female midwives. It might even be argued that the widespread adoption of the term "obstetrician" as a replacement for "man-midwife" after around 1828 was of at least equal strategic importance with any technological advantage associated with forceps (Schnorrenburg, 1981: 400).

The development of a significant medical division of labor in the United States (Fryer, 1991) is one of three factors associated with the success achieved by American physicians in banishing midwives from involvement in the birth process. The other factors are: the effect of racial divisions and mass immigration in allowing midwives to be stigmatized as ignorant practitioners caring for impoverished clients; and the inheritance of the English tradition of laissez-faire as regards midwifery training, rather than of the continental European tradition of active municipal regulation of midwives [11]. During the course of the twentieth century, both in medicine and in other occupational spheres, the United States came to be widely perceived as having achieved great progress pushing occupational specialization to its limits. Near-universal hospitalization of birth came to be seen as the wave of the future, except in the Netherlands, until the "post-modern" backlash occurred, in almost all spheres, against the fragmentation of social roles and against the dehumanization of work in general and of health care in particular (Bakx, 1991).

Midwifery as an Occupation and Profession

Throughout history midwives have been and continue to be the major health care attendants at the birthing process. Estimates of midwife care range from two-thirds of all live births (Bayes, 1968) to three-fourths (Rooks 1997: 415) to four-fifths (Sousa, 1976). In most recent dictionaries a midwife is simply defined as a woman who assists other women in childbirth [12]. A more eclectic definition is offered by other dictionaries which specify that, in addition to the woman's physiological requirements, the assistance to be provided is to be extended to the emotional, religious (spiritual) and social needs as well. The World Health Organization (WHO) adds another component to this debate with the argument that midwives should be distinguished from TBAs; the term midwife should be reserved for only those with professional training and formal education. Perhaps, however, the most all inclusive sociological definition of midwife is offered by Cosminsky (1976: 231) who identifies this occupation as "a position which has been socially differentiated as a specialized status by the society. Such a person is regarded as a specialist and a professional in her own eyes and by her community".

Sociologically relevant questions, specific to midwifery as an occupation and profession, may now be posed, such as: (1) what are the criteria necessary for classifying an occupation as a profession?; and (2) why is midwifery not universally recognized as a profession? Answers to these questions will require analyses of the varieties of occupational statuses midwives occupy—inclusive of the TBA, lay and nurse midwife—and the norms attached to these statuses; and which of the aforementioned midwife types has the greatest potential of achieving professionalisation.

While midwives share the common occupational functions of assisting and caring for the health of women, great diversity characterizes the occupational status of midwives. Specifically, the norms associated with the TBAs in traditional societies and those associated with lay and nurse midwives in industrialized societies tend to vary in regard to such matters as recruitment, training, styles of practice, high or low esteem and prestige enjoyed in the community, and the economic rewards of the practice. Internal and external variations exist respectively within and between the statuses. Similarly, the norms associated with TBAs and lay midwives who received some medical training in a given society differ from those TBAs and lay midwives who lack such training. More so than variability, however, each of the different midwife statuses is characterized by common normative expectations and procedures unique to them which serve to identify as well as differentiate them from each other.

Birth Attendants in Traditional Society

In traditional societies, a midwife's authority comes from her "calling" (Cosminsky, 1982a; 1982b; Laderman, 1983; McCormack, 1982a; 1982b; Jordan 1978) which may come supernaturally (in the form of visions or dreams) or through custom (other family or community members). Traditional birth practices exist in many countries of the world such as Guatemala, Mexico, Kenya, Ghana and Haiti. In a few countries such as Egypt the functioning of the TBA is limited and repressed by state legislation (Itavyar, 1984). Generally, TBAs operate outside the organized health system and are older illiterate females with no formal training, whose sphere of expertise includes all matters having to do with the customary conduct of childbirth—usually learned as a consequence of working with another TBA in apprenticeship (Jordan, 1978; Leedam, 1985; McCormack, 1982a; 1982b). They themselves have borne children and adhere to a style of birthing that involved reliance upon herbs and traditional remedies for stimulating the uterus, have little use of modern obstetrical instruments and are devoid of orthodox medical training. In most societies, they are regarded with deference and command great respect as in Iraq (McCormack, 1982a; 1982b); Guatemala (Cosminsky, 1982a); Malaysia (Laderman, 1983): and the Sudan (El Hakim, 1980). On the other hand, research conducted by Jeffery et al. 1989 in rural India revealed how little respect was accorded to the untrained birth attendant or "dai" [13], in a culture overwhelmingly preoccupied with the desirability of avoiding pollution. In countries such as Guatemala and Nigeria some TBAs, under United Nations auspices, are given a brief training in basic hygiene and officially upgraded and integrated with the modern health care system (Itavyar, 1984; McCormack, 1982a; 1982b). Under these circumstances, the normative expectations of the midwife status—i.e. what tasks are expected and how they are to be pursued—tend also to change, in the direction of greater reliance on modern medicine. For the present, however, the care offered by most traditional midwives—inclusive of the physiological processes of gestation and delivery—can be understood in terms of a complex conceptual framework, grounded in close observation and tactile skills, which is simply incommensurable with that of the secular perspective of scientific medicine.

According to the WHO, health services throughout the world are expanding. Still, however, between sixty and eighty percent of births in developing countries take place not with the help of these services but with the help of a TBA or trained midwife (TMW) (Leedam, 1985; WHO, Maglacas & Simons, 1979; 1986; Sindiga, 1995; Mathews, et al., 1995). In Africa and rural India the percentage is even higher; an estimated eighty percent or more are assisted by TBAs (Barns, 1980). Concern, however, about the future of traditional midwives in Malaysia is expressed by Laderman (1983). For those indigenous midwives who are trained according to modern medical procedures, but are not able to treat diseases peculiar to their area, there is a real possibility that their usefulness may diminish and become obsolete as technological requirements for the status increase.

The contrast between the observations made by Jeffery and colleagues (1989), and those made elsewhere by Carol McCormack (1982a, b, 1986)—among the Mende of Sierra Leone in West Africa—brings out the connection between the status accruing to midwifery as an occupation and the degree of skill which a midwife can aspire to achieve through apprenticeship to an older woman. Clearly, social recognition for the value of TBA's skills passed on from one generation to the next has no place in a culture where the role of birth attendant is despised. McCormack's study revealed, moreover, that Mende midwives were also the practitioners of clitoridectomy at the time of the young girl's initiation ceremony—thus illustrating another aspect of the cultural diversity in and cultural expectation of birth practices. The variation in what a birth attendant does and how the work is viewed is in fact so enormous that it is even arguable that we incur a distortion in our understanding by applying everywhere the single term "midwife" (or "TBA" with the World Health Organization). There are societies where it is normal for the baby's father to be the birth attendant, as with the Chinantec-speaking Indians in Oaxaca, Mexico, among whom Browner's (1989) fieldwork was carried out. Alto et al. (1991) found that the Angal Heneng of Papua New Guinea had no midwives. Among the Bariba of Benin, West Africa, Sargent (1982; 1989) found that although there were women who specialized in helping to cope with minor birth complications, midwifery was not a distinct occupation with a specific title in the local language so much as a skill which happened to be acquired by particular individuals, some of them being trained healers for whom it was a natural extension of a recognized occupational role.

Midwives in the United Kingdom

In the U.K., midwives—most of whom are employed by the National Health Service (Rooks 1997: 414)—are legally recognized as practitioners in their own right, and may provide care for women throughout pregnancy, labor and the puerperium (Expert Maternity Group, 1993; Porter in this volume pp 145-154). Procedures which midwives may perform are defined by the social/cultural norms and relate to the status of the occupation. For example, in Britain breech deliveries are normally carried out by the medical staff, whereas in France midwives may undertake them (Rothman, 1983). Midwifery education in Britain has been changing rapidly in the 1990s when, after decades of midwifery education being predominantly a post-basic nursing training in nursing/midwifery colleges, it has become an academic undergraduate subject. Merger with "institutions of higher education have presented opportunities for extending the knowledge base of midwifery and for increasing academic rigour" (Roch 1993). At the same time a number of direct-entry midwifery courses were established (or better re-established).

Lay and Nurse-Midwives in the United States

In the U.S., however, traditional midwives have more limited status responsibilities [14]. The informally trained midwife is called or "lay" or "granny" midwife (Mongeau, et al. 1961) traditionally provided care for women in poorer urban and rural communities (Wasserman, 1975). Like the TBA in traditional society, the granny midwife is an older female who has trained as an apprentice to more knowledgeable midwives and has learned her skills from them (Peterson, 1983). Although granny midwives constitute a tiny minority of all US midwives, numerous accounts of pregnancy and childbirth and the role played by such practitioners appear in ethnographic studies of ethnic groups, such as the Ohio Amish (Campanella, 1983); Montana Hutterites (Converse, 1973); southern blacks (Schaffer, 1991; McMillen, 1990; Mongeau, et al. 1961) and whites (McMillen, 1990); New York Tonawanda Seneca Indians (Evanshko, 1982); Utah Greeks (Papanikolas, 1968); Utah and Arizona Mormans (Stark, 1982); and Oregon Muckleshoot Indians (Horn, 1982).

A second type of traditional midwife has evolved during the twentieth century. These tend to be characterized by varying degrees of training, deliver babies only in the home, and are not legally permitted to practice in most of the fifty American states [15]. Whereas the type of birth attendants described in the preceding paragraph have a low level of formal training or none at all and are found mainly in southern border states and central cities [16], this second group largely consists of women with a higher level of training, who may have received instruction at skills workshops and/or lay midwifery schools such as in Texas (Peterson, 1983). They tend to be concentrated in the northeast and far west (Yankauer, 1988). In general, lay midwives of both varieties regard birth as a domestically based family event and not as a medical happening, inasmuch as they reallocate knowledge and responsibility among all the participants and use childbirth technology only as a last resort if the baby cannot be born at home and must be transported to the hospital (Peterson, 1983; DeVries, 1982; Donegan, 1978; Litoff, 1978; Mongeau, et al. 1961). They are virtually never permitted hospital privileges (Declercq, 1992: 680).

Nurse-midwives, on the other hand, are certified registered nurses who have had a minimum of one year of nursing experience (not necessarily in obstetric nursing), have obtained their formative experience in hospitals and have graduated from one of the approximately fifteen midwifery programs of study approved by the American College of Nurse-Midwives (Wasserman, 1975; Record & Cohen, 1972). Nurse-midwifery licensing is determined by the individual cities and states (Harris et al., 1971; Rothman, 1983) [17]. Some states require nurse-midwives to have a special license whereas other states allow them to practice under their nursing license. Almost never self-employed, nurse-midwives work in hospitals, medical centers or private medical doctor group practices. Most importantly, however, they are not independent practitioners. They function largely within a physician directed environment—such as in a medically directed health service (DeVries, 1982: 87) and like Dutch (Van Teijlingen & McCaffery 1987) and other European midwives (WHO, 1985) attend only to women who are expected to deliver without complications (Rothman, 1981)—such deliveries almost always taking place in a hospital setting (Wasserman, 1975). Typically the physician is consulted whenever there is deviation from the normal pregnancy and delivery pattern (Harris et al., 1971; WHO, 1985).

Perhaps the most useful way to distinguish between lay midwifery and nurse-midwifery is to focus on the principal work norms associated with these statuses, or as DeVries (1982:96) suggests, "the context in which the midwife worked" [18]. In the early twentieth century most of the deliveries in the United States were home births attended by midwives (Litoff, 1978: 27; Declercq 1992). However, a national survey of U.S. birth data for 1975 to 1988 found a substantial increase in midwife attendance at births and where they occurred: (a) overall, the proportion of all births attended by midwives increased from 0.9 percent in 1975 to 3.4 percent in 1988; (b) virtually all (93.2 percent) of the increase occurred in hospital births; (c) the number of midwife attended births outside of hospitals decreased from 33.1 percent of all midwife-assisted births in 1975 to 12.7 percent in 1988.

Since lay midwives almost never have hospital privileges (Wasserman, 1975) and 98 percent of all births in the U.S. take place in hospital—most of which are under the direct supervision of an obstetrician with the nurse-midwife responsible for the remaining percentage (Reid, 1989)—it is reasonable to hypothesize the decreasing importance of the lay midwife and eventual status dominance of nurse-midwifery (Ventre et al., 1995; Jackson, et al. 1995; Josefson, 1995). Even nurse-midwives, however, may in due time be defined out of existence since they too are not ideally suited to today's technologically dominated world. The nature of their norms tends to be too restrictive and confining. As a group, work norms of the nurse-midwife are geared to a one to one supportive care orientation. Since they are not independent, self-employed practitioners—and function largely within a physician directed environment—they will probably not be able to make the necessary decisions associated with adopting and using medical technology that could ensure their survival.

Specific problems facing the licensed traditional midwife and the certified nurse midwife (CNM) include: (a) restrictions on the capacity of the CNM to admit patients in hospitals in their name (Langton & Kammerer, 1989); (b) cancellation of malpractice insurance as occurred in 1985 for 1400 CNMs (Radosh, 1986); (c) mutual distrust between Colorado lay midwives and CNMs which prevented the former from achieving professional status (Tjaden, 1987); (d) midwife licensing laws that have resulted in a decrease in the autonomy of midwives in favor of increased control by physicians—notably in the variations in the practices of certified and non-certified midwives (DeVries, 1982); (e) physicians' refusal to cooperate with the CNM i.e. the widespread unwillingness among physicians to provide the required prenatal screening examination and medical backup (Sullivan & Weitz, 1984); (f) inability of CNM to be self-governing—i.e. CNMs tend to be confined to hospitals or birthing centers, to be required to work under the supervision of physicians and to be limited by statutes and licensing requirements (Evenson, 1982). Such problems can also be found among independent midwives in the UK who operate outwith the NHS (Stapleton 1997:55-6).

Professionalization

It seems reasonable to assume that a first step in seeking an answer to the "professionalisation" question would be to examine the extent to which the status of midwife is organized as a group, and correspondingly to review the professionalisation process as it pertains to the physician—a group who perform the same child delivery function as the midwife but, unlike the midwife, have already been successful in achieving professional status.

Physicians as Professionals

There tends to be little consensus among sociologists on what constitutes a profession (Dingwall, 1976: 91-5; Anisef & Basson, 1979; Abbott, 1991; Denton, 1978). Flexner (1910), for example, in his comprehensive report on the status of the American medical profession introduced six criteria (Becker, 1970: 88); Wilenski (1964) and Greenwood (1957), set out five criteria of professional activity; Foote (1957), three; and Freidson (1970) succinctly defined a profession in terms of one trait: "an occupation which has assumed a dominant position in a division of labor so that it gains control over the determination of the substance of its own work". Additional criteria necessary are that a profession should be characterized by a relatively long period of training and an esoteric body of knowledge that creates experts. Earlier, however, Goode (1957; 1960; 1969) offered one of the most sociologically comprehensive explanations of professionalisation. Beginning with two attributes—an extensive body of abstract, theoretical knowledge and an orientation toward providing a highly specialized service for others—he expanded the two into ten characteristics of a profession, as follows:

(a) The profession determines its own standards of education and training, and is able consequently,

(b) To demand high caliber students for formal medical education, and insist that students go through a more rigorous socialization experience than the learner in other occupations.

(c) Professional practice is often legally recognized in some form of licensure.

(d) Licensing and admission boards are staffed by members of the profession.

(e) Most legislation concerned with the profession is shaped (controlled) by that profession.

(f) The occupation enjoys (acquires) high income, power, esteem and prestige ranking.

(g) The practitioner is relatively free of lay evaluation and control.

(h) The norms of practice are enforced by the profession, and are more stringent than legal controls.

(i) Members are more strongly identified and affiliated with the profession than are members of other occupations with theirs.

(j) The profession is more likely to be a terminal occupation, i.e. members do not care to leave it.

These characteristics, according to Goode (1960), as social relationships are closely interrelated and therefore assert mutual and reciprocal obligations and rights between patient and professional, professional and colleague, and professional and organization. Consequently, an important feature of the process whereby an occupation becomes a profession is the gradual and eventual institutionalization of the various social relationships. Of all of Goode's characteristics it would appear that the most important are (a), (b), (f) and (g) since only these are unique to medicine and may therefore be applied to the professionalisation of medicine. Of all occupations, for example—professional and non-professional—only medicine remains relatively free of lay evaluation and control; only medicine has the power to determine the standards of performance of its members and to keep the evaluation of the profession in the hands of its own members; only medicine has the power to successfully demand highly qualified and able students thereby controlling who enters into the profession; and only medicine can determine the increased rewards (monetary and prestige) that stem from professional status. Flexner (1915) offered another relevant distinction between a profession and other similar occupations. Only a profession, such as medicine, possesses the quality of "unequal responsibility" for the application of scientific knowledge to the community. Although pharmacy, for example, contains most of the qualities of a profession, it does not include original or primary responsibility. "The physician thinks, decides and orders; the pharmacist obeys....and does not originate. Pharmacy therefore is an arm added to the medical profession, a specially and distinctly higher form of handicraft, not a profession."

However, the above taxonomic approach has been challenged by both Marxist and Weberian analysis. The former holds that professions (1) act as a stabilizing force in capitalist society, and (2) are largely dominated by the monopolistic interests and bureaucratic forces of contemporary capitalism. The latter set of theories is associated with the neo-Weberian idea of occupational closure (e.g. Parkin 1979; Saks 1983; Turner 1987:133-9; Witz 1990; 1992). Both Marxist and (neo-)Weberian approaches criticise the taxonomic approach for taking claims by professionals at face value. These two approaches argue that professionals are not working altruistically for the common good. Instead they emphasise the notion of 'autonomy' which is based on the profession being able to exercise power and control over, for example, other occupations, policy makers, and clients. Relating professionalisation to strategies of occupational closure or exclusiveness serves to supplement and amplify these two perspectives. From the work conducted by Freidson (1970; 1977; 1990) we could define a profession as a particular kind of occupation, namely one in an advantageous position in the division of labour, enjoying autonomy and some degree of dominance over the work and the clients.

Midwives as Professionals

Whether any type of midwife satisfies the preceding criteria for what constitutes a profession or possesses the potential for achieving professionalisation remains highly problematic. In a cross-cultural comparison of midwifery in Great Britain and the United States, Anisef and Basson (1979: 353) found that only in Britain has midwifery achieved institutionalization, and offered the hypothesis that "the greater the emphasis on childbirth as a normal physiological process by the medical profession and their patients, the more likely the retention of midwifery and its eventual professionalism". At least one writer (Reid, 1989: 220-1), however, has excluded American lay midwives from such serious consideration by suggesting that they are not strictly comparable to professions since they do not work within the orthodox framework of society, and are domestically based and informally organized.

On the other hand, if we apply the select Goode criteria and Flexner's criterion and organize the midwives along a continuum—with those who possess the quality of "unequal responsibility", have stringent socialization and formal education experience, are often legally recognized in some form of licensure, and use most of the tools of technology at one end, and those who lack these attributes at another end—it would appear that the nurse-midwife has the greatest potential for achieving professionalisation status. One ongoing, apparently insurmountable limitation, however, of nurse-midwives ever achieving professional status is that even though they do work with some independence, they are restricted from attending high-risk labors and deliveries, and from using much of the available medical technologies. They remain, consequently, subordinate to and dependent upon the authority of the physician for occupational accountability and viability. This question of independence is dealt with by Allison and Pascall (1994) in their essay on the suitability of midwifery as a career for women. Their conclusion: midwives lack autonomy in practice, the successful challenge to this autonomy having come from a male dominated obstetrics profession whereby hospital delivery and obstetric management have demoted midwives and fragmented their work.

A brief comment on Freidson's (1970) conceptualization is also in order here. Emphasis by Freidson is clearly not on the personal characteristics, such as the commitment, competence or integrity of the individual occupying the particular status position. Only the structural position of the occupation in the division of labor is important. Important features center on control, power and autonomy, i.e. on the decision making ability and power to control one's own occupation (Rothman, 1985). As applied to the midwife and medical doctor, midwives do not instruct physicians what to do and how to do it or to which instruments they may have access. To the contrary, physicians typically offer such instruction, and the norms of practice are legally regulated—such control having been successfully engineered by the medical profession. According to this perspective, then, midwifery is not a profession, and can never be until and unless control by midwives over their occupation becomes a reality.

Van Teijlingen and Van der Hulst (1995) discuss a related question concerning the professionalisation process as regards the midwife—i.e. whether midwifery is a semi-profession. In defining a semi-profession, the authors focus on the power and control features of Freidson's conceptualization. A semi-profession is an "occupation that is less powerful and has less control than a profession, but is more powerful and has more control than a trade. ... A semi-profession attempts to exert power over the other occupations, clients, and the state, but achieves this to a lesser degree than a profession. ... In short, one can only make comparative statements regarding the professional status of an occupation". They hypothesize that midwifery in the Netherlands is more than a semiprofession in that it has more power and autonomy than midwifery in other industrialized nations vis-à-vis the medical profession. To support this proposition they offer the following evidence: Dutch midwives have been legally recognized as independent medical practitioners since 1865, and are trained separately from nurses. They can practice obstetrics without the supervision of a doctor when pregnancies and deliveries show no indication of medical complications. Training takes place in direct-entry schools of midwifery and the length of training was increased from three to four years in 1994 (Rooks 1997: 414). Legislation permits the midwife to conduct blood tests and give advice on a variety of pregnancy-related health matters, normally the province of physicians. During a home birth in the Netherlands the midwife will normally be assisted by a subordinate occupational specialty—the "maternity home care assistant" (Van Teijlingen, 1990; and this volume pages: 163-172).

PART TWO: MEDICALIZATION OF CHILDBIRTH AND MIDWIFERY

The second of our major themes centers on childbirth as an event that has already in varying degrees been medicalized in the technologically advanced regions of the world such as North America and Western Europe. The medicalization process has also significantly begun, and will probably continue to evolve, in areas such as Africa, the Middle and Far East, and Central and South America. Especially significant about this process, however, is the gradual displacement of the midwife as the childbirth authority—where the midwife loses control or autonomy over being able to act independently in the birthing process—with the consequent transfer of such authority to the medical doctor and hospital.

Medicalization of Midwifery in Britain, United States and the Netherlands: a Socio-Historical Perspective

Midwives in Pre-Industrial Europe

The first main point which needs to be made about pre-industrial midwives is that here too, just as in the context of anthropological accounts, one can easily be misled by the use of the one term "midwife" for women with quite different levels of skill (Green, 1989). There were often several women present at birth (though normally no men); consequently, an older woman was likely to have witnessed many births, and to have some notion of what needed to be done. In the light of later developments, it is reasonable to ask: from what period can we date midwifery as a recognized occupation? When did some women begin to be "professional midwives" rather than "experienced amateurs"? Biller (1986: 43-4) says that as early as the thirteenth century, it was already common to distinguish between trained and untrained midwives. By the fifteenth century, provision was being made for municipal employment of midwives. This in turn eventually led to measures for assessing candidates' suitability for public authorization to practice (Greilsammer, 1991: 296-300; Wiesner, 1993 and this volume).

This takes us to a second issue: the relationship between midwives and doctors. The word "doctor" here has to be used with no less caution that the word "midwife", for medicine (however defined) was still at an early stage in the process of becoming a profession. The view sometimes put forward, that male doctors in the Middle Ages were never asked to play an obstetric role, is undermined by the fact that as early as 1299, Jaime II of Aragon wanted Queen Blanca to be attended by the university-trained court physician (McVaugh, 1986).

Although restricted by taboos against intimate physical contact with patients, by the late fifteenth century ambitious medical men were anxious to achieve the status of authorities on everything to do with health, not excluding female reproductive functions (Lemay, 1985). One way of summarizing the growth of medical influence over the management of birth is to say that it grew in step with the wider aspirations of doctors to claim jurisdiction over anything that could be defined as detrimental to good health. In 1460, we find a woman who wishes to be licensed as a midwife in Lille being examined by a doctor (Jacquart, 1981: 49). Though the trend towards ascribing superior knowledge about how to manage obstetric emergencies to doctors cannot be clearly traced, the idea took root that midwives confronted with difficult births did well to seek medical advice. In fifteenth century Nuremburg, a physician was supposed to be consulted over retention of the placenta, while in Regensburg the regulations of 1555 directed midwives to ask for medical assistance in all emergencies (Benedek, 1977: 556). In Paris, too, the doctors helped to supervise midwifery after 1560 (Petrelli, 1971: 279).

Establishing the basic principle that doctors must be deemed more adept in handling abnormal births than midwives was certainly a social and political accomplishment. Historians differ as to how far this presumption rested on gender bias and social prejudice, or on respect for the pioneering work of men like Amboise Paré, Francois Mauriceau or the Chamberlen family in Britain. The indirect consequence which ensued from it was that it paved the way for a stronger claim on the part of the medical profession: the claim to surpass women in skill at managing normal births as well. How is one to explain the fact that this claim too came to be widely accepted? Eccles (1982: 120) speculates that it was thanks to a greater awareness of "the necessity of conciliating the patient". But she also (ibid: 124) ascribes it to, "a quite rational evaluation by women themselves of the respective merits of male and female midwives". At any rate, in France before 1700, and in Britain by the 1730s practitioners of the various forms of medicine—surgeons, apothecaries, accoucheurs, and less often physicians—were beginning to do all they could to propagate the belief that it was preferable for even normal births to be attended by a male professional rather than a female midwife (Donnison, 1977: 20-2; Gélis, 1988: 315; Loudon, 1986: 85-99). Research in recent decades has traced in detail the processes whereby after about 1720 midwives steadily lost ground, especially in urban Britain and later in North American cities, to their male competitors (for valuable summaries see Donnison, 1977; Leavitt, 1986; Loudon, 1992a; 1992b; Wertz & Wertz, 1989). Among the leading "male midwives" of the eighteenth century were William Hunter and Fielding Ould. Both were pivotal figures in the evolution of unskilled midwifery into modern obstetrics. Ould became master of the Dublin Lying-in Hospital and helped found that city's school of obstetrics. He is known especially for his treatise of midwifery which discussed many important obstetrical problems including the mechanism of labor, use of opiates, and episiotomy (Longo, 1995). Hunter practiced midwifery in London, and is especially known for his opposition to the increasingly widespread use of forceps (Wilson, 1985).

The British Experience

The following sketch concentrates on three issues: the attitudes of doctors towards female midwives; training in midwifery for women; and the place of birth.

Characteristics of British Midwives

As we have noted above, the word "doctor" can have a range of meanings in the context of earlier centuries (Pelling, 1987; Parry & Parry, 1976; Starr, 1982). Furthermore, one must remember that unqualified medical practitioners abounded in eighteenth century England. But a common feature distinguished all branches of medicine from midwifery; the collective interests of those who had undergone the required training were always defended by some national body able to speak on their behalf. Midwives generally lacked a collective voice, even though as the century went on, occasional individuals published eloquent statements of their viewpoint. The clientele over whom competition raged can be crudely divided into three categories: the wealthy, the less-well-off and the indigent. From the 1720s onwards in Britain, and in North America from the 1760s, it quite rapidly became the established fashion for well-to-do women to desire medical attention in childbirth, and this lucrative end of the market preoccupied writers of the fiercely polemical literature generated by the conflict. A doctor might hope, by acquiring a reputation for skill as an accoucheur, to become accepted as the regular provider of medical services to whole families. Loudon (1992a: 170, cf 184-5) illustrates this with the example of a small-town surgeon-apothecary so worried about competition from midwives that he scarcely dared to leave home for fear of losing a case to them. The lower end of the income scale attracted less competition, and it was here, especially in the countryside, that midwives stood the best chance of retaining their traditional role. But as living standards rose over the course of the eighteenth and nineteenth centuries, and as the medical ranks were swelled by more and more recruits, the income-level at which women were content with a midwife's services fell. Attending poorer patients was never lucrative work, of course, even for a doctor, and it certainly offered no great income for a midwife. The fact that most midwives in Britain could only charge very little—in view of their clients' limited resources—helps to explain their inability to influence political debates about the best way forward in restructuring the health professions. A low-paid occupation was in no position to support an effective campaign for its members' interests. As to the care of destitute women in childbirth, this was a concern which was increasingly being addressed by private initiatives, the indirect beneficiaries being doctors rather than midwives. The lying-in hospitals provided clinical material for research and for the teaching of medical students (Versluysen, 1981). It is true that midwives were trained in these institutions, but not in great numbers.

The low average incomes of midwives were, then, one cause of this inability to influence Parliament to legislate in their favor by establishing an official regulatory body to set standards of midwifery training and practice. Proposals along these lines were made, in conjunction with schemes to formalize the standing of the profession. After all, maternity care was by now regarded as an element in professional health care, so there was an obvious anomaly in allowing it to go unregulated when provided by women rather then by men (Donnison, 1977: 46). The opposition of the London medical elite to any change in this matter reflected the low standing of doctors engaged in this work. Not until the 1820s did it acquire a distinct name as a branch of medicine, being christened "obstetrics". The fact that women with no formal instruction in anatomy continued to practice this skill was felt to lower its value (Loudon, 1992a: 173). The obvious remedy, in some people's eyes, was to ensure that midwives received such instruction; but few medical men had this as their primary concern, at a time when even a doctor was under no requirement to have undergone training in obstetrics. Anticipating arguments later used in North America (see History section), others contended a satisfactory situation could never be reached until midwives were altogether excluded from attending births (Donnison, 1977: 49; 57).

Training in Midwifery for Women

What finally overcame British reluctance to see organized midwifery training for women? The hesitation to legislate seems to have reflected broad ideological concerns for free markets and minimal state interference, as well as professional self-interest. But a voice raised in favor of change was that of the Registrar-General's Statistical Superintendent William Farr, whose reports from 1841 onwards constantly drew attention to the need for something to be done about the rate of maternal mortality. Knowledge about the extent of the problem was not in itself sufficient, of course. Practical experience with schemes for training added to the impetus, partly by demonstrating what could be done and partly by ensuring larger numbers of well-trained midwives (and of doctors aware of their skill). By 1902, in the light of the Boer

War setbacks, the climate of opinion was affected by a new concern for effective public health measures to improve the country's military potential.

Place of Birth

Finally, in our consideration of the nineteenth century, we come to a topic which will loom much larger in the twentieth century context, namely the place of birth. We have alluded to the provision of hospital in-patient maternity care for the needs of the poorest women and for research and training. These were not places where women would go by preference. Institutional births accounted for only 4% of births in England and Wales in the 1890s (Loudon, 1992a: 195-6). Whatever the problems that might arise when the baby was delivered, it was at home that normal and abnormal births alike took place, in any family that could afford to pay for care. It was here above all that differences in attitudes towards time between doctors and midwives tended to manifest themselves. Attending childbirth is often a matter of waiting. What was expected of a midwife was patience, and maybe some help with household duties, as much as expertise; but what of a doctor? As a professional, trained to manage a variety of threats to health, he was more likely to begrudge the time spent waiting.

The pressure on doctors' time underlay two different phenomena: the rise of the "monthly nurse", whose job was to do the waiting and then call the doctor; and the alacrity with which many doctors used forceps (Donnison, 1977: 52-3; Loudon, 1992a: 218-9; Shorter, 1982: 154). When doctors and midwives were competing for home deliveries, general practitioners were liable to feel that keeping their clientele cost them a heavy price. Once the advent of antiseptic precautions in hospitals from the 1880s onwards made them less risky places for giving birth, it is not surprising that many general practitioners showed little regret at seeing their middle-class patients switch from home births to hospital birth, for they had plenty of other claims on their own time. But for community midwifery, the trend was to have far more drastic consequences.

The American Experience

From Britain, we now turn to consider twentieth-century developments in North America—not least, a trend towards hospitalization of birth, which proceeded at a faster rate than anywhere else. Here again, there will be three guiding threads, which we shall follow. Having first asked who the midwives were, we shall return to considering doctors and their attitudes towards midwives. The third topic we shall address is the use of statistics on maternal mortality in the rhetoric deployed by those campaigning on behalf of the American medical profession for the legal restriction of midwifery.

Characteristics of American Midwives

As we have already seen, wealthier Americans had already begun to prefer doctors to midwives as childbirth attendants from the 1760s onwards (Scholten, 1977), and during the nineteenth century this attitude gradually became more widespread in the white population. The black population in the south was largely unaffected by it, however, (Ferguson, 1950); nor was it shared as a rule by the immigrants who flooded into the United States at the end of the century. Consequently, calling in a midwife to assist at childbirth came to be associated with low status. From research conducted in the early years of the twentieth century, the picture of the unhygienic immigrant midwife gained credence (Crowell, 1907; Loudon, 1992a: 302-7). This charge may have had some validity; it certainly contributed to the spreading of the stereotype of midwives as dirty, ignorant, and incompetent (Litoff, 1978: 31-2; Wertz & Wertz, 1989: 214-7). The reality, however, was that some of the immigrant midwives had received very thorough training; indeed, it was conceded by two leading opponents of midwifery that "the average graduate of an American medical school would have difficulty in passing with distinction" the examination undergone by a prospective midwife in Germany (Emmons & Huntington, 1912). Many of the immigrant midwives were German, and the journal *American Midwife* carried a German language section (Borst, 1988: 615, n34). Others had been trained elsewhere in Europe, and a few in the U.S. Those who lacked a midwifery-school training had often made up for this by studying as apprentices in America—in many cases, with local doctors. However, there were also "neighbor-women" who had turned to midwifery without any formal training. The majority of midwives were middle-aged women whose children were either of school age or adult. Most attended mainly the women of their own ethnic group. They were preferred to doctors because midwife-delivery was part of their clients' culture, and because their competence was respected: moreover, they charged only half of what a doctor would charge (Borst, 1988; Declercq, 1985; Declercq & Lacroix, 1985).

Attitude of Doctors toward Female Midwives

Why then, was there a strong body of medical opinion opposed to them? The first point to make in this context is that one should not exaggerate the extent of this opposition, for as we have seen, there were plenty of doctors prepared to take on midwives as apprentices. Kobrin (1996: 353) distinguishes four standpoints adopted by different sections of the medical profession. Some anticipated a time when midwife training throughout the United States could be raised to the level already achieved in Europe and now envisaged in Britain. Newark and New York City had shown the way, they argued. Others, in the southern states, doubted whether this was feasible everywhere, but believed that it was realistic to aim at requiring minimal acceptable standards of midwifery, and that this would have to suffice. And among those wishing to bring about a situation where maternity care would be provided only by doctors, there were the gradualists, who pointed to the current lack of adequate obstetric facilities and personnel as a reason for proceeding slowly in this direction, and the hard liners. These favored legal measures to abolish midwifery, along the lines already followed in Massachusetts, where the 1894 law giving qualified doctors a monopoly in the provision of medical care was interpreted by the courts as covering maternity care.

The whole question was bound up, not only with the economic issue of doctors' incomes, but also with the medical profession's insistence on self-regulation despite the inadequacy of the training which many of its members had received. One fact which must never be lost from sight is that the standards of obstetric competence among American doctors at the turn of the century gave little ground for complacency. There were scarcely any suitably experienced people available to teach obstetrics in medical colleges; hence, to expect high standards of maternity care from their graduates was unrealistic (Williams, 1912).

What, then, explains the determination of obstetricians who were well aware of this fact to press for the abolition of midwifery, at least in the large cities? Essentially, their argument rested on two beliefs: first, that standards in American medical education were about to rise dramatically, to a point where doctors would become much more competent than midwives in managing childbirth; and secondly, that once this objective had been achieved, the availability of midwives would perpetuate a double standard of maternity care, with pregnant women on lower incomes being tempted to save money at the expense of their own health and that of their babies. They interpreted the situation in Germany and Austria as evidence that once the public respected the competence of midwives, it became harder for doctors to establish the complete monopoly which they desired (DeLee, 1915).

These two beliefs lay at the heart of the process whereby childbirth became medicalized, initially in North America (see Laforce, 1990 in French Canada), and later in almost every industrialized country. The first of them amounted to a faith in the potential of medical science to overcome all major threats to health, once adequate funding could be assured for teaching based on ever more thorough research. The second article of faith, namely the conviction that midwife care would then inherently constitute a second-best option, rested on the assumption that until a woman had been safely delivered, one can never exclude in advance the possibility of complications in labor. A pithy formulation of this principle is commonly cited: "Labor is normal only in retrospect". The inference drawn by men like Williams and DeLee was that every woman needed a doctor's care through the whole process of childbirth: if a woman began by being under the care of a midwife but complications developed, the midwife could not be trusted to recognize and acknowledge the necessity of handing over her client to a doctor in every such case. Moreover, practical difficulties might arise over transporting the woman to a hospital for the highly-skilled care required. In North America (though not elsewhere) the conclusion was drawn that even if women were brought to a hospital at the onset of labor, no one but a doctor could be relied on to manage the birth process satisfactorily; so anyone else attending a woman in labor must be assigned the status of an obstetric nurse following a doctor's orders.

In addition midwifery suffered from two major demographic changes, namely a decline in immigration into North America and a decreasing family size (DeVries 1997: 252). Fewer immigrants meant that the social context in which midwifery was standard diminished and that fewer trained midwives entered North America, whilst a decrease in family size brought hospital deliveries, once regarded as a luxury by immigrant families, within their reach. Moreover, standards did rise in medical science and the training of doctors in the United States after the Flexner report (Starr, 1982), and that midwifery was eliminated from many states during the first half of the twentieth century in the wake of Massachusetts, are facts beyond dispute (DeVries, 1985; 1996; Butter & Kay, 1988). What has been debated is whether the ensuing improvements in the well-being of American mothers and babies would have been less impressive had this policy of replacing midwives with doctors not been followed. The contrary view is that greater reductions in maternal and perinatal mortality might otherwise have been achieved—to say nothing of the avoidance of complaints about the dehumanization of childbirth which have helped to stimulate the revival of traditional midwifery since the 1970s. Mention of this debate can serve to lead us on to considering the ways in which statistical data were being used by advocates of the policy alternatives.

Campaign by American Physicians for Legal Restrictions on the Practice of Midwifery: Use of Statistics

Some of the arguments put forward in these policy discussions were without evidence, and their use can be understood only in the light of the paramount importance attached to the image of the medical profession. Midwives were resented not simply because they undercut doctors' fees, but also because of a fear that people might suspect delivering babies was surely not so difficult (or so worthy of high remuneration), if women without any medical qualifications could do it. To show that midwives were causing unnecessary loss of life seemed like a necessary first step towards dispelling this misapprehension. Accordingly, part of the campaign which was consciously being waged to reinforce the already prevalent stereotype of the dirty and ignorant midwife consisted of repeated assertions that mothers who relied upon midwives to deliver their babies ran a greater risk of dying in childbirth. The unhealthy physical environment in which many low income black and immigrant families were living lent additional plausibility to this proposition (Devitt, 1979: 87-8). However, it did not follow that maternal mortality could be reduced simply by ensuring that these mothers received a doctor's services. To establish this, it would have been necessary to show that medical care led to lower mortality than midwife care in comparable conditions.

Initially, the evidence was lacking. Williams (1912) tried to circumvent this problem by asking a sample of medical respondents for their subjective impressions, but he shrank from accepting the majority opinion that doctors tended to do worse that midwives. Such a conclusion, he wrote, "is contrary to reason". He justified this, not by any appeal to other evidence, but by conflating the two separate issues at stake: what was currently happening, and what should be done in the future. It is worthwhile to reconstruct the logic of his argument, because it was by thinking along these lines that the opponents of midwifery were able to convince themselves and others of the rightness of their case. If it were true that "women in labor were as safe in the hands of admittedly ignorant midwives as in those of poorly educated medical men", then the right policy would be "the restriction of obstetrical practice to the former, and the abolition of medical practitioners, which would be manifest absurdity". In other words, Williams rejects the guess made by most of his respondents on the factual question of comparative mortality rates, on the grounds that if future policy were shaped by their belief, the medical profession might be deprived of the chance of eventually reaching standards of excellence quite beyond the reach of midwives. Deprived of access to the full range of "clinical material", researchers would never find solutions to all the complications of labor. His logic can be summarized by saying that he raised the spectre of a self-fulfilling prophecy: unless people placed their confidence in the medical profession collectively by entrusting them with the entire responsibility for maternity care, they would never become worthy of that responsibility. Consistently with this position, Williams argued that there was nothing to be gained by giving better training to doctors and midwives alike, because the resources devoted to midwife training would be resources diverted from medical training.

One has to bear in mind this underlying logic in the anti-midwife position in order to understand the long-term outcome of the New York maternal mortality survey of 1930-1932 (King, 1991:500). The analysis followed the convention of ascribing the deaths of women attended by a midwife to that midwife, even in cases where a doctor had immediately been summoned. Despite this, the overall mortality rate for births attended by doctors was half as high again as the overall rate for midwife-attended births (Devitt, 1979b: 175) with many deaths in hospital being classified as preventable. Yet the lesson drawn from these findings was not that midwifery was worth preserving, but that specialist obstetricians should in future replace general practitioners as the medical attendants at childbirth. It is hard to escape the conclusion that the publicity campaign in favor of a medical monopoly over maternity care had generated such momentum by this time that statistical evidence was no longer relevant to the question of whether midwifery should be preserved, but only to the issue of which section of the medical profession should be entrusted with the role of normal attendants at childbirth. This also emerges when one considers how little interest was taken in the achievements of the Frontier Nursing Service in Kentucky. This was an initiative undertaken by Mary Breckinridge, who realized that in remote rural areas of the United States it was unrealistic to expect that women would always have access to a doctor. To her nursing qualification, she decided to add a midwife's training, for which purpose she went to Britain. In 1925 she set up a system of nurse-midwifery care, thus laying the foundations for a new American profession (Dye, 1983; Loudon 1992a: 318-21; Rooks 1997).

The extent of and reasons for the decline of midwifery in the United States can be summarized as follows. By 1935, only 5% of births to white mothers were attended by midwives, though for black mothers the corresponding figure was 54% and the overall proportion was greater than one in ten; this fell to 3% in 1953. Even in the black population the figure had by then dropped to 20% (Sullivan & Weitz, 1988: 14). There were demographic reasons for the decline of midwifery, in addition to the growing prestige of the medical profession: immigration was greatly reduced, which meant that the ranks of European trained midwives were not replenished; and couples were having fewer children, so they could more easily afford a doctor's fees and even the cost of hospital delivery. Hence midwifery became increasingly confined to the southern part of the U.S. (Loudon, 1992a: 298, 311-8). The restrictive legislation, enacted by many states, typically permitted a woman who was already established as a midwife to continue her work. Though efforts were made in the South to provide training courses for younger black women, mothers often preferred these "granny" midwives (Mongeau et al., 1961; Schaffer, 1991). In the eyes of public health professionals, the links between midwifery and low education, and between being poor and being attended by a midwife, were thereby further strengthened.

Thus, by the advent of the second-wave women's movement in the 1960s, doctors were close to establishing a monopoly over maternity care in the country where ideals of progress in medical science had perhaps a greater resonance than anywhere else in the world and where maternal mortality rates had fallen even more rapidly than elsewhere over the previous thirty years (Loudon, 1992a: 152-4; 390)—though this was also a country where rather less success had been achieved in reducing the national rate of neonatal mortality than in many other parts of the industrialized world.

The Dutch Experience

From the U.S. we turn finally, in our socio-historical overview, to the Netherlands, which by the 1960s was alone among Western countries in maintaining a largely autonomous midwifery profession geared to enabling women to give birth at home if they preferred it (Oppenheimer, 1993; Van Teijlingen & McCaffery, 1987; Van Teijlingen, 1993; Smulders & Limburg, 1988; Kloosterman, 1978; Rooks 1997).

Uniqueness of Dutch Midwifery: Evolution toward an Autonomous Status

We have already seen that the training of midwives had been organized more systematically in German cities and other parts of continental Europe long before the twentieth century legislation addressed this task in Britain. (On Germany see Wiesner, 1993; on France, Gélis, 1988 and Loudon, 1992a: 403-6; on Italy, Filippini, 1993; on Sweden , Romlid 1997 and Loudon, 1992a: 406-15). The puzzling question is: What was there about the evolution of Dutch midwifery that might help to explain why this country did not follow the trend toward hospital birth and the subordination of midwives to hospital-oriented obstetricians?

1. Role played by civil authorities in local communities. When considering this question, it is helpful to go back to the early days of the Dutch Republic—when the War of Independence against Spain has not been decisively won. This was not simply a war fought to drive out foreign rulers, but also a war of religion. Subjection to the Spanish crown meant living under a regime where childbirth came within the orbit of the Church's efforts to regulate people's conduct, as did many other spheres of life. (See Greilsammer, 1991: 308-13 for details of how this applied in neighboring Flanders.) By contrast, the ethos which characterized life in the Dutch Republic was one wherein secular concerns were regulated by the civil authorities, so far as regulation was needed (Schama, 1987; Schilling 1992:388-401). For city dwellers, this meant that the municipal council was expected to try to ensure the availability of good maternity care. The council licensed midwives, endorsing their claims to competence; some it employed to attend women who could not afford to pay a fee.

The civic responsibility for safeguarding the health and reproduction of the population was not, of course, unique to the Netherlands. But the strenuous efforts of the various Dutch municipalities in the seventeenth and eighteenth centuries to improve the maternity care system did place them at the forefront of contemporary endeavors to reduce levels of maternal mortality. Each city and town was largely self-governing, and treasured its autonomy. The energy and foresight put into dealing with such municipal concerns in each place could be seen as a measure of that community's collective well-being and vitality. Some sense of competition based on local pride seems to have underlain the vigor with which people set about implementing the best possible arrangements for maternity care.

During the second half of the seventeenth century, first Delft and later Amsterdam required their local medical corporations to teach reproductive anatomy and physiology to women aspiring to become licensed midwives and to examine them in these subjects (Marland, 1993a). Emphasis was laid on the theoretical knowledge needed so that in practice a midwife would recognize those complications of labor for which a doctor should be called. The importance of determining a clear distinction between normal and abnormal births is a thread running through Dutch maternity-care arrangements for over three hundred years. Perhaps because administrators and doctors identified this distinction early on—which it was crucial to establish as clearly as possible—there seems to have been less of a tendency in the Netherlands than in Britain for man-midwives to compete with their female counterparts over the work of attending normal births. The requirement that midwives be given formal instruction in obstetrics also helped to enhance the status of this branch of medicine, and several Dutch cities had a Collegium Obstetricum or, as in Amsterdam, a Collegium Medicum et Obstetricum. By the middle of the eighteenth century, at a time when doctors in Britain were seeing midwives as their rivals, many Dutch municipalities had created arrangements that presupposed a view of midwifery as complementary to medicine. Municipal man-midwives were employed, as in Haarlem in 1744, partly to teach obstetrics and partly to be responsible for attending difficult deliveries.

Meanwhile, the more traditional pattern continued whereby a younger woman was apprenticed to an experienced midwife for practical instruction, and this was built into the official system. In urban areas, as well as licensed midwives there were unlicensed practitioners, who perhaps had been unable to afford the fees for the initial course of study, for the license itself and for the affiliation to the surgeons' guild. Moreover, the licensing system did not apply to rural areas, where the only midwives available were women who had learnt by apprenticeship. Some of them might be highly skilled, as was Catherina Schrader, whose notebooks still survive and give evidence of her competence (Marland, 1987; 1993a; 1993b).

2. Role played by national government. With the French invasion and the establishment of a more centralized Dutch monarchy after the Napoleonic Wars, the system inevitably changed. The intention was to extend to rural areas the type of arrangements which had existed in urban settings. Provincial committees for examining and licensing midwives were set up, and in theory each midwife was supposed to report annually all the cases where she had been confronted with complications in labor.

The 1818 law sought to create a nation-wide division of labor in healthcare, demarcating the boundaries between the work of obstetric doctors, man-midwives and (female) midwives. The latter were restricted to attending 'natural' births, being obliged to call in either an obstetric doctor or a man-midwife in difficult cases (Klinkert, 1980: 45). Nevertheless, female midwives in the Netherlands were required to pass an examination, administered by the authorities in the provinces where they lived. There were two routes to achieving this. One was to follow an apprenticeship. The other was to attend a course of study, similar to an apprenticeship, in a 'clinical school'. These courses included a bare minimum of theoretical instruction. They attracted only a minority of aspiring practitioners, and in the second half of the nineteenth century were replaced by midwifery schools offering a more theoretically-oriented two-year course which prepared students for a standardized national qualification. (Meanwhile, the special category of man-midwife gradually disappeared, as the education legally required of al doctors to incorporate obstetric training.)

A low limit was set to the number of student-midwife admissions each year, and competition for entry into these schools became increasingly stiff. The quality of those who successfully completed the courses was high enough to command the respect of 60% of doctors surveyed in 1897; by 1911, this figure had risen to 80% (Van Lieburg & Marland, 1989: 311-3). This respect may help to explain why the tensions found elsewhere between doctors and midwives never reached the same pitch in the Netherlands, even though general practitioners were by now competing with midwives for normal deliveries (Marland 1993a; 1993b).

3. Role played by medical profession. There is another feature of the Dutch medical scene which has contributed to the greater autonomy of midwives: the orientation of the leading obstetricians (Hiddinga, 1993: 68-70). A low level of government funding for medical research, and a dearth of maternity beds in Dutch hospitals, together had the effect that the education of future doctors and midwives tended to have higher priority than extending the frontiers of scientific knowledge, and unlike many of their counterparts in other countries, Dutch obstetricians continued for a long time to insist on the need to view birth as a normal physiological process in most instances, rather than emphasizing the various forms of pathology.

The Process and Consequences of the Medicalization of Midwifery

The process and consequences of the medicalization of midwifery may be examined within a sociological framework on at least five levels [19]: (1) the technological level, where perhaps the single most important factor responsible for changing the status of midwife has been, and continues to be, obstetric technology; (2) the conceptual level, at which a medical vocabulary—possessed and used only by medical personnel, usually physicians—serves to exclude all except this small minority from full participation in the birthing process; (3) the interactional level, at which physicians treat women in childbirth as medical problems; (4) the control level, at which organized groups such as medical doctors, hospitals, insurance and drug companies, and state and local governments are the principal administrators, supervisors, opinion formers and decision makers in political, economic, and educational matters relating to the reproductive process; and (5) the gender status level, from which the birthing experience may be viewed as largely a reflection of the process of male domination and control—i.e. movement of birth from a female dominated experience to one controlled by obstetric specialists who, not surprisingly, are most often male (Oakley, 1976; 1977; Rich, 1976; Corea, 1977; Wertz & Wertz, 1989; Ehrenreich & English, 1973).

Technological Level

In its broader, sociological context, Zola (1972) suggests that medicalization is part of a larger process of social change that can be termed the bureaucratization of society or of the technological dimension— which has spread to all aspects of life. An important consequence is societal reliance on technical experts. In the health field, this has resulted in the strengthening of professional control, especially as pregnant women are increasingly expected to rely on doctors as technical experts for an evaluation of their condition. The history of midwifery suggests that technology is an important factor in changing the character and meaning of the occupational status of midwife. Technology, in fact, has been one of the most effective factors in diminishing the importance and influence of the practice of midwifery (Arms, 1975; Walker, 1972; Jordan, 1987a; 1987b). Use by medical doctors, for example, of technological innovations—such as oxytocin to bring on labor, electronic fetal monitors to follow the baby's progress through labor, antibiotics, anesthesia, analgesia, forceps [20] and stirrups—have been instrumental in perpetuating the decline of midwifery in industrialized societies mainly because: (a) midwives lacked or were denied access to knowledge of this technology; (b) the technology proved to be successful which led to its cultural acceptability—initially, at least, by the middle and upper classes; and (c) by being successful, the technology created doubts about many of the existing techniques and procedures, sources of knowledge and definitions that surround birth; in brief, it challenged the legitimacy and authority of midwifery—which is, after all, a practice characterized by low technology and one-to-one supportive care (DeVries, 1993: 133-4; 141; DeVries n.d.).

Conceptual Level

As childbirth became more medicalized—especially in regard to the proliferation of obstetric technology—maternity care became more standardized (Riessman, 1983); the shifts in location of childbirth from home to hospital were facilitated, and acceptance of the belief that the hospital was a germ-free place where safe birth could occur became widespread (Romalis, 1981: 20-3). Several consequences of the shifts are that a redefinition of birth occurred: from a family and community-centered event to a hospital, medically managed process (Butter, 1993; Starr, 1982); and from midwives being the principal birth attendants to medical doctors dominating this process. The medical profession was able to redefine this home to hospital shift in that it was successful in establishing "cultural authority" over definitions of health and disease as well as how, where and when health care should be provided—the results of which are that an increase in the hospitalization of births occurred—from fifty-five percent of all births in 1940 to ninety-nine percent in 1969 (Starr, 1982). Pregnant women have tended to regard their condition in the idiom of illness (Oakley, 1975), and have been successfully encouraged to see themselves as patients entrusting their physical well-being in childbirth to medical management.

That the medical profession is, in fact, able to successfully establish "cultural authority" over definitions of health and illness is further illustrated in the following discussion regarding the variable nature of risk as a concept. Gifford (1986) recently demonstrated how risk is a concept, which can take on different content and meaning depending on whether the language being used is clinical, epidemiological, or lay. Kaufert and O'Neill (1993)—in their study of childhood among the Canadian Inuit—applied the Gifford construct and showed how the development of these three languages of risk may be used to affirm or challenge existing relationships of power and control (Harwood, 1988; Nash & Kirsch, 1988). Whereas the lay-woman's definition of risk tends to be community based and revolves around risk as a subjective experience, epidemiologists see risk as a statistical construct, a particular way of analyzing data. Clinicians, on the other hand, abstract the vocabulary of the epidemiologist from its scientific discourse and incorporate it into their own arguments about childbirth. The Canadian Medical Association, for example, has used risk to legitimate its opposition to home births; obstetricians have also been known to use a lowering of risk as justification for introducing new forms of technical and/or clinical intervention in the birthing process (Kaufert & O'Neill, 1993: 32-3). Ultimately the question of who has the power to successfully define risk—the woman or the physician—is of paramount concern (Van Teijlingen 1994: 254-96; Kaufert & O'Neill, 1993: 32; 51).

Interactional Level

Eighteenth century medical men—who themselves had nothing medically sound to offer women in labor—were quick to contemptuously dismiss the herbal remedies, potions and charms employed by midwives to assure conception and prevent miscarriage (McLauren, 1984: 54-5; Shorter, 1982: 51-90). Contemporary physicians in the USA also tend to view the midwife as an irregular and dangerous practitioner (e.g. Cook 1982). They resemble their earlier colleagues in that their hostility and opposition to midwifery is consistent and very public. They differ from them, however, in that childbirth is placed within a medical frame of reference as a condition for which the evidence of doctors is needed and hospitals—which once were only for the poor sick and dying—become the proper place of birth (Oakley, 1977: 19). Birth with medication, medical technological intervention—inclusive of episiotomy, forceps and electrical fetal monitoring (Annandale, 1988)—use of pharmacological resources of modern scientific obstetrics (Jordan, 1981; 1987a), and managing the birth without a close social and emotional relationship built up between the midwife, family and community (Oakley, 1977; Romalis, 1981; Peterson, 1983; Goldthorpe & Richman, 1974; Bryar 1995) have all become synonymous with the medical model of childbirth.

Control Level

In the present discussion, we will focus on one facet of control: the major transformation in the management of childbirth that has come to be associated with the transfer of power from one occupational group to another, i.e. from midwives to medical doctors [21] (Oakley, 1976; 1977). In modern industrialized societies the legal, economic and professional status of the midwife remains fragile, highly circumscribed and subject to various measures of social control by associations or organized groups—the results of which have diminished the importance, perhaps even the success of midwifery as an occupation.

Organized medicine, especially, enjoys an aura of prestige, expertise and legitimacy which allows it to dominate other health systems in the western world (Freidson, 1970: 5). Unlike the European experience, American medical doctors strongly opposed the practice of midwifery. As early as 1913, for example, unqualified opposition to the future education and licensing of midwives was expressed by a Professor of Obstetrics at the University of Pittsburgh (Ziegler, 1913; also this volume). The demise of midwifery in the U.S. was very rapid and was brought about in part by medical doctors who were able to: (a) successfully adopt for use the technological inventions and discoveries from European medical experience (which was denied midwives); (b) "sell" their healing methods of bloodletting and purging to both upper and middle class women; (c) organize into politically effective professional medical organizations on the local, state, and national levels to promote legislation that would eliminate or effectively reduce the practice of midwifery by redefining birth as dangerous, birth attendance as increasingly scientific (e.g. use of particular drugs administered to women during delivery), and by casting midwives as dangerously unskilled (Declercq, 1994; Devitt, 1979a, b; DeVries, 1996; Romalis, 1971); and (d) set the standards of medical school education and training (Flexner Report) for the physician obstetricians (Wertz & Wertz, 1990). That is to say, the shift to obstetric control of midwifery had more to do with politics than with an assessment of the medical data available (Allison & Pascall, 1994) [22]. Although in most cases efforts to license lay midwifery in the United States have been initiated by midwives—who view licensure as the avenue to independent and legally safe practice—this vision is seldom realized (DeVries, 1986: 1147-50, and this volume). Instead, midwifery practice has been subjected to a multitude of sanctions designed to replace it (Butter, 1993) or place it under the authority and control of physician-obstetricians (Wertz & Wertz, 1990: 148-60; DeVries, 1986: 1147-50). Control was also made possible by the ability of this group to control the instruments and procedures that may be used in the birthing process. Regulatory legislation was enacted in America in the early 1900's which prohibited the midwife from administering drugs and using instruments which were available to physicians. Forceps were used by physicians with no training of midwives in their proper use—which obviously resulted in the absolute monopoly of a desired service. Additional advances in medical science, such as in surgery—to open the bowels and stimulate contractions, use of anesthesia to eliminate pain, and performing Cesarean sections—strengthened the claim of specialized knowledge and expertise.

Joining forces with the medical establishment have been medical insurance companies [23] who have threatened loss of malpractice insurance of physicians providing backup to midwives (Sullivan & Weitz, 1988); politicians who have pursued legislative procedures to prohibit (Butter & Kay, 1988) and prosecute (Mitford, 1990) midwifery practice; and hospitals which have provided inferior treatment to women transferred as emergency cases by midwives to their hospital (Sullivan & Weitz, 1988), and terminated hospital privileges of physicians who collaborate with midwives (Martin, 1981).

Gender/Status Level

A second facet of control focuses on a gender difference in the structure of control, i.e. on the transfer of control in the birthing process from female to male. During the Middle Ages, major control of childbirth remained securely in the hands of women who had developed expertise through participation in their own and other women's births. From the fourteenth to the seventeenth centuries, however, the church—and the doctors who had received their education at church sponsored universities—began to see lay women healers as threatening witches. Consequently, church dominated witch hunts prevailed during this period according to Ehrenreich and English (1973) and Romalis (1981). However, this view that midwives disproportionately suffered during the witchcraze has been contested, is outlined in the introduction to and some of the papers included in the 'History of Midwifery' section in this reader.

Although the female midwife continued to be the principal birth attendant during the Renaissance (15th to 16th centuries), a measure of control was exercised during this period through licensing requirements by municipal boards in urban centers (Donnison, 1977; Benedek, 1977)—along with regulations stipulating that midwives consult physicians (who were almost always male) in case of difficulty (Benedek, 1977). From the 16th to the 19th century, male doctors with the cooperation of male barber surgeons—who since the 13th century had the exclusive right to use surgical instruments—began to successfully encroach on the female practice of midwifery. In addition licensing requirements during this period, other methods of control, denied the midwife, included the use of technological innovations such as obstetrical forceps (1700s) and anesthesia (1800s) which proved to be sufficient to tip the scales in favor of the male doctors. Most importantly, however, it was not until the arrival of the germ theory of disease at the turn of the 20th century that institutionalized dominance of the male doctor over the female midwife could occur (Romalis, 1981).

There is no question but that any discussion of the medicalization of childbirth must consider the displacement of the midwife as the principal childbirth attendant. Displacement is synonymous with loss of control by the midwife over the childbirth process—such authority now being transferred to the obstetrician and hospital. Feminists have tended to focus on childbirth in terms of this issue of control, and women's desire to reclaim the power to control their birth experiences. They see control of childbirth, however, to be only one of the many facets of women's larger struggle to control their life circumstances. They reject the biomedical model which today dominates industrialized society, whereby birth is defined as a risk to be managed by the application of science and technology, and sociocultural factors are considered either neutral or an impediment to the birthing process (McClain, 1982). They further view this model as having been derived from a male perspective; a perspective which is translated into a power relationship of male dominance over the medical profession and the birthing process.

Most writers agree that the transition from control by lay women to control by medically trained men in industrialized society [24] is one of the most crucial changes that has occurred in the management of childbirth over the last one hundred years (Oakley, 1976; 1977: 23; Romalis, 1981: 13-20). It is a mistake, however, to attribute this transition simply to the organizational efforts of the medical establishment. The decline of midwifery and the institutionalization of the dominance of the male doctor over the female midwife could not have occurred without the rise of obstetric science (DeVries, 1982), the successful incorporation of the various technologies in the birthing process, and the arrival of the germ theory of disease at the turn of the century. Not unimportant also is the cultural acquiescence of the general population to all of these "scientific benefits".

Cultural Demedicalization of Childbirth and Midwifery: Is it Possible?

A number of writers, largely American, have hypothesized that although a significant expansion of medical jurisdiction over reproductive matters has occurred, the medicalization problem is overstated; and have, instead, suggested that recent developments indicate that a contrary trend toward cultural demedicalization may be occurring (Fox, 1990; Strong, 1979)—where birth is in the process of being redefined as a "natural", family, and not simply medical, experience; one where organized groups have initiated significant changes in the delivery of care in childbirth which have tended to add to—rather than detract from—the stature and success of midwives. Associations composed of medical doctors together with hospitals have begun adding nurse-midwives to their staff, and companies specializing in health care equipment have begun advertising and selling products designed for this "new" market (DeVries, 1993). Consumer demand, insurance reform and research on safety issues have also aided the midwifery movement and begun to force new changes in hospital policies (Eastman & Loustanau, 1987).

Other evidence indicative of the trend towards cultural demedicalization is found in opinion poll data regarding the recent decrease in the number of primary care physicians in the United States. Most medical students and graduates are expressing less of an interest in family medicine, general obstetrics, and general paediatrics—fields they consider too general in focus and which provide lower incomes and less predictable work hours. Instead, they are choosing specialities such as dermatology, ophthalmology, radiology, and surgical subspecialities (Young, 1993). According to the American College of Nurse-Midwives (ACNM), the number of nurse-midwives practicing in the U.S. tripled two decades ago (in the period from 1963-1973). In New York City, for example, 102 nurse-midwives were working in 1973 in 18 hospitals, compared with 22 in three hospitals ten years before (Klemesrud, 1973). This same organization reported in 1975 a total nationwide membership of 945 (Miller, 1977). In 1998 the ACNM listed 6,400 members, approximately 5,200 were in clinical practice (ACNM 1998).

Data drawn from secondary historical sources and interviews with midwives, their clients and activists, are used to chronicle the reemergence of midwifery in the United States and Canada in terms of the role played by two ideologies—science and feminism (Rushing, 1993). Both ideologies have been used by midwives and their supporters to legitimate midwifery in health care systems. The rhetoric of science has been used in establishing the safety of home birth and natural childbirth; and feminist principles and rhetoric often underlie claims about the economic and political advantages of midwifery made by its advocates. Both nurse-midwives and lay midwives have used these ideologies to justify their struggles for occupational legitimacy. They have, however, been more important to the latter's struggles for occupational legitimacy (Rushing, 1993).

Using participant observation and data from contemporary publications, Ruzek (1980) argued that the medical establishment has responded to women's health movement efforts to maximize women's control over obstetrical and gynecological care in patterned ways. While most changes were resisted at first, gradually changes such as more egalitarian interpersonal style and self help—which do not seriously threaten the medical profession's status, income or control over medicine—have been accepted. Changes such as alternative abortion and midwifery services controlled by non-physicians—which do threaten medical dominance—have been fought vigorously. Some innovations have been co-opted and transformed into more conventional, medically controlled services, e.g. in hospital "home-style" birth programs and medically supervised "self-care" (Ruzek, 1980).

A recent study was completed at Glasgow (Scotland) Royal Maternity Hospital of a randomized control trial of 1299 pregnant women who had been screened early in their pregnancy and had no medical obstetrical complications (Turnbull, *et al.*, 1996). The trial shows that prenatal, intrapartum and postpartum care could be given safely by midwives with outcomes for women and babies as good as with care provided by doctors. This finding is of paramount importance for countries such as the United States and Canada where primary care during pregnancy and birth for most women without complications is given by obstetrician doctors (Wagner, 1996). It is instructive also for all other countries who are presently in the process of adopting a purely medical model of childbirth, since it highlights the importance of the Turnbull finding that midwife managed care for healthy women is as clinically effective as that offered by doctors while also being capable of enhancing women's satisfaction with maternity care (Beesley, 1995).

Perhaps one of the most convincing arguments for justifying the cultural demedicalization of childbirth and midwifery—should this trend in reality be taking place—is put forward by Wagner (1988). Wagner proposes that infant mortality in the U.S. is not a health problem, but a social problem with health consequences. The experience of those industrialized countries with the best record for lowering infant mortality indicates that an extensive system of social and financial benefits for families with pregnant women and infants lowers infant mortality rates. In addition, every country in Europe with perinatal mortality and infant mortality rates lower than the U.S. uses midwives as the principal and only birth attendant for at least 70% of all births, indicating that a strong independent midwifery occupation is an important counterbalance to the medical profession in preventing excessive interventions.

BIBLIOGRAPHY

Abbott, G., 'The midwife in Chicago,' *American Journal of Sociology* 20: March 1919, 684-99.

Abbott, A., 'The order of professionalisation & empirical analysis,' *Work & Occupations*, 18 1991, 355-84.

ACNM, 1998 membership figures available on web page: *http://www.midwife.org/prof/basicfct.htm*

Alaska Midwifery Teaching Guide for Public Health Midwives, Juneau: Department of Health & Welfare, 1966.

Allison, J. & Pascall, G., 'Midwifery: A career for women?' pp. 203-17 in *Women and Career: Themes and Issues in Advanced Industrial Societies*, Evetts, J. (Ed.): London: Longman, 1994.

Anisef, P. & Basson, P., 'The institutionalization of a profession,' *Sociology of Work and Occupations*, 6(3): August 1979: 353-72.

Annandale, E.C., 'How midwives accomplish natural birth: managing risk and balancing expectations,' *Social Problems*, 35: 1988, 95-110.

Alto, W.A., Albu, R.E. & Irabo, G., 'An alternative to unattended delivery—A training program for village midwives in Papua New Guinea,' *Social Science and Medicine*, 32(5): 1991, 613-18.

Arms, S., *Immaculate Deception, A New Look at Women and Childbirth in America*, Boston: Houghton Mifflin Co., 1975.

Bakx, K., 'The eclipse of folk medicine in Western society,' *Sociology of Health & Illness*, 13: 1991: 20-38.

Barns, T., 'The indigenous midwife in India,' pp.311-22 in *Maternity Services in the Developing World*, Proceedings of 7th Study Group Royal College of Obstetricians & Gynecologists, Philpott, R.H. (Ed.), 1980.

Bayes, M., 'Maternity care in the world,' in *Report of Macy Conference: The Midwife in the U.S.*, New York: Josiah Macy, Jr. Foundation, 1968.

Beals, R.L., *Cheran: A Sierra Tarascan Village*, Publication No. 2, Washington: Smithsonian Institute of Social Anthropology, 1946.

Becker, H.S., *Sociological Work*, Chicago: Aldine Co., 1970.

Beesley, K., 'Home birth. The delivery of safe and satisfying care to women and their families,' *Journal of Nurse Midwifery*, 40(6): Nov.-Dec. 1995, 463-5.

Benedek, T., 'The changing relationship between midwives and physicians during the Renaissance,' *Bulletin of the History of Medicine* 51: 1977, 550-564.

Benoit, C., *Midwives in Passage: A case study of occupational change*, St. Johns, Newfoundland: ISER Press, 1991.

Benton, J.F., 'Trotula, women's problems and the professionalisation of medicine in the middle ages,' *Bulletin of the History of Medicine* 39: 1985, 30-53.

Biller, P., Childbirth in the middle Ages, *History Today* **36**: August, 1986, 42-49.

Blanguernon, C., *LeHoggar*, Paris: B. Arthaud, 1955.

Borst, C.G., 'The training and practice of midwives: a Wisconsin Study,' *Bulletin of the History of Medicine*, **62**: 1988, 606-627.

Browner, C.H., 'The management of reproduction in an egalitarian society' pp.58-72 in *Women as Healers: Cross-Cultural Perspectives*, McClain, C.S. (Ed.), New Brunswick, N.J.: Rutgers University Press, 1989.

Bryar, R.M., *Theory for Midwifery Practice*, London: Macmillan, 1995.

Buss, F.L., *La Partera, Story of a Midwife*, Ann Arbor: University of Michigan Press, 1980.

Butter, I.H., 'Premature adoption and routinization of medical technology: Illustrations from childbirth technology', *Journal of Social Issues*, **49**(2): 1993, 11-34.

Butter, I. & Kay, B., 'State laws and the practice of lay midwifery,' *American Journal of Public Health* **78**:1988, 1161-9.

Butter, I.H., 'Premature adoption and routinization of technology: illustrations from childbirth technology,' *Journal of Social Issues* **49**(2): Summer 1993, 11-34.

Campanella, K., Korbin, J.E. & Acheson, L., 'Pregnancy and childbirth among the Amish,' *Social Science & Medicine* **36**(3): 1993, 333-42.

Canadian Medical Association, Obstetrics, 1987. A Report of the Canadian Medical Association on Obstetrical Care in Canada, *Supplement to Canadian Medical Association Journal*, March 15, 1987.

Clarke, R., 'The last stand?' *Nursing Times* **89**(11): March 17, 1993, 36-37.

Conrad, P. & Schneider, J.W., 'Looking at levels of medicalization: A comment on Strong's critique of the thesis of medical imperialism,' *Social Science and Medicine*, **14A**(1): 1980, 75-79.

Converse, T.A., Buker, R.S. & Lee R.V., 'Hutterite midwifery', *American Journal of Obstetrics and Gynecology*, **116**(2): 1973, 719-725.

Cook, W.A., *Natural Childbirth: Fact and Fallacy*, Chicago: Nelson-Hall, 1982.

Corea, G., *The Hidden Malpractice: How American Medicine Treats Women as Patients and Professionals*, New York: Wm. Morrow & Co., 1977.

Cosminsky, S., 'Cross-cultural perspectives on midwifery,' pp.229-248 in *Medical Anthropology*, Grollig, F.X. & Haley, H.B. (Eds.), The Hague: Mouton, 1976.

Cosminsky, S., 'Midwifery and medical anthropology,' pp. 116-126 in *Modern Medicine and Medical Anthropology in the United States-Mexican Border Population*, Belimrovic, B. (Ed.), Washington, D.C.: Pan American Health Organization, 1978.

Cosminsky, S., 'Childbirth and change: A Guatemalan study,' pp.205-230 in *Ethnography of Fertility and Birth*, McCormack, C.P. (Ed.), New York: Academic Press, (1982a).

Cosminsky, S., 'Knowledge and body concepts of Guatemalan Midwives,' in *Anthropology of Human Birth*, Kay, M. (Ed.), Philadelphia: F.A. Davis, (1982b).

Cosminsky, S., 'Traditional birth practices and pregnancy avoidance in the Americas,' pp.75-89 in *The Potential of the Traditional Birth Attendant*, Maglacas, A.M. & Simon, J. (Eds.), Geneva: World Health Organization, 1986.

Crowell, F.E., 'The midwives of New York,' *Charities and the Commons*, **17**: 1907, 667-677. Reprinted in Litoff, 1986: 36-49.

Davis-Floyd, R.E., 'The Technological Model of Birth,' *Journal of American Folklore*, **100**: 1987, 479-95.

Davis-Floyd, R.E., *Birth as an American Rite of Passage*, Berkeley: University of California Press, 1992.

Davis-Floyd, R.E., & Sargent, C.F. (Eds.), *Childbirth & Authoritative Knowledge: Cross Cultural Perspectives*, Berkeley: University of California Press, 1997.

Declercq, E.R., 'The nature and style of practice of immigrant midwives in early twentieth century Massachusetts,' *Journal of Social History*, **19**: 1985, 113-129.

Declercq, E.R. & Lacroix, R., 'The immigrant Midwives of Lawrence: The conflict between law and culture in early twentieth-century Massachusetts,' *Bulletin of the History of Medicine* **59**: 1985, 232-246.

Declercq, E.R. 'The transformation of American midwifery: 1975 to 1988,' *American Journal of Public Health* **82**(5): May 1992: 680-684.

Declercq, E.R. 'The trials of Hanna Porn: The campaign to abolish midwifery in Massachusetts,' *American Journal of Public Health* **84**(6): June, 1994, 1022-1028.

DeLee, J.B., 'Progress towards ideal obstetrics,' *Transactions of the American Association for the Study and Prevention of Infant Mortality* **6**: 1915, 114-123.

Denton, J.A., 'The professionalisation process,' in *Medical Sociology* J.A. Denton (Ed.). Boston: Houghton Mifflin, 1978: 180-90

Devitt, N., 'How doctors conspired to eliminate the midwife even though scientific data supported midwifery,' pp.345-370 in *Compulsory Hospitalization or Freedom of Choice in Childbirth?*, Stewart, D. & Stewart, L. (Eds), Marble Hill, Mo: NAPSAC, 1979a.

Devitt, N., 'The statistical case for elimination of the midwife: fact versus prejudice, 1890-1935,' *Women and Health* 4(1): 1979b, 81-96 and 169-186.

DeVries, R.G., *Barriers to midwifery: An international perspective*, Dept. of Sociology, St. Olaf College, Northfield, Minnesota, unpublished paper (n.d.)

DeVries, R.G., 'A cross-national view of the status of midwives,' pp.131-146 in *Gender, Work & Medicine, Women & the Medical Division of Labor*, Riska, E. & Wegar, K. (Eds.) Newbury Park, Calif.: Sage, 1993.

DeVries, R.G., 'Midwifery & the problem of licensure,' *Research in the Sociology of Health Care* 2: 1982: 77-120.

DeVries, R.G. *Regulating Birth: Midwives, Medicine & the Law*, Philadelphia: Temple University Press, 1985.

DeVries, R.G., 'The contest for control, regulating new and expanding health occupations,' *American Journal of Public Health* 76(9): September 1986, 1147-1150.

DeVries, R. G., *Making Midwives Legal*, Ohio State University Press, 1996

Dingwall, R., 'Accomplishing profession,' pp.91-107 in *Studies in Everyday Medical Life*, Wadsworth, M. & Robinson, D. (Eds.) Martin Robertson & Co., Ltd., 1976.

Donegan, J.B., *Women and Men Midwives, Medicine, Mortality and Misogyny in Early America*, Westport, Connecticut: Greenwood Press, 1978.

Donnison, J., *Midwives and Medical men: A History of the Struggle for the Control of Childbirth*, London: Heinemann, 1977; 2nd (Ed) New Barnet, Herts: Historical Publications, 1988.

Dye, M.S., 'Mary Breckinridge, the Frontier Nursing Service and the introduction of nurse-midwifery in the United States,' *Bulletin of the History of Medicine*, 57: 1983, 485-507. Reprinted in Leavitt, 1984: 318-26.

Eastman, K.S. & Loustaunau, M.O., 'Reacting to the medical bureaucracy: Lay-midwifery as a birthing alternative,' *Marriage and Family Review*, 11(3-4): 1987, 23-27.

Eccles, A., *Obstetrics and Gynecology in Tudor and Stuart England*, London: Croom-Helm, 1982.

Ehrenreich, B. & English, D., *Witches , Midwives and Nurses: A History of Women Healers*, Glass Mountain Pamphlet No. 1, Old Westbury, New York: Feminist Press, 1973.

Ehrenreich, B. & English, D., *For Her Own Good: 150 Years of the Expert's Advice to Women*, Garden City, New York: Anchor Press, Doubleday, 1978.

El Hakim, S.Y., 'Village midwives in the Sudan,' pp.282-92 in *Maternity Services in the Developing World*, Proceedings 7th Study Group Royal College Obstetricians & Gynecologists, Philpott, R.H. (Ed.), 1980.

Emmons, A.B. & Huntington, J.L., 'The midwife: her future in the United States,' *American Journal of Obstetrics and the Diseases of Women & Children*, 65: 1912, 383-404. Reprinted in Litoff, 1986: 117-26.

Engelmann, G.L., *Labor Among Primitive Peoples*, St. Louis: Chambers 1884.

Etzel, R.A., 'The birth and development of midwifery, Liberian obstetrics,' Part 1, *Journal of Nurse Midwifery*, 21(4): Winter 1976: 24-37.

Etzel, R.A., 'The birth and development of midwifery, Liberian obstetrics,' Part 2, *Journal of Nurse Midwifery*, 22(1): Spring 1977: 18-30.

Expert Maternity Group, *Changing Childbirth* Part 1, London: HMSO, 1993.

Ferguson, J.H., 'Mississippi midwives,' *Journal of the History of Medicine*, 5: 1950, 85-95.

Evaneshko, V., 'Tonawanda Seneca childbearing culture,' in *Anthropology of Human Birth*, M. Kay (Ed.) Philadelphia: F.A. Davis, 1982.

Evenson, D., 'Midwives: survival of an ancient profession,' *Women's Rights-Law Reporter*, 7(4): 1982, 313-30.

Filippini, N.M., 'The church, the state & childbirth: the midwife in Italy during the 18th century,' pp.152-75 in *The Art of Midwifery: Early Modern Midwives in Europe*, Marland H. (Ed.) London: Routledge, 1993.

Flexner, A., *Medical Education in the United States and Canada*, New York: Carnegie Foundation for the Advancement of Teaching, Bulletin No. 4, 1910.

Flexner, A., 'Is social work a profession?' *School & Society*, 1: 1915, 905.

Foote, N.N., 'The professionalisation of labor in Detroit,' *American Journal of Sociology*, **LVIII**: January 1957, 371-80.

Ford, E., 'Notes on frequency and parturition in the D'Entrecasteaux Islands,' *Medical Journal of Australia*, **2**: 1940, 489-501.

Ford, C.S., *A comparative Study of Human Reproduction*, Yale University Publications in Anthropology, No. 32, New Haven, Connecticut: Yale University Press, 1945.

Forman, A.M. & Cooper, E.M., 'Legislation and nurse-midwifery practice in the USA,' *Journal of Nurse-Midwifery*, **21**(2): 1976, 1-53.

Fox, R.C., 'The medicalization and demedicalization of American society,' pp.409-413 in *The Sociology of Health and Illness*, 3rd edition, Conrad, P. & Kern, R. (Eds.), New York: St. Martin's Press, 1990.

Freedman, L.Z. & Ferguson, V.M., 'The question of 'painless childbirth' in primitive cultures,' *American Journal of Orth-Psych.*, **20**: 1950, 336.

Freidson, E., *Profession of Medicine, A Study of the Sociology of Applied Knowledge*, New York: Dodd, Mead, 1970.

Freidson, E., 'The futures of professionalisation', In: *Health and the Division of Labour*, Stacey, M., Reid, M., Heath, C. & Dingwall, R. (eds.), London: Croom Helm, 1977.

Freidson, E., 'The centrality of professionalism to health care', *Jurimetrics Journal*, **30**: 1990, 431-45.

Galba-Arauja, 'The traditional birth attendant in Brazil,' pp.293-310 in *Maternity Services in the Developing World*. Proceedings 7th Study Group Royal College of Obstetricians &Gynecologists, Philpott, R.H. (Ed.), 1980.

Gélis, J., *La sage-femme ou le médecin. Une nouvelle conception de la vie*, Paris: Fayard, 1988.

Gifford, S.M., 'The meaning of lumps: A case study of the ambiguities of risk,' pp.213-46 in *Anthropology & Epidemiology*, Craig, J., Stall, R. & Gifford, S. (Eds.) Dordrecht, Netherlands: D. Reidel Pub. Co., 1986.

Goldthorpe, W.O. & Richman, J., 'Reorganization of the maternity services: a comment on domiciliary confinement in view of the expense of the hospital strike 1973,' *Midwife & Health Visitor*, **10**: 1974, 265-70.

Goode, W.J. 'Community within a community: The professions,' *American Sociological Review*, **22**: 1957, 194-200.

Goode, W.J., 'Encroachment, charlatanism, and the emerging profession: Psychology, sociology and medicine,' *American Sociological Review*, **25**: 1960, 902-914.

Goode, W.J., 'The theoretical limits of professionalisation,' in *The Semi-Profession and Their Organization: Teachers, Nurses and Social Workers*, A. Etzioni (Ed.) New York: The Free Press, 1969.

Gorer, G., *Himalayan Village: An Account of the Lepchas of Sikkim*, London: Michael Joseph, 1938.

Green, M., 'Women's medical practice and health care in medieval Europe,' *Signs*, **14**(2): 1989, 434-473.

Greenwood, E., 'Attributes of a profession,' *Social Work* **II**: July 1957, 45-55.

Greilsammer, M., 'The midwife, the priest & the physician: the subjugation of midwives in the Low Countries at the end of the Middle Ages,' *Journal of Medieval & Renaissance Studies*, **21**: 1991, 285-329.

Gupta, K., 'Qualified personnel or traditional midwives?, Women's choice in rural India,' *International Nursing Review*, **25**: 1978, 175-181.

Haire, D.B., *A Cultural Warping of Childbirth*, Milwaukee: International Childbirth Education Association, 1972.

Harley, D., 'Ignorant midwives—A persistent stereotype,' *Bulletin of the Society for the Social History of Medicine*, **28**: 1981, 6-9.

Harley, D., 'Historians as demonologists: the myth of the midwife-witch,' *Social History of Medicine*, **3**: 1990, 1-26.

Harris, D., Daily, E.F. & Lang, D.M., 'Nurse midwifery in New York City,' *American Journal of Public Health*, **61**: January 1971, 64-77.

Harwood, A., 'A discussion about discourse,' *Medical Anthropology Quarterly*, **2**(2): 1988, 99-101.

Hiddinga, A., 'Dutch obstetric science: emergence, growth & present situation, ' pp.45-76 in *Successful Home Birth & Midwifery: The Dutch Model*, Van der Mark, E.A. (Ed.), Westport, Conn.: Bergin & Garvey, 1993.

Hilger, M.I., *Araucanian Child Life and its Cultural Background*, Smithsonian Miscellaneous Collection, Vol. 133, Washington: Smithsonian Institution, 1957.

Holmberg, A.R., *Nomads of the Long Bow: The Siriono of Eastern Bolivia*, Publication No. 10, Washington: Smithsonian Institute, Institute of Social Anthropology, 1950.

Horn, B., 'Northwest Cosat Indians: The Muckleshoot,' pp.361-376, in *Anthropology of Human Birth*, M. Kay (Ed.), Philadelphia: F.A. Davis, 1982.

House of Commons, Health Committee, *Health Committee second report on the maternity services (Winterton Report)*, Vol. 1, London: HMSO, 1992.

Illich, I., *Medical Nemesis*, London: Calder & Boyers, 1975.

Illsley, R., 'The sociological study of reproduction and its outcome,' pp.75-141, in *Childbearing: Its Social and Psychological Aspects*, S.H. Richardson & A.F. Guttmacher (Eds.), Williams and Wilkins Co., 1967.

Itavyar, D.A., 'A traditional midwife practice, Sokoto state Nigeria,' *Social Science & Medicine*, **18**(6): 1984, 497-501.

Jackson, M.E. *et al.*, 'Home birth with certified nurse-midwife attendants in the U.S., an overview,' *Journal of Nurse Midwifery*, **40**(6): Nov.-Dec. 1995, 493-507.

Jacquart, D., *Le milieu médical en France du XII au XV siècle*, Geneva: Droz, 1981.

Jeffery, P., Jeffery, R. & Lyon, A., *Labour Pains and Labour Power: Women & Childbearing in India*, London: Zed Books, 1989.

Jeffery, R. & Jeffery, P., 'Traditional birth attendants in rural India,' pp.7-31 in *Knowledge, Power & Practice: The Anthropology of Medicine and Everyday Life*, Lindenbaum, S. & Lock, M. (Eds.) Berkeley: University of California., 1993.

Jones, L.J., *The Social Context and of Health and Health Work*, Houndsmills, Basingstoke: Macmillan, 1994

Jordan, B., *Birth in Four Cultures. A Cross-cultural Investigation of Childbirth in Yucatan, Holland, Sweden and the United States*, St. Albans, Vermont: Eden Press, 1978.

Jordan, B., 'Studying childbirth: The experience and methods of a woman anthropologist,' pp.181-215, in *Childbirth: Alternatives to Medical Control*, Romalis, R. (Ed.), Austin: University of Texas Press, 1981.

Jordan, B., 'High technology: the case of obstetrics,' *World Health Forum*, **8**: 1987a, 312-319.

Jordan, B., 'The hut and the hospital: information, power & symbolism in the artifacts of birth,' *Birth*, **14**(1) March 1987b, 36-40.

Jordan, B., *Birth in Four Cultures. A Cross-cultural Investigation of Childbirth in Yucatan, Holland, Sweden and the United States*, 4th edition, Prospect Heights, Ill.: Waveland Press, 1993.

Josefson, D., 'U.S. midwives have low caesarian rate,' *British Medical Journal*, **311**: Nov. 25, 1995, 1387.

Justice, J., 'Can socio-cultural information improve health planning? A case study of Nepal's assistant nurse-midwife,' *Social Science & Medicine*, **19**(3): 1984, 192-198.

Kaufert, P.A. & O'Neil, J., 'Analysis of a dialogue on risks in childbirth,' pp.32-53 in *Knowledge, Power and Practice: The Anthropology of Medicine & Everyday Life*, Lindenbaum, S. & Lock, M. (Eds.) Berkeley: University of California Press, 1993.

King, C.R., 'The New York maternal mortality study: a conflict of professionalisation,' *Bulletin of the History of Medicine*, **65**: 1991, 476-502.

Kitzinger, S., *Birth at Home*, N.Y.: Oxford Univ. Press, 1979.

Kitzinger, S., 'The social context of birth: Some comparisons between childbirth in Jamaica & Britain, Nana: The midwife,' pp. 181-190, in *The Ethnography of Fertility & Birth*, McCormack, C. (ed.), N.Y.: Academic Press, 1982.

Kitzinger, S., 'Childbirth and Society,' pp.99-109, in *Effective Care in Pregnancy and Childbirth*, M. Enkin, M.J.N.C. Keirse & I. Chalmers (Eds.), Oxford: Oxford University Press, 1989.

Klinkert, , J.J., 1980, *Verloskundigen en artsen verleden en heden van enkele professionele beroepen in de gezondheidszorg*, (PhD thesis), Alphen a/d Rijn: Stafleu's wetenschappelijke uitgeversmaatschappij

Kloosterman, G.L., 'The Dutch system of home births,' in *The Place of Birth*, S. Kitzinger & J. Davis (Eds.) Oxford: Oxford University Press, 1978.

Kobrin, F.E., 'The American midwife controversy: a crisis of professionalisation,' *Bulletin of the History of Medicine*, 40: 1966, 350-394. Reprinted in Leavitt, 1984: 318-326.

Laforce, H., 'The different stages of the elimination of midwives in Quebec,' pp.36-50 in *Delivering Motherhood*, Arnup, K., et al., (Eds.) London: Routledge, 1990.

Laderman, C., *Wives and Midwives: Childbirth & Nutrition in Rural Malaysia*, Berkeley: University of California Press, 1983.

Langton, P.A. & Kammerer, D.A., 'Childbearing and women's choice of nurse-midwives in Washington D.C. hospitals,' *Women and Health*, 15(2): 1989, 49-65.

Leavitt, J.W., 'Science enters the birthing room: Obstetrics in America since the eighteenth century,' *Journal of American History*, 70(2): September 1983, pp.281-304.

Leavitt, J.W. (Ed.), *Women and Health in America*, Madison: University of Wisconsin Press, 1984.

Leavitt, J.W., *Brought to Bed: Childbearing in America 1750-1950*, New York: Oxford Univ. Press, 1986.

Leedan, E, 'Traditional birth attendants,' *International Journal Gynecology & Obstetrics*, 23: 1985, 249-74.

Lemay, H.R., 'Antonius Guainerius and medieval gynecology,' pp.317-336, *Woman of the Medieval World*, Oxford: Blackwell, 1985.

Lévi-Strauss, C., 'The effectiveness of symbols,' pp.186-205 in *Structural Anthropology*, Vol. 1, N.Y.: Basic Books, 1963.

Lieburg van, M.J. & Marland, H., 'Midwife regulation and practice in the Netherlands during the 19th century,' *Medical History*, 33: 1989, 296-317.

Linton, R., 'Marquesan culture,' p.163 in *The Individual & His Society*, Kardiner, A. (Ed.), New York: Columbia University Press, 1939.

Litoff, J.B., *American Midwives: 1860 to the present*. Westport, Connecticut: Greenwood Press, 1978.

Litoff, J.B., (Ed.) *The American Midwife Debate*, Westport, Connecticut: Greenwood Press, 1986.

Lockett, C., 'Midwives and childbirth among the Navajo,' *Plateau*, 12: 1939, 15-17.

Longo, L.D., 'A treatise of midwifery, in three parts,' *American Journal of Obstetrics and Gynecology*, 172(4 pt1): April 1995, 1317-19.

Loudon, I., *Medical Care and the General Practitioner, 1750-1850*, Oxford: Clarendon Press, 1986.

Loudon, I., *Death in Childbirth: An International Study of Maternal Care and Maternal Mortality, 1800-1950*, Oxford: Clarendon Press, 1992.

Malin, M. & Hemminki, E., 'Midwives as providers of prenatal care in Finland—past and present,' *Women and Health*, 18(4): 1993, 17-34.

Mathews, M.K., 'Training traditional birth attendants in Nigeria—the pictorial method,' *World Health Forum*, 16(4): 1995, 409-13.

McCormack, C.P., 'Biological, cultural and social adaptation in human fertility and birth: A synthesis,' pp.1-23 in *The Ethnography of Fertility and Birth*, McCormack, C.P. (Ed.), N.Y.: Academic Press, 1982a.

McCormack, C.P., 'Health, fertility and birth in Moyamba District, Sierra Leone,' pp.115-139 in *The Ethnography of Fertility and Birth*, McCormack, C.P. (Ed.), N.Y.: Academic Press, 1982b.

McCormack, C.P., 'The articulation of Western & traditional systems of health care' in *The Professionalisation of African Medicine*, Last, M. & Chavundaka, G.L. (Eds.) Manchester, UK: Manchester University Press, 1986.

Macintyre, S., 'Childbirth: the myth of the golden age,' *World Medicine*, 12(8): June 15, 1977, 17-22.

McClain, C., 'Toward a comparative framework for the study of childbirth: A review of the literature,' in *Anthropology of Human Birth*, Kay, M. (Ed.), Philadelphia: F.A. Davis Co., 1982.

McLauren, A., *Reproductive Rituals: The Perception of Fertility in England from The Sixteenth Century to the Nineteenth Century*, London: Methuen Co., 1984.

McMillen, S.E., *Motherhood in the Old South: Pregnancy and Infant Rearing*, Louisiana State University Press, 1990.

McVaugh, M., 'The births of the children of Jaime II,' *Medieval*, 6: 1986, 7-16.

Maglacas, A. M. & Simons, J. (Eds.), *The Potential of the Traditional Birth Attendant*, Geneva: World Health Organization (WHO), 1979 and 1986.

Marland, H., (Ed.), *The Art of Midwifery: Early Modern Midwives in Europe*, London: Routledge, 1993a.

Marland, H., 'The burgerlijke midwife: the stadsvroedvrouw of eighteenth-century Holland,' pp.192-213 in *The Art of Midwifery: Early Modern Midwives in Europe* Marland, H. (Ed.), London: Routledge 1993b.

Marland, H., 'The midwife as health missionary: the reform of Dutch childbirth practices in the early twentieth century,' pp.153-79 in *Midwives, Society & Childbirth: Debates & Controversies in the Early Modern Period*, Marland, H. & Rafferty A.M. (Eds.) London: Routledge, 1997.

Martin, W.D., *Hearings on Nurse Midwifery: Consumer's Freedom of Choice*. Testimony before the Subcommittee on Oversight & Investigation, 96th congress, December 15, 1980, Washington D.C.: United States Government Printing Office, 1981.

Mead, M, *Growing up in New Guinea: a study of adolescence and sex in primitive societies* Harmondsworth: Penguin, 1942 (original published 1930)

Mead, M, *Coming of age in Samoa*, New York: Morrow, 1928.

Mead, M. & Newton, N., 'Cultural patterning of perinatal behavior,' pp.142-244 in *Childbearing: Its Social & Psychological Aspects*, Richardson, S.A. & Guttmacher, A.F. (Eds.), Baltimore: Williams & Wilkins, 1967.

Mitford, J., 'Teach midwifery, go to jail,' *This World*, October 21, 1990, 7-12.

Mongeau, B., Smith, H.L. & Maney, A.C., 'The granny midwife: changing roles and function of a folk practitioner,' *American Journal of Sociology*, **66**: 1961, 497-505.

Muecke, M., 'Health care systems as socializing agents: childbearing the North Thai and Western ways,' *Social Science & Medicine*, **10**: 1976, 377-383.

Naaktgeboren, C., 'The biology of childbirth,' pp.795-804 in *Effective Cure in Pregnancy and Childbirth*, Chalmers, I., Enkin, M. & Keirse, M.J.N.C. (Eds.) Oxford: Oxford University Press, 1989.

Naroll, F., Naroll, R. & Howard, F.H., 'Positions of women in childbirth,' *American Journal of Obstetrics and Gynecology*, **82**: 1961, 943.

Nash, J. & Kirsch, M., 'The discourse of medical science in the construction of consensus between corporation and community,' *Medical Anthropology Quarterly*, **2**(2): 1988, 158-171.

Nettleton, S, *The Sociology of Health & Illness*, Cambridge, UK: Polity Press

Newton, N., 'Pregnancy, childbirth and outcome: A review of patterns of culture and future research needs,' pp.147-243 in *Childbearing: Its Social and Psychological Aspects*, Richardson, S.A. & Guttmacher, A.F. (Eds.), Baltimore: Williams and Wilkins, 1967.

Oakley, A., 'The trap of medicalized motherhood,' *New Society*, 34(689): Dec., 1975, 639-641.

Oakley, A., 'Wise women and medicine man: Changes in the management of childbirth,' pp.17-58 in *The Rights & Wrongs of Women*, Mitchell, J. & Oakley, A. (Eds.) Harmondsworth, UK: Penguin, 1976.

Oakley, A., 'Cross-cultural practices,' pp.18-33 in *Benefits and Hazards of the New Obstetrics*, Chard, T. & Richards, M. (Eds.), London: Wm. Heinemann Books, 1977.

Oakley, A., *Essays on Women, Medicine and Health*, Edinburgh: Edinburgh University Press, 1993.

Oppenheimer, C., 'Organizing midwifery led care in the Netherlands,' *British Medical Journal*, **307**: 1993, 1400-2.

Papanikolas, H.Z., 'Margerou: The Greek midwife,' *Utah Historical Quarterly*, 1986, 51-60.

Parkin, F., *Marxism and Class Theory: A Bourgeois Critique*, London: Tavistock, 1979.

Parry, N. & Parry, J., *The Rise of the Medical Profession*, London: Croom-Helm, 1976.

Patten van, N., 'Obstetrics in New Mexico prior to 1600,' *Annals of Medical History*, 2D series 4: 1932, 203-212.

Pearson, M., 'Old wives or young midwives? Women as caretakers of health: The case of Nepal,' pp.116-130 in *Gender and Geography in The Developing World*, Monsen, J. & Townsend, J., (Eds.), London; Hutchinson, 1987.

Pelling, M., 'Medical practice in early modern England: trade or profession?' pp.90-128 in *The Professions in Early Modern England*, Prest, W. (Ed.) London: Croom-Helm, 1987.

Peng, J.Y., 'The role of the traditional birth attendant in family planning in Southeast Asia,' *International Journal of Gynecology and Obstetrics*, **17**: 1979, 108-113.

Peterson, K.J., 'Technology as a last resort in home birth: The work of lay midwives,' *Social Problems*, **30**(3): 1983: 272-283.

Petrelli, R.L., 'The regulation of French midwifery during the Ancien Régime,' *Journal of the History of Medicine*, **26**(3): 1971, 276-292

Radosh, P.F. 'Midwives in the United States: Past and present,' *Population Research and Policy Review*, **5**(2): 1986, 129-146.

Recio, D.M., 'Birth and tradition in the Philippines,' pp.66-74 in *The Potential of the Traditional Birth Attendant*, Maglacas, A.M. & Simons, J. (Eds.), Geneva: World Health Organization, 1986.

Record, J.C. & Cohen, H.R., 'The introduction of midwifery in a prepaid group practice,' *American Journal of Public Health*, **62**: March 1972, 354-360.

Reid, M., 'Sisterhood and professionalisation: A case study of the American lay midwife,' pp. 219-238 in *Women as Healers: Cross-Cultural Perspectives*, McClain, C.S. (Ed.) New Brunswick: Rutgers University Press, 1989.

Rich, A., *Of Women Born*, New York: W.W. Norton & Co., 1976.

Riessman, C.K., 'Women & medicalization,' *Social Policy*, Summer, 1983, 3-18.

Riley, M., *Brought to Bed*, New York: A.S. Barnes, 1968.

Robinson, S., 'Midwives, obstetricians and general practitioners: the need for role clarification,' *Midwifery*, **1**: 1985: 102-113.

Roch, S., 'Excellence in midwifery education', *Modern Midwife*, **3**:1993, 36-8

Romalis, S., (Ed.) *Childbirth: Alternatives to Medical Control*, Austin: University of Texas Press, 1981.

Romlid, C., 'Swedish midwives and their instruments in the eighteenth and nineteenth centuries' pp.38-60 in *Midwives, Society & Childbirth: Debates & Controversies in the Early Modern Period*, Marland, H. & Rafferty A.M. (Eds.) London: Routledge, 1997.

Rooks, J.P, *Midwifery and Childbirth in America*, Philadelphia: Temple University Press., 1997.

Rothman, B.K., 'The social construction of birth,' *Journal of Nurse-Midwifery*, **22**(2): Summer, 1977, 9-13.

Rothman, B.K., 'Awoke and aware, or false consciousness: The cooption of childbirth reform in America,' pp.153-154 in *Childbirth: Alternatives to Medical Control*, Romalis, S. (Ed.) Austin: University of Texas Press, 1981.

Rothman, B,K,, 'Midwives in transition: The structure of a clinical revolution,' *Social Problems*, **30**(3): February 1983, 262-271.

Rothman, B., 'Childbirth management and medical monopoly,' pp.117-135, in *Women, Biology and Public Policy*, V. Sapir (Ed.), N.Y.: Sage Publications, 1985.

Rushing, B., 'Ideology in the reemergence of North American midwifery,' *Work & Occupations*, **20**(1): 1993, 46-67.

Ruzek, S.B., 'Medical response to women's health activities: Conflict, accommodation and co-optation,' *Research in the Sociology of Health Care*, **1**: 1980, 335-354.

Sargent, C.F., *The Cultural Context of Therapeutic Choice, Obstetrical Care Decisions Among the Bariba of Benin*, Dordrecht: D. Reidel Publishing Co., 1982.

Sargent, C.F., 'Women's roles and women healers in contemporary rural and urban Benin,' pp.204-218 in *Women as Healers: Cross-Cultural Perspectives*, McClain, C.S. (Ed.) New Brunswick, New Jersey: Rutgers University Press, 1989.

Saks, M., 'Removing the blinkers? A critique of recent contributions to the sociology of professions', *Sociological Review*, **31**: 1983, 1-21

Schaffer, R.C., 'The health and social functions of black midwives on the Texas Brazos Bottom, 1920-1985,' *Rural Sociology* **56**(1): 1991, 89-105.

Schama, S., *The Embarrassment of Riches: An Interpretation of Dutch Culture in the Golden Age*, New York: Knopf, 1987.

Schilling, H., 1992, *Religion, Political Culture and the Emergence of Early Modern Society: Essays on German and Dutch History*, Leiden: E.J. Brill

Scheepers, L.M., 'Jidda: The traditional midwife of Yemen,' *Social Science & Medicine* **33**: 1991, 959-62.

Scholten, C.M., 'On the importance of the obstetric art: Changing customs of childbirth in America, 1760-1825,' *William and Mary Quarterly*, **34**: 1977, 426-45.

Schnorrenberg, B.B., 'Is childbirth any place for a woman? The decline of midwifery in 18th century England,' *Studies in Eighteenth Century Culture*, **10**: 1981, 393-408.

Shorter, E., *A History of Women's Bodies*, New York: Basic Books, 1982.

Shorter, E., 'The management of normal deliveries and the generation of William Hunter,' pp. 371-383 in *William Hunter and the Eighteenth Century Medical World*, Bynum, W.F. & Porter, R. (Eds.), Cambridge, UK: Cambridge University Press, 1985.

Sindiga, I., 'Towards the participation of traditional birth attendants in primary health care in Kenya,' *East African Medical Journal*, 1995.

Sousa, M., *Childbirth at Home*, Englewood Cliffs, New Jersey: Prentice Hall, 1976.

Sleep, J., Roberts, J. & Chalmers, I., 'Care during the second stage of labour,' pp.1129-1144 in *Effective Care in Pregnancy and Childbirth*, Chalmers, I., Enkin, M. & Keirse, M. (Eds.) Oxford: Oxford University Press, 1989.

Smulders, B. & Limburg, A., 'Obstetrics and midwifery in the Netherlands,' in *The Midwife Challenge*, S. Kitzinger (Ed.), London: Pandora, 1988.

Sparks, B., 'A descriptive study of the changing roles and practices of traditional birth attendants in Zimbabwe,' *Journal of Nurse-Midwifery*, **35**(3): 1990: 150-61.

Stark, S. 'Mormon childrearing,' pp. 341-361 in *Anthropology of Human Birth*, M. Kay (Ed.), Philadelphia: F.A. Davis, 1982.

Strong, P. M., 'Sociological imperialism and the profession of medicine: A critical examination of the thesis of medical imperialism,' *Social Science & Medicine*, **13A**: 1979, 199-215.

Sullivan, D.A. & Weitz, R., 'Obstacles to the practice of licensed lay-midwifery,' *Social Science & Medicine*, **19**(11): 1984, 1189-96.

Sullivan, D. & Weitz, R., *Labor Pains: Modern Midwives and Home Birth*, New Haven: Yale University Press, 1988.

Stanton, M.E., 'The myth of 'natural' childbirth,' *Journal of Nurse-Midwifery*, **24**(2): 1979, 25-29.

Stapleton, H., 1997, 'Choice in the face of uncertainty', in. *Reflections on Midwifery*, Kirkham, M.J. & Perkins, E.R. (eds.), London: Ballière Tindall

Starr, P., *The Social Transformation of American Medicine*, New York: Basic Books, 1982.

Stout, D.B., *San Blas Cuna Acculturation: An Introduction*, New York: Viking Fund Publ., 1947

Sumner, W.G., *Folkways*, Boston, 1907.

Tatlock, L., 'Speculum feminarum: gendered perspectives on obstetrics and gynecology in early modern Germany,' *Signs* **17**(4): Summer, 1992, 725-760.

Teijlingen van, E.R. & McCaffery, P., 'The profession of midwife in the Netherlands,' *Midwifery* **3**: 1987, 178-86.

Teijlingen van, E.R., 'The profession of maternity home care assistant and its significance for the Dutch midwifery profession,' *International Journal of Nursing Studies*, **27**: 1990, 355-366.

Teijlingen van, E.R., 'Maternity home-care assistant: A unique occupation,' in pp.161-71 *Successful Home Birth and Midwifery: the Dutch Model*', E. Abraham-Van der Mark (ed.), London: Bergin & Garvey, 1993.

Teijlingen van, E.R., *A social or medical model of childbirth? Comparing the arguments in Grampian (Scotland) and the Netherlands*, (unpublished PhD Thesis), Aberdeen: University of Aberdeen, 1994.

Teijlingen van , E.R. & van der Hulst, L., 'Midwifery in the Netherlands, more than a semi-profession?,' pp. 178-86' In: Larkin, G., Johnson T. & Saks, M. (eds.), *Health Professions and the State in Europe*, London: Routledge, 1995.

Tew, M., *Safer Childbirth? A Critical History of Maternity Care* , N.Y.: Routledge, Chapman & Hall, 1990.

Tew, M., *Safer Childbirth? A Critical History of Maternity Care* (third edition), London: Free Association Books, 1998.

Tjaden, P.G., 'Midwifery in Colorado: A case study in the politics of professionalisation,' *Qualitative Sociology*, **10**(1): Spring, 1987, 29-45.

Turnbull, D., Holmes, A., Shields, N., *et al.*, 'Randomized controlled trial of efficacy of midwife-managed care,' *The Lancet*, **348**(9022): July 27, 1996, 213-18.

Turner, B.S., *Medical Power and Social Knowledge*, London: Sage Publications Ltd, 1987.

Ventre, F., 'The transition from lay-midwife to certified nurse-midwife in the U.S.,' *Journal of Nurse Midwifery*, **40**(5): Sept.-Oct., 1995, 428-37.

Versluysen, M.C., 'Midwives, medical men & poor women labouring of child: lying-in hospitals in 18th century London,' pp.18-49 in *Women, Health & Reproduction*, Roberts, H. (Ed.), London: Routledge, 1981.

Voorhoeve, A.M., Kars, C. & Van Ginneken, J.K., 'Modern and traditional antenatal and delivery care,' pp. 309-372 in *Maternal and Child Health in Rural Kenya*, Van Ginneken, J.K. & Muller, A.S. (Eds.) London: Croom-Helm, 1984.

Wagner, M.G., 'Birth and power,' in *Perinatal Health Services in Europe—Searching for Better Childbirth*, Phaff, J.M.L. (Ed.) WHO Regional Office for Europe, 1986.

Wagner, M.G., 'Infant mortality in Europe: Implications for the United States,' *Journal of Public Health Policy*, **9**(4): Winter, 1988, 473-484.

Wagner, M., 'Midwife-managed care,' *The Lancet*, **348**(9022): July 27, 1996, 208.

Walker, J., 'The changing role of the midwife,' *International Journal of Nursing Studies*, **9**: 1972, 85-94.

Walker, J., 'Midwife or obstetric nurse? Some perceptions of midwives and obstetricians of the role of the midwife,' *Journal of Advanced Nursing*, **1**: 1976, 129-138.

Wallace, E. & Hoebel, E.A., *The Commanches: Lords of the South Plains*, Norman: University of Oklahoma Press, 1952.

Wasserman, M., 'The new nurse-midwives,' *The Progressive*, **39**: October 1975, 32-35.

Wertz, R.W. & Wertz, D.C. *Lying In: A History of Childbirth in America*, N.Y.: Free Press, 1977; and New Haven: Yale University Press, 1989.

Wertz, R.W. & Wertz, D.C., 'Notes on the decline of midwives and the rise of medical obstetricians,' pp148-160 in Conrad, P. & Kern, R. (Eds.) *The Sociology of Health and Illness*, 3d ed., New York: St. Martin's Press, 1990.

Wiesner, M., 'The midwives of south Germany and the public/private dichotomy,' pp.77-94 in *The Art of Midwifery: Early Modern Midwives in Europe* Marland, H., London: Routledge 1993a.

Wilensky, H.L., 'The professionalisation of everyone,' *American Journal of Sociology*, **LXX**: Sept. 1964, 137-58.

Williams, J.W., 'Medical education and the midwife problem in the United States,' *Journal of the American Medical Association*, **58**: 1912, 1-7. Reprinted in Litoff, 1986: 86-101.

Wilson, A., 'William Hunter and the varieties of man-midwifery,' pp.343-369 in *William Hunter & the 18th Century Medical World*, Bynum, W.F. & Porter, R. (Eds.), Cambridge UK: Cambridge University Press, 1985.

Witz, A., 'Patriarchy and Professions: The gendered politics of occupational closure', *Sociology*, **24**, (4): 1990, 675-90

Witz, A., *Professions and Patriarchy*, London: Routledge, 1992.

World Health Organization, *Traditional Birth Attendants: An Annotated Bibliography on Their Training, Utilization and Evaluation*, Geneva: World Health Organization (WHO), 1979.

World Health Organization, Regional Office for Europe, *Having a Baby in Europe*, Report of a Study, Public Health in Europe, Copenhagen: 1985.

Wright, J., 'Collective review—the views of primitive peoples concerning the process of labor,' *American Journal of Obstetrics and Gynecology*, **2**: 1921, 206-210.

Ben-Yehuda, N., 'The European witchcraze of the 14th to 17th centuries: A sociologist's perspective,' *American Journal of Sociology*, **86**(1): July, 1980, 1-32.

Young, D., 'Crisis in primary care: Will midwives meet the challenge?' *Birth*, **20**(2): June, 1993, 59-60.

Yankauer, A., 'Editor's note,' *American Journal of Public Health*, **78**: Jan. 1988, 96.

Ziegler, C.E., 'The elimination of the midwife,' *Journal of the American Medical Association*, **60**: January 4, 1913, 32-38; and in this reader.

Zola, I.K., 'Medicine as an institution of social control,' *Sociological Review*, **20**(4): 1972, 487-504.

[1] A term originally introduced by the sociologist William Graham Sumner in his *Folkways*, 1907 to mean the tendency that people have of viewing and evaluating other cultures in terms of the values of their own culture, and ultimately concluding that their culture is superior.

[2] Birth is an abnormal deviation from the norm and a hazardous medical condition. A visit to the obstetrician to diagnose a pregnancy is little different from that to diagnose an ovarian tumor and the entire prenatal period involves careful surveillance in anticipation of pathology and illness (Romalis, 1981: 7).

[3] In a comparative study of the biological process of childbirth, Jordan (1978) found that a high value was placed on collaboration between women and their midwife attendants in Yucatan (Mexico), Sweden and the Netherlands—such collaboration positively influencing a woman's physical and emotional well-being. This involvement and support of birth participants is in sharp contrast with the culture of birth in industrialized societies where the woman is relatively isolated and considered by physicians as too ill-informed and incompetent to be involved in making medical decisions (Romalis, 1981: 10).

[4] Perhaps the most accurate rendering of the relationship between pregnancy and illness is that the pregnant woman should be treated as if she is or might become ill (Oakley, 1977: 20).

[5] In almost all non-industrialized societies childbirth is defined as a normal function and is regarded as an integral part of ordinary family life (Mead & Newton, 1967; Riley, 1968). That is, beliefs and practices related to reproduction and integrated with those characterizing social life generally. Only a handful of traditional societies resemble the Western attitude toward childbirth. The Cuna Indians of Panama (Newton, 1967) and the Araucanian Indians of South America (Hilger, 1957), for example, regard childbirth as sickness or illness.

[6] Even in those few traditional societies, for example where TBAs practice a broad range of healing arts—with midwifery being only one of the services they provide (Jordan, 1978; McCormack, 1982)—their beliefs and practices are commonly shared by all TBAs.

[7] Instead of using "subculture" to describe the shared set of beliefs and practices of the Bariba midwife, Sargent used the terms "therapeutic system".

[8] Although unattended birth does occur in traditional culture (Alto, 1991: 613), it is a rare event to be gossiped about in the same manner as an American birth taking place in an ambulance (Newton, 1967: 169). In certain regions of the world, however—especially where populations are sparse and dispersed as in Alaska, New Guinea and Africa—there is no indigenous status of midwife (Alto, 1991: 613; Alaska, 1966; McCormack, 1982) or midwives may serve alongside spirit mediums and herbalists to advise and assist the woman in childbirth (McCormack, 1982). Even in those societies, however, with no recognized position of midwife there are established customs and procedures associated with child delivery and child care.

[9] Of the 76 non-European societies surveyed in one study, 62 used upright and not supine positions (Ford, 1945: 58; Oakley, 1977: 26).

[10] It is a romantic myth that women in traditional societies always approach childbirth joyfully and casually and deliver without fear and pain and the need for intervention. (Macintyre, 1977: 17; Stanton, 1979: 27; Ford, 1940, 1945). As a matter of fact, women from these societies acquire many negative attitudes toward pregnancy and birth, and are subjected to all kinds of intervention—many of which resemble those in modern societies (Romalis, 1981: 6).

[11] In Lille, for example, the grant of a license to practice as a midwife is on record in 1460, and 1600 there was a printed register of qualified midwives allowed to practice in Paris (Petrelli, 1971: 279, 281).

[12] For much of the twentieth century, the view of midwives as doctors' assistants has gained ground in almost every part of the world. The other view of a midwife, as a person whose job is to be with a childbearing woman, is far older. It is there in the word used in the English language to refer to such a person—the "mid" in midwife meaning "with", and "wife" meaning "woman".

[13] The delivery is typically attended by married women from the laboring woman's close marital kin (e.g. mother-in-law)—or other senior attendants from neighboring households—who remain in control of the conduct of the delivery and in decisions regarding what the birthing position should be and whether the labor should be accelerated. The other major actor in childbirth is the "dai", who is called when the mother-in-law decides the labor is well established, and who performs only those practices which both Hindus and Moslems consider "disgusting" and "polluting" such as delivering the baby, cutting the umbilical cord, disposing of the placenta, washing birth clothes and cleaning up the blood (Jeffery & Jeffery, 1993: 16-17; Barns, 1980: 312-334; Gupta, 1978).

[14] For a detailed analysis of the many normative elements that differentiate the status of American lay midwives from that of certified nurse-midwives see DeVries (1982: 79-101) & DeVries (1996).

[15] Unlike nurse-midwifery which is nationally recognized (Evenson, 1982), not all states in the United States permit lay midwives to practice (DeVries, 1982). Lay midwifery may be legal because (a) midwives have attended an approved course of study and passed a state qualifying examination; (b) there are no laws prohibiting the practice of midwifery; or (c) midwives are permitted simply to register as midwives (Reid, 1989: 220-1; see DeVries in this volume).

[16] Litoff (1978) gives a picture of this type of midwife who was prominent in early twentieth century America. She would most likely have been a married woman who had borne several children. She would have had little or no formal training in midwifery but would have received her first learning experience from her mother or some older woman. Since she would not have been familiar with modern obstetric techniques she would have adopted a policy of non-intervention, i.e. of letting nature take its course. Other norm requirements of the status would have been that she would often be expected to perform household or non-medical tasks such as cooking and cleaning. Abbott (1919), in her study of midwives in early 20th century Chicago, adds to this period image of the American midwife. She found that almost all of the midwives in this city were foreign born and lived in foreign neighborhoods where their practice was almost exclusively confined to immigrant women of Polish, German, Italian, Bohemian and Slovak extraction. She also found these midwives to be largely untrained; therefore labeled them "careless, dirty and dangerous".

[17] DeVries (1982) contends that it was the licensing and regulation requirements in the various states and cities which initially led to the development of two distinct practitioners: the lay midwife and the CNM. The CNM is now able to practice legally in all states and jurisdictions—having been awarded formal recognition as a status in 1971 by the obstetricians' professional association (the American College of Obstetricians and Gynecologists).

[18] Norms associated with the lay midwife continue to focus on the patient with little or no involvement with the formally established health care delivery system inclusive of hospitals, physicians, and high technology obstetrics (DeVries, 1982).

[19] In an earlier paper, Conrad and Schneider (1980) suggested that medicalization occurs on three levels: the conceptual, institutional, and interactional. In their discussion, however, midwifery was only one of a multitude of medicalization features described.

[20] Forceps have been frequently associated by historians of medicine with the demise of the traditional female midwife and the rise of male attendance in childbirth (Litoff, 1978: 7). Wilson (1985: 343-51) contends, however, that William Hunter, the leading male midwife in mid-eighteenth century London, was strenuously opposed to the midwifery use of forceps, and that, at least initially, male midwives were preferred to traditional female midwives by the families of the mother because they believed that the birth might be difficult and male midwives were better able to handle abnormal birth. Leavitt (1983: 284), in discussing eighteenth-century obstetrics in America, adds further insight into this subject by suggesting that women had good reason to believe that physicians, who were almost all males, could provide services that midwives, largely female, could not—primarily because men had access to education (typically northern-European universities in London, Edinburgh, and Leiden) then denied women, which provided them with a theoretical understanding of female anatomy and the process of parturition.

[21] A case in point is with the passage of the 1902 Midwives Act in the U.K., where the midwives surrendered their autonomy to medical control (Clarke, 1993). Although the Act legally acknowledged the practice of midwifery, it did not give midwives the right to define for themselves the scope of their professional authority and sphere of control. Most importantly, however, the right to practice remained under control of medical doctors.

[22] At least one writer, however, focusing on non-political features to explain this demise Loudon (1992) suggests that maternal care in the U.S. has been primarily dictated by local circumstances, and dominated by a commercialized competitive and free market system in which women were expected to pay for maternity care. The "youthfulness" of the U.S.—with numerous geographically isolated communities and highly mobile populations—made potential or real legislation to establish systems of medical care difficult to enforce. Most of all, it was the tradition of "rugged individualism" and the frontier mentality which provoked hostility to "unnecessary interference" in social and medical matters.

[23] In a comparative study of midwifery in five Western countries (Britain, Canada, Sweden, the U.S. and the Netherlands) Benoit (1991) distinguishes between "midwifery" and "medical" models of care. Because Britain, the U.S. and Canada have "medical" models of care, midwives in these countries tend to have little autonomy, and function largely as assistants to the obstetrician. The health care systems of Sweden and the Netherlands, however, have "midwifery" models of care that allow the midwives to play an independent and more important role. It is concluded that policies—by the respective governments (for example, their regulations, funding and licensing requirements) and the rules of private insurance companies concerning insurability of midwives—in these five countries have been important in determining the relative importance, and probability of success, of midwifery as an autonomous, independent occupation. See also McKay in this volume.

[24] One notable exception to this transfer of control based on the present sex status model is found in the study by Malin and Hemminki (1993) of Finnish female midwives. In Finland, midwives—who are credited with contributing significantly to one of the lowest perinatal mortality rates in the world (6.4 per 1000 births in 1986)—are losing their long standing status as independent caregivers during pregnancy due in large part to their being replaced by public health nurses, who are themselves also largely female. Midwives, up until recently, provided prenatal care and were considered to be specialists in pregnancy, childbirth and puerperium. As a result of new legislation passed in 1986, however, public health nurses are beginning to provide prenatal care and health education, and may in the future replace midwives in the prenatal care function—with midwives returning to caring only for normal hospital births.

HISTORY OF MIDWIFERY: INTRODUCTION

Edwin R. van Teijlingen

Midwifery is one of the oldest professions in the world. This is well expressed by Breckinridge (1927:1147): "The midwife's calling is so ancient that the medical and nursing professions, in even their earliest traditions, are parvenus beside it." This sections highlights four related themes in the history and development of midwifery as recognized in the literature:

1. division of labor/competition with male doctors;
2. the ignorant midwife theme;
3. midwives and witches;
4. licensing and regulation of midwifery practice.

These four themes are introduced in some detail in this section followed by a selection of essays on the history of midwifery. The links between each contribution and the four themes are highlighted. In this historical section a number of themes are presented in more or less chronological order, although there are overlaps in time between the themes. Some contributions cover a wider period in the history of midwifery than others do; consequently a certain minimal amount of leaping in time and/or overlap between papers occurs. Since it is impossible to include all historical topics related to midwifery, only the major themes and issues are highlighted in this overview section and the relevance of these selected papers to the themes is indicated.

THE DIVISION OF LABOR: COMPETITIVE STRATEGIES

In Roman times midwives normally attended childbirth, according to French (1987:72 and this volume pp. 53-62), and "male physicians might attend particularly difficult births". Making the first reference to the division of labor between midwives and doctors. In the late Middle Ages "midwives were omnipresent, comprising perhaps one third of all female medical practitioners" (Minkowski 1992:292). One recurring pattern is the decline of female-dominated midwifery vis-à-vis male-dominated medicine. "The clashes in and controversies surrounding the birthing room in Western culture from the seventeenth century to the present are the subject of an expanding corpus of scholarship" (Tatlock 1992:727). Indeed many contributions in this section describe and analyze this 'take-over' process. For example, Wiesner (1986:94 and this volume pp. 63-74) states that "the entrance of men into the field pushed the female practitioners out, as was the case in so many other fields."

Linking this theme to those outlined below, Wiesner (1986:94-5 and this volume 63-74) suggests that "the very identification of witches and midwives shows that the community recognized the power which midwives had—they *were* able to make the difference between life and death, just as witches were perceived to". It is always difficult to put a date on the start of most historical processes; some argue that the signs of the decline of midwifery were already visible in the late Middle Ages (Greilsammer 1991). Studying the status of Flemish midwives in the period from the fourteenth to the seventeenth century, she linked the degradation of midwifery to the disappearance of female doctors in the same period. Despite this down-grading or, perhaps more accurately, degradation of midwifery it was probably still one of the most important occupations open to 'lower middle-class' women (Wiesner 1986; 1993). Van Lieburg and Marland (1989:311 and this volume pp. 151-172) remind us that in the late nineteenth century Dutch midwives "were portrayed, both professionally and socially, in a negative light by many members of the medical profession".

However, it was felt that at least one historical contribution arguing in favor of degrading midwives should be included, since this reader is not necessarily 'a tribute to the midwife', but a sociological collection collated to enrich our understanding of social processes around services provided to women in childbirth. The paper by Ziegler (1913 and this volume) was published in one of the leading medical journals, namely the *Journal of the American Medical Association*, arguing in favor of the elimination of the midwife. This paper is characteristic of the considerable pressure that American midwifery came under in the early twentieth century (see also Litoff 1978; Wertz & Wertz 1989; Devitt 1979; Leavitt 1983; Evenson 1982). In a paper presented to the American Association for the Study and Prevention of Infant Mortality two years earlier, Emmons and Huntingdon (1912:393) argued that women in labor were "in their hours of greatest need require the attention of men and women thoroughly grounded in obstetrics". Furthermore, "the midwife never has and never can make good until she becomes a practising physician, thoroughly trained; that midwives should not be lisensed save in those States where they are so numerous that they cannot be abolished at once". Whilst this discussion about the future of the midwife was in progress, American women were turning away from midwives. In her autobiography, the well-known anarchist Emma Goldman (1970) recalled her experiences as a midwife for the poor in New York at the turn of the century. According to her, only the poorest immigrants used the services of the midwife. "Those who had risen in the scale of material Americanism lost their native diffidence with many other traits. Like the American women they, too, would be confined only by doctors.... Ten dollars was the highest fee; the majority of the women could not even pay that" (Goldman 1970:185).

During the first decades of this century, midwifery rapidly became a low status occupation in the United States. Wiedenbach (1960:256) pointed out the negative connotation acquired by the term midwife, which in the United States of America had come to mean: "well-intentioned, but uneducated, old woman." However, when mortality statistics were analyzed, midwives did better than expected, considering that they worked with the poorer, worse nourished, poorer housed population (Devitt 1979). Even though the American midwives at the turn of the century had a pretty bad press, some doctors admitted that a "poorly trained physician does far more harm than the midwife ..." (Lobenstine 1911:877). Devitt (1979) analyzed the campaign waged by the American medical profession in the first third of this century to eliminate the midwife. He pointed out that many doctors argued their case without being able to back up their arguments with facts. Leavitt (1983) summarized the developments taking place in the United States in the period 1760-1940. According to Leavitt (1987) in a later article, doctors were only occasionally called in to help with deliveries in the United States before the 1880s. From 1880 to 1920, however, although most births still took place at home, the medical profession gradually increased its authority over the birth process (Leavitt 1987). Darlington (1911:870) estimated that "50 per cent of the births in the United States are attended by midwives". However, by the 1930s hospital deliveries had overtaken home deliveries. In the hospital setting, control over the management of birth became almost exclusively a medical matter (Leavitt 1987).

THE IGNORANT MIDWIFE THEME

There appears to be a recurrent dispute in historical papers as to whether midwives were ignorant, unskilled and untrained healers attending those women in the population who could not afford any other kind of care, or whether midwives were knowledgeable, skilled and reasonably well-trained compared to other healers and birth attenders at the time. This question is often referred to as the 'midwife question' and links in with the issue of interprofessional competition from predominately male doctors. In many European countries and America, the "midwife question" came to the fore during the late nineteenth century.

The idea that the midwife throughout history was ignorant, superstitious and without formal training, and that her social standing was low, can be found in several essays. Among nineteenth century authors on midwifery Aveling (1872:1-10) made such observations, and among twentieth century authors Forbes (1962a) is a prime example. Friesian midwife Catharina Schrader (1656-1746), who left us her detailed diaries and whose importance is outlined in the essay by Marland (1987), did not write in a flattering way about her midwifery colleagues (Van Lieburg 1987:19). The low status of midwifery is also clear from Catharina Schrader's notebook. She commented that one of the most important obstacles to her responding to God's call to midwifery was the burden of the vocation and the consideration "that it was for me and my friends below my dignity" (ibid.:18). In Schnorrenberg's contribution to this reader we find reference to the stereotype of the midwife as the fat, dirty, drunken old woman whose image culminated with Sairey Gamp in *The Life and Adventures of Martin Chuzzlewit* (Dickens 1844). According to Schnorrenberg: "She is an old literary type, found in stories at least since the late Middle Ages, who still appears in popular novels about old and ignorant times." Darlington (1911:871) suggested that reports published in the USA at the turn of the century proved "conclusively that the midwife, with very few exceptions the country over, is dirty ignorant, and totally unfit to discharge the duties which she assumes." A view which is shared by Edgar (1911:881), according to whom "midwives, . . . , except in some rare instances, are ignorant, untrained, incompetent women, and some of the results of their obstetric incompetence are unnecessary deaths and blindness of the infants, and avoidable invalidism, suffering and death of the mothers". The notion that midwives perform deeds that cause them to be held in low esteem in the community can also be found in more recent times. For example, (Beeman & Bhattacharyya 1987:297) noted that in Gavaki, a village in Iran, only women "without shame" would be involved in midwifery, because it (a) involves intimate contact with a woman's sexual parts; (b) is associated with vaginal excreta which were thought to be polluting; and (c) midwives received payment, which puts them at the same social level as servants and washerwomen.

The idea that midwives were relatively knowledgeable, skilled and trained has found equally strong proponents. Marland (1993) presents a number of essays in *The Art of Midwifery: Early Modern Midwives in Europe,* which demonstrated the inadequacy of the ignorant midwife theory. Her argument is that across Europe the early modern period (1400-1800) was "... a period of great diversity, of variation between and within Western European countries, in terms of midwives' practices, skills and competence, their socio-economic background and education, their training and qualification to work and their functions and image" (Marland 1993:2). Despite this diversity and variation, Marland (1993:4) still concludes that midwives shared certain characteristics: "most were mature women, married or widowed, who started to practice when they had grown-up families, most were trained by some form of apprenticeship, formal or informal, most were of middling status, the wives of artisans, craftsmen, tradesmen or farmers, for whom the practice of midwifery, though not necessarily vital for the family income, was a useful addition." Harley (1993:35) insists that midwives in Lancashire and Cheshire (England) in the period 1660-1760 were "central figures in women's culture, acting as advisors and conciliators as well as organizing the rituals surrounding childbirth, but at times they also had to represent the more respectable section of the town or village." Wiesner's paper (this volume pp. 63-74) concludes that the early modern midwife was a woman on whose skills and knowledge one could depend. Discussing the changes taking place in midwifery in America between 1760 and 1825, Scholten (1977:429) also takes the view that "until educated male physicians began to practice obstetrics, midwives enjoyed some status in the medical profession, enhanced by their legal responsibilities in the communities they served."

The history of midwifery is not all doom and gloom, at least one recent work argued that the work of the traditional midwife in the early modern period has been idealized by feminist historians. Shorter (1982) argues that the idea of old-fashioned natural childbirth in which birth attenders abstained from intervention is a myth. "Women have never really controlled their own births, and birth has always been subject to a web of custom and community regulations which reduces the scope of choice open to an individual mother" (Shorter 1982:68). In his view those around the pregnant women felt "compelled to take a hand in Nature's work, *except* on those occasions when a little 'intervention' might have been welcome to the mother" (ibid:49). Wilson (1985:144) argued a slightly different line, namely that the seventeenth century midwife and man-midwife were both paid practitioners and "Correspondingly, the seventeenth century mother was perhaps less a participant, and more a patient, than we might wish to believe." Thus the mother and the midwife did not necessarily have identical viewpoints.

MIDWIVES AND WITCHES

In the late Middle Ages the church developed its attack on women healers, branding them as witches. In their now classic publication *Witches, midwives & nurses: A history of women healers* Ehrenreich and English (1973) popularized the idea that midwives were prime victims during the witchcraze. "In particular, the association of the witch and the midwife was strong." (Ibid:13). The idea that midwives in that period were singled out as victims of the witchcraze originated from the work of Thomas Forbes (1962a; 1966). In his article 'Midwifery and Witchcraft' Forbes (1962a) argues that midwifery was generally a low status occupation in the fifteenth, sixteenth and seventeenth century. "Ignorant, unskilled, poverty-stricken, and avoided as she often was, it is small wonder that the midwife could be tempted, in spite of teachings of the Church, to indulge in the superstitious practices and even in witchcraft" (Forbes 1962a:264-5). In this respect Dominican Inquisitors Kramer and Sprenger (1986) are often quoted. In their infamous *Malleus maleficarum* (Hammer of Witches) published in the period 1487-89 they claimed that: "No one does more harm to the Catholic Faith than midwives" (Kramer and Sprenger 1986:161). This book was a major guideline to witch hunters and in the opinion of Ben-Yehuda (1980:11) "The importance of the *Malleus* cannot be overestimated." Ben-Yehuda (1980:19-20) also commented that one of the main explanations as to why the population did not increase during the sixteenth to seventeenth century in Europe after the major plagues had passed, was the widespread use of contraception and the rise of infanticide. Ben-Yehuda (1980:22) underlines that "midwives were experts in birth control and no doubt helped and cooperated in infanticide." It is then clear why midwives were among the chief suspects of witchcraft. Although Ireland largely escaped the witchcraze, one story was recorded in 1913 by St. John D. Seymour (1989:160-1):

> "Most wonderful and unpleasant were the bodily contortions that an Irish gentleman suffered, as the result of not having employed a woman who to the useful trade of *sage-femme* added the mischievous one of witch–it is quite conceivable that a country midwife, with some little knowledge of medicine and the use of simples, would be classed in popular opinion amongst those who had power above the average."

Further evidence to suggest that midwives were suspected of being involved in witchcraft lies in the reasoning behind the first attempts to license or register midwives in England in about 1550. These were based on concerns that the women used "witchcraft, charms, sorcery, or innovations, and.... had ever exhibited behaviors offensive to the Church" (Achterberg 1990:123). This is in itself not evidence that midwives were disproportionately persecuted during the witchcraze, but it is an indication that "the authorities sensed a connection between witchcraft and midwifery." (Ibid.:122). Wiesner (1986:94) summarizes the above argument as follows: "Historians have noted the frequent identification of witches as midwives and have seen a decline in the role and status of the midwife during the sixteenth and seventeenth centuries because she was tainted with witchcraft."

The opposite view, namely that midwives were unlikely to be perceived as witches, has been put forward by several authors. Demos (1982:80) quotes both Forbes (1966) and Ehrenreich and English (1973) when he referred to the theme of the midwife and witch sometimes (often) being the same person. However, Demos (1982:80) concluded that in early New England generally witches were not midwives, "at least not in a formal sense. It is clear, moreover, that scores of midwives carried out their duties, in many towns and through many years, without ever being touched by imputations of witchcraft." Purkiss (1996) also indicated that there is no evidence that those accused of witchcraft were commonly midwives. This point of view is developed by Harley (1990) in 'Historians as Demonologists: The Myth of the Midwife-witch'. Harley (1990) argues that "midwives were generally immune from witchcraft prosecution unless they fell foul of a zealous magistrate or there was some special local belief." In England, rather than being prosecuted, midwives were called upon as expert witnesses to examine the body of the witch for the witchmark, from which demons or Satan himself would suckle blood, or to determine whether a convicted woman was pregnant and might thus be granted a stay of execution (Purkiss 1996:21). Thus midwives were part of the system of social control, and their knowledge of women's bodies was no threat to the state and church powers. Following this line of argument Purkiss (1996:8) concludes that there is no evidence that the midwives were more likely to be accused of witchcraft, since: "midwives were more likely to be found helping witch-hunters." Harley (1990:6) adds to this argument that "The good reputation of a midwife was essential in her trade since it was her best credential and her only advertisement". This notion of 'good reputation' was pointed out earlier by Forbes (1962b) in the case of a midwife called Perrette accused of witchcraft in 1408. She was found to be skilful and of good character and not guilty of practicing witchcraft; in fact her "skills and blameless reputation earned for her the King's mercy" (Forbes 1962b:129).

Although it is generally recognized that *women* were the prime suspects of witchcraft (Macfarlane 1970; Demos 1982:62-3), it seems unlikely that *midwives* were especially singled out as victims. The impact of the witchcraze on its victims was great, and one does not have to be a great believer in conspiracy theories to see the witchcraze as 'orchestrated' by "a partnership between Church, State and the medical profession" as Ehrenreich & English (1973:19) suggested. However, it is highly questionable whether the witchcraze was specifically directed against midwives. Thus the midwife-witch theme is largely a sub-theme of the ignorant midwife theme. There is some indication that midwives had a good reputation and therefore were protected against allegations of practicing witchcraft.

LICENSING AND REGULATION OF MIDWIFERY PRACTICE

A third theme is the increasing regulation and licensing of midwifery. In the late Middle Ages midwives were to some extent subject to external control. This initially took the form of regulations laid down by the church and later by the town council, i.e. first the ecclesiastic authorities followed by the secular authorities. Schilling (1992:389) points out that the supervision of midwives was "among those social matters over which the medieval church had assumed responsibility." One of the main reasons for such supervision was the concern to preserve the infant's soul in the event of the mother's death and/or its own death (Donnison 1988:14-6). Therefore the church had to ensure that "midwives knew the baptismal formula and that they led moral lives which guaranteed their conscientious use of the sacrament" (Schilling 1992:389). Wiesner (1992:106-7) refers to the printed regulations of the city of Nuremberg during the period of the Reformation informing midwives how to conduct 'emergency baptism'. Also in Germany, the Trier synod of 1310 obliged midwives to pour water over the head of the child in order to baptize the baby in cases when the head was born first but the birth could not be completed (Thiele-Ochel 1972:3-4).

The first known European municipal system of midwife regulations was introduced in 1424 in Brussels, according to Greilsammer (1991:296). This is at least a century earlier than the often quoted regulation of 1552 found in Regensburg in the south of Germany (Green 1989:450; Ketch 1983:280; Benedek 1977:553; Van Teijlingen 1994:51). It is also suggested that French midwives were being sworn in as early as 1385 (Kalisch *et al.*, 1981 and this volume 93-108). The nature of regulating authorities differed from country to country; for example, in Scotland (Armet 1962:146-7), Germany (Ketch 1983:280), Spain after 1523 (Ortiz 1993:99) and the Low Countries (Greilsammer 1991:296; Houtzager 1993:61-6) regulation of midwives was in the hands of municipal authorities, while England required episcopal licenses for centuries (Donnison 1988:26-7). In England the local bishop was given the responsibility for examining anyone seeking a license to practice midwifery and for punishing unlicensed practitioners. Regulations also covered the prohibition of the use of instruments, the administration of 'drugs' by midwives, and midwives' general character. In the early eighteenth century "medical men were replacing the clergy as signatories of the majority of Chester (England) testimonials, which suggests a medicalization of the midwife's social role", according to Harley (1993:31). In Spain in the period 1477-1523 the *Protomédicos* (the king's physicians and the highest medical authority) examined all medical practitioners, including midwives, before licensing. After 1523 midwives needed permission to practice in areas covered by municipal regulations (Ortiz 1993: 98-9).

Donnison (1988:47 and this volume) quotes Mrs. Elizabeth Nihell's *A Treatise on the Art of Midwifery* as arguing in favor of rigorous examinations of English midwives, whereby "ignorant practitioners of either sex" were to be excluded through governmental regulation as obtained in Holland, with prohibition of practice by all unqualified persons. The issue of registration and licensing and subsequent control over the midwifery profession continued to dominate the debate in England in the late nineteenth century and early twentieth century (Donnison 1988; Towler & Bramall 1986). The debate around licensing and regulating is a recurrent issue in the twentieth century, for example, in the U.S.A. (DeVries 1982), and Ontario, Canada (Kaufman 1991; Bourgeault 1996).

OUTLINE OF THE PAPERS INCLUDED

The first paper by Valerie French (1986) distinguishes between 'trained' literate midwives for the rich and 'untrained' illiterate midwives for the poor in Roman times. This paper addresses the theme of the 'ignorant' midwives, although care should be taken in attaching the labels such as 'untrained' and 'unskilled' to women who learned midwifery through apprenticeships rather than through a formal training program. This division of labor can still be seen clearly today in developing countries, where the poor might receive help from a traditional birth attendant whilst the better-off receive maternity care from western-style trained midwives. The division of labor, which is described in this paper, fits in with the gender division outlined above, whereby Roman midwives attended normal deliveries and doctors were called in difficult cases.

Wiesner (1986) in her case study of early modern midwifery also addresses the ignorant midwives theme. Her paper points out that early modern midwifery (in Nuremberg, Germany) was not viewed by its contemporaries as an anachronistic relic, but as a skilled and knowledgeable and respectable occupation. In a similar way to the contribution by French (1987), Wiesner argues that the work of midwives was based on their reputation. Wiesner links all four themes outlined above, namely that of the 'ignorant midwife', 'midwives and witches', 'competition between male doctors and female midwives', and 'regulating midwifery'. Wiesner's case study of Nuremberg also functions as a link to the following paper, which is a case study of an individual midwife, Louyse Bourgeois, who was a major figure in the history of French midwifery (P.A. Kalisch *et al*.1981). Bourgeois was the first midwife to publish on obstetrics as well as on midwifery, and her "texts were widely used in the generations which followed her" (Perkins 1996:ix). There have been a number of other midwives over the past three or four centuries who have left writings about their work: for example, the French midwife Mme du Coudray (1715-1795) and the Dutch midwife Catharina Schrader (1656-1746). Du Coudray was commissioned to travel throughout France to teach illiterate peasant women how to deliver babies safely (Gelbart 1993, 1995). Schrader has left us her detailed notebook (Van Lieburg 1984), which she mostly wrote-up straight after having assisted at a delivery (Van Lieburg 1987:8). Marland (1987) has published an English summary of this diary. This account of a Dutch midwife is particularly interesting because of the rural background of Catharina Schrader.

The process of take-over of normal childbirth from midwives by doctors is analyzed by Schnorrenberg (1981). She found that the decline of midwifery in eighteenth century England could be attributed to three factors: "The least important of these was the increase in scientific knowledge and medical skills. Far more important were the professionalization of medical practitioners and the emergence of what we usually call 'Victorian' ideas of role, abilities and status of women." (Ibid:393.) The latter is stressed in particular by Scholten (1977:443) who suggests that "The crowd of supportive friends and family disappeared with the arrival of the doctor in the delivery room." Thus, as the male physician took over from the female midwife, for some American women childbirth ceased to be an open ceremony. This process is also described in Wilson (1995).

Forbes (1962b) translated French court documents relating to an episode of witchcraft involving Perrette (wife of Thomas of Rouen) in fifteenth century Paris. She was accused of witchcraft in 1408, but her skills and blameless reputation earned for her the King's mercy. In the letters of pardon by Charles VI of 17 May 1408 one reads (Forbes 1962b:128):

> "Her service, office, or skill is very necessary to the public welfare, and likewise several pregnant women place great reliance in her knowledge and diligence and from day to day come to her and ask her to deliver their children. Therefore we have by our special grace and royal authority discharged, forgiven and pardoned Perrette of Rouen in respect to the above mentioned case."

From the 1720s onwards, more and more men were coming into the field, and, according to Donnison (1988), they were beginning to take over the routine cases. Donnison (1988:52) suggests that lack of government recognition, regulation and provision and subsidy of instruction were allowing male practice to become more general in England than anywhere else in Europe.

The next paper by Hélène Laforce provides an excellent historical overview of the change in Canada from the French tradition in midwifery, of peaceful co-existence between doctors and midwives, to the Anglo-Saxon tradition of doctors dominating and eliminating midwifery. The latter tradition is outlined in more detail in the contribution by Donnison.

The organization of midwifery in the Netherlands is radically different from all other industrialized countries, as highlighted in the sections *Midwifery in Contemporary Western Societies* and *The Politics of Midwifery* of this reader. Van Lieburg and Marland outline the historical developments in the nineteenth-century midwifery regulation, education, and practice in the Netherlands in order to help understand the relatively strong position of the Dutch midwife at present.

REFERENCES

Achterberg, J., 1990, *Woman as healer: A comprehensive survey from prehistoric times to the present day*, London: Rider

Armet, H. (ed.), 1962, *Extracts from the Records of the Burgh of Edinburgh, 1689 to 1701*, Edinburgh: Scottish Record Society

Aveling, J.H., 1872, *English midwives*, London: Churchill

Beeman, W.O. & Bhattacharyyam A.K., 1978, 'Towards an assessment of the social role of rural midwives and its implication for the Family Planning Program: An Iranian case study', *Human Organization*, 37:295-300

Ben-Yehuda, N., 1980, 'The European Witch Craze of the 14th to 17th Centuries: A Sociologist's Perspective', *American Journal of Sociology*, 86:1-31

Benedek, T.G., 1977, 'The changing relationship between midwives and physicians during the Renaissance', *Bulletin of the History of Medicine*, 51:550-564

Bourgeault, I.L., 1996, 'Delivering midwifery into the Ontario (Canada) health care system', *Medical Sociology News*, 22:43-7

Breckinridge, M., 1927, 'The nurse-midwife–A pioneer' *American J. of Public Health*, 17:1147-51

Darlington, T., 1911, 'The present status of the midwife', *American Journal of Obstetrics and Diseases of Women and Children*, 63:870-6

Demos, J.P., 1982, *Entertaining Satan: Witchcraft and the Culture of Early New England*, Oxford: Oxford Univ. Press

Devitt, N., 1979, 'The Statistical Case for Elimination of the Midwife: Fact versus Prejudice, 1890-1935 (Part 1)', *Women & Health*, 4 (1):81-96

DeVries, R.G., 1982, 'Midwifery and the problem of licensure', In: *Research in the Sociology of Health Care*, Vol.2, Ruth, J. & Ruzak, S. (eds.), London: JAI Press, 77-120

Dickens, C., 1844, *The Life and Adventures of Martin Chuzzlewit*, London

Donnison, J., 1988, 'The decline of the midwife', *Midwives and Medical Men: A History of the Struggle for the Control of Childbirth*, New Barnet, Herts: Historical Publications

Edgar, J.C., 1911, 'The remedy for the midwife problem' *American Journal of Obstetrics and Diseases of Women and Children*, 63:881-884

Ehrenreich, B. & English, D., 1973, *Witches, midwives & nurses: A history for women healers*, New York: The Feminist Press

Emmons, A. B. & Huntingdon, J. L., 1912, 'The Midwife', *The American Journal of Obstetrics and the Diseases of Women and Children*, 65 (3):393-404

Evenson, D., 1982, 'Midwives: Survival of an Ancient Profession', *Women's Rights Law Reporter*, 7(4):313-30

French, V., 1986, 'Midwives and maternity care in the Roman world', *Helios*, 13 (2):69-84

Forbes, T.R., 1962a 'Midwifery and Witchcraft' *Jrn of the History of Medicine*, 17:264-83

Forbes, T.R., 1962b, 'Perrette the midwife: a 15th century witchcraft case', *Bull. of the History of Medicine*, 36:124-9

Forbes, T.R., 1966, *The Midwife and the Witch*, New Haven, Conn.: Yale University Press

Gelbart, N., 1993, 'Midwife to a nation: Mme du Coudray serves France', In *The Art of Midwifery: Early Modern Midwives in Europe*, Marland, H. (ed.), London: Routledge

Gelbart, N.R., 1995, 'Delivering the goods: Patriotism, property, and the midwife mission of Mme du Coudray', In. *Early Modern Conceptions of Property*, Brewer, J. & Staves, S (eds.), London: Routledge

Goldman, E., 1971, *Living my Life* (reprint of 1931 edition), New York

Green, M., 1989, 'Women's medical practice and health care in medieval Europe', *Signs*, 14 (2):434-73

Greilsammer, M., 1991, 'The midwife, the priest, and the physician: the subjugation of midwives in the Low Countries at the end of the Middle Ages', *Jrn. of Medieval & Renaissance Studies*, **21** (2):285-329

Harley, D., 1990, 'Historians as Demonologists: The Myth of the Midwife-witch' *The Society for the Social History of Medicine,* **3**:1-26

Harley, D., 1993, 'Provincial midwives in England: Lancashire and Cheshire, 1660-1760', In: Marland, H. (ed.), 1993, *The Art of Midwifery: Early Modern Midwives in Europe*, London: Routledge

Houtzager, H.L. ,1993, *Wat er in de kraam te pas komt: opstellen over de geschiedenis van de verloskunde in Nederland*, Rotterdam: Erasmus Publishing

Kalisch, P.A., Scobey, M. & Kalisch, B.J., 1981, 'Louyse Bourgeois and the emergence of modern midwifery', *Jrn. of Nurse-Midwifery*, **26**, (4):3-17

Kaufman, K.J., 1991 'The introduction of midwifery in Ontario, Canada', *Birth* **18**:100-3

Ketch, P., 1983, *Frauen im Mittelalter*, **1**, Düsseldorf: Schwann-Bagel

Kramer, H. & Sprenger, J., 1986, *Malleus Maleficarum* (reprint), London: Arrow Books

Laforce, H., 1990, 'The different stages of the elimination of midwives in Québec', In: *Delivering Motherhood*, Arnup, K., Levesque, A. & Pierson, R.R. (eds.) London: Routledge

Leavitt, J.W., 1983, '"Science" enters the Birthing Room: Obstetrics in America since the Eighteenth Century', *Jrn. of American History*, **70** (2):281-304

Leavitt, J.W., 1987, 'The growth of medical authority: technology and morals in turn-of-the-century obstetrics', *Med. Anthropol. Q.* (new series), **1**:230-55

Lieburg van, M.J. (ed.), 1984, *C.G. Schrader's memory boeck van de vrouwens. Het notitieboek van een Friese vroedvrouw 1693-1745 (with an obstetric commentary by G.J. Kloosterman)*, Amsterdam: Rodopi

Lieburg van, M.J., 1987, ' Catharina Schrader (1656-1746) and her notebook', In: *Mother and child were saved: the memoirs (1693-1740) of the Frisian midwife Catharina Schrader* Marland, H. (ed.), Amsterdam: Rodopi

Lieburg van M.J. & Marland, H., 1989, 'Midwife regulation, education, & practice in the Netherlands during the nineteenth century', *Medical History*, **33**:296-317

Lobenstine, R.W., 1911, 'The influence of the midwife upon infant and maternal morbidity and mortality' *American Journal of Obstetrics and Diseases of Women and Children*, **63**:876-80

Litoff, J.B., *American Midwives: 1860 to the Present*, Greenwood Press, Westport, Conn, 1978.

Macfarlane, A.D.J., 1970, *Witchcraft in Tudor and Stuart England,* London: Routledge & Kegan Paul

Marland, H., 1987, 'All well for mother and child', *Nursing Times*, **83** (40):49-51

Marland, H. (ed.), 1993, *The Art of Midwifery: Early Modern Midwives in Europe*, London: Routledge

Minkowski, W.L., 1992, 'Women Healers of the Middle Ages: Selected Aspects of Their History', *American J. of Public Health*, **82** (2):288-295

Ortiz, T., 1993, 'From hegemony to subordination: midwives in early modern Spain', In: *The Art of Midwifery: Early Modern Midwives in Europe*, Marland, H. (ed.), London: Routledge

Perkins, W., 1996, *Midwifery and Medicine in Early Modern France: Louise Bourgeois*, Exeter: University of Exeter Press

Purkiss, D., 1996, *The Witch in History: Early Modern and 20th-Century Representations*, London: Routledge

Schilling, H., 1992, *Religion, Political Culture and the Emergence of Early Modern Society: Essays on German and Dutch History*, E.J. Brill

Schnorrenberg, B.B., 1981, 'Is childbirth any place for a woman? The decline of midwifery in Eighteenth-Century England', *Studies in Eighteenth-Century Culture*, **10**:393-408

Scholten, C.M., 1977, 'On the Importance of the Obstetrick Art: Changing Customs of Childbirth in America 1760-1825', *The William & Mary Quarterly: A Magazine of Early American History*, **34**:426-445

Shorter, E., 1982, 'A typical birth then', *A History of Women's Bodies*, London: Allen Lane

Seymour, St. John D., 1989, *Irish Witchcraft and Demonology*, London: Portman Books

Tatlock, L., 1992, 'Speculum Feminarum: Gendered Perspectives on Obstetrics and Gynecology in Early Modern Germany', *Signs: Journal of Women in Culture and Society*, **17**:725-760

Teijlingen van, E.R., 1994, *A social or medical model of childbirth? Comparing the arguments in Grampian (Scotland) and the Netherlands*, (unpublished Ph.D. thesis), Aberdeen: University of Aberdeen

Thiele-Ochel, F.G., 1972, *Zur Geschichte des Hebammenwesens in Köln* , (unpublished Ph.D. thesis), Cologne, University of Cologne

Towler, J. & Bramall, J., 1986, *Midwives in history and society*, London: Croom Helm, chapters 7-8.

Wertz, R.W. & Wertz, D.C., *Lying In: A History of Childbirth in America*, Yale Univ. Press, New Haven, 1989.

Wiedenbach, E., 1960, 'Nurse-midwifery: purpose, practice and opportunity', *Nursing Outlook*, 8:256-9

Wiesner, M.E., 1986, 'Early modern midwifery: a case study', In: *Women and Work in Preindustrial Europe*, Hanawalt, B.A. (ed.), Bloomington: Indiana U.P. Published before as: 'Early modern midwifery: a case study', *International Journal of Women's Studies*, (1983) 6:26-43

Wiesner, M.E., 1993, 'The midwives of south Germany and the public/private dichotomy', In: *The Art of Midwifery: Early Modern Midwives in Europe*, Marland, H. (ed.), London: Routledge

Wilson, A., 1985, 'Participant or patient? Seventeenth century childbirth from mother's point of view', In: *Patients and practitioners: Lay perceptions of medicine in pre-industrial society*, Porter, R. (ed.), Cambridge: Cambridge U.P.

Wilson, A., 1995, *The making of man-midwifery*, London: UCL Press

Ziegler, C.E., 1913, 'The elimination of the midwife', *Journal of the American Medical Association*, 60:32-8

MIDWIVES AND MATERNITY CARE IN THE ROMAN WORLD[*]

Valerie French[†]

The birth of a child marks one of the great events of life in any culture, but in most societies it carries with it a high probability of death or serious illness for both mother and child. Neonatal mortality rates—deaths at less than four weeks—vary considerably in the modern world: in communities that do not employ asepsis in obstetrical care, neonatal mortality can be as high as 50 deaths per 1000 live births.[1] Maternal mortality rates for deaths associated with pregnancy and childbirth also range considerably, but even at their highest they fall significantly short of neonatal mortality. If we retroject the worst mortality rates of the modern world back into the Greco-Roman one, we would estimate that about 5% of all babies born alive would die before they reached the age of one month, and that among every 20,000 women giving birth, five would die.[2] If we include late fetal and in-childbirth deaths, the probability of infant mortality climbs from 5% to 8%.[3]

The dangers of childbirth must have made it an occasion of great anxiety for everyone concerned. The death of a woman or her baby was an all too common occurrence. Caesar's daughter Julia died in childbirth. The younger Pliny reports that both daughters of one of his friends, Helvidius, died during labor.[4] And the Athenian philanthropist, Herodes Atticus, was grief-stricken when his first child, a son, died on the day of his birth.[5] The anxiety and grief of the elite was surely paralleled among the lower classes.

Accustomed as we are to the procedures of late twentieth-century obstetrics with its emphasis on prenatal care, asepsis, and medical technology, our reactions to some of the methods and medications used for normal, uncomplicated childbirth in the Greco-Roman world are likely to range from mild amusement to outright revulsion. While we can make only educated guesses about the mortality rates associated with childbirth in antiquity, we can reconstruct a fairly detailed description of Greco-Roman maternity care and recover a partial picture of the women who attended this epochal life event—the midwives.

Both Pliny the Elder and Soranus provide detailed information about midwifery and obstetrical practices; other medical writers such as Celsus and Galen supplement their accounts and offer some additional evidence. We are fortunate that Pliny and Soranus treat maternity care from significantly

[*] An earlier version of this paper was read at the 1981 Berkshire Women's History Conference. I am very grateful to a number of people for their useful suggestions, particularly anonymous referee; Sarah Pomeroy; and Ronnie Lichtman, a practicing midwife and member of the faculty of the Nursing Midwife Program, College of Physicians and Surgeons, Columbia University.

There is a rather scant bibliography on ancient maternity practices; most of the book-length studies of the history of obstetrics give only a cursory treatment of antiquity. See Hugo Blummer, *Die römischen Privataltertumer* (Munich: Oskar Beck, 1911), pp. 299-306; Theodore Cianfrani *A Short History of Obstetrics and Gynecology* (Springfield, Ill.: Charles C. Thomas, 1960), pp70-83; Martial Dumont, "L'Obstetrique et la gynecologie dans la Rome antique," *Cahiers Medicaux Lyonnais*, 41 (1965), pp. 83-91; Palmer Findley, *Priests of Lucina* (Boston: Little, Brown, 1939), pp. 38-65; Harvey Graham, *Eternal Eve* (Garden City, N.Y.: Doubleday, 1951), pp. 56-70; Harold Speert, *Iconographica Gyniatrica* (Philadelphia: F. A. Davis, 1973), pp. 83-84.

[†] Helios, **13** (2), 1986:69-84

different vantage points. In his *Historia Naturalis,* Pliny reports primarily on the practices of folk medicine, whereas Soranus's *Gynecology* describes the obstetrical care recommended by the medical profession. Together Pliny and Soranus probably cover the full range of the different kinds of maternity care found in the Greco-Roman world.

I. FOLK MEDICINE

Pliny's descriptions of childbirth practices chiefly concern ways to hasten and ease labor. Boys, he says, are more easily delivered than girls.[6] According to Pliny, fumigations with the fat from hyaena loins produce immediate delivery for women in difficult labor; placing the right foot of a hyaena on the woman results in an easy delivery, but the left foot causes death.[7] A drink sprinkled with powdered sow's dung will relieve the pains of labor, as will sow's milk mixed with honey wine.[8] Delivery can also be eased by drinking goose semen mixed with water or "the liquids that flow from a weasel's uterus through its genitals."[9] Pliny also describes medications made of herbs and plants that were used for childbirth. The root of vervain in water, scordotis in hydromel, and dittany leaves are recommended for the lying-in woman.[10] Amulets and other objects were also thought to be efficacious. Pliny says that some people used the after-birth of a bitch that had not touched the ground to withdraw the infant, placing the canine placenta on the thighs of the woman.[11] Others tied a snake's slough to the thigh of the woman but took care to remove it immediately after delivery. Some people believed that a "stick with which a frog has been shaken from a snake" was helpful.[12] A vulture's feather might be placed under the woman's feet to aid delivery.[13] Celsus remarks on other folk nostrums, reporting that sneezing relieves a difficult labor;[14] Celsus also recommends drinking hedge mustard in tepid wine on an empty stomach for difficult labor.[15]

It is difficult to determine just how efficacious—or harmful—these treatments might have been. Understandably, contemporary midwives and obstetricians are unwilling to experiment with any of them. At the very least, we can conjecture that the presence in the delivery room of hyaena's feet, snake sloughs, canine placentas, sticks, and vulture feathers may have increased the risk of infection for both mother and child, especially if such objects came in contact with the vaginal area. But we ought not to underestimate the potential for a placebo effect in some of these treatments. If a woman in the throes of labor were told, and believed, that a vulture feather or snake slough would ease her pains, she might well have relaxed and felt better. The practice of giving the parturient liquids, however, was probably beneficial since they would tend to prevent dehydration, a potentially serious problem in protracted labor.

Pliny also reports on ways to bring away the placenta. Here too the treatments are apt to strike us as distasteful. Among his recommendations are earthworms taken in raisin wine; the membrane covering newborn goats, dried and then taken in wine; and linozostis or parthenion. Another is hare's rennet applied with saffron and leek juice.[16] Celsus recommends a draught of four measures of ammoniac salt or Cretan dittany dissolved in water.[17]

Pliny's reports are no doubt drawn from a vast reservoir of traditional folk medicine. And it is important to recognize that Pliny, a highly educated and sophisticated man, did not make light of these treatments. He seems to think that they are sound and efficacious maternity practices. We are on firm ground in assuming that the maternity care of most women in the Greco-Roman world was conducted along the lines described by Pliny. Regardless of the lack of attention to hygiene and sanitation and the likelihood that the medications employed did little good—except as they exercised a placebo effect and prevented dehydration—we must remember that, at the very least, the maternity care described by Pliny was very personal and attentive to the mother. She was at home, not in a strange, alien environment; she was not left alone, sometimes for hours, to sweat out the initial stages of labor by herself. She had the constant company of some of her female relatives and the midwife to encourage her and to divert her mind from the pains of labor. On an emotional level, Greco-Roman maternity care is probably preferable to the production line, impersonal procedures of some modern hospitals. An intensely emotionally supportive atmosphere is of considerable importance to the health of both the new mother and the new baby.[18]

II. MIDWIVES

With the physician Soranus, who wrote in the early second century A.D., we find attitudes and beliefs about obstetrics more familiar to the modern world.[19] Soranus begins his discussion of childbirth with a description of the good midwife. To Soranus, the demands of the profession require a highly competent woman; he implies that some midwives are simply unfit for their work. "A suitable person," Soranus writes, "will be literate, with her wits about her, possessed of a good memory, loving work, respectable and generally not unduly handicapped as regards her senses (i.e., sight, smell, hearing), sound of limb, robust, and, according to some people, endowed with long slim fingers and short nails at her fingertips."[20] Soranus also insists that the midwife be of sympathetic disposition (though she need not herself have borne a child) and keep her hands soft, presumably so she would not cause discomfort to either mother or child.[21]

Soranus argues that the best midwives should be literate so that they can be knowledgeable about obstetrics and pediatric theory.[22] Soranus's demand for literacy presumes that there was material for the midwives to read. Soranus probably intended that midwives read his work; and it appears that he prepared a shorter, condensed version as a sort of *vademecum*.[23] One wonders whether Soranus would have put Pliny the Elder on his recommended reading list for midwives; probably not, for Soranus says the midwife must be free from superstition "so as not to overlook salutary measures on account of a dream or omen or some customary rite.... "[24]

Soranus's references to other medical writings also indicate that obstetrical practice was not limited to midwives; a male physician might attend particularly difficult births.[25] But the literary sources make it clear that midwives normally attend childbirth.[26] Unfortunately, we can reconstruct only a partial picture of the women who practiced midwifery. In the Eastern end of the Mediterranean basin, some women advanced beyond the profession of midwife (*maia*) to that of obstetrician (*iatros gynaikeios*), for which formal training was surely required. Moreover, there were some gynecological tracts written by women with Greek names. It would appear that obstetrical care in the East was a respectable profession in which respectable women could earn their livelihoods and enough esteem to publish works read and cited by male physicians.[27]

In the Roman West, the situation appears to be somewhat different. Among the thousands of funeral epitaphs recorded in *CIL* (the *Corpus Inscriptionum Latinarum*), only sixteen commemorate the deaths of women who were identified as midwives.[28] Of those sixteen, nine either come from the *columbaria* of the great noble houses of Rome or are clearly members of the *familia Caesaris*. It seems, then, a reasonable inference that large, wealthy households had their own midwives.

Only one of these midwives died a slave; the others appear to be freedwomen or the daughters of freedwomen. Two hypotheses are suggested by this admittedly small sample. The first is that midwifery was not a profession to which freeborn women of families that had enjoyed free status for several generations were attracted; thus, it seems likely that most midwives were of servile origin.[29] Second, since midwifery is an occupation that can be practiced successfully into old age, emancipation cannot be explained by the owner's desire to shuffle off a useless slave.[30] Thus, we can propose that midwives were generally valued enough, and earned enough income, to be able to gain their freedom.

The *praenomina* of these women confirm a hypothesis of servile origin. Of the thirteen inscriptions in which the full name of the midwife is still extant, eight have Greek names; the Latinate names of the others—Secunda, Imerita, Hilara, Veneria—are also associated with slaves. Unfortunately, it is not possible to determine from their epitaphs alone whether these slaves, freedwomen, or daughters of freedwomen were born, raised, and trained in Italy or were brought to Rome from the East.

Nor can we tell how particular slave women were selected for training as midwives. Possibly mothers taught their daughters, or slave girls may have been apprenticed. Such training may well have begun at an early age; one epitaph records the death of Poblicia Aphe, obstetrix, dead at age twenty-one (# 9723). Two others died in their early thirties (# 6647 and 9724).

Midwives married, and three of the epitaphs record the name of the dead woman's husband or *contubernalis* (# 6647, 8192, and 9720). Two of the midwives were commemorated by their fathers (# 9724 and 8207), two by their sons (# 8948 and 9720), and only one by her husband (#6647).[31]

Despite the paucity of evidence about the training of midwives, it seems a reasonable hypothesis that well-trained midwives were more likely to come from the Eastern, Hellenized end of the Mediterranean basin, and that midwifery and obstetrics were more highly esteemed professions, conferring greater prestige on their female practitioners, in the East than in the West. It also seems likely that wealthy Romans secured medical expertise in midwives—as they did in doctors—by purchasing highly educated and trained slaves from the East. The hypothesis of lower status for midwives in the Roman West is corroborated by legal commentary on the *Lex Aquilia,* passed probably in the third century B.C.; practitioners of medicine, including midwives, were placed in a relatively low social status.[32]

Whatever the regional or socioeconomic background of midwives, their services were not inexpensive. In Plautus's *Miles Gloriosus,* Periplectomenus complains that women always ask for more money—even the midwife, who protested the sum Periplectomenus had sent to her.[33] A mid-third-century A.D. marriage contract from Oxyrrhynchus in Egypt stipulated that the husband should give to the wife forty drachmae for her confinement if she was pregnant at the time of any separation; the sum probably was intended to cover more than the midwife's fee, but a substantial portion no doubt was to be used for her services.[34] Soranus admonishes midwives not to be greedy for money.[35] A number of Roman legal provisions strongly suggest that midwives enjoyed status and remuneration comparable to that of male doctors.[36]

But there were, no doubt, people who simply did not have the resources to pay for a capable midwife. There may have been some "midwives" who performed their services for a pittance. Soranus certainly implies that some midwives were much better trained than others. What poor women did is not known. We can only guess that if they could not afford a trained midwife, they turned to *sagae,* wise women who appear to have served at least in part as midwives in early Rome,[37] or to their female relatives who would have given whatever assistance they could. Whether the rate of maternal and infant mortality was lower for births handled by competent midwives, we do not know.

III. OBSTETRICS

After his description of the good midwife and a highly dubious discussion of female reproductive physiology, Soranus turns to delivery proper. He describes in detail the equipment used for normal labor and delivery. The midwife must have olive oil (clean, not previously used in cooking), warm water, warm fomentations (ointments applied to the body), soft sea sponges, pieces of wool, bandages (to swaddle the infant), a pillow (on which to place the infant), things to smell (pennyroyal, dirt, barley groats, apples, quinces, lemons, melons, cucumbers; these were used as we use spirits of ammonia to revive someone who has fainted), a midwife's stool or chair (this was the property of the midwife; she brought it with her to the home where the delivery was to take place), two beds (a hard one for use during labor and a soft one for rest after delivery), and a proper room (of medium size and moderate temperature).[38]

Soranus provides a good description of the midwife's stool; this chair was used only during the actual delivery, not during labor. Apparently both midwives and physicians believed that normal delivery was easier when the mother sat upright.[39] In the seat of the chair was a crescent-shaped hole through which the baby would be delivered. The sides of the chair had arm-rests, in the shape of the letter "pi," for the mother to grasp during delivery. The chair was to have a sturdy back against which the parturient was to press her hips and buttocks. Soranus's description implies, however, that some midwives' stools did not have backs and that an attendant stood behind the parturient to support her, a less desirable arrangement because of the danger that the parturient might recline or slip backwards.[40]

Soranus recommends that the sides of the chair from the seat to the floor be completely closed in with boards while the front and back be left open for the midwife's work. Soranus mentions later that if a midwife's stool is not available, the parturient can sit on the lap of another woman, who, understandably, must be robust enough to bear the mother's weight and hold her still.[41] It seems a reasonable conjecture that the children of the poor may have been born without a midwife's stool if the midwives they employed did not have the wherewithal to purchase a birthing stool. Indeed, one of Alciphron's letters describes a midwife who carries with her only a kit.[42]

At the onset of labor, the midwife was summoned and the necessary equipment made ready. During labor, the parturient lay on her back on a hard, low bed with a support under her hips; her feet were drawn up together, her thighs parted. Soranus directs the midwife to ease the labor pains with gentle massage, with a cloth soaked in warm olive oil laid over the abdomen and genital area, and with the equivalent of hot-water bottles—bladders filled with warm oil—placed against the woman's sides. As the cervix begins to dilate, the midwife is to encourage the process of dilation by gently rubbing the opening with her left forefinger (with its nail cut short); the finger is to be generously smeared with olive oil. When the cervix is dilated to the size of an egg, the parturient is moved to the midwife's stool, unless she has become very weak; in the latter case, the delivery is to be made on the hard bed.[43]

For the actual delivery, the midwife needs three assistants to stand both sides of the chair and at the back. Soranus stresses that these assistants should be "capable of gently allaying the anxiety" of the mother.[44] The woman who stood behind the chair had to be strong enough to keep the parturient from swaying; in addition, she was to hold a small, flat piece of cloth at the anus to avoid hemorrhoids.[45] The midwife herself, covered by an apron, sat in front of the mother and throughout the delivery reassured her that all was going well.[46]

Clearly Soranus, and presumably most midwives, expected the parturient to do the work of expelling the fetus from the womb during a normal delivery. There is no indication that anything like an episiotomy was performed. One of the midwife's duties was to instruct the mother on proper breathing and on how to push downwards during a contraction.[47] The assistants who stood by the sides of the chair were to assist in delivery by gently pressing downwards on the parturient's abdomen. Soranus's discussion, supplemented by passages from later medical writers, is similar to the instructions now given to women choosing natural childbirth, except that the father plays no role in the delivery Soranus describes and, more importantly, the instruction in breathing and pushing comes during delivery rather than in a prenatal training program.

In a normal headfirst delivery, the midwife might stretch the cervical opening slightly to help the fetus's head and shoulders through, after which she gently pulled out the rest of the infant's body. The midwife was also to take care that the umbilical cord was not distended and to remove gently the placenta immediately after the birth of the baby. Soranus instructs the midwife to wrap her hands in pieces of cloth or thin papyrus so that the slippery newborn does not slide out of her grasp; Soranus seems to think that if the midwife's hands are so wrapped, she will not inadvertently squeeze the baby too hard in her efforts to maintain a firm hold.[48]

In the fourth book of his treatise, Soranus discusses difficult labor and delivery. In addition to physical problems such as an overly small pelvic opening, malnutrition, or obesity, he recognizes that a woman's attitude and state of mind can have an important bearing on the ease of her delivery: thus Soranus's counsel that midwives work hard to allay the fears and anxieties of the mother. When the parturient suffers from excessive "grief, joy, fear, timidity, lack of energy, anger, or extreme indulgence," labor and delivery are difficult.[49] Soranus notes that inexperienced women have more difficulty than those who have had babies before and that women who do not believe that they are pregnant also have difficult labor.[50]

In a lengthy section, Soranus treats the conditions under which the fetus itself causes a difficult delivery and gives detailed instructions for handling various kinds of cases, including those in which the fetus is dead.[51] Unfortunately, it is impossible to tell even roughly what proportion of births were subject to these complications. But the very length of Soranus's discussion implies that midwives could expect to encounter a significant number of complicated births. And although the obstetrical procedures described seem basically sound, many otherwise healthy fetuses probably died during a difficult delivery.[52]

A number of small reliefs provide visual evidence for ancient childbirth. For example, a rather crudely fashioned, second-century A.D. terracotta from the tomb of Scribionia Attica in the cemetery on the Isola Sacra at Ostia (tomb 100) depicts three women: the parturient seated on a birthing chair; an attendant who stands behind the birthing chair with her arms supporting the parturient's upper torso; and the midwife who sits on a low stool in front of the chair and appears to be about to pull the infant from its mother's womb. The presence of this relief in the tomb may indicate that its owner was a midwife.

A more elegantly crafted ivory relief from Pompeii (Museo Nazionale, Naples, No. 109905) depicts a similar scene. Here there are four women: the parturient sits in the birthing chair; an attendant stands behind and supports the new mother; the midwife, again seated on a low stool and holding a sponge in her right hand, assists the delivery; the fourth woman, who stands behind the midwife with her arms outstretched, appears ready to take the infant or to offer a blessing.

A marble relief from a private collection provides an even more detailed image of childbirth. Delivery has taken place in a well furnished room of an apparently wealthy household. The parturient, naked in this rendition, is sprawled across a chair (not a birthing chair) with a cushion at her back; her lower torso and legs are entirely off the chair, her left leg propped on a low stool. The midwife sits or crouches at the parturient's feet with the newborn baby on a cushion in front of her. A slave attendant stands behind the midwife. Standing behind the parturient are two men, probably physicians; one of them holds an instrument that appears to be an ancient version of obstetric forceps. Both men grip the left arm of the parturient. This visual evidence, meager as it is, confirms and perhaps supplements the verbal pictures of childbirth in Pliny and Soranus.[53]

IV. CARE OF THE MOTHER

Soranus follows his description of normal delivery with a discussion of care of the new mother, which, unfortunately, is very fragmentary. The sole surviving section deals with care of the mother's breasts, including treatment of intumescence or engorgement. He recommends preventive measures such as sponging the breasts with "mildly contracting things (such as diluted vinegar...or tender dates triturated with bread and diluted vinegar)" or confining them with "a close fitting bandage".[54] If swelling occurs, however, poultices made of bread, water, and olive oil or hydromel, or of linseed, wheat or fenugreek, and water should be applied. If the breasts are too tender to stand the poultices, the fluids should be gently pressed out while soaking the breasts in warm oil. If the breasts become inflamed and suppurate, surgery is necessary to remove the pus and fluid.[55] Soranus also tells how to stop lactation in women who do not intend to nurse their new babies themselves.[56] Presumably, the midwife is to administer this care, at least up to the point of surgery for intumescence. The clear implication is that the new mother remained under the care of the midwife for at least several days after the delivery, and so probably did the newborn infant.[57]

If we compare Soranus's recommendations for the care of the breasts of the new mother with Pliny's descriptions of folk medicine, we again see significant differences. Indeed, the methods of treatment described by Pliny seem not only useless but also perhaps sufficiently distasteful to make breast-feeding and the attendant folk remedies something to be avoided. Pliny suggests drinking mouse dung diluted with rain water and ass's milk for intumescences.[58] Rubbing the breasts with sow's blood, goose grease with rose oil and a spider's web, or the fat of bustards is also supposed to relieve swelling.[59] And a poultice of partridge egg ash, zinc oxide ointment and wax might be used to keep the breasts firm.[60]

For breasts that inflame to the point of suppuration, Pliny recommends laying earthworms across the breasts to draw out the pus and adds that earthworms drunk with honeywine stimulate the flow of milk.[61] We may reasonably doubt the efficacy of such treatments; if the breasts were at all abraded, these treatments could cause serious infections. We must assume, however, that these were the kinds of treatment employed for most mothers. Only a relatively few families had the money or the inclination to engage midwives trained according to the medical theories propounded by the leading physicians; nor were there likely to have been many such midwives even in major urban areas.

V. CARE OF THE NEWBORN AFTER DELIVERY

Once the baby had been safely delivered, the midwife carefully inspected it for any congenital deformities. Apparently the midwife made the initial recommendation about whether the newborn was healthy and fit to rear.[62] Soranus suggests several tests for determining the health of the infant. First, when placed on the ground, it should cry lustily; babies that do not cry, or cry only weakly, are suspect. Second, its body should be normal; the openings for the nose, ears, urethra, and anus should be clear; its arms and legs should bend and stretch readily. Finally, by pressing her fingers against the skin of the newborn, the midwife should be able to elicit a reaction, indicating that the infant is sensitive to such sensations.[63] Soranus also instructs the midwife to consider whether the mother has been in good health during pregnancy and whether the length of gestation was normal.[64]

We might well ask under what circumstances a midwife would declare a baby unfit. Not all weakly infants nor all those with some kind of congenital defect such as a club foot were regarded as unfit. Probably the midwife made a determination about the chances for the infant's survival and would likely recommend that a newborn with any severe congenital problem be exposed.

After inspecting the child and letting it rest a bit, the midwife severs the umbilical cord. Soranus recommends using a knife and castigates other methods as superstitious. He says that some midwives use a piece of glass or a potsherd (presumably unwashed), a reed, or even a thin crust of hard bread.[65] Soranus indicates that such materials are apt to cause inflammation, showing at least some awareness of a connection between dirt and disease. Instead of cauterizing the cord, as many midwives do, Soranus directs her to gently squeeze the blood from it, to ligate the end with a stout woolen (not linen) thread, and finally to gently press the bent cord into the umbilicus or navel.[66]

With the umbilical cord tied off properly, the midwife is then to cleanse the newborn. In the course of his discussion of washing the infant, Soranus describes the practices of many other groups of people and rejects them all as harmful to the newborn. Soranus recommends that the midwife sprinkle the infant with a moderate amount of "fine and powdery salt, or natron or aphronitre."[67] All these chemicals are mildly astringent and were recommended primarily for their ability to cut through the residue of amniotic fluid, vernix, and placenta on the newborn's skin and also to make the skin less prone to develop rashes; however, astringents would also tend to make the baby's skin dry out and flake or crack. Soranus suggests mixing the salt with honey, olive oil, or the juice of barley, fenugreek, or mallow so the granules are less likely to abrade the baby's delicate skin. The emulsion is to be washed away with warm water and the process repeated a second time. Next, the midwife is to clear any mucus from the nose, mouth, and ears and to clear the anus of any membranes that might impede regular bowel movements. She is to put a little olive oil into the infant's eyes to clear away any birth residue and to place a small piece of wool or lint soaked with olive oil over the umbilical cord. Soranus indicates that some people use cumin here, but he states that cumin is too pungent to be used on an infant.[68] Throughout his discussion of the care of the newborn, Soranus stresses the delicacy of the infant and recommends those treatments he thinks least likely to cause it discomfort.

VI. CONCLUSIONS

The vast majority of women in the Greco-Roman world very probably received their maternity care (assuming they could afford to pay for it; no doubt many could not) from midwives who employed the methods and medications described by Pliny. While the traditions of folk medicine probably did little to make childbirth safer (and some practices may have been harmful), it does seem clear that efforts were made to give emotional support to the parturient.

There is insufficient evidence to reach any firm conclusions about the characteristics of the women who practiced midwifery. In the Hellenized East, they seem to have had a higher status than their sisters in the Roman West. Although some women of free birth went into midwifery as a profession, the bulk of them were probably of servile origin or the daughters of women of the lower classes. A very few women became obstetricians of some note.

For the wealthy elites, maternity care was potentially much better. The corpus of medical literature certainly shows that some physicians and midwives employed enlightened techniques that at the very least were unlikely to harm either the mother or the baby. It seems probable, therefore, that the rates of maternal and infant mortality in the Greco-Roman world varied with the socio-economic class of the family and with the family's choice between traditional folk medicine and professionalized obstetrical care.

---

[1] World Health Statistics Annual (1979), pp. 16-28.

[2] Calvin Wells has recently argued that the incidence of female death in childbirth in antiquity has been significantly overestimated; a relatively poorer diet will account for the shorter lives of ancient women, Wells contends. "Ancient Obstetric Hazards and Female Mortality," Bulletin of the New York Academy of Medicine, 51 (1975), 1235-49.

[3] World Health Statistics Annual (1979). Keith Hopkins Death and Renewal (Cambridge: Cambridge University Press, 1983), p. 225, estimates that 28% of Roman babies who were born alive died by their first birthday.

[4] Ep. 4.21.1-3.

[5] Fronto, ad M. Caesar 1.6.7 and Epis. Graec. 3.

[6] HN 7.6.4 1.

[7] HN 28.27.102.

[8] HN 28.77.250. The drying and powdering of the dung probably would have reduced its bacterial content, but ingestion of even some E. coli (colon bacillus) would be dangerous.

[9] HN 30.143.124 (Loeb translation). Semen has a high sugar content and would have supplied the parturient with energy.

[10] HN 26.90.160-61. Vervain (radix verbenicae) comes from the family of verbena and has been used for medicinal purposes, chiefly for fevers, colds, convulsions, and nervous diorders; it was valued for its nervine, tonic, emetic, and sudorific properties. Scordotis (teucrium scordium) is probably related to garlic and was thought to have antiseptic, sudorific, and alexipharmic properties; it has been used particularly for inflammations. Dittany (origanum diciamnus) is a pink flowered plant, probably of the mint family. For descriptions of the plants prescribed, see R. C. Wren, Potter's New Encyclopaedia of Botanical Drugs and Preparations (Devon: Health Sciences Press, 1975), and Walter H. Lewis and P. F. Elvin-Lewis, Medical Botany (New York: John Wiley, 1977).

[11] HN 30.143.123.

[12] *HN* 30.44.129 (Loeb translation), Although Pliny does not say specifically what was done with the stick, we can probably assume that it was not used in the process of delivery; rather it was valued for its presumed magical properties.

[13] *HN* 30.44.130.

[14] *Med.* 2.8.16.

[15] *Med.* 5.25.14. Hedge mustard is a common form of wild mustard and is said to be a digestive stimulant, expectorant, and diuretic.

[16] *HN* 30.43.125; 28.77.255; 25.18.40; 28.77.248. Linozostis is probably annual or perennial mercury (*mercurialis annua* or *perennis*), a toxic plant whose leaves can cause gastroenteritis and allergic reactions in the lungs; it is possible that the cramps of gastroenteritis were confused with uterine contractions and that the plant, therefore, seemed to aid delivery. Parthenion is a plant with white ray flowers; *P. hysterophorus* (the bastard feverfew) and *P. integrifolium* are used medicinally. Pliny notes that linozostis and parthenion were recommended as emmenagogues, remedies to induce menstrual bleeding. None of the plants recommended by Pliny or Celsus are known at present to be oxytocic agents, substances that stimulate uterine contractions. But the emetic properties of some of them could induce vomiting which, with its abdominal spasms, is sometimes helpful in separating the placenta from the uterus. The folk practices described by Pliny and Celsus are similar to contemporary folk medicine. See A. Mangay-Maglacas and H. Pizurki, *The Traditional Birth Attendant in Seven Countries* (Geneva: World Health Organization, 1981).

[17] *Med.* 5.25.13.

[18] Recent research has shown how important emotional support is. See Aidan Macfarlane, *The Psychology of Childbirth* (Cambridge, Mass.: Harvard, 1978), pp. 29-31; Joyce Prince and Margaret E. Adams, *Minds, Mothers, and Midwives* (New York: Churchill Livingstone, 1978), pp. 116f; and Barbara L. Blum, ed., *Psychological Aspects of Pregnancy, Birth, & Bonding* (New York: Human Sciences Press, 1981), pp. 144-45.

[19] A careful edition of the Greek text of Soranus was published by Johannes Ilberg as volume four of the *Corpus Medicorum Graecorum* (Leipzig and Berlin: Teubner, 1927). For an English translation of Soranus with an excellent introduction, see Owsei Temkin, *Soranus' Gynecology* (Baltimore: Johns Hopkins, 1956). A physician himself, Temkin presumes a fair amount of obstetrical knowledge on the part of his readers. Unfortunately, the section of Soranus' work treating normal delivery is fragmentary. But Temkin's translation fills in many of the lacunae with passages from later gynecological treatises that were based on Soranus, especially the works of Caelius Aurelianus and Muscio. Soranus's extant work, supplemented by later writers, provides the best description of the best obstetric care in the Greco-Roman world.

[20] *Gyn.* 1.1.3 (Temkin translation).

[21] *Gyn.* 1.2.4.

[22] *Gyn.* 1.1.3.

[23] Temkin, p. xxxvii.

[24] *Gyn.* 1.2.4 (Temkin translation). Soranus's reference to the dreams of midwives may parallel anthropological findings. In some cultures, women are selected as midwives on account of a dream vision in which they are taught the skills and knowledge of the profession. We do not know how Greco-Roman women became midwives, but Soranus's brief statement might suggest that dreams played a role in the selection process. See Sheila Cosminsky, "Cross Cultural Perspectives on Midwifery" in *Medical Anthropology,* eds. S. Grollig and H. Haley (The Hague: Mouton, 1976), pp. 231-32.

[25] Temkin, p. xxxvii. But the male physician gave directions; the midwife did the work (Galen, *Nat. Fac.* 3.3. 1 5 1).

[26] In Plautus's comedy *Amphitryon*, Alcmena delivers twins without anyone present (line, 1070-72). However, the birth story here parallels that of Heracles so strongly that the absence of a midwife should not be taken too seriously, even though Alcmena's family surely could have afforded one.

[27] For women as midwives and physicians in the East, see Sarah B. Pomeroy, "Technikai kai Mousikai," *AJAH,* 2 (1977), 58-60, and "Plato and the Female Physician," *AJPH.* (1978), 496-500. A few female physicians are also attested in Rome; see Susan Treggiari, "Jobs for Women," *AJAH,* 1 (1976), 86, and Natalie Kampen, "Social Status and Gender in Roman Art: The Case of the Saleswoman," in *Feminism and Art History,* eds. Norma Broude and Mary Garrard (New York: Harper & Row, 1982), p. 70, and *Image and Working Women in Ostia* (Berlin: Gebr. Mann Verlag, 1981), pp. 69-72 and (Gyn. 3.3.1) draws a clear distinction between the midwife (*maia*) and the physician obstetrician (*iatros gynaikeios*); in Latin, *ob(p)stetrix* and *medicus/a* parallel Soranus' terminology.

[28] *CIL* 6: # 4458, 6325, 6647, 6832, 8192, 8207, 8947-9, 9720-5, and 37810. We should not assume that because so few women are identified as midwives that there were few midwives in general. Until more research is done on analyzing the occupational titles recorded in funeral epitaphs, we cannot conclude anything about the relative numbers of people engaged in different occupations.

[29] *Contra*: Treggiari (above, note 27), 87; she sees the women commemorated by #9722, 9724, and 9725 as just as likely to be freeborn as freed. Treggiari suggests, therefore "that free women might train for this work and that only

in domestic service would slaves be the rule." Kampen (above, note 27), p, 116, argues for the servile background of most midwives.

[30] For midwives working expertly at an advanced age, see Cosminsky (above. note 24) p. 23 1.

[31] In the other eleven epitaphs, the name of the commemorator is not given.

[32] John Scarborough, *Roman Medicine* (London: Thames and Hudson, 1979). P. 19 See *Dig.* 9.2.9. 1; Ulpian describes the application of the *Lex Aquilia* to *obstetrices*.

[33] *M. Gl.* 697.

[34] *P. Oxy.* 1273, lines 33-34. The potential income of a midwife suggested by this contract compares favorably with other wages from this period and region. Stewards, for example, earned approximately 40 drachmas a month (*P. Lond.* 1226 and *P. Flor-* 321 and 322); ox drivers made between 34 and 48 drachmae a month (*P. Flor.* 321); common laborers could expect around four to eight drachmae a month *(P. Flor.* 322); estate managers received between 60 and 128 drachmae a month (*P. Oxy.* 1577-78). See Allan Chester Johnson, *An Economic Survey of Ancient Rome*, vol. 2, ed. Tenney Frank (Paterson, N. J.: Pageant, 1959), II, pp. 309-10.

[35] *Gyn.* 1.2.4.

[36] *Cod. Iust.* 6.43.3 provides that slave *medici* and *obstetrices* left to legatees had equal value (60 *solidi*). *Dig.* 50.13.1 gives a list of people for whom Provincial governors were to hear suits on contracts for wages; at 50.13.1.2 the midwife is given equal access to the official because she is regarded as practicing medicine just as doctors do *(quae utique medicinam exhibere videtur)*. See J. A. Crook, *Law and Life of* Rome (Ithaca: Cornell University Press, 1967), pp. 204-05, and Kampen (above, note 27), pp. 70 and 11 7.

[37] Scarborough (above, note 32), p. 18; W. W. Fowler, The *Roman Festivals of the Period of the Republic* (London: Macmillan, 1899), p. 292, connects the Carmentes, birth goddesses, with the *sagae*.

[38] *Gyn.* 2.2.2.

[39] Recent research indicates that an upright as opposed to a recumbent position is more comfortable for the parturient and reduces the time of both labor and delivery. See Susan McKay and Charles S. Mahan, "Laboring Patients Need More Freedom to Move," *Contemporary OB/GYN*, July 1984, 90-119. I am grateful to Dr. Celeste Phillips for her assistance on this question.

[40] *Gyn.* 2.2.3,

[41] *Gyn.* 2.3.5.

[42] *Letters* 2.7. 1.

[43] *Gyn.* 2.2.3-2.3.4. Galen's brief description of the midwife's duties during delivery (*Nat. Fac.* 3.3.151-52) closely parallels Soranus's account. Midwives today use massage and warm oil to soothe the parturient during labor. But the practice of trying to hasten dilation by rubbing the cervix is potentially dangerous, for the midwife's finger even if smeared with oil, is likely to introduce foreign bacteria. However, since birth took place at home, there was less likelihood that the parturient could be contaminated with bacteria from sick people.

[44] *Gyn.* 2.3.5.

[45] Hemorrhoids usually develop during pregnancy, if they occur at all; Soranus's advice may well have prevented internal hemorrhoids from becoming external during delivery. The cloth held at the anus may also have prevented fecal matter from contaminating the perineum and vagina.

[46] *Gyn.* 2.3.5.

[47] *Gyn.* 2.3.6. According to Pliny, HN 7.6.42, women who do not hold their breath during delivery experience greater difficulty; Pliny also adds that gasping may prove fatal.

[48] Gyn. 2.3.6. It is hard to see how the midwife would he able to reach the cervix once the baby's head had emerged. Soranus may mean the perineum. More serious is the instruction to try to remove the placenta immediately after delivery. Premature removal of the placenta, especially if the midwife attempted to reach into the uterus, would be likely to cause infection and even hemorrhage. Modern practice is to allow the placenta to separate itself from the uterine wall and then to have the parturient push to expel it.

[49] *Gyn.* 4.2.2.

[50] *Gyn.* 4.2.2.

[51] *Gyn.* 4.2.3f.

[52] Galen says that infants present feet first, laterally, or with an arm or leg first in only of many thousands of births *(de Usu Partium* 15.7). We should properly take this observation with a grain of salt, since neither Galen nor any one else in antiquity ever tried to make an accurate count of such occurrences. But clearly, Galen thought these births unusual. Modern statistics suggest that in about five percent of deliveries, the infant presents in a difficult position—breech, transverse, compound, or face/brow first. By far the most common, breech occurs in about three to four percent of deliveries. Breech presentations are especially associated with prematurity and poor nutrition, conditions at least as likely in the Greco-Roman world as today. As a general rule of thumb, 85-90% of all births in a generally healthy female population are normal and uncomplicated. See Harry Oxorn, *Human Labor and Birth,* 4th edition (New York: Appleton Century Crofts, 1980).

[53] See plates 1-111 (in original, not reproduced in this reader). For the Ostia and Pompeii reliefs, see Kampen (above, note 27), pp. 69-72. For the relief depicting obstetrical forceps, see Harvey Graham, *Eternal Eve* (Garden City: Doubleday, 1951), pp. 68-69. Professor Silvestro Baglioni, the owner of the relief reportedly found near Rome, dates it to the second or third century B. C., but its authenticity is not secure. For ancient obstetric surgical instruments, see John Stewart Milne, *Surgical Instruments in Greek and Roman Times* (New York: Oxford, 1907), pp. 152-58.

[54] *Gyn*. 2.5.7 (Temkin translation). A terracotta figurine in the Athens National Museum (No. 5666) shows a woman bandaging both her breasts, since she has a rather flabby abdomen, the figurine may well depict this method of caring for the breasts after delivery, a method also used by modern midwives.

[55] *Gyn*. 2.5.7. Fenugreek (trigonella foenumgraecum), a leguminous annual herb with aromatic seeds, has been used as an insulin substitute. Plutarch's wife apparently underwent surgery for a "bruised nipple" incurred while nursing her son Charon; Plutarch praises her action as "noble" and indicative of "true mother love" (*Mor*. 609E). The tenor of Plutarch's remarks suggests that such surgery was very painful.

[56] *Gyn*. 2.5.8.

[57] Despite the fullness of Soranus's description of the duties of the midwife, she may have been expected to do even more. For example, Horace refers to a midwife washing the blood stained cloths used in delivery (*Epod*. 17.51). It may well be that some midwives brought with them the cloths they used in childbirth; if so, one is relieved to learn that they were washed.

[58] *HN* 30.43.124 and 28.77.250.

[59] *HN* 28.77.250 and 30.45.131.

[60] *HN* 30.45.131.

[61] *HN* 30.43.125.

[62] Varro, *apud* Nonius 528.12; Soranus, *Gyn*. 2.6. 1 0.

[63] *Gyn*. 2.6.10. The author of the biography of Clodius Albinus comments that normal children are red at birth *(SHA*, Clod. 4.4). Surprisingly, Soranus does not mention the newborn's skin color as an indication of its health.

[64] *Gyn*. 2.6.10. The normal period of gestation was believed to vary between seven and ten months. Without a system of prenatal care, the midwife would have to rely on the mother's determination of her health and length of pregnancy; such determinations were, no doubt, often in error.

[65] It is possible that poor midwives used such readily available implements in order to save the cost of purchasing a knife.

[66] *Gyn*. 2.7.1 1. The potential problem with cauterization, apart from the pain it probably causes the infant, is that it will not always completely close the blood vessels and thus increases the possibility of umbilical hemorrhage. Pressing the cord into the umbilicus is not likely to insure an indented navel. Oribasius gives similar instructions for ligating the umbilical cord. It is to be cut at a distance of about four finger widths (about three inches) from the stomach with a sharp knife, neither a reed nor a piece of glass should he used in order to keep the contusion as slight as possible. After cutting, the blood should be gently squeezed from the cord, and then the end is to be wiped and bound with wool *(Collect. Med. Liv. Incert*. 12.1).

[67] *Gyn*. 2.8.12-13. Natron is the mineral, hydrated sodium carbonate, rather like baking soda; aphronitre is probably some kind of foaming saltpeter, either potassium or sodium nitrite.

[68] *Gyn*. 2.9.13. Cummin is a plant from the same family as parsley and celery and a sharp, distinct taste and odor.

EARLY MODERN MIDWIFERY: A CASE STUDY

Merry E. Wiesner[*]

The most important occupation in which women were involved during the medieval and early modern period, in terms of impact on society as a whole and recognition by government and church authorities, was midwifery. The midwife's vital role is often overlooked by modern historians, however, as they consider her only in passing while focusing on other developments. Medical historians tend to limit themselves to examinations of the development of obstetrics and gynecology, tracing the advances in the field made by university-trained physicians beginning in the early modern period, viewing the midwife as superstitious and bungling. They often skip from the theorists of ancient Greece to the Chamberlen brothers (who invented the forceps) in seventeenth-century England[1]. This ignores the fact, however, that the midwife's practices and methods during the intervening 1500 years were no more bizarre or occult than those of contemporary physicians, and were based on beliefs about the body and bodily processes current during the time period in which she worked.

Historians have noted the frequent identification of witches as midwives and have seen a decline in the status and role of the midwife during the sixteenth and seventeenth centuries because she was tainted with witchcraft, particularly in France and England. They point out that witches and midwives were often members of the same social group—poor, elderly women, often widows, with some knowledge of herbs and charms. This decline in midwifery, they feel, allowed for the entrance of male midwives—accoucheurs—and physicians into the field[2]. One wonders if the cause and effect relationship here is not the reverse, however, i.e., that the entrance of men into the field pushed the female practitioners out, as was the case in so many other fields. In addition, the very identification of witches and midwives shows that the community recognized the power which the midwives had—they *were* able to make the difference between life and death, just as witches were perceived to. Even during the period of "decline," cities and rulers took as great care with the regulation of midwives as they did with the regulation of physicians and surgeons. They did this because the midwife had an extremely important role, not only handling nearly every birth, but also performing additional medical services, distributing public welfare, serving various religious functions, and giving testimony in legal cases.

Her multifaceted role can be seen clearly in a close examination of midwifery in one community. For this I have chosen the city of Nuremberg. Nuremberg had a system of midwives which was the envy of and later model for those in many other parts of Germany. Although there are no means of determining their actual effect on infant mortality, the fact that Nuremberg's midwives were sought by other cities and rulers indicates that their skills and teaching were highly regarded. Unfortunately, there are no diaries or case books from Nuremberg midwives, so it is difficult to perceive how they saw themselves or defined their own role, but the activities in which they were involved were so varied and their testimony taken so seriously that they are clearly seen as able and trustworthy. This despite their low social position, evidenced by the fact that they are always referred to by first name in court records, city council minutes, and private diaries.

---

[*] This chapter originally appeared in *International Journal of Women's Studies* 6, no. 1:26-43. All translations are my own.

HISTORICAL BACKGROUND

Nuremberg's population grew from about 23,000 in 1430 to about 54,000 in 1620, making it one of the three largest cities in Germany, along with Cologne and Augsburg[3]. A small city council *(Rat)* governed the city, making all decisions from the most important—foreign policy, declarations of war, religious change—to the most trivial—the permitted width of fur trimmings, the price of fruit and nuts, the proper method for washing clothing. Unlike most other German cities, there were no independent guilds, and all organized crafts had to swear an oath of obedience to the council. As a free imperial city, Nuremberg was not controlled by any secular or ecclesiastical prince, but swore allegiance only to the emperor.

During the fifteenth and sixteenth centuries, the city was a commercial and cultural center whose merchants and products were to be found throughout Europe. The work of her goldsmiths, artists, and printers was in demand everywhere, and the new ideas of humanism and later Protestantism found ready acceptance among the leaders of the city. The city council assumed control of public welfare and hygiene very early on, and Nuremberg's hospitals and system of poor relief would be emulated by other cities.

As in other social and intellectual concerns, the city stood in the forefront in the area of midwifery as well, first organizing and developing a system of midwives in the early fifteenth century. The first record of a midwife active in the city dates from 1381, and midwives first appeared as sworn city officials in the *Aemterbüchlein,* the list of all occupational groups required to take an annual oath before the council, in 1417[4]. Sixteen women were listed this first year; their number varied from eight to twenty-one over the next 200 years.

In 1463, the council instituted the office of *Ehrbare Frauen,* women from the patrician class given responsibility to oversee and control the midwives. They had no medical function, but assigned midwives and distributed food and clothing to indigent mothers, as well as disciplining women they felt were not living up to their midwives' oath. They were responsible for making an annual report to the city council immediately after Easter, reporting any problems or deficiencies among the midwives. The number of women in this office was surprisingly large, varying from seventeen when first established to a high of fifty-five in 1530, but then dropping throughout the sixteenth century to as few as nine by 1620, to two one hundred years later[5]. From about 1560 on, each year's *Aemterbüchlein* includes a note calling for the appointment of more *Ehrbare Frauen,* with no success. It appears that the office was no longer seen as prestigious by upper-class women.

Acting on the report of the *Ehrbare Frauen* and complaints by the midwives, the council created another office in 1549, the *Geschworene Weiber*[6]. These women were the wives and widows of craftsmen and minor officials who were to act as overseers, watching for the misuse of public welfare or any other infractions, and helping midwives in particularly difficult cases. Although no specific reason is given for the creation of the *Geschworene Weiber,* this was a period of more rigid social stratification in Nuremberg, leading one to speculate that the *Ehrbare Frauen* no longer wished to mix with the lowest classes, and called for this new office to deal with the poorest women.

The council paid the *Geschworene Weiber* twelve Rhenish gulden (fl.) annually, although the upper-class *Ehrbare Frauen* were not paid anything. The *Geschworene Weiber* were also given small tips by the midwives and the expectant mothers, but they were warned by the council not to demand or take too much "food, drink, or payment"[7]. Their number varied from four to ten from 1550 to 1650.

The total number of women involved in the city's midwife system thus increased from sixteen in 1417 to a high of sixty-five in 1530 and then stabilized at forty to fifty for the next one hundred years. Of these, about one third were active midwives.

As noted above, the population of Nuremberg during the late medieval and early modern period ranged between 25,000 and 50,000. Although a determination of the exact birthrate for any area before the advent of accurate record-keeping is impossible, several studies of preindustrial Europe have found the birthrate to be roughly 40-50 births per thousand population[8]. Thus one would expect somewhere between 1000 and 2500 births per year in the city.

With the number of midwives varying between eight and eighteen, the number of births per midwife would have varied between 60 and 300 a year. This latter pace—an average of nearly one birth a day—would have been very difficult to maintain and would not have allowed for any postnatal care, which midwives were also often paid to do. Thus one can understand the constant concern of the council that more women be trained, particularly whenever the total number of midwives in the city dropped below ten.

These figures may be somewhat high, because there were undoubtedly some women who gave birth without the aid of a trained midwife. If a woman had already had numerous children without complications, was generally healthy, and had friends and relatives who could attend to her, she may not have summoned a midwife. If the child was born prematurely, there may not have been time for one to reach her. Certainly women in the rural areas during this period did not expect the services of a midwife for each delivery.

However, given the fact that the council provided for the services of a midwife for every indigent mother, and carefully spelled out the proper charges for women of all social classes, one may assume that most births in the city itself were handled by a midwife. Three to five births per week was probably average for an experienced midwife.

FEES AND REGULATIONS

Midwives' actual fees varied with the social class of the mother involved. Sebastian Welser, a wealthy cloth merchant and council member, recorded in 1534 that he paid the midwife 1½ fl. for a delivery and 1 fl. more for the care of his wife during the three months after delivery[9]. Wives of craftsmen would generally pay half that, and wives of day laborers even less. In 1561, midwives were granted 42 pfennig by the council for caring for indigent women[10]. Midwives were also rewarded for medical services during times of an epidemic.

These payments compare relatively well with the salaries of craftsmen and journeymen, depending on how many births a midwife attended. Carl Sachs has determined the average salary for journeymen and apprentices in 1510 to be 15-33 pfennig a day, and that of a master 47-60 d, depending on the time of year and length of the work day[11]. Because of inflation during the sixteenth century, the payment granted to midwives for indigent mothers 1561, 42 d, was probably very close to the average daily salary of a journeyman at that time. As one birth was all any midwife could physically handle in a day, the salaries are roughly comparable.

The council encouraged experienced midwives to move into the city by granting them free citizenship rights and often an initial salary as well. In some cases they seem to have paid the usual fee, but generally their entry in the new citizen lists *(Neubürgerlisten)* is accompanied by the note *dedimus*, i.e., granted free of charge[12].

Only in very unusual cases was a midwife allowed to leave the city and render services elsewhere, despite the high position and prestige of those who requested one. In 1496, a woman was sent to Heidelberg to serve the wife of a Count Palatine; he had personally written asking for a midwife[13]. In 1506 the city of Ulm asked for one, and in 1541, Dorothea, the wife of Duke Albrecht of Saxony, did as well[14]. In the first case the council refused to send one, as it felt none could be spared[15]. The decision in the latter case is not recorded. The city of Heilbronn requested an experienced midwife to teach local women in 1606, and the council again refused, claiming a shortage in the city at that time would not allow it[16].

The regulations governing midwives were promulgated in a series of ordinances, to be given to all of them annually before the oath-swearing. The first systematic ordinance was put forth in 1522, with amendments and alterations made as new problems arose[17]. From these ordinances, and the day-to-day cases before the city council, we can get an idea of the wide variety of activities in which midwives were involved. The most basic rules concerned their conduct vis-à-vis pregnant women. They were to treat all alike, rich and poor, and especially not to leave a poor woman to attend a rich one for whom they would be paid more. No birth was to be hurried; if a midwife needed rest during a particularly long or difficult birth, she was to call another sworn midwife, and not simply her maid. She could be fined five fl. and deprived of her office for leaving a woman in need. Excessive wine-drinking was repeatedly forbidden.

Midwives were not allowed to dispense strong drugs, only "common medicines, juices, nectars and the like, that cannot be mishandled easily but used safely every day"[18]. These they could obtain from an apothecary, however, without referral by a doctor. If their patients could not pay for the medicine themselves, the city paid the apothecary.

The period of apprenticeship for a midwife was four years. Apprentices were required to stay with one mistress the whole period, or else prove that they had left through no fault of their own; this restriction is the same as those in other craft regulations. If the council found a maid had valid reasons for leaving her first mistress, such as cruel treatment, the maid would be assigned to another. As punishment, the old mistress could take on no new apprentices until her previous one had finished her training, even though she was now learning with another woman[19].

Midwives were admonished to take on no "young, light-headed" girls. A later amendment forbade married women with families as well, for fear they would be too busy with their own concerns and housework. Apprentices could not be sent to any case alone until they had served one year, and then only to women who had already had several children. Unlike most occupations, there was no required grace period after one apprentice left before another could be taken on. On the contrary, the council asked that another be accepted within three months.

Bonuses were offered to encourage the acceptance of an apprentice. In 1483, four midwives were granted two to three lb. a year when they took on apprentices; the following year this was raised to five pounds[20]. In 1517, the council increased this even more: "From now on, the sworn midwives are to be given 32 lb. to teach each maid, but (payable) only when she has completed her instruction and sworn her oath"[21].

During the middle of the sixteenth century, the council called for even stronger measures to encourage the teaching of more apprentices: "Each midwife is to be told once again to be prepared to take on a qualified apprentice, or the council will punish her in earnest"[22]. This did have some effect for several years.

Further changes were made in the seventeenth century, ordering midwives and their maids to report any miscarriages, forbidding the marriage of any maid during her training period, and suggesting more midwives be sent to the rural areas which the city controlled[23].

A picture of the typical midwife, or at least one which the council hoped was typical, emerges clearly from these ordinances. She was a widow, or an older, unmarried woman, not especially well-off financially as she did not have her own household. The fact that admonitions against married midwives continued indicates that not all were of the marital status considered proper, however.

DELIVERY PROCEDURES

We must first examine the most important activities—delivery and child care. The regulations and ordinances give us little information about actual techniques and methods, but the early sixteenth century saw the publication of an extremely influential midwives' manual which does address these questions, and which covers the beliefs about gynecology and obstetrics which were certainly current in Nuremberg. This was Eucharius Rösslin's *Den Swangern frawen und hebammen Roszgarten* (The rosegarden for midwives and pregnant women). It was first printed in 1513 by Martin Flach in Strassburg, with two more editions printed in Hagenau that same year. Nearly 100 additional editions were published during the next 200 years in various languages—English, French, Latin, Dutch, Italian, Spanish and Czech[24]. It was always illustrated with woodcuts and engravings, although these varied from edition to edition.

Although objections may be raised against using a printed manual as a source of popular beliefs, in the case of the *Rosengarten* this may be justified on three grounds. First, midwives seem to have been much more literate than has previously been assumed. In Nuremberg, for example, they were given printed copies of their oath and of baptism regulations so that they would be able to refer to them if questions arose; no provision was made to have these read to midwives who were illiterate[25]. The number of editions and widespread popularity of Rösslin's manual and its copies also point to a large body of readers interested in its advice. Second, although midwives actually learned through an apprentice system and never from a manual alone, the *Rosengarten* gives hints and tips for medicines and techniques that could easily have been adopted by the most enlightened midwives and then passed on to their assistants and apprentices. Third, although Rösslin names only classical authors as the source of his ideas, he also often adds the comment "as is widely known" or "as is known by wise women" after describing certain treatments; clearly he had talked to midwives and women about their practices while writing his manual.

The pictures and much of the text of the *Rosengarten* stem from classical authors; Rösslin himself lists Hippocrates, Galen, Averrois, Rhazes, Avicenna, and Albertus Magnus as his sources. He does not mention his most important source, however, a Latin translation of a gynecological text by Soranus of Ephesus, written about 100 A.D.[26]. The translation from Greek was made in the sixth century by Muscio (Moschion), and usually bore the title *Gynaecia Muscionis*; numerous copies from the ninth to the fifteenth century are still extant. One copy of this book was in Heidelberg at the time Rösslin wrote the *Rosengarten*, and it may have been the copy he used.

The pictures which Rösslin adopted from Soranus of the baby in utero were not only included in further reprints and translations, but were copied by Jakob Rueff, Ambroise Paré, Jacques Guillimeau and others in their own works until nearly 1700.

The actual text begins with a discussion of the normal position of the baby in the uterus, the normal duration of pregnancy (40 weeks), and how to tell if a woman is likely to have a miscarriage or difficult birth. Expectant mothers are urged to watch their diets in order to prevent constipation (which was linked to difficult births) and maintain their strength.

Certain foods, such as broth, juices, fried apples, figs, goose fat, and linseed or fenugreek oil are advised to make the mother wider in the pelvis, and also warmer, moister, and more pliable, all of which aided in delivery. Warm herb baths also served this purpose. In no case was the woman simply to lie in bed, but keep to her normal routine of moving and working. Specific advice for the mother and midwife during labor and delivery was as follows:

When the mother finds an increase in pain and some dampness that begins, appears and flows to her genitals, she should prepare herself in two sorts of ways. The first is to make a shortened descent and passage out for the child. The second way is a lessening of the accompanying pains and aches; she should sit down for an hour and then stand up, climb up and down the stairs crying loudly. The woman should also breathe heavily and hold her breath so that she pushes her insides down.

The woman should also drink one of the medicines which follow so that she pushes the child out to its birth. When she discovers that the uterus has opened and the liquid is flowing freely, she should lie down on her back, but not completely lie down nor stand up. It should be midway between lying and standing with the head more toward the back than the front. In upper German lands and in Welfish countries the midwives have special chairs for use when the women bear. They are not so high, but are cut out in the middle.

The chairs should be made so that the woman can lean back on her back. These chairs should be covered and padded at the back with cloths. When it is time the midwife should lift up the cloths firmly and turn the woman first onto the right side and then onto the left. The midwife should sit in front of her and pay careful attention to the movement in the mother's body. The midwife should control the mother's legs and movements with her hands which have been coated with white lily oil or almond oil or the like. With her hands the midwife should also advise, instruct and direct the mother, nourish her with food and drink and encourage her with gentle words to exert herself so that she breathes deeply. She should also lightly press on the stomach above the navel toward the hips. The midwife should also comfort the mother with the happy prospect of the birth of a boy[27].

In case of abnormal presentation, the midwife was first to attempt to turn the child around to bring about a head-first position by pushing the feet upwards. If this was impossible, a feet-first presentation was the next best, with care taken that the arms were at the child's sides, not alongside its head. The midwife could bind both feet together with a linen bandage in order to make delivery easier. Any other presentation, breech, knee, shoulders, or hand-first, was to be handled in this way as well, the midwife first attempting to effect a head-first presentation and then a feet-first if that was easier. In all cases she was to handle the baby carefully and gently. The midwife was also to treat any post-delivery illnesses of the mother, which Rösslin felt came either from an incomplete cleansing and purification, which led to fever, or from a loss of too much blood. Barley-water, broth, and pomegranates are advised to bring down fever, as well as numerous potions and mixtures to alleviate pain. Bandages and cloths soaked in herb mixtures could be placed on the mother's vagina, or the mixtures poured directly into the uterus.

Rösslin next discusses premature births and miscarriages, and here his dependence on classical authors emerges most clearly. He cites both Avicenna and Hippocrates in giving reasons why a woman would miscarry: If she was too fat or too thin, ate the wrong foods, took too long or too hot baths, went out in the night air, suffered from diarrhea or constipation and took any strong drugs to alleviate this condition, was frightened or injured in any way. External factors could cause a miscarriage as well: unseasonal temperatures or other climatic conditions (especially an unusually cold summer), or meteorological phenomena such as eclipses or comets.

The midwife and the mother were to recognize the signs of an imminent miscarriage, particularly the collapse or shrinking of one of the mother's breasts. Again, following Hippocrates and Avicenna—"If the right breast shrivels then a boy will be miscarried, as normally a boy lies on the right side, and a girl on the left side"[28]. Various methods are suggested to prevent miscarriages: mild laxatives, moderation in food and drink, blood-letting, no vigorous exercise, drugs that will make the mother's vaginal opening narrower.

Perhaps the most unpleasant task a midwife had to deal with was handling a baby which had died inside the mother. Rösslin lists twelve ways to tell if the child had died, some of which make sense—if the mother had great pain or a fever, or poor color, if she couldn't sleep or felt no movement. Others have no biological basis—if the mother's breasts shriveled, if her urine or breath stank, if the whites of her eyes turned brown or her nose or ears grew numb, stuck out or turned blue, if she wanted to eat and drink unusual things.(!)

Once it was determined the baby was actually dead, the midwife could either attempt to force it out by administering medicines or cut the child apart and remove it piece by piece. Medicines and treatments recommended vary widely: the woman could sit over a smoldering fire of donkey's dung so that the child would be smoked out; she could drink a brew made of figs, fenugreek, rue, and wild marjoram, which would make the child slip out; she could drink the milk from another woman who had borne a dead child before her; she could bathe in an herb bath made with rain water, and afterwards drink crushed date seeds and saffron mixed with wine.

If none of these, nor the numerous other recommended treatments worked, the midwife was forced to use surgery:

The woman should be laid on her back with the head down and the legs up. She should be lifted on both sides and her arms bound tightly so that she cannot pull away when the child is drawn out. Then the midwife should make the woman's opening wider with her left hand—which had been greased with white-lily oil or with something else that makes it smooth and slippery—with the fingers spread. Then she should reach in the opening of the woman and search for the limbs of the dead child, so that she knows where to put the hook and how to pull the child out. If the child is lying in its mother's body with the head toward the opening then the midwife should put the hook in one eye of the child, in the gums of the mouth, under the chin in the throat, in one armpit or in another part of the child where the hook goes in easily. If the dead child comes with its feet first then the midwife should force the hook into a bone above the pelvis of the child, as in the middle ribs, or in the bones of the breast or behind in the back. When she has forced one hook in she should lift with her right hand, but not pull, and reach with her left hand inside the woman and push another hook in on the opposite side of the dead child from the first hook. Then the midwife should pull with both hands together and not only one, so that the dead child will be pulled equally on both sides. She should jerk slowly and gently from one side to the other, and while doing this should grasp inside the woman with a well greased pointer finger and loosen the child on all sides from the mother, moving it toward the opening and loosening it if it is stuck anywhere. She should do this until the child has been removed completely from the mother's body.

It may happen that the dead child has one hand forward without the other which cannot be easily pushed back in the mother's body because the opening to the uterus is too narrow. Then a cloth should be tied tightly around the child's hand so that it cannot slip off easily and the midwife should pull on the hand until the entire arm emerges completely and then cut off the arm at the armpit. The same thing should be done at the elbow when both arms of the dead child emerge and cannot be pushed down to their correct position.

When one or both feet appear and the body will not follow, they should be pulled out and cut off by the pelvis. The barber-surgeon or midwife should have special instruments or tools for this like scissors, iron tongs and iron hatchets so that such things are easily pulled out and cut. Then she should pull the rest of the dead child out wholly or in pieces until the dead child comes completely out of the mother.

If the head of the dead child is swollen or enlarged with evil fluid and liquid so that it cannot come out of the mother's opening because it is too narrow, the midwife should have a sharp little knife between her fingers and should rip open the head of the dead child. Then the head will shrink as the liquid flows out of the head. If the head comes out of the mother's body and the chest of the dead child is too large or the passage too narrow and it won't emerge, then the breast should be squeezed and split and the armpits used to pull on it so it will come out....

In a case where the mother is dead, which one can tell by the normal signs of a dead person, and there is hope that the child lives, then the mother's mouth, uterus and vagina should be kept open, so that the child has air, as women normally know. Then the dead woman should be cut open on the left side with a shearing knife, because the left side is more open and free than the right because the liver lies on the right side. And when you have cut open this woman, reach inside with both hands and pull out the child. We read in the history of the Romans that the first emperor, named Julius, was cut from his mother's body. For that reason one who is cut from his mother's body is called a Caesarean[29].

From Rösslin's text and contemporary woodcuts depicting women in childbed, one can get the truest picture of the normal activities of a midwife, and the usual methods of delivery. The mother was seated on the birthing stool, gripping the handles, with the midwife seated directly in front of her to assist in bringing about a normal presentation. Often a number of other women bustled about, preparing broth, wine, and other drinks for the mother, and a meal for the midwife. Normally a warm herb bath was prepared for the baby and care was taken to have clean swaddling clothes. The scene is usually shown as one of great joy and contentment, with the midwife often asleep beside the bed after her job has been successfully completed.

Dr. Christoph Scheurl, a Nuremberg lawyer, pictures just such a scene at the birth of his son George:

> The birth occurred in the back of the house, in our normal eating room along Rosenpadt street. I was banished before the bed was prepared. Frau Margrethe Endres Tucherin, Ursula Fritz Tetzlin, the widow Magdalena Mugenhoferin and Anna the midwife assisted her[30].

The social position of the midwife can be seen from the fact that Scheurl refers to her by first name only, and to the other women of his own social class who were also present by their complete names.

Despite the pictures of happiness and calm, on reading the *Rosengarten* one can easily see why the slightest complication could so often be fatal, and why a period of rest three to six weeks in duration was recommended after childbirth. The chance of infection from the midwife's hands or the local treatments was great, as was the possibility of puncturing the uterus when using clumsy iron tools. No matter how skilled the midwife, her basic techniques and anatomical knowledge were the same as those used 1500 years earlier.

Thus it is readily, though unfortunately, understandable why Rösslin includes a section instructing midwives how to tell if a mother was dying:

> This can be recognized if she grows weak or falls unconscious, and becomes oblivious to the things around her and loses her memory; if her limbs become heavy and cannot be moved; when one calls to her or talks to her and she gives little or no answer, especially if she answers very weakly when one calls her with a loud voice; when her face clouds over and she won't eat anything; when her pulse grows fast and weak and her pulse twitches, flutters and beats wildly. Through these signs one knows that the woman cannot be helped and cannot be kept alive. Then she must be commended to God[31].

OTHER MEDICAL FUNCTIONS

Midwives often served as back-up medical assistants during outbreaks of the plague and other epidemics. In 1534, one was granted a special payment of one pound for services during a recent epidemic (*Sterbslauf*)[32]. Fifty years later, another was removed from office because she was "such an unruly woman"; the next year this same woman was asked to take care of pregnant women in the *Lazarett*, the special infirmary set up for plague victims[33]. She was to be paid half a florin a year for this and reinstated in her office after the plague had passed.

One of the midwives or *Ehrbare Frauen* assisted in the *Sondersiechenschau*, the annual examination of those suffering from leprosy and other diseases, looking at all the woman to determine if they actually did have leprosy[34].

Midwives were used by physicians in all vaginal inspections, as a physician never performed manual vaginal exploration[35]. As noted above, midwives also did caesarean sections on dead or dying mothers and removed babies which had died in the uterus. This probably led to their doing other minor surgery, such as the removal of boils or the opening of abscesses, especially if they were located in a woman's genital area.

The midwives were a vital link in the city's welfare system. They were responsible for handing out the *Arme Kindbetterin Almosen* (alms for poor expectant mothers), which consisted of bedding, bread, and lard, to needy women. The council found they were often misusing this, however, and requesting it for women who didn't need it once these women had agreed to call them and not another midwife. If this collusion was proved, the midwife was immediately removed from office.

Some authors have commented that the *Almosen* could actually include a bed and care in the home of one of the *Ehrbare Frauen* during the time of delivery[36]. This seems to be a misreading of the word *Bett,* however, which at that time could simply mean bedding, as in "feather-bed"; at any rate, no specific mention is to be found in the *Ratsbücher* of such a practice[37].

Baptism

It was the duty of the midwife to carry any child which she had delivered in its baptism ceremony. She was not to send her apprentice, nor bring along any other members of her family, and had to be sure that all babies were baptized and registered in the parish in which they were born[38]. Baptism was primarily a female affair; the child's father and godfather were the only men allowed at the church ceremony[39].

The midwife was also held responsible if any sumptuary laws were broken at the baptism:

> All midwives should warn all new mothers that they should stay within the laws at baptism and other parties.
> If they don't tell the parents and guardians the limitations, and therefore help them to break them, or if they
> allow extravagances on purpose, they, as well as the parents, should be punished[40].

With the coming of the Reformation, and the city's assumption of all church functions, closer attention was paid as to how midwives carried out emergency baptism. Initially Luther and other Protestant theologians had accepted the Catholic doctrine of baptism "on condition," which meant that foundlings and other children who had been baptized by lay people, if there was some question about the regularity of this baptism, could be baptized "on the condition" that they had not been properly baptized before[41]. This assured parents that their child had been baptized correctly, while avoiding the snare of rebaptism. In 1531, however, Luther rejected all baptisms "on condition" if it was known any baptism had already been carried out, and called for a normal baptism in the case of foundlings.

Andreas Osiander, the preacher at St. Lorenz, one of Nuremberg's two main churches, and a leader of the Reformation in Nuremberg, disagreed with Luther, and the issue was not discussed at all in the church ordinances of Nuremberg and Brandenburg from 1533, leaving the matter open. By 1540, however, most Lutheran areas, including Nuremberg, were no longer baptizing "on condition" and those who still supported the practice were occasionally branded Anabaptists[42]. As Gottfried Seebass notes, this avoided casuistry in dealing with problems of the validity of baptism, but it also made it much more important that midwives and other lay people knew how to conduct an emergency baptism correctly.

The midwives were examined, along with pastors, church workers, and teachers, in the visitations conducted by members of the city council and pastors of the main churches. The council found what it considered shocking irregularities, and ordered the pages from the baptism ordinance which dealt with emergency baptism (*Jachtauffen*) to be printed up and a copy given to each midwife[43]. The midwives were bound in their oath to perform all baptisms correctly; every time they swore the oath, the council was to make sure each had a copy of this ordinance. Later that year the whole baptism ordinance was actually published with the *Getrenksbüchlein*[44]. The midwives were all called together, given the pamphlet, and sworn to abide by it with the threat of punishment. If any midwife could not be at the meeting, she was to come some other time and get the rules. Interestingly enough, no provision was made for midwives who were illiterate; no mention is made that these women were to have it read to them. Given the popularity of midwives' manuals, perhaps the council could safely assume that all midwives in Nuremberg could read.

In 1578 the city published an entirely new set of baptism regulations (*Kindtaufbüchlein*) with a special section on emergency baptisms[45]. This was later revised, and the city council again stressed that "the midwives are to be bound in their oath to uphold the new set of baptism regulations and do or allow nothing which violates it"[46].

As baptism was an important social occasion and a chance for the flaunting of wealth and social position, an early emergency baptism was often hushed up if the child lived, so the whole normal church ceremony could be carried out. In areas of Germany where Anabaptism flourished, Anabaptist midwives were charged with claiming that they had baptized babies when they really had not. The opposite seems to have been the case in Nuremberg, where parents paid the midwife to conveniently forget she had baptized their child.

The problems with emergency baptisms continued throughout the seventeenth century. An addition to the midwives' ordinance from 1660 demands that they pay more attention to their oath "so that they do not commit such inexcusable mistakes in emergency baptisms." One from 1704 reads: "They shall be required to report all children who have had an emergency baptism immediately in the parish churches, so that they may be registered in the normal manner"[47].

Abortion, Infanticide and Foundlings

Midwives appear most often in the city council records *(Ratsbücher)* in connection with criminal cases, particularly abortion and infanticide. Their oath required them to report immediately all illegitimate children—who the parents were, whether the child was alive or dead, where the mother was. The council recognized that illegitimate children would be those most likely to be aborted, killed, or abandoned, for there were no means of public support for them; the *Arme Kindbetterin Almosen* was only given to the wives of citizens or permanent residents whose children were legitimate. As noted above, the council punished midwives who did not make these reports.

A woman suspected of aborting or killing her child was taken in to the *Loch,* the city jail, where she was examined by a midwife to see if she had been pregnant, which generally meant only seeing if she had milk[48]. If the suspect was from a rural area, she was often brought into the city in chains, at night or in the early morning[49].

The midwife also questioned her, as an admission of guilt was needed for capital punishment, particularly after the institution of the *Carolina Constitution Criminalis,* the set of legal procedures drawn up by Charles V and adopted by the city in the 1530s[50]. Her house was searched for anything suspicious like bloody cloths or clothes, and apothecaries and neighbors questioned as to her activities and purchases. Often the suspect was held for weeks or months while the investigation continued[51].

A midwife and often a barber-surgeon were sent out to search for the body of the child, to examine it for signs of violence and an indication that it had been born alive. This occasionally involved an autopsy to see if it had drawn breath: "On the report of the sworn midwives as to how they had found the dead child with a piece of wood stuck in its mouth it is recommended that the child be cut open and examined further"[52].

The body was exhumed from the field, dung-heap, or cow-stall where it had been buried, examined, and then reburied with a simple ceremony conducted by the midwife[53]. In one particularly gruesome case, a woman had killed the child which had been conceived in incest with her father, but had not buried it deep enough and the body was dug up by the neighborhood dogs; the midwife was dispatched to bury what was left[54].

The council usually called the midwives who were active in the area where the body was found to make the examination. If they conducted it alone, they sent a report to the council; if a barber-surgeon was also involved, the opinions of the midwives or *Geschworene Weiber* were included in his report[55]. Not until 1624 was the presence of a trained physician *(Medicus)* required at an autopsy, and then only if there was a suspicion of force in the death[56]. Even after this date, in the case of newborns, the testimony of midwives often stood alone.

The child's corpse was generally brought in to the mother in order to shock her into confession. Occasionally reports of this are particularly macabre. A child found three days after its death was shown to its mother:

And then the midwife said, "Oh, you innocent little child, if one of us here is guilty, give us a sign," and immediately the child raised its left arm and pointed at its mother[57].

The unfortunate mother was later executed by drowning.

The council did recognize that confessions were not always valid. In 1610 a woman accused of child-murder confessed out of fear of torture. Her confession proved untrue, as no bodies could be found where she claimed they were, and she was released[58].

Great care was taken to prove that the child had actually lived and that the mother's actions had in fact caused its death. If this was at all in doubt, the mother was not executed, even if she had tried to abort or kill the child and failed.

Between the years 1533 and 1599, fifty-five cases of infanticide were reported[59]. More than half the women involved were not from Nuremberg, and most were pregnant outside of marriage[60]. Children were usually killed when they were only a few hours old, and most often by stabbing, strangling, or not tying the umbilical cord so that they bled to death[61]. The city executioner drowned or beheaded nineteen women for infanticide in the forty years between 1578 and 1617[62].

Along with actual infanticides, midwives were often called in to give opinions in cases of suspected abortion. Various methods were tried to abort a child, including witchcraft and sodomy with farm animals, but the usual ones were draughts or douches of drug and herb mixtures. In 1614, a woman tried to abort her child with herbs, although she was unsuccessful. The council asked the *Geschworene Weiber* "whether one can abort a child with such herbs"[63]. The dosage proved too weak, so the mother was simply given an imprisonment for fornication, although the council warned her that she would have been banished except for its mercy.

A midwife suspected of aiding in or covering up an abortion or infanticide was just as harshly handled as the mother was. One was banished for not reporting that an unmarried woman had killed her own child[64]. Another was imprisoned in the *Loch* for questioning, "because she has helped and advised Anna Müllner as to how she could kill her child"[65].

The council also wanted midwives to report all illegitimate births so that it could trace foundlings more easily. Popular sites for leaving foundlings were the gates to the city, church doorways, in front of the houses of clergy or wealthy citizens, and the doorway of the supposed father[66].

All citizens were admonished to watch for mothers leaving children, and were rewarded for reporting this to the council[67]. City officials were also rewarded for finding a child's mother: "The mother should be followed and taken into custody and the watchman honored with a tip"[68]. The council questioned those living near the place where a child had been set out, as well as friends or relatives of any suspect[69].

If the mother could not be found, or if it was certain that she had left Nuremberg, the child was taken into the orphanage. or given to a wet nurse[70]. He or she was baptized immediately, and given a first name, often the saint's name of the day it had been found[71].

Mothers who left foundlings were banished, with a slight fine often added, but were not punished corporally. There was no church punishment either before or after the Reformation for setting out a foundling, only for bearing an illegitimate child. Women were treated with increasing severity, however, throughout the sixteenth century, with the suggestion made in 1597 that any woman having a child secretly be banished, no matter what she had done with the child[72].

Midwives were called in to examine any female prisoner who claimed she was pregnant, along with those charged with infanticide or abortion. In the fifteenth century pregnant women were not tortured, although this special treatment was gradually lessened during the sixteenth century. The council's medical counselors still advised a milder handling, for otherwise "they (the mother) could become unconscious and hurt the child in their bodies"[73]. Corporal punishment was still used, however. Throughout the period, a woman who claimed she was pregnant and was found not to be so was dealt with more sharply. In 1581, a woman accused of repeated theft and other crimes was sentenced to death, but then claimed she was pregnant and demanded a stay of execution. The four midwives who examined her could not agree, so the council ordered that she be held in the *Loch* until they could be sure[74]. Three months later there were still no signs of pregnancy, and she was executed[75].

Thus we find midwives active in a broad spectrum of medical, legal, and religious activities. Their opinions and judgments were taken seriously and their essential power over life clearly recognized. No other group of women received more frequent consideration by the city council or was more closely watched as to conduct, numbers, and skill.

At least in Nuremberg, then, the early modern period does not see a significant decline in the role of midwives. Their social utility continued to be recognized, and we find no male midwives operating in the city until the eighteenth century. Nuremberg may be a peculiar case, as it was so tightly controlled by a conservative city council, which was apparently quite satisfied with the system it had developed, and as it also had no executions for witchcraft during the whole period. One suspects, however, that the general thesis of the decline in midwifery with the advent of professional obstetrics needs to be modified, or at least pushed back several centuries. The early modern midwife was not viewed by her contemporaries as an anachronistic relic, holding to old techniques out of ignorance and fear, but as a woman on whose skills and knowledge they depended.

[1] See, e.g., Palmer Findley, *Priests of Lucina: The Story of Obstetrics* (Boston, 1939) or Irving S. Cutter & Henry R. Viets, *A Short History of Midwifery* (Philadelphia, 1964). For more balanced views, see, e.g., Audrey Eccles, *Obstetrics and Gynecology in Tudor and Stuart England* (Kent, Ohio, 1982) or Ann Oakley, *The Captured Womb: A History of the Medical Care of Pregnant Women* (London, 1984).

[2] Thomas Rogers Forbes, *The Midwife and the Witch* (New Haven: Yale Univ. Press, 1966).

[3] Rudolph Endres, "Zur Einwohnerzahl und Bevölkerungsstruktur Nürnbergs im 15./16. Jahrhunderts," *Mitteilungen des Verein für Geschichte der Stadt Nürnberg (MVGN)* **57** (1970):242-11; Otto Püchner, "Das Register des

gemeinen Pfennigs der Reichsstadt Nürnberg," *Jahrbuch fur fränkische Landesforschung* 34/35 (1974-75):909-48; Caspar Ott, Bevölkerungsstatistik in der Stadt und Landschaft Nürnberg (Berlin: R. Trenkel, 1907).

[4] Friedrich Baruch, "Das Hebammenwesen in Reichsstädischen Nürnberg," (Dissertation, Erlangen, 1955), p. 8; Aemterbüchlein, Nuremberg, Staatsarchiv (StN), Repertorium 62, Nr. 1-139.

[5] StN, Repertorium 62, Nr. 5-139.

[6] StN, Ratsbücher (RB), Repertorium 60b, Vol. 24, fol. 299 (1549).

[7] StN, Amts-und Standbücher (AStB), Repertorium 52b, Vol. 100, fol. 126.

[8] Carlo Cipolla, "Four Centuries of Italian Demographic Development,"" in *Population in History*, ed. D.V. Glass (London: Edward Arnold, 1965) finds the crude birth rate in Lombardy in the eighteenth century varies between 37 and 45 per thousand. J.C. Russell, *British Medieval Population* (Albuquerque: Univ. of New Mexico Press, 1948) finds the birth rate in England to be about 53 per thousand. T.H. Hollingsworth, *Historical Demography* (London: Sources of History, 1969) determines the birthrate in England and Wales in the eighteenth century to be 44 per thousand, and notes this was the same in Spain and Prussia.

[9] Nuremberg, Stadtarchiv, Quellen zur Nürnbergische Geschichte, Repertorium F5, Nr. 168 (unpaginated): "Abschrift des Journals des Sebastian Welser (1530-1539)."

[10] RB 31, fol. 197' (1561). A short note on monetary values: The basic unit was the silver pfennig (d); 120 d made up one "new" pound, which was strictly a money of account. The gold Rhenish gulden (fl) was generally figured at two pounds, 12 d, although its value fluctuated. Over the fifteenth and sixteenth centuries, the value of the gulden increased as Bohemian silver created a glut on the market.

[11] "Nürnbergs reichsstädtische Arbeiterschaft des Amtszeit des Baumeisters Michel Behaim," *Mitteilungen aus der Germanische National Museum (MGNM)*, 1914/15, pp. 141-209.

[12] AStB, Vol. 305-306 "Nürnberger Neubürgerlisten." The percentage of all new citizens that were women varied between 0 and 15%, although it was usually about 1%.

[13] RB 6, fol. 155 (1496).

[14] Baruch, p. 12.

[15] StN, Briefbucher, Repertorium 6, Nr. 57, quoted in Baruch, p. 13.

[16] RB 64, fol. 236' (1606).

[17] AStB Nr. 100, fol. 180-182 & Nr. 101, fol. 100-103.

[18] Baruch, p. 14, from a report by Joachim Camerarius, a doctor in Nuremberg during the late sixteenth century.

[19] AStB; Vol. 100, fol. 182.

[20] RB 3, fol. 265' (1483) & RB 4, fol. 54 (1484).

[21] RB 11, fol. 102' (1517).

[22] RB 29, fol. 268' (1556).

[23] Baruch, p. 32.

[24] A facsimile reprint of the first Hagenau edition was published in 1910 in Munich as volume 2 of the series *Alte Meister de Medizin und Naturkunde,* with accompanying notes by Gustav Klein. This reprint was the edition used here.

[25] AStB 103, fol. 323', "Einer Hebamme auf dem Land verneuerte Pflicht."

[26] Klein, *Rosengarten,* p. x, and Cutter/Viets, p. 217.

[27] Rösslin, pp. 26-27. It was widely believed that the birth of a girl was more difficult than the birth of a boy, which partially explains the last sentence.

[28] Ibid., p. 63.

[29] Ibid., pp. 70-73.

[30] "Schuld und Rechnungsbuch Dr. Christoph Scheurl," unpublished manuscript in the Germanische Nationalmuseum, fol. 10.

[31] Rösslin, p. 70.

[32] RB 16, fol. 148 (1534).

[33] RB 43, fol. 53 (1584) & RB 44, fol. 106' (1585).

[34] J.F. Roth, *Fragmente zur Geschichte der Bader, Barbiere, Hebammen, Ehrbare Frauen und Geschworene Weiber in der freien Reichsstadt Nürnberg* (Nuremberg, 1792), p. 12; Willi Ruger, "Die Almosenordnungen der Reichsstadt Nürnberg," *Nürnberger Beiträge zu den Wirtschafts-und Sozialwissenschaften* 31 (1932):24.

[35] Paul Diepgen, *Frauen und Frauenheilkunde in der Kultur des Mittelalters* (Stuttgart: Thieme, 1963), p. 224.

[36] Roth, p. 42.

[37] The *Arme Kindbetterin Almosen* was a charity fund totally administered by women. It was directed by a *Pflegerin,* an upper-class woman appointed by the city council, and received many contributions from wealthy widows. It continued as a separately endowed charity until the city was taken over by Bavaria in 1806.

[38] Parish registration of baptism began in the 1540s; unfortunately no sixteenth-century baptism rolls survive.

[39] AStB, Vol. 232, "Wandelbuch Ordnung und Gestez," fol. 165.

[40] Joseph Baader, "Nürnberger Polizeiordnungen," *Bibliothek des litterarische Vereins Stuttgart,* 63 (1862): 69-70.

[41] This issue is discussed fully in two articles by Gottfried Seebass: "Das Problem der Konditionaltaufe in der Reformation," *Zeitschrift fur bayerischen Kirchengeschichte,* 35 (1966):138-68, and "Die Vorgeschichte von Luthers Verwerfung der Konditionaltaufe nach einem bisher unbekannten Schreiben Andreas Osianders an Georg Spalatin vom 26. Juni 1531," *Archiv für Reformationsgeschichte* 62 (1971):193-206.

[42] Seebass, "Vorgeschicte," p. 195.

[43] RB 27, fol. 360 (1554).

[44] RB 28, fol. 53 (1554).

[45] RB 37, fol. 176 (1578) & AStB, Vol. 250 "Kindtaufbüchlein."

[46] RB 69, fol. 53' (1614).

[47] Baruch, p. 39, quoting from *Hebammenordnung.*

[48] StN, Ratsverlässe (RV), Rep 60a, 2908, fol. 108.

[49] RV 1034, fol. 24' (1549).

[50] Kaiser Karl des fünften peinliche Gerichtsordnung (Carolina Constitution Criminalis), ed. Reinhold Schmidt (Jena, 1835).

[51] E.g., RV 1109, fol. 1, 3, 9, 25 (1554).

[52] RV 1141, fol. 33'-34.

[53] E.g., RB 29, fol. 354' (1557); RB 35, fol. 125' (1578); RB 56, fol. 507 (1597).

[54] RB 33, fol. 219' (1568).

[55] E.g., RV 1141, fol. 33' 34, 34'; (1556); RV 1496, fol. 32 (1583); RV 1538, fol. 2, 5 (1586).

[56] Jurgen Dieselhorst, "Die Bestrafung der Selbstmörder in Territoriums der Reichsstadt Nürnberg," MVGN 44 (1953):112.

[57] AStB, Vol. 226a "'Malefizbücher" (1549).

[58] Achtbuch 1610, fol. 172, quoted in Hermann Knapp, Das Lochgefängnis, Tortur und Richtung in Alt-Nürnberg (Nuremberg: Heerdegen-Barbeck, 1907).

[59] Karl Roetzer, "Die Delikte des Abtreibung, Kindstötung sowie Kindsaussetzungen und ihre Bestrafung in der Reichsstadt Nürnberg" (Jur. Dissertation, Erlangen, 1957), p. 86.

[60] Ibid., p. 103.

[61] Ibid., p. 97.

[62] Meister Franz Schmidts Scharfrichter inn Nürnberg all sein Richten (Leipzig, 1913). This is Schmidt's own record of all the people he either executed or gave corporal punishment to during his period as city executioner (Scharfrichter), 1578-1617. Interestingly, Schmidt first convinced the council in 1588 to behead women rather than drown them. He reported that the Pegnitz River had been frozen several times when he was supposed to carry out an execution. The council accepted his reasoning and also came to the conclusion that a beheading had more shock value than a drowning, when no one could see the actual death. There were still those who argued that beheading was more difficult, especially in the case of women, as the victim often fainted or sank to the ground in fear, making it hard for the executioner to do his job with the first stroke (Knapp, p. 71). Until 1515, women had been buried alive, but the council decided at that time to switch to drowning "in consideration of what a horrible death being buried alive is for women and that such punishments are no longer being carried out in many imperial areas." (Knapp, p. 73, from Nürnberg Kriminalrecht, p. 56. This is also noted in RB 10, fol. 223').

[63] RB 69, fol. 545, 549 (1614).

[64] RB 12, fol. 96 (1522).

[65] AStB Vol. 221 "Malefizbücher," fol. 48' (1514).

[66] Roetzer, p. 97.

[67] E.g., RV 1936, fol. 3; RV 1942, fol. 46; RV 1080, fol. 31; RV 1874, fol. 34.

[68] RV 1140, fol. 14' (1557).

[69] E.g., RV 969, fol. 3'(1544); RV 845, fol. 6 (1540).

[70] RV 575, fol. 3 (1514).

[71] RV 923, fol. 22 (1540).

[72] Roetzer, p. 104.

[73] StN, Repertorium 51, Ratschlagbücher, Nr. 10 (1530).

[74] RB 40a, fol. 287' & 290'. (1581~.

[75] RB 40a, fol. 378' (1582).

LOUYSE BOURGEOIS AND THE EMERGENCE OF MODERN MIDWIFERY[*]

Philip A. Kalisch, Margaret Scobey & Beatrice J. Kalisch[†]

ABSTRACT

As a contribution to establishing the antecedents of nurse-midwifery, this article focuses on the career of Louyse Bourgeois (1563-1636), a major figure in the history of modern midwifery. She was the first midwife to publish a book on obstetrics and the first to publish on midwifery. Within her writings she outlined clear guidelines for sound clinical practice and articulated an ethical code to govern the practice of midwives. For example, Bourgeois recommended induced labor in cases of contracted pelvis; she was the first to discuss the management of umbilical prolapse; she offered a detailed description of face presentation and its management; and she was the first to cut the cord between two ligatures, when it was wrapped about the neck. She was an ambitious woman, not only for her personal advancement but for the advancement of female midwives as a group. More than 350 years ago she called for improvements in the training of midwives and saw the value of providing midwives with theoretical framework in support of clinical practice. As midwife to the Queen of France and to other influential families, Bourgeois took advantage of every opportunity to improve her own position and that of her calling. Her eventual fall from prominence, due to attacks by physicians and surgeons, is remarkably similar to the emotional conflict that surrounds present day nurse-midwife and medical profession confrontations over practice issues.

The life and career of Louyse Bourgeois, sworn midwife of the city of Paris, offers an excellent starting point for an examination of the history of modern nurse-midwifery and maternity care. She practiced her art in the late sixteenth and early seventeenth centuries, in the city which would become, by the mid-1600s, the recognized European center of childbirth training. At the time Louyse Bourgeois began her work, Parisian midwives provided the only childbirth assistance available for normal births. The only time a male surgeon might be called to assist would be when natural labor failed, and the surgeon would enter to remove the infant, usually stillborn. Despite their utility and monopoly of maternity care, midwives enjoyed little social or intellectual esteem. The role Louyse Bourgeois carved for herself in Parisian society—as a midwife of integrity and intelligence—altered the traditional conception of a midwife's humble status. In many ways, Louyse Bourgeois stands as a prototype of the respectable and educated

[*] *Journal of Nurse-Midwifery*, 1981, **26** (4) 3-17. Reprinted by permission of Elsevier Science. Copyright 1981 by the American College of Nurse-Midwives.

[†] Philip A. Kalisch, Ph.D., is Professor of History and Politics of Nursing at the University of Michigan, School of Nursing, Ann Arbor. Beatrice J. Kalisch, R.N., Ed.D., F.A.A.N., is the Titus Distinguished Professor of Nursing, Chair for Parent-Child Nursing, and Director of the Graduate Program in Parent-Child Nursing also at the University of Michigan. They have been co-investigators on a series of federally funded research projects over the past 12 years on various aspects of the history and politics of nursing. Among the book they have co-authored are: *The Advance of American Nursing* (Little Brown, 1978), *Nursing Involvement in Health Planning* (HEW, 1978), *The Politics of Nursing* (Lippincott, in press) and *The Image of the Nurse on Television* (Springer, in press). They have also co-authored numerous articles and book chapters. Margaret Scobey, M.A., a research associate in the History and Politics of Nursing, University of Michigan and is currently completing her Ph.D.

teaching midwives, who would dominate their field through the following two centuries. While elevating the social status of Parisian midwives, Bourgeois also, albeit unintentionally, eroded the traditional monopoly of the female midwife in maternity care.

The advent of Louyse Bourgeois' career coincided with the advent of the Bourbon dynasty in France—in effect, the end of the medieval socio-political order. Indeed, Bourgeois' close association with the royal family of Henry IV and his Queen, Marie de Médicis, so enhanced her reputation as to guarantee her a respectful audience. Louyse Bourgeois, of course, was not the first royal midwife, but she was the first royal midwife to use her position for ends beyond immediate personal gain. Capitalizing upon her court position, she became the first female midwife to write and to publish treatises on the art of midwifery. Her publications not only helped her own career but also served to promote improvements in the practice of midwifery. Her writings provide a unique source of information about the standards of midwifery at the dawn of modern times as well as insight into the conflicts and competitions within the medical-surgical professions.

Louyse Bourgeois did not typify Parisian midwives during the late sixteenth century. From her own account of her entry into practice as well as from secondary sources, the typical Parisian midwife was an illiterate, middle-aged, multiparous woman who had learned her trade by observing and helping her friends and by assisting an established midwife. Financial need motivated these wives and widows of small-time tradesmen and artisans. Lacking the basics of elementary education, most midwives had no intellectual defense against superstitious beliefs. Certainly midwives possessed only the rudest and often erroneous conceptions of anatomy and physiology. (It must be noted, that neither physicians nor surgeons of the time really understood the physical process of childbirth, although they held a variety of fanciful theories.) For all their faults, midwives provided the only source of help for women in labor, and the wise, experienced midwife knew enough to let nature take its course.[1]

The practice of midwifery in Paris remained largely outside public control. Hundreds of women practiced on a part-time basis, limiting their clients to their poor neighbors. For those relatively few midwives who sought to attract a wider, more affluent clientele, certification of their suitability by municipal officials was necessary. The city registers of 1601 showed that only sixty women in Paris qualified as sworn midwives.[2] The first municipal regulation of midwives appeared in 1560, although evidence of earlier and less systematic regulation existed as far back as the thirteenth century.[3] When Bourgeois presented herself for certification, she had to provide a witness to her good moral character and to submit to an examination of her skill and knowledge by a panel of a physician, two surgeons, and two senior, sworn midwives. Upon successful completion of the examination, the midwife would take an oath and receive a diploma. The oath required the midwife to report practice by any noncertified midwife and to call in a physician, surgeon, or more experienced midwife in cases of difficult labor and delivery.[4] It is unknown if any midwives were actually prevented from practicing without certification or if any sworn midwives were fined or reprimanded for failing to live up to their oaths.

The content of the examination remains unknown, too, but to judge by Louyse Bourgeois' experience in 1598, the physician and surgeons left the task to the midwives, who concerned themselves more with the candidate's family background than with her knowledge. No standards of training or minimum preparation existed for midwives; the usual course was an unspecified apprenticeship with a sworn midwife. Probably the personal recommendation of a sworn midwife counted for more than an objective evaluation of skill in determining a candidate's suitability. The lying-in wards of the large charity hospital, the Hôtel-Dieu, provided a rudimentary apprenticeship program; the institution used four apprentice-midwives to assist the chief midwife for three-month periods. The Hôtel-Dieu did not provide a salubrious environment for childbirth, nor did its childbirth techniques seem better than average; however, its large number of obstetrical patients, estimated at over 100 births per month, gave the apprentice an opportunity to witness and to help in a wide variety of deliveries in a short amount of time.[5] Both the examining midwives who tested Louyse Bourgeois had some experience working in the Hôtel-Dieu.

Even among the elite of sworn midwives, Louyse Bourgeois represented an anomaly and nearly failed to acquire certification because of the jealousy she aroused among her examiners. As her name suggests, Louyse Bourgeois, born in 1563/4, came from a relatively affluent middle-class family of the Faubourg St. Germain. Her father owned property in the area, and as a young girl she received a sound elementary education—she was fully literate and skilled in fine needlework, as would befit a daughter of a family of substance. She married Martin Boursier, a barber-surgeon and long-time student of the famed surgeon Ambroise Paré,[6] and expected to raise her family in comfortable circumstances. The final years of a long and bloody civil war culminated in Paris, 1588-1594, and the consequent destruction of property ruined her family's financial security. Faced with the need to help support her family, Louyse took up midwifery at the suggestion of her own midwife, who said that if she had known how to read and write like me that she could have done wonders. She felt in her heart that I could be the best in my field in a short time, for my husband, who had lived for twenty years in the home of the late master Dr. Ambroise Paré, first surgeon to the king, could teach me a lot.[7]

Louyse confessed that it had been a hard decision to make because certain of the midwife's duties, such as carrying newborn babies to Baptism, were considered unsuitable to a well-born woman. She swallowed her pride, however, when she considered the needs of her children.[8]

Louyse's training also did not fit the customary pattern. She explained that she read the works of Ambroise Paré, who had written an important book on obstetrics, and simply began delivering babies for the poor women of her neighborhood. After five years of experience, in 1598 she presented herself for certification as a sworn midwife. The two senior midwives who examined her, Madame Dupuis and Madame Peronne, immediately recognized Louyse Bourgeois as a formidable challenger to their own preeminence in the field. Undoubtedly the midwives took offense at Louyse's unusual training; after all, she had not done homage in the service of an established midwife. But their greatest objection was to Louyse's social class and marriage to a surgeon. They feared that her higher social status and her husband's connections would give her unfair advantages in attracting important clientele—as indeed they would. Madame Dupuis tried to stop or delay the certification; she told the other midwife, "We should only receive the wives of artisans who understand nothing of our business."[9] Despite Madame Dupuis' antipathy, Louyse Bourgeois became a sworn midwife, free to practice throughout the city.

Louyse put her own education and family connections to good use. Within three years of her certification, so well known had she become among influential aristocratic families that several important ladies supported her efforts to secure the position of midwife to Marie de Médicis at her first confinement in late 1601. In addition, Louyse enjoyed a good reputation among the court physicians, and one of them, whose daughter Louyse had delivered several times, recommended her to his colleagues who were trying to find a midwife to replace Madame Dupuis, the King's choice, whom the Queen did not like. (Madame Dupuis had delivered several of the King's illegitimate children, an association the Queen did not approve.) Louyse mobilized all the ladies whom she had delivered, and her husband's clients also sought to promote Louyse's chances, However, no one dared openly introduce a new midwife to the Queen for fear of arousing the King's displeasure. Secret negotiations arranged for Louyse to meet the Queen by accident. In a brief encounter outside the Queen's carriage, Louyse favorably impressed Marie de Médicis, who determined then and there that no other would deliver her. Just a few weeks before the expected birth, Marie de Médicis finally told her husband that she did not like Madame Dupuis, and Henry graciously acquiesced to his wife's preference, but not before checking Louyse Bourgeois' reputation and qualifications with over a dozen ladies of good family who had been delivered by her. Madame Dupuis' career as royal midwife ended before it began, and from Louyse's own statements, it was clear that the usurper took pleasure in displacing her old antagonist. At the end of August 1601, Louyse packed her trunk and joined the caravan of royal coaches taking the Queen to Fontainebleau, where delivery would take place.[10]

Louyse Bourgeois secured her future as royal midwife by her masterful handling of the Queen's first delivery. To understand the effect of Louyse's efforts, the significance of this particular royal birth must be emphasized. Every royal birth was important, not only to secure succession to the throne but also to provide sons and daughters to be used in international diplomacy, in an era when marriages between royal and princely families gave physical reality to treaty arrangements and aided future cooperation between monarchs. The expected child of Marie de Médicis represented far more than the usual royal birth, and all of Europe anxiously awaited the results of the Queen's labor. By 1601, Henry IV had pacified his kingdom, but at age forty-eight he had yet to produce a legitimate child. Indeed, no male heir had been born and survived infancy in the French royal family for over eighty years, a situation that contributed not a little to the incessant dynastic squabbles and civil wars of the previous decades. The birth of a healthy son would insure the Bourbon dynasty and the future peace of the realm.

In the highly charged, emotional environment surrounding this birth, Louyse Bourgeois' calm, resolute approach impressed the sovereigns and earned their respect. In the midst of hundreds of anxious courtiers and the greatest aristocrats of France, the good midwife went about her work as if she were delivering the child of just any woman. When she not only predicted the birth of a male but also brought him into the light of day, on September 26, 1601, she earned the post of premier midwife in all of France. After the birth of the Dauphin, the future Louis XIII, Louyse Bourgeois delivered the Queen's subsequent children, five more before Henry's death in 1610.[11] Not surprisingly, as midwife to the Queen, Louyse attracted the most prestigious clientele in Paris, and she delivered most of the babies of Parisian aristocrats until around 1627.

Louyse Bourgeois' reputation and influence surpassed any other midwife of her day, but even her service to the Crown could not secure her place in the history of maternity care. In 1609, Louyse began to write of her knowledge and experience in midwifery, and it is through her writings that she achieved lasting fame. No other midwife had ever published a treatise on her art, and it is a tribute to Louyse Bourgeois' intelligence and ambition that she not only attempted it but succeeded in winning a wide European audience.

Between 1609 and 1634, she wrote three books of *Observations,* one *Apology Against the Physicians,* and one *Collection of Secrets.*[12] Her work went through several editions and translations. Latin, German, and Dutch translations came out during her lifetime and new editions continued to appear throughout the seventeenth-century, the latest known in 1710. It would be impossible to measure her influence; writers of the time borrowed freely from published works without indicating their sources. Even Louyse Bourgeois took information from Ambroise Paré without noting her dependence upon him. Suffice it to say, she enjoyed influence unprecedented for a self-taught female midwife.

The body of her work reveals an unevenly developed intelligence. From the practical point of view, her best work was her first, *Diverse Observations on Sterility, Miscarriage, Fertility, Delivery and Diseases of Women and Newborn Infants,* 1609. Thereafter, she added little improvement to her clinical portrait of maternity care. Her later efforts did, however, demonstrate the development of her own sense of importance and of her confidence in the well-trained midwife. Her articulation of the duties and ethical standards of her profession (found in a section of advice to her daughter, dating from 1617) revealed a highly refined conception of the role of midwife. Yet much of her later work, the second (1617) and third (1626) books of *Observations* and her *Collection of Secrets* (1634) included unsubstantiated anecdotes of unusual deliveries and bizarre gynecological problems. Given Louyse Bourgeois' innate intelligence and common sense, these later accounts appear inconsistent with her earlier work. Yet it must be remembered that she had no advanced education—in itself no immunity to credulity—and certainly no conception of scientific reasoning. Also, there was a hint that she succumbed to the temptations of popularity. Having put all she knew of childbirth into a successful first book, she was encouraged to publish more. What better subject than anecdotes of the "Believe It Or Not" variety, such as the case of the "pregnant woman whose baby stuck out his arm and then pulled it back in two months before delivery"?[13] Her next to the last work appeared in 1627 and marked the end of her long public career. Her *Apology Against the Physicians* offered her defense from the lightly veiled charge of incompetence broadcast about her by physicians and surgeons apparently jealous of her influence.

In the summer of 1627, Louyse Bourgeois was at the height of her fame. She wore the gold cross and velvet collar of the royal midwife, as well as a velvet cap usually reserved for royal nurses. Her newly expanded work had been published just the year before. Her family was consolidating its position in the medical-surgical world of Paris. Her husband continued to practice surgery; one son qualified as an apothecary; one daughter married a doctor of medicine; and the youngest daughter, also married to a doctor,[14] followed in her mother's footsteps by entering an intensive training program in midwifery, arranged by Louyse's friends at the Hôtel-Dieu. In all, the Bourgeois-Boursier clan represented a real force in the competitive, closed society of ministering to the wealthy and aristocratic families of the city. The most influential member of the clan, Louyse herself, realized her own power and made no concessions to the delicate egos of the physicians and surgeons who also attended the families of quality.

In her first writings, Louyse Bourgeois dealt with physicians and surgeons with deference and even reverence for their skills and knowledge. By 1626, she had lost all awe of them. Undoubtedly her politic appreciation of the court physicians aided her rapid rise to influence in 1601; the *Diverse Observations* of 1609 expressed her trust and admiration for the doctors without reservation. Frequently she told her reader to call in a physician whenever doubt as to the course of delivery arose. Consistently she sided with doctors and surgeons against the midwives, who frequently let their ignorance lead them to folly.

> Many are astonished when I say that if the midwife can't do it to have it done by a good surgeon; extreme remedies are necessary in cases of severe illness. Inasmuch as midwives find things going badly in only one case out of a hundred that they see, they tend to get upset when things go badly. The surgeon, on the contrary, is called only in hopeless cases that the midwife has not been able to resolve; he is as much accustomed to problems as the midwife is to things going well. There are midwives so over-confident that having made a few efforts to deliver a woman and knowing they can't do it hold out until all is lost. The poor surgeon is blamed for it all and is called an executioner, when if he had been called a little sooner he would have been

able to save both mother and child. Some are such enemies of the doctors that, having the relatives in the palms of their hands, they send the surgeon who was called by friends away, and thus leave the mother and baby to die. As for calling another midwife for help, I would not advise it, knowing that there is always the danger that she might spoil everything in case it is her first delivery.[15]

I am not speaking from opinion, but as a person who knows very well. The first thing that they do is to get into a dispute, forgetting the patient and their duties. I leave to your imagination what peace of mind is experienced by the assistants, seeing the life of their friend in the hands of two women out of their heads with anger. I wish that such women would be more good in fact that in name (the French word for midwife is *sage-femme*, literary, good woman). Therefore, I conclude that it is better to stay alive in the hands of a competent surgeon who dares to do the right thing, than to die in those of an ignorant and timid midwife who believes that time alone will get her out of a bad spot. I do not doubt that there are some very able midwives, but their numbers are not as great as the other kind.[16]

In this passage, the midwife Bourgeois identified herself with the physicians and surgeons more than with members of her profession. In fact, she professed low regard for most midwives. Further on, Louyse Bourgeois credited the good doctors as her best allies.

I have never been so happy as when the women that I am helping send for their doctors, because I feel that the doctors are on my side. All those who like to meddle and give prescriptions (families and friends) are forced to keep quiet, or if they make a proposition the doctor decides on it. He knows the history of the patient, and knows how to prescribe what is necessary for her. Everything that I have said about remedies and their effects comes from the learned doctors with whom I have practiced.[17]

Eight years later, either Louyse Bourgeois had forgotten her debt to learned doctors or else dropped her ingratiating manner because she felt herself no longer in need of their support. The second book of *Observations,* 1617, contained no deferential remarks about physicians and surgeons. From being a grateful disciple, Louyse had become a self-confident practitioner, rarely in need of medical support. She did not attack the physicians or surgeons directly, but when she mentioned them, it was almost always in a case which showed her to be the primary giver of care. She presented herself as the equal of any doctor and their superior in maternity matters.

For example, in the second book of *Observations,* she recalled the case "of a woman I was called to help who had been in labor for nine days." In an interesting reversal of roles, she informed her reader that a doctor asked her to accompany him to see a patient who was close to death despite his ministrations. "In spite of this, he very much wanted to have my opinion to help him do everything possible for the sake of those who had sent him." Although Louyse found the woman in a moribund condition, "I knew we had to do what my profession demanded ... He (the doctor) put the entire affair in my hands." Louyse's treatments enabled the woman to give birth, and although the baby died two days later, the mother survived.[18] In the very next case of the "English woman who carried her baby for eleven months," Louyse recalled that she attended the woman, although was not present at the delivery itself. The woman died, although she was attended by several doctors and surgeons who consulted among themselves and made erroneous conclusions as to the woman's condition. Bourgeois did not state that the doctors were at fault or that she could have saved the woman's life, but subtly she reminded the reader that doctors frequently found natural events "incomprehensible."[19]

In "Two Deliveries of a Woman of Lorraine," Louyse defended midwives who suffered by the dishonesty of a surgeon—a complete reversal of her opinions found in the 1609 denunciation of the faults of most midwives. "The two most esteemed midwives" of the country were called to attend the young beloved wife of a wealthy man of Lorraine. It was the woman's first pregnancy, and although the midwives did all that "their art dictated," the labor was slow but completely normal. The family became impatient, and the husband called in a local surgeon, who quickly turned the situation to his own advantage. He found the woman about to deliver in a normal fashion; he informed the husband that his wife needed his surgical help, but promised to deliver a healthy child and mother. Within minutes he fulfilled his promises. The midwives and their objections were dismissed, while the quick-witted surgeon received a handsome fee. Several years later, at the lady's second confinement, the surgeon was brought in three months early. The entire household catered to his whims, and the husband trusted him completely. The mother-to-be went into labor while her husband was gone; this time, the infant malpresented, and the surgeon, in his panic, killed both the infant and mother. He left the house under cover of darkness, before anyone discovered his failure.

Louyse Bourgeois summed up the tragedy as "a terrible punishment for the wrong that he had done the midwives."[20]

In the case of a "woman who wouldn't take orders while in labor and died because of it," Louyse described the stillborn birth of a premature infant. The umbilicus had detached from the placenta, requiring some intervention to expel the placenta. Louyse remembered, "I did this operation in the presence of Drs. Hautin, Duret, and Sequin and a surgeon who ordinarily helps women to give birth. He wanted to help me but I wouldn't let him inasmuch as I felt capable of doing it without harming the woman."[21] Whether or not she intended to imply the surgeon's inescapable clumsiness or not, the midwife, by 1617, saw herself equal to all and more capable than many male doctors.

In her recollections of the births of Marie de Médicis' children, composed eight years after the last birth, Louyse Bourgeois presented herself as the central figure in the dramas. Whenever doctors or surgeons were mentioned, it was to note their absence from the delivery room. In her account of the birth of the Dauphin, in 1601, she listed all the famous doctors gathered for the event, who, after visiting the Queen, "retired to a nearby place right away." The doctors did enter the room from time to time, and she told them what was happening. According to Louyse, they asked her what she would recommend to ease the Queen's colic, and then they promptly ordered it administered. Of course, the Queen recovered. Furthermore, the King ordained that the doctors and midwife be in agreement on the Queen's treatment.[22] Henry IV may well have respected the midwife and had been impressed with her demeanor, but it seems unlikely that at the birth of his first child and probable heir to the throne, he would have elevated a young and relatively unknown midwife to a position equal to his court physicians and surgeons. Nor would it seem natural for the court doctors to make a public deference to the prescriptions of a lowly midwife at so noble a confinement.

At future royal births, the doctors and surgeons did even less to help the midwife. During the labor and delivery of the fourth royal child, Dr. Honoré stood in attendance, "but he did not even come into the Queen's room either during or after the delivery." Dr. du Laurens asked Louyse to let him intervene in case something unusual happened—the Queen being larger than at previous deliveries, but the self-confident midwife replied that she "didn't forsee any problems for the Queen."[23]

By the time her third book of *Observations* appeared in 1626, Louyse's memory of her role in the royal delivery room had changed again, to the further detriment of the physicians. She recalled:

> It is well known that medicine is a body from which come out several branches, such as pharmacy, surgery, and all its dependencies, which are numerous and which depend upon practice rather than theory. The late king realized this upon the birth of his son, when, in the presence of four doctors, perhaps the most learned in France, he put me over them, enjoining them not to make the queen take anything unless I felt it was a good idea, and to listen to my ideas and follow them because my art lay more in experience than in science, and that I had seen more than hundreds whereas they had seen only a few ...."[24]

Not only did Louyse present herself as being the most favored obstetrical consultant in the palace, in her third book of *Observations* she dared to present herself as the doctors' superior in almost all health matters. From the tone it would appear that she considered herself a doctor in all but name; she described situations in which she herself applied bloodletting remedies, the traditional duty of the surgeon. Nor did she stop at asserting new prerogatives for herself; she even published a criticism of one of the court physicians.[25]

She told of "a woman dead on the sixth day of her labor and its cause." This woman had been treated by a court physician for five and a half months, during which time she had considerable hemorrhaging. The woman, distrusting her doctor, consulted Louyse Bourgeois after the bleeding stopped. The physician had diagnosed her as "hydropic" but Louyse declared her pregnant; she advised her client to wait for normal delivery and not to consult the doctor. Some time later, the woman delivered a premature infant who died three hours after birth. The placenta was not expelled, but Louyse refused to intervene for fear of causing further harm. The surgeon who did intervene was unable to complete the entire removal of the placenta, and three days later the patient died. Thus she accused both a court physician of a bad diagnosis and a court surgeon of clumsy methods.[26]

It is easy to understand why many court physicians and surgeons might have come to resent Louyse Bourgeois, given her ability to do without them. As she led her aristocratic patients to view the physicians and surgeons as superfluous in matters of childbirth, she challenged one of their cherished and lucrative prerogatives—to stand ready in case of abnormalities. The learned doctors may well have caballed against the pretentious midwife in 1627; Louyse certainly believed they did.

In the summer of 1627, Louyse Bourgeois was called to deliver the first child of the young Marie de Bourbon, Duchess of Orleans, married to Gaston, the only surviving brother of the new king, Louis XIII. Before her marriage, Marie de Bourbon was the Duchess of Montepensier in her own right and as such the wealthiest heiress in France. Marie de Médicis, now the Queen Mother, doted upon the Duchess since her infancy and early on intended her as the bride for one of her sons. Louis XIII, in the seventeenth year of his reign, appeared physically weak and remained childless after twelve years of marriage. Because Marie de Médicis had been feuding for years with her son and his wife and councillors, she put much hope in the birth of Gaston's heir, who might one day gain the throne and restore his grandmother to a position of influence at court. None of her plans succeeded; with the dashing of Marie de Médicis' hopes, coincidentally, Louyse Bourgeois' own star began to wane. The child born on May 29, 1627 survived, but was a girl; in addition, the Duchess died nine days after the birth. In her grief and disappointment Marie de Médicis called for an autopsy; ten surgeons and physicians rushed to do her bidding and published the results. Their findings indicate to the modern reader a case of virulent puerperal peritonitis; the surgeons and physicians suggested that the cause of the infection was a small piece of the placenta that had been left in the uterus and hardened.[27] The doctors never mentioned the midwife at all, but the publication of the protocol, an unusual procedure, clearly meant to destroy Louyse Bourgeois' long-held reputation among the aristocracy.

She quickly rushed into print an *Apology*, defending herself and attacking the signers of the postmortem. She began:

> I, the undersigned, having read the printed protocol of the dissection of the dead body of her late Highness, etc. which the doctors and surgeons who operated upon her ladyship, the Duchess, during her recovering from confinement, have written and published, by which they tried to justify themselves and put the cause of her death entirely upon my shoulders; find it necessary for the saving of my honor to reveal the entire cause, truthfully and thoroughly, of what happened after and during her illness; by which statement it will appear as clear as daylight that the cause of her death did not proceed from the small remains of placenta, as has been wrongfully stated in the protocol.[28]

Louyse attributed death to "cancer in the lower parts of the abdomen," as did the doctors who pronounced the Duchess dead. Bourgeois accused the doctors of inventing the diagnosis before the postmortem began for the sole purpose of discrediting her. (There is more than a little irony in the cause of death suggested by the signers of the postmortem. They accused Louyse of leaving a piece of the placenta in the uterus, indirectly causing the death of the patient. In a similar situation, described in the third book of *Observations,* Louyse had accused a court surgeon and physician of botching the delivery and afterbirth of a patient, failing to retrieve the entire placenta as noted previously.[29]) She considered that her credentials supported her innocence:

> I have practiced my profession now for fully thirty-four years, faithfully, diligently, and honorably, and acquired not only a good certificate, after various examinations, but have also written books treating on this subject, which have been printed and published in several editions and were translated into foreign languages, for which trouble many noted physicians have rendered me thanks and have gladly confessed that they were of great use to humanity. If I had knowingly left a piece of the placenta inside the matrix, I would have mentioned it in time, in order to have asked advice and help.[30]

Furthermore, none of the noted writers on midwifery, read by Bourgeois, had ever described a case in which a piece of the placenta could cause death.

A few days after Louyse's defense appeared, an anonymously authored pamphlet appeared on the streets of Paris. In it, the author reported that the midwife to the Duchess forced her to assume a strenuous position to facilitate the afterbirth and that the midwife herself squeezed and pressed the "delicate Princess" too tightly.[31] At a distance of 350 years, it is impossible to determine who bore responsibility for the Duchess death; given the large number of attendants, anyone could have introduced the deadly infection. What does seem obvious is that a group of physicians and surgeons took advantage of an opportunity to reduce the influence of a pretentious and powerful midwife, who had taken pains to dismiss their contributions on many occasions. The damage to the aging midwife's reputation ended her active career among the notables of Paris.

She retired, ungracefully, from the arena. Two years before her death she published once more; in 1634 appeared her *Collection of Secrets,* filled with "rhapsodies the most pitiable, and with nostrums of the silliest."[32]

The work also showed Louyse at her most pretentious, as she wrote up treatments for all manner of physical ailments not merely those limited to obstetrics and gynecology. The accusations of her enemies and the writings of her dotage ought not efface the merit of her life and career. A brief examination of her earlier work, from a clinical perspective, demonstrates the basis of her justly won reputation.

The author of *Diverse Observations,* 1609, drew upon all sources of knowledge available to her, from folk traditions to the classical authors. To this melange of superstition and hypothesis, she added her own keen observations and understanding of human nature. The resultant mixture is both amusing in its fanciful explanations and surprising in its frequent approximation of modern clinical practice. Louyse Bourgeois did not write as a simple midwife but as a midwife conversant with the ideas and theories held by her learned medical colleagues. As far as is known, she could not read Latin, so came by her medical theories by way of vernacular sources such as Paré, perhaps translations, and undoubtedly by conversations with doctors and under the tutelage of her husband, a surgeon. She recognized the value for midwives to have theoretical knowledge to support their practice. At one point in her work, she implored doctors to arrange anatomy lessons for midwives. She herself included theoretical explanations for physical conditions. The cause she identified may have had little to do with the treatment prescribed, but her attempts to link scientific theory to clinical observations should not be dismissed, however fanciful they now appear. She tried to place midwifery on a sounder intellectual plane by identifying, whenever possible, the confluence of medical, surgical and obstetric concerns.

For example, a good deal of late Renaissance medical theory dealt with the functioning and malfunctioning of bodily fluids. Louyse Bourgeois frequently explained a physical condition on the tendency of these fluids to chill, overheat, rise, fall, vaporize, and accumulate in the wrong places, thus throwing the body's normal course out of balance. One cause of sterility, according to Bourgeois, could be due to the following situation:

> ... there is a great deal of moisture in the womb, coming from the brain and following a course along the spine and across the kidneys. This moisture passes through the womb and makes it damp, cooling it off so much that its natural heat does not warm it in order to preserve and maintain the semen, whose purpose it is to form the baby. It acts like a storm falling upon newly-seeded ground, washing away the seed and making trenches where the drops of water collect.[33]

Thus did Louyse Bourgeois not only display her own knowledge of anatomy and physiology, but put the theoretical idea into a concrete analogy that might be grasped by those midwives less learned than she. Following this explanation, she proceeded to describe the dessicative, or drying-out, remedy that should cure the sterility.

Often when she seemed short on scientific theory, she often stood on firmer ground, clinically speaking. She described the symptoms of chlorosis, which she called "the disease of pale coloring," in exact detail and much better than others before her. She attributed it to "an obstruction of the liver and the spleen." Clearly she had little understanding of the cause of the disease, even hypothetically, but not only did she describe its clinical manifestation with great exactitude, she also published the cure for it—a homemade iron supplement administered daily in prescribed doses.[34] The section on chlorosis was typical of Bourgeois' basically ordered and practical mind and her mission of disseminating the best medical knowledge she had to others. She never let the absence of a scientific hypothesis hinder her from tackling a problem, and she never revealed the secretive, self-serving approach common among practitioners anxious of establishing their reputations on the possession of secret remedies. If Bourgeois knew the formula of a helpful drug or a proven technique, she would invariably share it with readers.

Louyse Bourgeois originated very little in terms of theory or clinical skills. Her greatest contributions, in the opinion of a late nineteenth-century French doctor who studied her work, consisted of her treatment of chlorosis, her description of podalic version for use in several types of malpresentation, and her recommendation to force delivery if a woman should experience uncontrollable bleeding.[35] None of these discoveries can be attributed to Bourgeois. The use of iron for chlorosis was known among the Italians for many years; Ambroise Paré reintroduced podalic version to public knowledge and may have suggested forced delivery to control hemorrhaging. However, Bourgeois practiced these cures and techniques much more often than any of her masters; furthermore, she can be credited with putting these techniques and recommendations into a clearly defined clinical setting, spelling out for her readers exactly when and how to employ them.

Important as the publication of these clinical treatments and techniques might have been in advancing childbirth care in the early seventeenth century, Louyse Bourgeois' unique and original place in the history of maternity care is based upon the attitude and approach to midwifery that she reiterated in all of her writings, from the 1609 treatise to her last work. She articulated an approach to childbirth designed to give every woman the best chance of a happy delivery and recovery, and many of her precepts have been creeping back into maternity care teaching in the last twenty years. The foundation of her approach to childbirth lay in her profound respect for the power and mystery of nature. She saw the midwife's role as standing ready to assist nature or, if need be, to intervene in order to help nature back on its course. Her respect for nature and her experience with childbirth did not lead her to superstitious or mystical practices; nor did she easily abandon a woman to her fate. Louyse Bourgeois had perhaps the greatest of virtues: she knew when to leave well enough alone.

In a metaphorical description of the midwife's role, she likened the midwife to a pilot at sea. The experience of the pilot could mean the survival of the ship and its passengers (the mother and child), for a good pilot recognized what measures to take to best secure the safety of his charges in the frequently treacherous seas surrounding them. She fully appreciated the power of the sea to overwhelm the frail vessel and cargo, but she just as fully appreciated the value of having at the helm a mature and experienced pilot who would not panic during a storm.[36] The clinical result of this approach to childbirth led Bourgeois into advocating a conservative, non-interventionist approach to labor and delivery. Whenever patience could lead the patient to a successful delivery, no matter how time-consuming the effort, Louyse Bourgeois stood resolute against those who recommended interventions. Although neither she nor her colleagues could understand the significance of this approach, undoubtedly the midwives who so practiced experienced fewer maternal deaths simply from the decreased likelihood of infection through unnecessary intrusions and manipulations with dirty instruments. This implicit understanding of the generally productive course of nature recurred in all her practical advice.

She counselled against an intrusive internal examination to diagnose pregnancy in its early stages. She realized that a true pregnancy would soon reveal itself with external symptoms, and the danger of the mother and child of an ignorant person intervening outweighed the possible benefit of an early diagnosis.[37] She told her readers never to puncture the membrane containing the waters, when it seemed delayed, nor force delivery if the waters should break a long time before labor: "I have found that nature is too provident to get rid of all its commodities, leaving nothing for later." She advised in cases of premature breakage, to keep the woman in bed to await God's time.[38] She strongly denounced the practice of pulling on the cord to retrieve the placenta, or worse, going in search of the placenta; the danger of hemorrhage, or pulling on the wrong organs, or tearing the afterbirth were clearly more dangerous than waiting for natural expulsion. She did practice mild stimulants to prod nature, but never forceful efforts.[39]

Louyse Bourgeois also recognized that the mother's efforts and her frame of mind were vitally important in a successful labor and delivery. She told her readers to let the mother do as she pleased, as long as she did not harm herself. In other words the good midwife Bourgeois did not hew to any absolute and orthodox position for delivery or schedule of events. The midwife was to support the mother's efforts and allow her to find her most comfortable position. Never be obstinate she warned her daughter: "The pain of childbirth is extreme, and this is why you must consider and accommodate (without harming her) the whims of the patient, no matter how difficult it is for you. Your are only there to help and to serve her."[40] Thus, if the mother wanted to walk around up until delivery, let her, as long as there was someone to walk with her. If she wanted to eat something or drink something, give her nourishment in moderation. If she refused certain preparations, do not force them, but if the recommendation were vitally important to the mother's well being, try to convince her with sweetness and reason. Position the mother for delivery so that gravity helps the mother's labor. Pull gently on a malpresented infant after repositioning it and pull with the contractions.

She decried the friends and relatives of new mothers who frightened the younger woman with horror stories of disastrous and painful deliveries. She instructed midwives to give their patients courage and to reassure them. Midwives should make their preparations quickly and quietly, without drawing attention to things that might frighten the mother. For example, she told of a midwife who so imperiously ordered silk and scissors be brought to her, for the care of the umbilicus, that the new mother went into convulsions of fear of what the midwife was preparing to do to her.[41] The midwife should also reassure the family and friends that the mother is all right. By the same token, she realized that often the greatest challenge to a midwife's skills would come from well-meaning family and friends who would plead with her to intervene in a long labor or suggest tactics that the midwife knew not to be in the mother's best interests. Despite a family's anxiety, "it is necessary to wait until the hour ordained by God, particularly in natural births where there are no problems."[42] In the era when births took place in the home, with family and friends in attendance, often it was difficult for the midwife to establish her authority in the midst of competing factions.

Perhaps her best single bit of advice, which appeared frequently in her discussions of various episodes, was to treat each pregnancy as a unique and individual occurrence. No two women were alike, and no two pregnancies, even of the same woman, could be counted upon to proceed in a similar fashion. The good midwife, even in the most obviously normal deliveries, always stayed alert for possible complications.

In an interesting section of her second book of *Observations,* 1617, Bourgeois instructed her daughter in the ethics of midwifery, and in so doing left a series of precepts that could easily be applied to the modern profession.[43] Often Louyse rambled and digressed onto topics that seemed to bother her, such as the decline in moral standards among young women. However, most of her dicta were very much to the point of elevating the practice of midwifery to a noble calling, despite the large numbers who practiced it unworthily. A good midwife should have "a total fear of God ... total charity, and an overwhelming desire to do well." The good midwife must "keep learning up until the last day of (her) life," for which she would need humility. Never experiment either on the rich or the poor with unproven remedies, and never keep good remedies secret. The good midwife should speak freely of what she is doing, both to instruct and to keep her reputation clean. The good midwife should serve the poor with the same affection as shown the rich, and never charge the truly poor for her services. Despite the scorn often shown to the profession of midwife, the good midwife will continue her search for perfection and not sully her good name by entering into fights with ignorant women who work as midwives. She especially warned her daughter about involving herself in the service of corrupt women, who might involve her in their immorality; especially heinous to Bourgeois was the attempt to induce abortion.[44]

Louyse Bourgeois saw herself as the founder of a new line of midwives, who would continue to improve themselves by learning and sharing their experiences. Furthermore, she saw midwifery as a profession equal to medicine, if not slightly superior because of its noble purpose. She invoked the "wise Phanarote, mother of the great physician Socrates," as the source of her decision to become a midwife.

> She told me that because of her, whose adopted daughter I would be, all of her son Socrates' disciples would be favorably disposed toward me ... When Lucina, the goddess of childbirth, saw that Phanarote had given me such great favors she was jealous, and out of envy sent me her own favors ...And she commanded Mercury ... to lead me into the most illustrious places of the realm ... Be advised, daughter, of how much better than me you could do, since you are the grandaughter of Phanarote, a disciple of Lucina, and mistress of Mercury because Lucina made him subject to your mother.[44]

Perhaps Bourgeois merely meant to display her acquaintance with classical authors and mythology, but more likely she meant to sound the clarion call that midwifery sprang from noble antecedents and would in the future be modelled on the best elements of science and service.

Louyse Bourgeois' daughter did not live up to her mother's expectations; at least she left no trace of her life and work. Yet the seeds of a professional identity and ethics found in Louyse Bourgeois' work did bear some fruit, although it is difficult to attribute any of the changes in the profession of obstetrics and midwifery directly to Louyse Bourgeois. The medical and surgical professions were already undergoing a process of transition when Louyse Bourgeois came on the scene, but she did appear to have been influential in establishing a new role for the male practitioner-primary birth attendant, or *accoucheur*. Her efforts to lift midwifery from the status of a vile and menial occupation paid off in unexpected ways. The role she carved for herself among the royal and aristocratic families of the court was an enviable one. She turned the tables on the traditional role of male doctors and surgeons attending a birth. Prior to her appearance on the scene, doctors and surgeons contented themselves with decorous role of offering occasional advice from afar, or occasionally intervening in cases of extreme emergencies. The actual handling of the mother and child fell beneath their dignity. Louyse Bourgeois advertised that in fact these good gentlemen were useless in the delivery room, with all the important decisions and work being done by the midwife. She exposed them as being inexperienced and often clumsy in the handling of birth. Furthermore, she earned great respect for herself from the many families she aided, and the watchful doctors and surgeons realized the great influence they might have by taking a more active role in attending women in labor. Even during her own lifetime, she witnessed an increased use of male doctors as primary birth attendants, which shocked her. After her death, men increased their role in the delivery room and established themselves as authorities in all facets of childbirth. These doctors trained themselves at the Hôtel-Dieu, and in 1670, an *accoucheur* actually attended the birth of an illegitimate child of Louis XIV.[45]

The impact of Louyse Bourgeois' works on the practices and attitudes of the hundreds of ignorant midwives practicing in Paris was slow and indirect. Since most midwives were illiterate, it could hardly be expected that they read her treatises. However, throughout the later seventeenth and eighteenth centuries, a series of well educated, literate, and respected female midwives did concern themselves not only with improving their own skills but also with trying to improve the general level of maternal-infant care in the city. Not long after Louyse Bourgeois' death, the Hôtel-Dieu began to formalize its course of childbirth training. A long series of influential female midwives headed the lying-in wards and published their knowledge; furthermore, they expanded the apprenticeship program to a full-fledged clinical learning experience for midwives from all over France.[46]

The inherent conflict between the better educated doctors and the more experienced midwives, so obvious in Louyse Bourgeois' life, did not evaporate after her death, although none of her successors seemed to offend the medical profession so strongly. Perhaps, however, an amelioration of the conflict between doctors and midwives, at least in Paris, may have emerged in an interesting social development that occurred after Louyse Bourgeois' death: the emergence of Aesculapiad families. At the time Louyse Bourgeois presented herself for examination in 1598, one of her examiners noted the unusual fact that she was married to a surgeon. Louyse herself mentioned in 1617 that her entire family—husband, sons, daughters, and sons-in-laws—had entered into branches of the medical-surgical professions. Undoubtedly Louyse's colleagues and enemies saw the effectiveness of combining such a variety of medical expertise in one family. In all the limited biographical information gathered on the famous Parisian midwives of the later seventeenth and eighteenth centuries,[47] all the midwives appear to have come from families of medical practitioners. By literally including midwives in the families of doctors, surgeons, and apothecaries, the status of the midwife naturally rose to the level of her family. By including midwives in the medical families, too, competition did not threaten the male practitioners.

The dissemination of Louyse Bourgeois' clinical techniques and her philosophy of midwifery remains to be explored. Not until the works of other important Parisian midwives and obstetricians have been examined can an evaluation of her true place in the history of maternity care be attempted.

The story of Louyse Bourgeois-Boursier, and her rise and fall from grace, opens several new avenues for research in both the social history of Parisian medicine and the history of the health sciences. It has already been established that French surgeons worked to improve their status in the seventeenth century, so that by the eighteenth century they acquired a parity with university-educated physicians, long their social superiors. The displacement or readjustment within the medical-surgical ranks caused by the advent of *accoucheurs* needs some attention as well as the fascinating world of medical-surgical-midwife families that appear to have emerged in the later seventeenth century.

Midwives alone offer a promising channel through which to examine early modern women and their work. These midwives practiced an identifiable skill or art; they charged fees for their services; and they enjoyed, or suffered, a limited measure of municipal control. Yet they never attempted to create a corporation to protect their interests and let competition and hostility among themselves undermine their strength. It would be useful, perhaps, to study the city records that deal with the certification of the midwives and to establish whether or not any serious effort was made to police the practice of midwifery at all. Midwifery was one of the few exclusively feminine occupations of the Old Regime, and better understanding of the midwives' number and customs could lay open a new area of women's history.

Figures such as Louyse Bourgeois expose how one-sided has been the history of maternity care. The written history of maternity care has been largely the history of the forceps and the development of other instruments for mechanical intervention in labor and delivery. Medical historians have left the history of midwifery and natural childbirth techniques to the anthropologists of primitive cultures, under the assumption that the persistence of midwifery in advanced, western culture was but the natural recidivism of the ignorant and poor. The result of this peculiar view of childbirth history has been to give a pedigree of historical respectability to the branch of medicine, obstetrics, that approaches childbirth as an abnormal condition requiring highly sophisticated intervention and control. Conversely, today the term midwife evokes an image of a tooth-less granny with powdered tree barks and stump water, ready to assist a woman in labor. The worthy history of female midwives, by being ignored, has become a mixture of folk tales and unexamined assumptions about their worth.

It might appear anachronistic to see Louyse Bourgeois as an important figure in the history of nursing, because we have become so accustomed to dating the appearance of modern nursing from Florence Nightingale's work in the Crimea in the 1850s. Yet in her way, Louyse Bourgeois attempted to establish the female midwife, in so many ways the prototype of the modern nurse, as a respectable, competent practitioner complete with a set of ethics peculiar to her occupation. Certified nurse-midwives, a recent development in the nursing profession in the United States, are providing excellent maternity care to a growing clientele. However, these nurse-midwives often are hampered by outmoded conceptions of what the midwife does. Establishing historic claims to respectability could only enhance their current position.

Knowledge of figures such as Louyse Bourgeois and her successors also may serve more practical and immediate considerations. The U.S. government has begun investigations into problems of maternal, fetal, and neonatal health, focusing largely on obstetrical practices now in vogue. Given the current climate of concern over escalating health care costs and patients' rights, evaluation of alternative forms of health care management demands that we recognize the way in which decisions were made in the past. Was the decision to promote interventionist physician-dominated childbirth management made with an eye to the mother's welfare or the welfare of the medical professions? Or at least were social and professional advantages weighed in the development of medical obstetrics? A history of midwifery will not tarnish nor denigrate the valuable contributions to maternal and infant health made by *accoucheurs*; it might, however, bring forth a more informed understanding of how current practices developed and challenge the assumptions upon which they are based.

---

[1] Little research has been conducted into the quality of midwifery services offered during this period. Contemporaries certainly had little good to say about most of the women who worked as midwives. Ambroise Paré proclaimed their general incompetence in one of his treatises, and Gervais de la Touche published, in 1587, a treatise entitled *Against the Ineptitude of Midwives, (Contre l'impéritie des sages-femmes)*. See: "Fragments de l'histoire de la Chirurgie au XVIIIe siecle," *Revue de Medico-Chirurgicale*, III, No. 5 (1848), p. 314. Louyse Bourgeois, herself, recognized that most of her fellow midwives were unworthy of the appellation "sage-femme" (the French term for midwife, which translates literally as good woman). See also, Jacques Gélis, "Sages-Femmes et Accoucheurs: l'obstetrique populaire aux XVIIe et XVIIe Siècles," *Annates: Économies, Sociétés, Civilisations*, 32, 5 (Sept.-Oct., 1977), pp. 927-957.

[2] Herbert M. Little, "Louise Bourgeois and Some Others," Montreal Med J 39:175 (March 1910).

[3] Alexis Delacoux, *Biographic des Sages-Femmes Célébres* (Paris, 1834), pp. 13-14. Both Delacoux and Little, op. cit., refer to early control over the practice of midwifery by both ecclesiastical and civil officials. The Church's interest in the midwife's work was limited primarily to assuring her honesty and morality. The midwife was in a unique position—if she were unscrupulous—to aid or conceal abortions and illegitimate births and even to help those involved in sorcery or witchcraft by her access to the products of childbirth, often used in occult practices. Most importantly, the midwife might have need to administer the sacrament of Baptism if the infant appeared in danger of dying before a priest could be found. Even in Louyse Bourgeois' day, the midwife had the humiliating duty of carrying babies to Baptism. For all these considerations, the Church wanted only religiously orthodox women to work as midwives. Evidence of civil involvement in the regulation of midwifery in France appeared in 1385, with the first reference to the sworn midwives—*Jurés du Roi*. Delacoux attributes the more formal examination and certification procedure experienced by Louyse Bourgeois to the efforts of barber-surgeons Pare and Guillemeau to improve the level of practice in the mid-16th century. See also, Richard L. Petrelli, "The Regulation of French Midwifery during the Ancien Régime," History Med. 26:3, 276-92. (1971).

[4] Little, p. 1975.

[5] On the Hôtel-Dieu see: Marcel Fosseyeux, *L'Hôtel-Dieu de Paris au XVIIe et au XVIIIe Siécle* (Paris, 1912). The Hôtel-Dieu had the oldest lying-in wards in Europe. The general conditions of the hospital are described in: Edwin M. Jameson, *Clio Medica: Gynecology & Obstetrics* (New York, 1936), p. 101. Despite the high maternal and infant mortality rates, the Hôtel-Dieu became a natural center of informal childbirth education in the seventeenth-century, attracting students from all over Europe by the mid-1600s; see: Walter Radcliffe, *Milestones in Midwifery* (Bristol, 1967), pp. 26-27.

[6] Ambroise Paré (1510-1590) worked as a barber-surgeon and served as military surgeon to armies of the King of France. So great was his skill that he became First Surgeon to Henry II. In addition to such important contributions as ligature of arteries to control bleeding—an alternative to the hideous practice of cauterizing wounds with a hot iron—Paré wrote several treatises on midwifery and gynecological surgery. He worked as a sort of house-surgeon at the Hôtel-Dieu, 1533-1536, where he acquired most of his obstetrical experience. In addition to Louyse Bourgeois' husband, Paré influenced several important surgeons of his day, notably Jacques Guillemeau, who published his own obstetrical treatise and who would become one of Louyse Bourgeois' most serious enemies.

[7] Louyse Bourgeois, *Observations de Louyse Bourgeois Ditte Boursier, Sage-femme de la Reyne. Livre Deuxiesme* (Paris, 1617), p. 108.

[8] Ibid.

[9] Ibid., p. 110.

[10] Ibid., pp. 112-136.

[11] Ibid., pp. 148-193.

[12] Louyse Bourgeois, *Observations Diversses, Sur La Sterilite, Perte de Fruict, foecondite, accouchements, & maladies des femmes, & enfans nouveaux naiz* (Paris, 1609); *Observations de Louyse Bourgeois Ditte Boursier, Sage-femme de la Reyne. Livre Deuxiesme* (Paris, 1617); *Observations diverses, sur la sterilite, perte de fruict, foecondiete, accouchements, et maladies des femmes, et enfants nouveaux-naiz. Amplement traictees, et heureusement praticquees* (Paris, 1626); *Apologia Contre Les Physicians* (Paris, 1627); and, *Recueil des Secrets* (Paris, 1634).

[13] *Observations* (Paris 1617), pp.10-12.

[14] Ibid., pp. 201-202.

[15] Ibid., pp. 74-75.

[16] *Observations*, 1609, pp. 47-49.

[17] Ibid., p. 107.

[18] *Observations*, 1617, pp. 12-16.

[19] Ibid., pp. 17-23.

[20] Ibid., pp. 41-46.

[21] Ibid., pp. 47-52.

[22] Ibid., Louis XIII's birth recounted, pp. 148-170.

[23] Ibid., p. 186.

[24] Louyse Bourgeois, *Observations diverses de Louyse Bourgeois dite Boursier, Sage-Femme de La Reyne, Mere du Roy. Troisiesme Livre* (Paris, 1652), pp. 18-19.

[25] Ibid., p. 17.

[26] Ibid., pp. 72-73.

[27] The entire protocol is reproduced in: W. H. Allport, M.D., "Louyse Bourgeois, An Old Midwife's Tale," Am J Obstet 65:841-845. (Jan-June 1912).

[28] Ibid., p. 846.

[29] Ibid., p. 847.

[30] Ibid., p. 849.

[31] Julien Roshem, "La Medicine dan le Passe, Une Sage-Femme (Louise Bourgeois)," Paris Med 12:831 (1913).
William Goodell, A *Sketch of the Life and Writings of Louyse Bourgeois* (Philadelphia, 1876), p. 51; Felix D'Amour, "Louise Bourgeois: Her Life and Work" (Doctoral dissertation, University of Paris, Faculty of Medicine, 1900), p. 74.

[32] Observations (Paris, 1609), p. 4.

[33] Ibid., pp. 16-25.

[34] D'Amour, p. 82.

[35] *Observations* (Paris, 1617), pp.228-229.

[36] *Observations* (Paris, 1609), pp, 31-32.

[37] Ibid., pp. 91-95.

[38] Ibid., pp. 108-113.

[39] *Observations* (Paris, 1617), pp.231-232.

[40] Ibid., p. 225.

[41] Ibid., p. 42.

[42] Ibid., pp. 200-251.

[43] Ibid., pp. 202, 203, 204, 205.

[44] Ibid., pp. 200-201.

[45] Delacoux, p. 7.

[46] Alexis Delacoux' *Biographie des Sages-Femmes Célèbres* (published in 1834), provides almost the only general treatment of French midwives, and this work is little more than a sketchy biographical dictionary. The most significant of the midwives attached to the Hôtel-Dieu and/or influential in the improvement of French midwifery included: Marguerite DuTerte Lamarche (1638-1706); Angelique-Marguerite Leboursier Ducoudray (1721-1789); Marie Jonet Duges (1730-1797); Marie-Louise Duges Lachapelle (1769-1821); and Marie-Anne Victoire Guillain Boivin (1773-1841). Almost all of these women left written treatises examining the state of the art of midwifery and deserve examination.

[47] Delacoux, passim.

IS CHILDBIRTH ANY PLACE FOR A WOMAN?
THE DECLINE OF MIDWIFERY IN
EIGHTEENTH-CENTURY ENGLAND

Barbara Brandon Schnorrenberg[†]

For many centuries, the normal assistant for all women in childbirth was a midwife. In the eighteenth century, however, the profession of midwifery began to decline markedly in England. By the nineteenth century midwives were mostly women of little education and generally no social status; their patients were the same. For the middle and upper classes, the stereotype of the midwife was the fat, dirty, drunken old woman whose image culminated with Dickens's Sairey Camp in *Martin Chuzzlewit*. She is an old literary type, found in stories at least since the late Middle Ages, who still appears in popular novels about old and ignorant times. This view of the midwife has also passed from fiction into fact to encompass all midwives in all periods in many serious works. The latest evidence of this can be found in Lawrence Stone's *The Family, Sex, and Marriage*.[1] How the profession of midwifery sank to this state is the subject of this paper. There were three major factors that depressed the role and reputation of the midwife in England during the eighteenth century. The least important of these was the increase in scientific knowledge and medical skill. Far more important were the professionalization of medical practitioners and the emergence of what we usually call "Victorian" ideas of the role, abilities, and status of women.

At the beginning of the eighteenth century, the position of the midwife in Britain seemed fairly secure.[2] Any woman could set herself up in practice as a midwife. She was supposed to have a license, issued by a bishop; its qualifications were concerned with good moral character rather than knowledge or experience in the job. Since the enforcement of licensing was the responsibility of the church courts, little was done to pursue it, especially after the Restoration.[3] The midwife's training was primarily through experience. The best served an apprenticeship with an established midwife, and some even received instruction from physicians. Various handbooks and treatises on midwifery and related subjects were also available, although the value of these was sometimes questionable. Certainly one of the most valid criticisms of English midwifery was its lack of any kind of required training and regulation.[4]

In the seventeenth century there had been attempts to remedy this situation. Under the Commonwealth the licensing of midwives had been placed in the hands of the physicians, but this change, which might have meant more training, lapsed in 1660. In the first half of the seventeenth century, members of the prominent family of man-midwives, Peter Chamberlen I and Peter II, attempted to establish a corporation for midwives which would have regulated itself and enforced requirements for training. But these proposals were opposed by both midwives and physicians and so came to nothing.[5] Whether licensed or not, however, the midwife who read the available literature and who received training under a reputable midwife or physician had practical education as good as most males.

The midwife was seldom involved in any kind of prenatal care. She was called in when labor began, having perhaps been consulted shortly before about supplies or equipment she might need for the delivery. At the beginning of the eighteenth century there were essentially no provisions for delivery in hospitals;

[†] *Studies in Eighteenth-Century Culture*, (1981), **10**:393-408

only in the second quarter of the century did lying-in hospitals and wards begin to be established in London, primarily for poor but respectable (married) women.[6] If the delivery was a normal one, all went well; the labor after all in such cases is that of the mother. If, however, things began to go wrong, the midwife was limited in what she could do. The better trained could use manual manipulation, but the midwife had no instruments. If things got really bad, the only recourse was to call in the physician or man-midwife. This provided another ground for criticism of the midwife; it was often said that she waited so late that even the skill of the physician was inadequate to save the mother or child. However, an examination of midwifery literature will show that he might well know little more than the midwife. The main difference between them was that the male, whether physician or man-midwife, used instruments.

By the early eighteenth century there were several basic texts for midwifery in circulation, and their number increased markedly throughout the century.[7] They reveal, however, the deficiencies of eighteenth-century medicine in general. What could be discovered by gross observation was clear and well understood. They could chart the development of the foetus and the various presentations of the child ready to be born. The finest of anatomical drawings, William Hunter's *The Anatomy of the Gravid Uterus,* appeared in 1774. But eighteenth-century physicians did not really understand the process of conception, the relation of the menses to reproduction, ova production, the causes of miscarriages. They were beginning to make some connections between such things as diet and exercise and a successful pregnancy and delivery, though all still believed firmly in the danger of marking the unborn child through the mother's external experiences.[8] All writers assumed that the midwife would officiate at a normal birth, though they urged that in difficult situations the physician be called in earlier rather than later.

The physician had instruments. In really abnormal births, the health of the mother was more important than that of the child. As Caesarian sections were universally fatal, they were not performed on living women. When natural childbirth failed, the physician used various instruments to crush and dismember the foetus in order to achieve its expulsion. More humane and more useful was the obstetrical forceps, which came into general use in the eighteenth century.[9] There are vague references in earlier literature to the use of forceps, but it appears that the efficient and practical prototype was developed in the seventeenth century by the Chamberlen family, man-midwives who came to England as Huguenot refugees in the later sixteenth century. They served the royal family and others; as they perfected the forceps they became widely known among their fellow professionals on the continent as well as in England. The exact design of the Chamberlen forceps was a highly guarded secret, although by the beginning of the eighteenth century various versions were being tried by other men. By about 1725 to 1730 the basic design had been developed and put to use by several practitioners, and by mid-century forceps were in general use among man-midwives.

The man-midwife was in a special category in England. Owing to the peculiar system of medical education and organization, they were a varied group. Whereas on the continent and in Scotland men practicing midwifery received standard university medical training, this was not necessarily true in England. Some of the men who practiced mainly in the area of obstetrics and gynaecology were university graduates; others were trained in the same way as their female counterparts. None of the Chamberlens, for example, held an English medical degree; those who did have university training received it on the continent. By the middle of the eighteenth century, graduates of Scottish universities dominated the man-midwife practitioners, especially in London.[10]

The whole system, if it can be dignified by such a term, of English medical education and professional organization and licensing was, by the eighteenth century, in need of major reform. Licensed medical men were divided into three separate organizations, but the actual practice of each was by no means so clearly divided or separated. The least prestigious group was the apothecaries. Although their original function had been to dispense drugs, by the eighteenth century many were serving, particularly in the provinces and among the urban poor, as general practitioners and even surgeons. They were trained by the apprenticeship system, not by formal education, and officially could charge only for drugs, not for attendance on a sick person. The regulatory body for the apothecaries was the Society of Apothecaries, which was essentially a London mercantile gild. Surgery was also controlled by what had originally been a London livery company, the Barber-Surgeons. By the eighteenth century the two functions of barber and surgeon had clearly divided; in 1745 the Surgeons Company separated from the older organization. In 1800 they were chartered by the King as the Royal College of Surgeons. The surgeons were not university-trained; a man could not be licensed as both a surgeon and a physician. The surgeons were the least numerous and probably the least important practitioners, especially outside the metropolitan area. Finally there were the physicians, organized under the Royal College of Physicians. The College, based in London like the other two companies, dominated the practice of its branch of medicine throughout the country. The College of Physicians was governed by the Fellows; admission to this body was by written and oral examination, which often seemed more concerned with the candidate's knowledge of Latin and whether he had an Oxford or Cambridge degree than with his medical knowledge. The Fellows administered examinations for the licensing of members of the College; the charter restricted licentiates to graduates of the two English universities. By the eighteenth century the Fellows had permission to grant licenses to others who might qualify, thus including the graduates of continental and Scottish universities if they chose to do so. To practice medicine in London and vicinity, a physician had to hold the College's license.[11]

The problem lay particularly in the limitation of the leadership of the profession to graduates of Oxford and Cambridge. Major changes in the study and teaching and the whole concept of medicine began in the seventeenth century and continued throughout the eighteenth. These emphasized an empirical approach to medical questions and a clinical approach to medical training. On the continent and in Scotland these ideas took hold, but England lagged far behind.[12] Some hospitals were founded, and by the mid-eighteenth century there were private medical schools in London offering lectures in anatomy and other medical subjects and training their students in the hospitals. But at Oxford and Cambridge, medical education continued in almost the same fashion as it had existed in the seventeenth century.[13] Nevertheless, the graduates of these two universities provided the political and organizational leadership of the medical profession. The often better trained and more skillful foreign or Scottish graduate was thus limited in his opportunity to achieve the fullest professional recognition.

There were also social implications in the question of any change in the organization of English physicians. Society assumed that a graduate of Oxford or Cambridge was a gentleman. Since the College of Physicians was controlled by these graduates, medicine was a gentlemanly profession, though it certainly ranked behind the church, the law, the military, or the civil service in the numbers it attracted and in prestige value.[14] But by the second half of the eighteenth century, English society itself was changing. The old order was being challenged, not just by political radicals but also by increasing industrialization. Those who were making the new society valued education and empirical results.[15] They were mostly outside the traditional establishment, and as their voice grew stronger, criticisms of the ruling class increased. There was demand for political reform and for change in various aspects of society. The gentleman physician whose main qualification was his Latin and his university degree was often a target. Obvious literary examples are Dr. Slop in *Tristram Shandy* and a number of doctors in the works of Tobias Smollett, himself a Scottish physician.[16]

Midwifery training and the relation of man-midwives to women midwives became a part of the larger issue of reform of medical education and licensing and the changing society of later-eighteenth-century England. Both men and women were practicing midwifery; no woman had a medical degree, and only some had acquired adequate training. Most of the man-midwives in London were not members of the College of Physicians; many had Scottish degrees, some were members of the Company of Surgeons. The College of Physicians had apparently recognized the problem of the man-midwife; in 1726 John Maubray and five other man-midwives were summoned before its Censorial Comitia for practicing without a license. Two years later another man-midwife was summoned; he argued that his profession did not need the College's license, and nothing more was heard on the subject for some years. In 1749 lectures on midwifery for men, sponsored by the College, were begun.[17]

By the forties a number of very distinguished man-midwives were practicing in London. The most important of these was William Smellie, a Scotsman whose teaching and writing on midwifery made him probably the most influential practitioner of the century. Older than Smellie were Frank Nicholls, the College's first lecturer on midwifery, and Sir Richard Manningham, also a College Fellow and the founder of a lying-in hospital. Students of Smellie were numerous; of them the most important was undoubtedly William Hunter, holder of a Scottish degree, anatomist as well as man-midwife.[18] Both Smellie and Hunter favored giving the same sort of lectures and clinical training to midwives as to men and had themselves begun private lectures and demonstrations for women. In 1752, with their endorsement, a proposal came before the College of Physicians to set up instruction for women in midwifery and to require this instruction before a midwife could get an episcopal license, but it was voted down.[19] Meanwhile Smellie published his *Treatise on the Theory and Practice of Midwifery* in 1751, followed by case history volumes in 1754 and 1764.[20] Smellie died in 1763; his place as the leading man-midwife was taken by Hunter. Aside from his *Anatomy of the Gravid Uterus,* Hunter made no original professional contribution. He was concerned with his own advancement, both financially and socially, so mixed in the leading political and intellectual circles of London. He became the fashionable man-midwife; he attended Queen Charlotte at the birth of her first son (later George IV) and at the births of the subsequent thirteen royal children. He died in 1783, before the birth of the Queen's fifteenth child. At the royal lyings-in, however, Hunter was not allowed in the room, where a midwife actually helped at the delivery. He also attended most of the nobility, including Lady Hester Pitt at the birth of the younger William Pitt.[21]

In 1767 the question of the relation of man-midwives to the College of Physicians again surfaced. Dr. Letch, a man-midwife, was rejected as a licentiate. He then went to the Court of King's Bench, asking the College to show cause for its actions. The Court found in favor of the College, but its judgement was tempered with a warning that the College ought to reform its practices. Meanwhile a number of licentiates of the College, including Hunter, formed the Society of Collegiate Physicians. The Society was closed to Fellows of the College of Physicians; its announced aim was the reform of the College. Twenty-three of these licentiates applied for admission as Fellows and were denied. The Society tried to debate with the Fellows, but this degenerated into an exchange of threats. The Society's members hired a gang from the neighborhood of the College's quarters and attempted to use force to break down the door to gain physical as well as paper admission. This action, known as the Battle or Siege of Warwick Lane, was clearly illegal, and the matter returned to the courts. There followed several lawsuits over the next years; in every case the College won, but always with strong advice from the judges to reform. These warnings finally took effect; in the seventies the College admitted some licentiates as Fellows and opened the possibility of more to come. The Society continued in existence, hearing papers and exchanging views until 1798, but its effectiveness as a reforming body declined rapidly after the mid-seventies.[22]

In the first reforms of the College, man-midwives were specifically exempted from the possibility of becoming Fellows.[23] Hunter, for example, who was admitted to the licentiate in 1758 on the strength of his Scottish degree, never became a Fellow. By the end of the seventies, however, the College had apparently decided that man-midwifery was there to stay. In 1783 they resolved to grant licenses to those qualified in midwifery only, for an entrance fee of £20. The number of those applying was small, but ten man-midwives were admitted to the College, including Thomas Denman, who succeeded Hunter as the fashionable man-midwife and whose training was entirely clinical.[24] Only a few man-midwives finally joined the College, although it was a far more prestigious body than the Company of Surgeons, which had been and continued to be the organization for many man-midwives. Those who attended royalty and society, such as Denman, Michael Underwood who attended the birth of Princess Charlotte, daughter of George IV, and Richard Croft, Denman's son-in-law, who let Charlotte die in childbirth, were all members of the College before it ceased to license man-midwives in 1804.[25]

As man-midwifery became socially respectable, these practitioners looked for a less awkward and contradictory name for themselves. Maubray, in his book of 1724, suggested that the man-midwife be called an "Andro-Boethogynist, or Man-Helper of Women"; it is not surprising that this name did not catch on. There was considerable use of the French term "accoucheur" in the eighteenth century, but doubtless many were not happy with the connotations a French word might carry. The term obstetrician seems to have come into use about 1828 and was apparently rapidly adopted by men to put themselves further from the midwives.[26]

In winning their own professional and social respectability, the man-midwives helped to depress the status and opportunities of their female counterparts. More and more by the end of the century, midwives attended the lower classes, who could not pay adequately; therefore, the lack of rewards meant the profession attracted fewer educated and qualified women. Of course there were exceptions, mainly London midwives who actually attended the births of royal children and who wrote books of instruction for their fellow practitioners.[27] Most of these books were positive statements of what a midwife could and ought to do. The bulk of the writing about midwifery, however, was increasingly vituperative criticism of men for taking over the profession. Although by the end of the century the best midwives were also using forceps, the most obvious ground for attack was the male's use of instruments. Actually the best men, such as Smellie and Hunter, were against their indiscriminate use. In 1751 Dr. Frank Nicholls published *A Petition of the Unborn-Babes*,[28] which accused man-midwives of killing both mothers and children by the misuse of instruments. It was said that Nicholls was paid for this support by the current royal midwife, but he was clearly sympathetic to the woman, for it was he who proposed in 1752 that the College offer lectures for midwives.[29]

The most vehement attack on man-midwives appeared in 1760, Elizabeth Nihell's A *Treatise on the Art of Midwifery, Setting forth Various Abuses therein, Especially as to the Practice with Instruments: the Whole Serving to put all Rational Inquirers in a fair Way of very safely forming their own Judgement upon the Question; Which it is best to employ, In Cases of Pregnancy and Lying-in, a Man-Midwife; or, a*

Midwife. Nihell was a midwife who had studied and worked for two years at the Hôtel-Dieu in Paris, where French midwives were trained. Her husband was an apothecary, and of course there were those who said he really wrote the book. Nihell's language was intemperate and her target ill-chosen, for much of her attack was against Smellie. An example of her style and views can be seen in her summary of her three essential points.

> The *first*, is that the origin of the men, insinuating themselves into the practice of midwifery, has absolutely no foundation in the plea of superior safety, and, consequently, can have no right to exact so great a sacrifice as that of decency and modesty.

> The *second*, for that they were reduced first to forge the phantom of incapacity in the women, and next the necessity of murderous instruments, as some color for their mercenary intrusion. And, in truth, the faculty of using those instruments is the sole tenure of their usurped office.

> The *third*, their disagreement among themselves about, which are the instruments to be preferred; a doubt which, the practices tried upon the lives and limbs of so many women and children trusted to them, have not yet, it seems, resolved even to this day.[30]

Her work was reviewed at length and extremely unfavorably in the *Critical Review*, probably by its editor Tobias Smollett. The review began by proposing that she adopt as a motto *Ex nihilo nihil fit*, and went on to attack her views of "the whole body of male-practitioners, as ruffians who never let slip the smallest opportunity of tearing and massacring their patients with iron and steel instruments." Among her other points were that women were more sympathetic in their attendance on those in labor, and midwives on the whole were better trained than their male counterparts. The *Critical Review* denied these claims.[31] Nihell replied in *An Answer to the Critical Review for March, 1760, Upon the Article of Mrs. Nihell's Treatise on the Art of Midwifery*.[32] The *Critical Review* noticed this refutation in a brief but sprightly call for an end to the exchange, saying "you have delivered yourself of a monstrous birth, that fully evinces your dexterity in the obstetric art: may it, however, be the last of our begetting!"[33] It is difficult to believe that the kind of attack Nihell made did much to improve the reputation of midwives.

Besides the unwarranted use of instruments, the other main attack on man-midwives was made on the grounds of propriety. Nihell raised this issue, which, as instruments were more accepted by women as well as men, became a key question in the employment of man-midwives. Especially by the end of the century, as what we usually refer to as "Victorian" attitudes about the purity and privacy of a woman's body came to be widely held,[34] the issue was raised as to whether a woman ought to let a man see and touch her. Midwives argued that they would not compromise a woman's purity. Stories of patients seduced by their male physicians, of poor women in lying-in hospitals being subjected to the harassment of examination by countless medical students, were repeated in various versions. Man-midwifery, along with boarding schools for girls, novels, and dancing (all French in origin), were ruining English women. Once women were lost, all society would crumble.[35] This Victorian attitude toward "touching," as it was usually called, did not, however, save the midwife. Rather it led to nineteenth-century gynaecology and obstetrics, with male physicians diagnosing and prescribing for women whom they had not really examined and whose propriety forbade them to describe their own condition adequately.[36] While concern for female modesty did not save the midwife as the primary agent of delivery care, other aspects of the "Victorian" view of women were certainly influential in her decline. A lady does not work, and no decent woman would voluntarily involve herself in such a physical (even sexual) and messy affair as childbirth. Therefore, the kind of woman who became a midwife was for yet another reason uneducated and lower-class, and thus even less likely to be engaged by the middle and upper classes.

One of the complaints of midwives against their male counterparts was that the men were taking away women's work. All through the eighteenth century this complaint was made about many occupations; midwifery is another example of women's loss of employment in pre-industrial society. The reasons men gave for their own advance were all what would now be called male chauvinism. A woman is more delicate than a man, less able to engage in strenuous activity. Therefore, was a midwife physically fit to do her job? Although the nineteenth-century mill owners argued that women's delicate and sensitive fingers made them more fitted to work in the textile mills for less money than men, the man-midwives argued that these fingers were not sensitive enough to manipulate obstetrical instruments. Since women's minds could not comprehend the mysteries of science, they could hardly be qualified to be obstetricians in the modern world. These arguments were in the end the most critical in the decline of the midwife. Women were excluded from the universities, the teaching hospitals (except as patients), from the professional organizations. Medicine, like other professions, was a male preserve, to be guarded jealously against incursion from illogical, unscientific, weak women. If medicine was to be scientific, it must be male. This is an attitude which has not died easily.

[1] *The Family, Sex and Marriage in England 1500-1800* (New York: Harper and Row, 1977), pp. 72-73, 79. Even so respected a medical historian as George Rosen makes these assumptions in "A Slaughter of Innocents: Aspects of Child Health in the Eighteenth-Century City," *Studies in Eighteenth-Century Culture,* vol. 5 (Madison: University of Wisconsin Press, 1976), pp. 293-316.

[2] General accounts of midwives and midwifery in the eighteenth century vary in value. Jean Donnison, *Midwives and Medical Men* (New York: Schocken Books, 1977) is concerned primarily with the nineteenth century; however, she has an extensive introductory section on the earlier period. This is also the best-documented account of midwives. Other surveys include Kate Campbell Hurd Mead, *A History of Women in Medicine* (Haddam, Conn.: Haddam Press, 1938), pp. 460-77; Gustave J. Witkowski, *Accoucheurs et sages-femmes célèbres* (Paris: G. Stemheil, n.d.); James Hobson Aveling, *English Midwives: Their History and Prospects* (London: J. and A. Churchill, 1872; reprinted, London, Hugh K. Elliott, 1967); Herbert Ritchie Spencer, *The History of British Midwifery 1650 to 1800* (London, John Bale Sons and Danielson, 1927; reprinted, New York, AMS Press, 1978), really about British writing on obstetrics; Thomas Rogers Forbes, *The Midwife and the Witch* (New Haven: Yale University Press, 1966); Barbara Ehrenreich and Diedre English, *Witches, Midwives, and Nurses* (Old Westbury, N.Y.: Feminist Press, 1973), a stridently feminist account; J. Elise Gordon, "British Midwives through the Centuries 3: From the 18th Century to Today", *Midwife & Health Visitor,* 3 (1967), 275-81; M. Olive Haydon, "English Midwives in Three Centuries," *Maternity and Child Welfare,* 3 (1919), 407-9; Alice Clark, *Working Life of Women in the Seventeenth Century* (London: George Routledge, 1919), pp. 265-85; Hilda Smith, "Gynecology and Ideology in Seventeenth-Century England," in Berenice A. Carroll, ed., *Liberating Women's History* (Urbana, Ill.: University of Illinois Press, 1976), pp. 97-114.

[3] See Aveling, Clark, and other sources cited above. Also see Thomas Rogers Forbes, "The Regulation of English Midwives in the Sixteenth and Seventeenth Centuries," *Medical History,* 8 (1964), 235-44, and "The Regulation of English Midwives in the Eighteenth and Nineteenth Centuries," *Medical History,* 15 (1971), 352-62; Thomas G. Benedek, "The Changing Relationship between Midwives and Physicians during the Renaissance," *Bulletin of the History of Medicine,* 51 (1977), 550-64.

[4] Compare what happened to midwifery in France. See Richard A. Petrelli, "The Regulation of French Midwifery during the Ancien Régime," *Journal of the History of Medicine & Allied Sciences,* 26 (1971), 276-92.

[5] Donnison, *Midwives and Medical Men;* Aveling, *English Midwives;* James Hobson Aveling, *The Chamberlens and the Midwifery Forceps: Memorials of the Family and an Essay on the Invention of the Instrument* (London, J. and A. Churchill, 1882; reprinted, New York, AMS Press, 1977); Smith, "Gynecology and Ideology."

[6] G. C. Peachey, "Notes upon the Provision for Lying-in Women in London up to the Middle of the Eighteenth Century," *Proceedings of the Royal Society of Medicine,* 17 (1923-24): Section of Epidemiology and State Medicine, 72-76; J. E. Donnison, "Note on the Foundation of Queen Charlotte's Hospital," *Medical History,* 15 (1971), 398-400; Donnison, *Midwives and Medical Men,* pp. 25-28.

[7] A useful survey of the various writers on the subject can be found in Irving S. Cutter & Henry R. Viets, *A Short History of Midwifery* (Philadelphia: W B. Saunders, 1964), pp. 10-44. Shorter and less-exhaustive summaries are John Byers, "The Evolution of Obstetric Medicine; With Illustrations from Some Old Midwifery Books," *British Medical Journal,* 15 June 1912, pp. 1345-50; Walter Radcliffe, *Milestones in Midwifery* (Bristol: John Wright, 1967); Miles H. Phillips, "Men-Midwives of the Past," *Bristol Medico-Chirugical Journal,* 52 (Summer 1935), 83-102; Ritchie Spencer, *History of British Midwifery.*

[8] This summary can be detailed from the secondary works cited above as well as contemporary works. I have read those available in the Lawrence Reynolds Collection, Lister Hill Library, University of Alabama in Birmingham: François Mauriceau, *Traité des maladies des femmes grosses ... ,* 4th ed. (Paris: Chez Laurent d'Henry, 1694. The first edition of this work was published in 1668; an English translation by Hugh Chamberlen appeared in 1672, titled *The Diseases of Women with Child and in Childbed);* John Maubray, *The Female Physician ...* (London: James Holland, 1724); William Buchan, *Domestic Medicine,* 3rd American ed. (Norwich, Conn.: John Trumbull, 1778; first published in Edinburgh in 1769). In the Rare Book Room, Medical History Section, Medical School Library, University of Rochester: Alexander Hamilton, *Outlines of the Theory and Practice of Midwifery,* 3rd ed. (London: T. Kay, 1791); John Burton, *An Essay Towards a Complete New System of Midwifery* (London: James Hodges, 1751). On microfilm from the National Library of Medicine: Paul Portal, *Midwives, or the True Manner of Assisting a Woman in Childbearing: . . .* (London: S. Crouch and J. Taylor, 1705); John Memis, *The Midwife's Pocket Companion: or a Practical Treatise of Midwifery ...* (London: Edward & Charles Dilly, 1765). See also Kenneth Dewhurst, "Locke's Midwifery Notes," *The Lancet,* 4 Sept. 1954, 490-91; Michael K. Eshleman, "Diet during

Pregnancy in the Sixteenth and Seventeenth Centuries," *Journal of the History of Medicine and Allied Sciences,* **30** (1975), 23-39.

[9] Cutter & Viets, *Short History,* pp. 44-69; Aveling, *The Chamberlens;* Kedarnath Das, *Obstetric Forceps: Its History and Evolution* (St. Louis: C. V. Mosby, 1929); Donald T. Atkinson, *Magic, Myth and Medicine* (Cleveland: World Publishing Co., 1956), pp. 163-66; John H. Peel, "Milestones in Midwifery," *Postgraduate Medical Journal,* Nov. 1947, pp. 523-29; Alban Doran, "Burton ('Dr. Slop'): His Forceps and His Foes," *Journal of Obstetrics and Gynaecology of the British Empire,* **23** (1913), 3-24, 65-86; and "Dusée: His Forceps and His Contemporaries," ibid., **22** (1912), 119-42, 203-7.

[10] William F. Mengert, "The Origin of the Male Midwife" *Annals of Medical History,* ns, 4 (1932), 453-65; R. W Johnstone, "Scotland's Contribution to the Progress of Midwifery in the Early 18th & 19th Centuries," *Journal of Obstetrics & Gynaecology of the British Empire,* **57** (1950), 583-94; Howard D. King, "The Evolution of the Male Midwife, with Some Remarks on the Obstetrical Literature of Other Ages," *American Journal of Obstetrics,* **77** (1918), 177-86; George Bancroft-Livingstone, "Louise de la Vallière and the Birth of the Man-Midwife" *Journal of Obstetrics & Gynaecology of the British Empire,* **63** (1956), 261-67; Steven A. Brody, "The Life and Times of Sir Fielding Ould: Man-Midwife & Master Physician" *Bulletin of the History of Medicine,* **52** (1978), 228-50.

[11] On these three companies and medical practice, see S. W F. Holloway, "The Apothecaries' Act: A Reinterpretation," *Medical History,* **10** (1966), 107-29, 271-36; Zachary Cope, *The Royal College of Surgeons of England: A History* (Springfield, Ill.: Charles C. Thomas, 1959); George Norman Clark, *A History of the Royal College of Physicians of London,* 2 vols. (Oxford: Clarendon Press, 1964-66); Frederick N. L. Poynter, *The Evolution of Medical Practice in Britain* (London: Pitman Medical Publishing Co., 1961); W J. Bishop, "The Evolution of the General Practitioner in England," in E. Ashworth Underwood, ed., *Science, Medicine and History: Essays on the Evolution of Scientific Thought and Medical Practice written in honour of Charles Singer,* 2 vols. (London: Oxford University Press, 1953), II, 351-57; Joseph F. Kett, "Provincial Medical Practice in England: 1730-1815," *Journal of the History of Medicine and Allied Sciences,* 19 (1964), 17-29; Bernice Hamilton, "The Medical Professions in the Eighteenth Century," *Economic History Review,* 2nd ser., 4 (1951), 141-69.

[12] Lester S. King, *The Road to Medical Enlightenment: 1650-1695* (London: Macdonald, 1970) and *The Medical World of the Eighteenth Century* (Chicago: University of Chicago Press, 1958); Albert H. Buck, *The Dawn of Modern Medicine* (New Haven: Yale University Press, 1920); Michael Kraus, "American and European Medicine in the Eighteenth Century," *Bulletin of the History of Medicine,* 8 (1940), 679-95; G. S. Rousseau, "'Sowing the Wind and Reaping the Whirlwind': Aspects of Change in Eighteenth-Century Medicine," in Paul J. Korshin, ed., *Studies in Change and Revolution: Aspects of English Intellectual History, 1640-1800* (London: Scolar Press, 1972), pp. 129-59; William R. LeFanu, "The Lost Half-Century in English Medicine, 1700-1750," *Bulletin of the History of Medicine,* **46** (1972), 319-48; Arnold Chaplin, *Medicine in England during the Reign of George III* (London, Henry Kimpton, 1919; reprinted, New York, AMS Press, 1977).

[13] Phyllis Allen, "Medical Education in 17th-Century England," *Journal of the History of Medicine and Allied Sciences,* **1** (1946), 115-43; James L. Axtell, "Education and Status in Stuart England: The London Physician," *History of Education Quarterly,* **10** (1970), 141-59; A. H. T. Robb-Smith, "Medical Education at Oxford and Cambridge Prior to 1850," in Frederick N. L. Poynter, ed., *The Evolution of Medical Education in Britain* (Baltimore: Williams and Wilkins, 1966), pp. 19-52; Arnold Chaplin, "The History of Medical Education in the Universities of Oxford and Cambridge, 1500-1850," *Proceedings of the Royal Society of Medicine,* **13** (1919-20): pt. 3, Section of the History of Medicine, 83-107; Charles Singer and S. W F. Holloway, "Early Medical Education in England in Relation to the Pre-History of London University," *Medical History,* **4** (1960), 1-17; Charles Newman, *The Evolution of Medical Education in the Nineteenth Century* (London: Oxford University Press, 1957), pp. 1-55.

[14] Axtell, "Education and Status"; Edward Hughes, "The Professions in the Eighteenth Century," *Durham University Journal,* ns, 13 (1951-52), 46-55; N. D. Jewson, "Medical Knowledge and the Patronage System in 18th-Century England," *Sociology,* **8** (1974), 369-85.

[15] J. H. Plumb, "Reason and Unreason in the Eighteenth Century: The English Experience," in *In the Light of History* (Boston: Houghton Mifflin, 1972), pp. 3-24.

[16] William White, "A Survey of the Social Implications of the History of Medicine in Great Britain, 1742-1867," *Annals of Medical History, ns,* 10 (1938), 279-300; Rousseau, "Sowing the Wind and Reaping the Whirlwind"; Doran, "Burton ('Dr. Slop')"; W. H. Allport, "Tristram Shandy and Obstetrics," *American Journal of Obstetrics and Diseases of Women and Children,* **65** (1912), 612-17; Arthur H. Cash, "The Birth of Tristram Shandy: Sterne and Dr, Burton," in R. F. Brissenden, ed., *Studies in the Eighteenth Century* (Toronto: University of Toronto Press, 1968), pp. 133-54; G. S. Rousseau, "Pineapples, Pregnancy, Pica, and Peregrine Pickle," in G. S. Rousseau and P. G. Boucé, ed., *Tobias Smollett Bicentennial Essays Presented to Lewis M. Knapp* (New York: Oxford University Press, 1971), pp. 79-109; Cecil K. Drinker, "Doctor Smollett," *Annals of Medical History,* 7 (1925), 31-47; E. Ashworth Underwood, "Medicine and Science in the Writings of Smollett," *Proceedings of the Royal Society of Medicine,* **30** (1937), 961-74; Claude E. Jones, "Tobias Smollett (1721-1771) The Doctor as Man of Letters," *Journal of the History of Medicine and Allied Sciences,* **12** (1957), 337-48.

[17] Clark, *Royal College of Physicians,* II, 502-3.

[18] Cutter and Viets, *Short History,* pp. 15-38; Johnstone, "Scotland's Contribution"; George C. Peachey, "William Hunter's Obstetrical Career," *Annals of Medical History,* ns, 2 (1930), 476-79.

[19] Clark, *Royal College of Physicians,* II, 504-5; William Hunter to William Cullen, London, 22 Feb. 1752, John Thomson, *An Account of the Life, Lectures, and Writings of William Cullen M.D.,* 2 vols. (Edinburgh: William Blackwood, 1859), I, 543-44.

[20] Tobias Smollett was a friend of Smellie; in the fifties and sixties, while editor of the *Critical Review,* he also edited and supervised the publication of Smellie's work. Jones, "Tobias Smollett"; Lewis M. Knapp, *Tobias Smollett, Doctor of Men and Manners* (Princeton: Princeton University Press, 1949); Claude E. Jones, "Tobias Smollett on the 'Separation of the Pubic Joint in Pregnancy,'" *Medical Life,* **41** (1934), 302-5; G. S. Rousseau, "Tobias Smollett: Doctor by Design, Writer by Choice," *Journal of the American Medical Association,* **216** (1971), 85-89.

[21] Johnstone, "Scotland's Contribution"; Cordon, "British Midwives"; Jane M. Oppenheimer, *New Aspects of John and William Hunter* (New York: Henry Schuman, 1946); Charles W. F. Illingworth, "William Hunter's Influence on Obstetrics," *Scottish Medical Journal,* **15** (1970), 58-60; Cutter and Viets, *Short History,* pp. 33-37; Olwen Hedley, *Queen Charlotte* (London: John Murray, 1975).

[22] Iwan Waddington, "The Struggle to Reform the Royal College of Physicians, 1767-1771: A Sociological Analysis," *Medical History,* **17** (1973), 107-26; Lloyd G. Stevenson, "The Siege of Warwick Lane: Together with a Brief History of the Society of Collegiate Physicians (1767-1798)," *Journal of the History of Medicine & Allied Sciences,* **7** (1952), 105-21; R. Hingston Fox, *Dr. John Fothergill and His Friends* (London: Macmillan, 1919), pp. 143-51.

[23] Dr. William Watson to Dr. John Fothergill, London, 16 Sept. 1771, Thomson, *Account of William Cullen,* I, 657-60.

[24] Clark, *Royal College of Physicians,* II, 588-89; Forbes "The Regulation of English Midwives in the Eighteenth and Nineteenth Centuries"; Cutter and Viets, *Short History,* pp. 41-42, 185-86.

[25] Clark, *Royal College of Physicians,* II, 636-37; Cutter and Viets, *Short History,* pp. 187-88; W J. Maloney, "Michael Underwood: A Surgeon Practicing Midwifery from 1764 to 1784," *Journal of the History of Medicine & Allied Sciences,* 5 (1950), 289-314,

[26] Forbes, "The Regulation of English Midwives in the Eighteenth and Nineteenth Centuries."

[27] Mead, *Women in Medicine,* pp. 472-77; Gordon, "British Midwives"; Witkowski, *Accoucheurs et sages-femmes;* Aveling, *English Midwives,* pp. 118-29.

[28] *The Petition of the Unborn-Babes to the Censors of the Royal College of Physicians of London* (London: M.Cooper, 1751).

[29] Clark, *Royal College of Physicians,* II, 503-5; Donnison, *Midwives and Medical Men,* p. 32; Cordon, "British Midwives."

[30] Nihell, *Treatise* ... (London: A. Morley, 1760), pp. xii-xiii.

[31] 9 (1760), 187-97.

[32] London: A. Morley, 1760.

[33] 9 (1760), 412. See also Aveling, *English Midwives,* pp. 118-26; Philip J. Kluhoff, "Smollett's Defense of Dr. Smellie in *The Critical Review,*" *Medical History,* 14 (1970), 31-41. Most of the other attacks on man-midwives used exactly the same material as Nihell with perhaps different emphases. For example, Philip Thicknesse, *Man-Midwifey Analyzed: and the Tendency of That Practice Detected and Exposed* (London: R. Davis, 1764), stresses the impropriety of men treating women.

[34] On this point see Muriel Jaeger, *Before Victoria* (London: Chatto and Windus, 1956); Cordon Rattray Taylor, *The Angel Makers* (New York: E. P. Dutton, 1974); Keith Thomas, "The Double Standard," *Journal of the History of Ideas,* 20 (1959), 195-216.

[35] Donnison, *Midwives and Medical Men,* pp. 28-31; Mengert, "The Origins of the Male Midwife." Nihell and Thicknesse make many of these points as well.

[36] Regina Morantz, "The Lady and her Physician," in Mary S. Hartman and Lois Banner, eds., *Clio's Consciousness Raised* (New York: Harper and Row, 1974), pp. 38-53; Jane B. Donegan, "Man-Midwifery and the Delicacy of the Sexes," in Carol V. R. George, ed., *'Remember the Ladies': New Perspectives on Women in American History* (Syracuse, N.Y.: Syracuse University Press, 1975), pp. 90-109; John S. & Robin M. Haller, *The Physician and Sexuality in Victorian America* (Urbana: University of Illinois Press, 1974). While these works deal with the United States, the results of these practices were the same everywhere.

PERRETTE THE MIDWIFE:
A FIFTEENTH CENTURY WITCHCRAFT CASE[*]

Thomas R. Forbes[†]

The relation of midwifery to witchcraft in western Europe in the fifteenth to seventeenth century has been reviewed in another paper.[1] Clearly, there was temptation for the midwife to practice the black arts. Witchcraft, according to a leading authority,[2,3] was wide-spread during this period, and its devotees were to be found everywhere. The midwife, at that time usually an ignorant and incompetent elderly woman, received meagre fees, occupied the lowest level of society, and lived a lonely and probably unhappy life. An opportunity for prestige in the community, power of sorts, the confidences of her neighbours, additional fees, and the unholy delights of the witches' Sabbath evidently drew some of these poor creatures into "the old religion," even at peril of merciless punishment if they were apprehended by the authorities and with the certain expectation, in any case, of eternal damnation.

The following translation of a court document relates an episode of witchcraft involving two midwives in fifteenth century France.[4] The Biographie des sages-femmes célèbres, anciennes, modernes et contemporaines, by A. Delacoux, Docteur en Médecine de la Faculté de Paris, etc., was published in Paris by Trinquart and Delacoux in 1834. On pages 130 through 137 appear a portrait and account of one Perrette, a midwife. Most of the material about her is also contained in a nineteenth century book by Witkowski,[5] who evidently drew directly on Delacoux's work. However, since neither volume is readily accessible and since the record is of considerable interest, it seems worthwhile to present a full translation of M. Delacoux's account, as follows:

Perrette (wife of Thomas of Rouen), sworn midwife of Paris in 1408.[6] Although the name Perrette is found neither in medical history nor in memoirs of the period, we nevertheless believe that we should make this midwife known, celebrated as she was as much for her integrity and her talents as for the ignominious sentence imposed on her for magic and sorcery. One part of the penalty incurred by this unfortunate woman was remitted because of her great renown and her skill at deliveries. The most important part of the history of this midwife is related in full in the letters of pardon granted by Charles VI on 17 May 1408, letters which we have exhumed from the registry of charters in the historical section of the Royal Archives. Our readers surely will be grateful to have in extenso this curious account, numbered 223 and entitled Remissio pro Perreta uxore Thome de Rothomago (Remission for Perrette, the wife of Thomas of Rouen).

"We, Charles, etc., make known to all present and to come that we have received the humble supplication of Perrette, wife of Thomas of Rouen, setting forth that for many years she has devoted herself to midwifery in order to secure the necessities of life for her husband, herself, and the fifteen children of their marriage, all of whom are still alive.[7] This office the supplication has performed and carried out well and dutifully for the space of twenty years and more. For a long time she has been a sworn midwife of our

[*] Read at the 34th annual meeting of the American Association for the History of Medicine, Chicago, Ill., May 18, 1961.

[†] Departments of Anatomy & the History of Science and Medicine, Yale University. *Bulletin of the History of Medicine* (1962); **36**: 124-9. Reprinted by permission of the John Hopkins University Press.

city of Paris without arousing any complaint; rather, by her loyalty, diligence and industry she has acquired the affection and favor of many noble ladies, women of the middle class, and others.

"Thus it was that about the time of the last feast of Saint John the Baptist a woman named Jehanne Chantre, called the Boudière[8] and known to the said Perrette because she had delivered her of three children, repaired to the said Perrette. The Boudière told here that if she could procure a stillborn infant, she would pay her as much as she would earn by delivering ten babies; she would give her twenty crowns. To this she answered that she could not, and would not know how to obtain (the infant). But the said Boudière told her that a great lord of France had become so afflicted with leprosy that he did not dare to come to our court. He had found a doctor who had promised to cure him but (who said) that a stillborn infant would have to be procured. He added that if the said Perrette would procure it for him he would give her the said twenty écus, and if the said lord could be cured he would make her such a rich woman that she would never have to deliver babies again. He implored the said Perrette so much that she agreed.

"The said Perrette related all this to a midwife named Katherine la Petionne (the little) with whom the said Boudière had previously spoken about the matter, telling her that if anyone came to her about it she should bring him to her house.[9] Every day, or at any rate very often, for about two months the said Boudière came to the said Perrette to learn if the said stillborn baby had been obtained, until finally in vexation Perrette told the said Boudière that she could not procure the said stillborn infant, would not know how to do so, and thereupon withdrew from the enterprise.

"About six weeks later the said Katherine came to the said Perrette, bringing in her pocket a stillborn baby as long as a hand, or thereabouts, which she delivered to the said Perrette, and told her to keep it until the said Boudière came to get it, and then left. Soon afterward the said Boudière came to the said Perrette and asked if the said Katherine had brought the said stillborn infant. She answered affirmatively and showed it to her, and the said Boudière departed, saying that she would speak to those who had commissioned her in this matter.

"The next day the said Katherine returned to the said Perrette and told her that she did not know what these people (the physician and the nobleman) wished to do with the stillborn infant and that her advice was that they (Perrette and Katherine) not deliver but bury it. Perrette agreed that this was good advice, and the two of them proceeded to inter it in a field. Later the same day, however, the said Boudière came to the said Perrette and demanded the stillborn infant, to which the said Perrette answered that she and the said Katherine had buried it in a field. At this the said Boudière was furious, saying that the said Perrette must take her for a chatterer and liar. She threatened the said Perrette, saying that she had done wrong and would be sorry. Nonetheless she also begged the said Perrette to go with her to those who had commissioned her (the Boudière), to help make her excuses to them.

"Perrette agreed to this and went with the said Boudière to the rue de Rosiers, to an inn where she found a tall nobleman dressed in gray, and another less important gentleman also dressed in gray, and another dressed in black, whom she did not know. The said Boudière told them that the said Perrette and Katherine had buried the said stillborn infant in the fields, at which the said three men were enraged and again threatened the said Perrette with punishment and injury. Then the said nobleman in gray, whom later the said Perrette heard addressed as Guiselin de Rebesnes, begged the said Perrette to deliver the said infant. He swore and protested that it was not to do anyone evil[10] but only to provide a little ointment with which to anoint the face of the leprous nobleman so that the crusts would fall from his face, and that afterward he would return and restore the said infant to the said Perrette for burial.

"So the said Perrette, who is a simple woman, accompanied by a young valet from the inn, left to disinter the infant, and brought it to the said inn, and delivered it to a man dressed in black who was said to be a physician, in the presence of the said Guiselin, the other man dressed in gray, and the said Boudière. The latter went to one of the rooms of the said inn and brought a dressing gown lined with fur, which she handed over as security to the said Perrette. She did not wish to accept it, but the said Boudière said and affirmed that she should take it, at least as a token. So Perrette took the said dressing gown and brought it to their home, and two or three days later the said Boudière brought there two francs, which she delivered to the said Perrette, and received from her and carried off the said dressing gown.

"All these things were and have been done without the knowledge of the said Thomas of Rouen. Because it came to the attention of the authorities that the said Guiselin and his accomplices in the matter of the stillborn infant wished to work sorcery or other witchcraft, the said Guiselin and several others were arrested and confined in the prison of Paris. Along with others the said Perrette of Rouen because of this matter has been a prisoner for the space of six weeks, or thereabouts, in the said prison in great privation and misery. Finally, by sentence of our Provost of Paris the said Perrette with the said Katherine was condemned to be turned on the pillory[11] and deprived of the said office of midwife. This sentence was executed in respect to the pillory, and then the said Perrette was released from prison. As a result, she and her said husband had the prospect of spending the rest of their lives in reproach and dishonour and in the greatest poverty and wretchedness. The said Thomas, who is an old man, a minstrel, hereafter can work little if at all at his profession and therefore plans to flee from the region where he was born, unless by our grace and mercy we grant their humble appeal for remission of sentence.

"Wherefore we have considered these things and wish to be merciful in this case rather than to exercise a rigorous justice. The said Perrette has always been an honest woman, leading a good life, reputable, and virtuous in speech without exception, having never been accused or suspected of making accusation or reproach. She had done or committed the above mentioned things more through simplicity and ignorance than through malice, expecting in addition that what was done would harm no one save only the law. The said Perrette, not only by her long detention in prison but also by the chastisement and disgrace of the said pillory, has been, and is, greatly punished. Her service, office, or skill is very necessary to the public welfare, and likewise several pregnant women place great reliance in here knowledge and diligence and from day to day come to her and ask her to deliver their children. Therefore we have by our special grace and royal authority discharged, forgiven, and pardoned Perrette of Rouen in respect to the above mentioned case. Be it known by these presents that we do discharge, forgive, and pardon the deed, case, and offence above described, together with the deprivation of her said office, and we restore to her good name and reputation in the said office or profession of midwife, without being sworn, and her goods which were not confiscated, satisfaction to be made under civil law if any were so (confiscated). Given by order to our Provost of Paris and to all other officials and officers or to their lieutenants present and to come, and to each one of them as it may pertain to him that by our mercy, remission, pardon, and vindication they permit, suffer, and allow the said Perrette to live justly and peacefully, without causing her, or suffering her to be caused, sent, or given hereafter any obstacle or impediment whatsoever in body, in goods, or in the exercise of her said profession or office. Let this be done, or arranged, or caused to be arranged at once and without delay for her full release and (restoration to) her original estate and due. We impose in this (matter) perpetual silence on our public prosecutor. And so that this be unalterable and established for always, we have caused our seal to be affixed by these presents, reserving in other matters each and all of our rights. Given at Paris the seventeenth day of May in the year of grace 1408 and of our reign the twenty-eighth.

"BY THE KING IN COUNCIL. CHARRON."

The history of the Middle Ages (M. Delacoux comments) continuously reveals to us superstition grappling with reason, in other words, feeble intellects battling with strong intellects. Seen in regard to the customs of the times, the deed imputed to Perrette was more than a profanation or even a crime; it was witchcraft. This unfortunate woman owed the remission of part of her punishment only to her superiority in the art which she practised and to the need for her skill; otherwise she would not have received mercy. Perrette survived a short time after her vindication, died in 1411 in the rue Aubribouché, or Aubrey-le-Boucher, and was buried in a church vault, according to the record of the parish of Saint-Jacques-de-la-Boucherie. (End of Translation).

Katherine's sentence seems to have been the same as that of Perrette. Nothing is said about the fate of the others who were arrested, but customarily the punishment for those convicted of witchcraft was ruthless indeed. Of Perrette we know nothing further. The pencil sketch of her which is printed with M. Delacoux's account is, one supposes, a product of the artist's imagination except as it shows some details of fifteenth century costume. In all other respects the story rings true, it is cheering to know that amidst the ignorance and harshness of the Middle Ages Perrette's skill and blameless reputation earned for her the King's mercy.

[1] T.R. Forbes. "Midwifery and witchcraft in fifteenth, sixteenth, and seventeenth century Europe". *J.Hist.Med.& Allied Sc.*, **17**:264-283.

[2] M.A. Murray. *The Witch-cult in Western Europe...*Oxford: Clarendon Press, 1921, pp.101, 279-280.

[3] M.A. Murray, "Witchcraft". In: *Encyclopedia Britannica*, London: Encyclopedia Britannica, 1937, **23**, pp. 686-8.

[4] The account from which the translation was made was discovered in the Wellcome Historical Medical Library in London. The research was made possible in large part by grants from the Wellcome Trust, London, and the National Science Foundation (G-8673) and Public Health Service (RG-6470), Washington.

[5] G-J. Witkowski. *Accoucheurs et sages-femmes célèbres*. Paris: G. Steinheil, 1891, p.4 et seq.

[6] In an effort to regulate the practice of midwifery and improve its standards, ecclesiastical and municipal authorities often required that midwives be examined as to their competence and character, be licensed, and swear to exercise their profession in keeping with specified standards.

[7] The interminable sentences of the Remissio have been divided into more manageable lengths by the translator.

[8] The word *boudière* does not appear in any of the dictionaries consulted by the translator. However, Godefroy's *Dictionnaire* (Frédéric Godefroy. *Dictionnaire de l'ancienne langue francaise et de tous ses dialectes du IXe au XVe siècle...Paris: Librairie des Sciences et des Arts*, 1937, vol. I, p. 695) lists *boudie* as equivalent to *ventre*, or abdomen.. *Ventrière* formerly signified midwife, and it seems very likely that *boudière* here meant the same.

[9] The reference of personal pronouns is obscure. Apparently this sentence means that the Boudière earlier had also asked Katherine la Petionne to notify the Boudière if any infant's body were obtained.

[10] A stillborn baby was sometimes an ingredient in brews prepared by witches as poisons, aids to enchantment, etc.

[11] Two kinds of pillory were in use at this time. One was like the stocks familiar in Great Britain and later in Colonial America. The other also consisted of an apparatus for confining the neck and arms of the prisoner, but the framework was mounted on a wheel on a vertical axis. The victim could thus be rotated and seen by all.

THE DECLINE OF THE MIDWIFE

J. Donnison [†]

The eighteenth century was a period of great change. Agrarian improvements, the move to industrialisation and urbanization, the increase in population, and the growth of prosperity all had far-reaching effects on people's lives, and especially on those of women. In the middle of the century women were still largely engaged in financially gainful work in their own homes, often acting as their husbands' partners in craft-work, business or agriculture. Over the next hundred years, however, the change to large-scale farming and the decline in domestic industries made this less and less possible. At the same time, the womenfolk of newly-prosperous tradesmen and farmers increasingly left the counter and the dairy for a life of leisure in the parlour—a poor qualification for earning a living should the future leave them unprovided for. Finally, the continuing professionalisation of other occupations, as for example, medicine, worked gradually but inevitably towards the exclusion of women.[1]

Even in the traditionally female occupation of midwifery, women were losing ground. From the 1720s onwards, more and more men were coming into the field. Moreover, they were no longer only called into attend abnormal labours, but were beginning to be engaged for routine cases. In consequence they were now in direct competition with the midwife. Thus work which since time immemorial had been the preserve of women, and in particular the resort of women with families to maintain, was gradually being lost to men.

There were several reasons for this change. As already noted by Jane Sharp, 'Men of Learning' who took up this work had higher status than midwives, irrespective of their skill. The distinction of the great men-midwives of the eighteenth century—men like Richard Manningham, Fielding Ould, William Smellie and William Hunter—was to reflect credit on every male practitioner, whether deserved or not. However, it was probably the introduction of the midwifery forceps, a development which occurred about 1720,[2] which precipitated the rapid acceleration in what was already an existing trend. The forceps enabled its user to deliver live infants in cases where previously either child or mother must have been lost, and also to shorten tedious labour. It thus gave the doctor or surgeon an additional advantage over the midwife (to whom custom did not allow the use of instruments as an accepted part of her practice) and so further enhanced the position of men.[3]

As in France, fashion played an important role in this process. Writing in 1724 in his *Female Physician*, John Maubray observes that the 'Politer Part of the World' had already begun to put themselves in the hands of men. Soon the 'middling classes' were following suit, and by the 1760s the practice was spreading to the tradesman and artisan class.[4] In this, as in many other occupations, men generally received higher remuneration than women; it was therefore important to the aspiring tradesman to show his neighbours that he could afford the higher-priced article.[5] Moreover, the growing prosperity of the times meant that increasing numbers were able to do so.

While these foregoing factors all favoured the male practitioner, another development worked directly to depress the midwife's standing in the community. Although episcopal licensing had been designed primarily as a means of social control, it had also served to confer status on the women who were licensed.

[†] *Midwives and Medical Men: A History of the Struggle for the Control of Childbirth.* With permission Historical Publications Ltd., London (1988).

But now, as the power of the Church waned, this system was breaking down. In London and surrounding areas it had ceased to operate by the 1720s, and although persisting longer in the provinces, in some places into the early 1800s,[6] it seems generally to have disappeared by the last quarter of the century. Even where licences were still granted, it does not appear that any prosecution of unlicensed persons took place, and, as with the midwife in *Tristram Shandy*, licences appear to have been sought purely for the official cachet they conferred,[7] rather than as an essential preliminary to practice.

In Scotland and Ireland more attention was given to midwife regulation than regulation in England. In 1726 Edinburgh had strengthened its law relating to midwife regulation and in 1740 the Glasgow Faculty of Physicians and Surgeons instituted a system of examination and licensing for midwives in the city and surrounding counties, which, as in Edinburgh, appears to have operated until the end of the century. Steps were also being taken for a similar system of midwife regulation in the New World. In 1716 the New York Common Council had passed an ordinance requiring midwives to take out licences, and to swear a version of the traditional midwives' oath.[8]

Scotland was also to be first with provision for organised midwife training. In 1726 Edinburgh Town Council had appointed a Professor of Midwifery, Joseph Gibson, the first such appointment in the British Isles. It is probable, however, that Gibson also took male pupils. From the standpoint of the young surgeon or apothecary, the attraction of midwifery was the entree it gave to medical practice proper. Once admitted to the lying-in room, the man-midwife might well become medical attendant to the whole family,[9] and many surgeon-apothecaries had in fact become 'general practitioners', though the term itself was not yet in use. By the middle of the century 'several hundred' men-midwives (though this may be an exaggeration) were said to be practising in London and its environs, and there was also a practitioner 'of standing' in every large town.[10]

As was to be expected, midwives viewed this trend with alarm. Clearly, the only way to arrest the progress of men, some of whom were anxious to drive women from the work altogether,[11] was to raise the general level of female practice. It was out of this concern for her 'Sister Professors in the Art of Midwifery' that in 1737 Mrs Sarah Stone, a Taunton midwife who had later moved to London, published her *Complete Practice of Midwifery*. This was the product of her thirty-five years' experience in the work, and Mrs Stone hoped that it would enable women even 'of the lowest capacity' to deliver their patients successfully without 'in every little seeming difficulty' calling in a man. Unless women showed themselves capable of dealing with difficult cases, she warned, the public would send for a man in the first place, as was already the fashion with the ladies of Bristol. Thus, merely for the lack of good 'Women-Midwives', practice would pass entirely to men, and 'the Modesty of our Sex will be in great danger of being lost.'[12]

Like Jane Sharp before her, Mrs Stone stressed the importance to the midwife of a thorough grasp of the relevant anatomical knowledge, reassuring her readers that it was 'not improper' for 'all in the Profession' to read anatomy or see dissections, as she had done. But thorough practical experience was also necessary; for 'had I inspected into them (dissections) all my Life, and had not been instructed by my Mother, and Deputy to her full six years, it would have signified but little'. Every midwife should therefore spend at least three years 'with some ingenious Woman' to learn her work; 'for if seven years must be served to learn a trade, I think three years as little as possible to be instructed in an art where life depends'.[13]

But it was not only midwives who objected to the growth of male practice. Opposition existed in the ranks of medicine itself, as shown by John Douglas's *Short Account of the State of Midwifery in London, Westminster,&c.* published in 1736. Douglas was a well-known London surgeon, and brother to James Douglas, the eminent man-midwife. Though Douglas himself saw a role for men in abnormal midwifery, he considered that such work belonged properly to the surgeon, and that physicians and apothecaries who practised it were trespassing beyond their province. Moreover, in order to strengthen their hold on the work, male practitioners were insisting that midwives should call in a man 'in every trifling little difficulty', reducing them to the condition of 'mere nurses'. Yet male assistance was not always available, even in London; and in the country, where midwives were more ignorant, it was often out of the question. Besides this, for reasons of modesty many women would not agree to send for a man, nor would their husbands allow it. More would refuse because they could not pay his fee, which, indeed, was often demanded beforehand. Why, then, asked Douglas, did not men, instead of forever blaming and rebuking midwives, do their best to instruct them as thoroughly as possible?[14]

Douglas' comments on the attitudes of male practitioners to the subject of midwives' instruction were not without justification. Though Edmund Chapman and other male writers for midwives expected that a midwife should be capable of certain manual operations, most were adamant that she should not use instruments. Moreover, in Thomas Dawkes' *The Midwife Rightly Instructed* (1736), a work written in the form of question and answer between surgeon and midwife, the surgeon refuses to tell the midwife how to deal with a haemorrhage. Even her objection that in country areas there may be no apothecary to whom she may send for medicines fails to move him. Warning her not to aspire beyond the capacities of a woman, he replies, 'I never designed, Lucina, to make you a Doctress, but to tell you how to practise as a Midwife.'[15]

This refusal to give women full instruction on the ground of their alleged incapacity to deal with difficult cases, was scornfully dismissed by Douglas as mere 'artful and groundless insinuation'. All ages had produced their learned women, as well as their illiterate, thick-headed physicians; it was not native deficiency, therefore, but the want of adequate instruction which disabled English women in the performance of this office. If proof of female ability were wanted, it could be found in the career of Madame du Tertre, a past Head Midwife of the Hôtel-Dieu, whose textbook for midwives demonstrated her status in the field.[16] English midwives, Douglas contended, could certainly reach the same standards if they had the opportunities available to French women. Recognizing the important part played by the Hôtel-Dieu in the training of French midwives, he demanded the establishment of lying-in hospitals in all the principal cities of England.[17]

Douglas was not the only one to deplore the lack of such provision in England. Three years later, in 1739, a beginning was made by a leading London man-midwife, Sir Richard Manningham, with the institution of a Charitable Infirmary for the relief of poor married women in two wards of St James' Infirmary, Westminster. Hitherto, Manningham explained in the advertisement of his Charity, 'due knowledge' of the practice of midwifery could not easily be obtained without going abroad, which for most pupils, especially women, was out of the question, with the result that they were not as fully qualified for their business as they should have been. However, it was as much Manningham's object to provide instruction for men as for women, and accordingly both sexes were admitted as pupils at the Hospital. Indeed, Manningham hoped that as the necessary knowledge had now 'come home to them', more young practitioners would study midwifery.[18]

It was also Manningham's hope that before too long Parliament would recognize its duty to establish a National Hospital which would serve all lying-in women, single and married alike. Until then, however, his 'little temporary one' would relieve married women only. But when in the next decade permanent lying-in hospitals were established (Manningham's institution does not appear to have lasted long)[19] they were the product not of Government action, but of the remarkable upsurge in organised private benevolence which was already making so much charitable provision for other categories of need.

The first of these permanent institutions was the Lying-in Hospital in Dublin (later the 'Rotunda Hospital'), founded in 1745. This was followed by the establishment of lying-in wards in the Middlesex Hospital in 1747, and the foundation of the British and City of London Lying-in Hospitals in 1749 and 1750. Next, in 1752, came the hospital in Jermyn Street (the General Lying-in Hospital—later, the Queen's Hospital, and, still later, Queen Charlotte's) and in 1765, the Westminster New Lying-in Hospital (in the nineteenth century known as the 'General Lying-in Hospital'). In Edinburgh, lying-in wards were opened in the Royal Infirmary in 1756. Dependent on public subscription, these institutions were of necessity small affairs, and it is likely that in their early years all the London hospitals together made less provision for lying-in cases than did the Hôtel-Dieu in Paris, where nearly fifteen hundred women were delivered each year.[20]

Like the voluntary general hospitals and other charities springing up in major towns, lying-in hospitals resulted in part from the initiative of medical men seeking a ready source of clinical material for their own and their pupils' study. But they were also an achievement of the active humanitarianism of the increasing numbers of affluent middle-class philanthropists, of whom the Thorntons, the Hoares and the Whitbreads were such outstanding examples. Such men saw the provision of hospitals as a duty, to be undertaken and only out of compassion for the 'distressed objects' of their charity, but also in the interests of their particular class and of the nation at large. The poor, potential subscribers were reminded, were the 'Riches of the Rich', and the 'Instruments of the Ease and Happiness of the Community'. They were also—and this was an important consideration in view of current fears that the population was falling—the source from which the fleets and armies for the defence of the country and its growing foreign acquisitions were supplied.[21]

The services of these new London lying-in hospitals were available, free of charge, to poor married women 'of good character', though the Westminster Hospital and the General Lying-in Hospital admitted single women pregnant with their first child. These hospitals were designed to serve the wives of soldiers, sailors, 'poor industrious Mechanics' and 'distressed Housekeepers' (householders). To qualify, applicants had to be respectable enough and persistent enough to obtain from a hospital subscriber one of the limited number of letters of recommendation allotted according to the yearly sum subscribed. They also had to come into the hospital (generally two weeks before labour was due), cleanly clad and free of vermin and contagious disease.

Women seeking free attendance in childbirth where there was no such charitable provision, organised or private, or who could not satisfy the charities' requirements as to their respectability or cleanliness had to resort to the Poor Law. Many Overseers of the Poor, however, did their best to whisk over the parish boundaries any 'great-bellied' woman who had no right of 'settlement' there (sometimes even when her labour had begun) in order to avoid the possibility that her pauper child, which by birth there would gain that right, might remain a long-term charge on the ratepayers.[22] Parturient women cared for under the Poor Law might be attended in the parish poorhouse, at an inn, or at home if they had such. The parish would pay for the attendance of the midwife (in some urban parishes a man-midwife might be called in for very difficult labours) and sometimes for a nurse to care for the mother during her lying-in, as well as for her maintenance.[23]

Like other voluntary charities, lying-in hospitals were run by Boards of Governors elected from among the subscribers. The 'Gentlemen of the Faculty' gave their services free, reaping the reward of public recognition in their private practice. The day-to-day running of the hospital, and responsibility for normal deliveries lay with the Matron—always a widow. For her exacting labours she received an annual salary of £25 to £30, plus board and lodging—equivalent to that of a housekeeper or lady's maid in a fairly well-to-do household. She was clearly subordinate to the Medical Officers, in whose hands was the overall responsibility for the patients, and whom she had to call in to abnormal labours.[24] In addition, the Medical Officers were also members of the Weekly Board which appointed and dismissed paid staff. The Matron's position thus contrasted unfavourably with that of the Head Midwife at the Hôtel-Dieu, who was independent of the medical staff and who called in the surgeon only when she considered instruments were necessary.[25]

Despite this, the lying-in hospitals were to play an important part in the future of the midwife, since in most of them instruction was available for women, though at a price. At the British Lying-in Hospital which, like the City of London, took no male students, the 'Gentlemen of the Faculty' gave theoretical instruction in 'all that is necessary for Women to know' for a fee of twenty guineas a head. Pupils had to pay a further ten shillings a week for board and lodging, 'exclusive of Tea, Sugar and Washing', and there may also have been fees to the Matron, who was responsible for practical training. All in all, including the cost of travel to London (the British Lying-in Hospital prided itself on serving the whole country), this must have amounted to more than £30 for a minimum stay of four months. Although this compared favourably with premiums paid for apprenticeships for young girls in millinery and dressmaking,[26] it was still a considerable sum for a married woman or a widow with a family to find, unless, as was the case with Mrs Wood, the midwife in Tristram Shandy, her training was financed by a local benefactor.[27] It was probably for these reasons that the Hospital appears never to have taken its full complement of twelve pupils a year, averaging at most between three and four.

Following general custom, the British Lying-in Hospital required its pupils to be married women to widows; they also had to be at least twenty-five years of age, and of good character. In general they came from the skilled tradesman class, being the wives or widows of shoemakers, tallow-chandlers, carpenters, maltsters, masons, butchers, and the like. Occasionally, there was the wife or widow of a farmer, an upper servant in a gentleman's household, or a minor government official. A few were married to apothecaries or surgeons,[28] and once in a while there was a clergyman's widow or the wife of a 'Gentleman', or of a junior army officer, presumably in reduced circumstances.

But as far as the actual provision of skilled assistance to lying-in women is concerned, a greater contribution was made by the outdoor charities which sprang up in London and provincial towns in the second half of the century. Many of the free dispensaries offering general medical services also attended midwifery patients, while other charities, like the London Lying-in Charity (later the Royal Maternity Charity) were created solely for this purpose.[29] Some lying-in hospitals also opened outdoor departments. The general pattern was for patients to be routinely attended in their own homes by midwives working under the general supervision of the institution's man-midwife, whom they had to call in to difficult cases.[30] Outdoor charities were not responsible for boarding, lodging, or nursing their mothers; in consequence their costs per case were lower, and the number of women attended by their midwives greatly exceeded the number delivered in hospital.[31] Moreover, since outbreaks of childbirth fever were a frequent occurrence in hospitals, out-door patients were without doubt far safer.[32]

Some of the larger out-door charities also trained midwives. These were women from a similar social background to the pupils of the lying-in hospitals, but the instruction they received was free. In return for their training, the midwives worked for the charity for an agreed period at specially low fees of 1s.6d or 2s.0d the case, compared with the half-a-crown or five shillings paid by the Overseers of the Poor for Poor Law work. At the same time they were free to take up private practice, and the charities took pride in the service which they were providing to the community by training women for work generally among the poor and 'middling' classes.[33] In some parishes the squire or parson might finance midwife's training, as did Parson Yorick in *Tristram Shandy*, or even pay her a small salary for attending the poor.[34]

By this time male practice appears to have been increasing more rapidly than ever,[35] arousing bitter hostility from those who saw this new development, along with many others, as a change for the worse. Opposition came not only from the midwives whose livelihood was in danger, but also from leading medical figures and from members of the general public. The more vocal of these opponents expressed their views in books, pamphlets and letters to the press. Though their more extreme opinions were probably shared only by a small minority, the repeated appearance and sale of similar publications during the next hundred years was to indicate a continuing opposition to man-midwifery.

To these adversaries of male practice its growing popularity had nothing to do with superior skill on the part of men. In his *Man-Midwifery Analysed*, the journalist Philip Thicknesse attributed it solely to a slavish desire to follow 'Fashion'. Once this French practice had been adopted by a few aristocratic ladies with negligent husbands, complained Thicknesse, the 'middling classes' who always felt bound to 'ape the quality', had copied them in this as in everything else.[36] However, the Queen herself still set an example to the nation in being attended by a midwife.[37]

But there was another factor. Men-midwives, it was said, anxious to establish their own importance in the eyes of the public, took every opportunity of helping Fashion do its work. To this end they exaggerated the dangers of childbirth and frightened women into believing that extraordinary measures, and therefore male attendance, were more generally necessary than they actually were. At the same time they made the most of every occasion to denigrate the understanding and competence of midwives, and to blame them, however unjustly, for anything that went wrong.

Finally, the male practitioner consolidated his position by making an ally of the monthly nurse. If a midwife were not employed, the nurse would not have to share the customary gifts from the attendant 'gossips', moreover, the man-midwife, anxious to win her goodwill might even tip her as well. By this means, writes Thicknesse, 'he convences Mrs Nurse almost to the bottom of her heart, that a female midwife is as dangerous about the person of a lying-in woman, as a rattlesnake about a man's leg, she sounds the Doctor's trumpet far and near, and all her kind mistresses, and indulgent masters are sure to have the warmest recommendation of Dr Blowbladder's art of touching'.[38]

The man-midwife controversy received light-hearted treatment at the hands of the novelist Sterne. In *Tristram Shandy*, with its comical figure of the 'scientific operator', Dr Slop, Sterne caricatures the well-known practitioner, Dr Burton of York, who so 'swore' by the 'new-invented forceps' that he could not understand how the world could have continued without them. As Sterne observes, 'Human nature is the same in all professions', and Dr Slop, like many members of emergent professional groups, is anxious about his status. Except on the occasion when he cuts his thumb and forgets to stand on his dignity, he rejects the homely, intelligible title of man-midwife, insisting on the newly fashionable French 'accoucheur'. Annoyed that the old midwife has been put in charge at Tristram's birth, and that he himself has been engaged, albeit at a fee of five guineas, only to wait in case instruments should be needed, the doctor cannot forbear asserting his superiority over her when the occasion offers. When, to his satisfaction, the midwife does ask for his assistance, he refuses to go upstairs to her, but demands that she come down to him. At the same time he takes the opportunity—unjustifiably, in view of her long years of successful practice—to belittle her in front of the Shandy family. Finally he applies his favourite instrument, and in so doing crushes the bridge of Tristram's nose.

Other comment was less restrained. Some of the publications condemning public appetite for salacious stories and so ensure their commercial success. For this reason they appealed to the age-old male fear than any relaxation in customs affecting women was likely to weaken wifely fidelity, from which it was only a short step to the collapse of society and the constitution of the State.[39]

One of the chief proponents of this view was Francis Foster, the puritanical author of *Thoughts for the Times but Chiefly on the Profligacy of Our Women* (1779). Here Foster rehearsed his anxieties about the decline in female virtue. The increasing number of divorces, he complained (then about three a year)[40] showed how far moral deterioration had progressed. Boarding-school education, French novels, and French dances like the cotillion and the allemande, all had their corrupting effect on women. But of all the pernicious influences at work in society, man-midwifery—which gave the enemy direct access to the very citadel of female virtue—was by far the worst.[41]

The argument was an old one, deriving from a fundamental male anxiety concerning supposed feminine weakness and inconstancy, and was a favourite among extreme opponents of the male practitioner. A woman handled by the man-midwife became 'polluted', and, in consequence, more likely to admit other men to similar familiarities.[42] Indeed, argued Thicknesse, if men-midwives were to resist all the temptations to which they were inevitably exposed, they had to be more, or less than ordinary men. Yet it was well known that under the sanction of the 'physician's great wig' and 'grave face', they took every opportunity to seduce their patients, travelling from one conquest to another 'like the Emperor of Morocco, or the Bashaw of Tangier, going to his seraglio'.[43]

The possibilities for amorous dalliance between the man-midwife and women consulting him had not escaped the ballad-writers, and in *The Man-midwife Unmasq'd* (1739), 'Doctor D....' is brought before the Grand Jury on a Bill of Indictment for rape. But although the Doctor had certainly taken advantage of the situation, he did not suffer in consequence. The Jury, (justly in this case), entertaining doubts about the accuser's own innocence in the matter...return'd the Bill 'Ignoramus'

And the Doctor has now got a Name that is famous.

How far men-midwives did succumb to their patients' charms is, of course, impossible to say, and Thicknesse's claim that the records of 'every court in the kingdom' would confirm his allegations[44] about the 'Touching Gentry' was no doubt exaggerated. One case of this sort did attract a great deal of notice, however, and was to provide the opponents of male practice with useful ammunition for a long time to come. This was an action for 'criminal conversation' brought in 1741 by a wealthy London merchant, George Biker, against a Dr Morley. The doctor had attended Biker's young and handsome wife in a miscarriage; later he had taken advantage of his subsequent acquaintance with the family to seduce her. The wife (possibly as a result of mental distress following the discovery of her adultery) died shortly afterwards in a madhouse, and the husband was awarded damages of £1,000. But like the doctor in the ballad, Dr Morley's practice does not seem to have been adversely affected by the publicity. In 1754 he was spoken of as a 'Physician of great Eminence in his Profession', and was substantial enough to have a further £1,000 damages awarded against him on account of his fatal negligence in a midwifery case.[45]

But if the attendance of men-midwives was open to such grave objections, so, protested their opponents, was the practice of allowing male students to learn their profession in the wards of lying-in hospitals. Even if the only patients they attended had forfeited their claim to virtue (the General and Westminster Lying-in Hospitals admitted single women), it was wrong to subject such wretched, frightened, harassed women to the indignity of being constantly available to the 'inspection and palpitation of a set of youths'. Nor was it right to expose these 'poor young pupils' to such shockingly indecent temptations to wantonness.[46]

Another continuing theme in the attack on men was their 'abuse' of instruments. Here, without doubt, the man-midwife's opponents were on stronger ground. The man-midwife Willughby had complained of this rashness over eighty years before and a strongly worded denunciation had appeared in 1724 in Dr John Maubray's *Female Physician*:

> However I know, some Chirurgeon-Practitioners are too much acquainted with the Use of *INSTRUMENTS*, to lay them aside; no, they do not (it may be) think themselves in their *Duty*, or proper *Office*, if they have not their cruel Accoutrements in Hand. And what is most unaccountable and unbecoming a Christian is that, when they have perhaps wounded the *MOTHER*, kill'd the *INFANT*, and with violent *Torture* and inexpressible *Pain*, drawn it out by Piece-meal, they think no Reward sufficient for such an extraordinary Piece of mangled Work.[47]

Similar admonitions figured in the writings of later practitioners, and the celebrated William Hunter is said to have shown his students his forceps, rusty from disuse, with the warning that 'where they may save one, they murder twenty'.[48]

This point had been strongly urged by Sarah Stone in her *Complete Practice of Midwifery* in 1737. Of recent years, she alleged, more mothers and children had died at the hands of raw recruits just out of their apprenticeship to the barber-surgeon than through the worst ignorance and stupidity of midwives. Yet by adopting a 'finished assurance' and claiming that their knowledge exceeded any woman's, these young 'Gentlemen-Professors' so secured their position that '...if Mother, or Child, or both, die, as it often happens, then they die *Secundum Artem*; for a Man was there, and the Woman-Midwife bears all the blame'.[49]

In 1751 the argument was forcibly restated in *A Petition of the Unborn Babes*, a pamphlet by Dr Frank Nicholls, Physician to George II, and an eminent member of the College of Physicians. In the *Petition* the 'Babes' accuse men-midwives of wickedly building their fortunes by preying on the ignorance of women and frightening them into engaging a male practitioner. Yet by their own misuse of instruments they were themselves often guilty of the death of both mother and child. Accordingly, the 'Babes' appealed to the Censors of the Royal College of Physicians for protection against these abuses.[50]

According to Wiliam Hunter, Nicholls' attack on men-midwives was motivated by jealousy of their success, 'because we get money, our antagonists none'.[51] Be that as it may, Nicholls himself is reputed to have profited from the exercise. It is said that as Mrs Kennon, midwife to Queen Caroline, lay on her deathbed, she gave Nicholls a banknote for £500 for her services to the midwives' cause. These services did not stop with the *Petition*, however, and the following year Nicholls proposed to the College of Physicians that the College itself should offer instruction for midwives. This should take the form of an annual course of free lectures, for women only, 'to render them as fully qualified in point of Knowledge to assist in Labour and the Disorders incident to Breeding Women as they are fitted for it by the Caution, Patience, Tenderness, and Decency natural to their sex'.[52] He himself offered the sum of £1,000 towards the cost, again said to have been donated by Mrs Kennon. But the College showed no interest in the proposal and it was allowed to die.

Nine years later, another midwife, Elizabeth Nihell, published her contribution to the controversy—a 400-page polemic against male practice under the title *A Treatise on the Art of Midwifery*. Mrs Nihell, who lived with her surgeon-apothecary husband in the Haymarket, was unusual in that she had obtained the privilege, rare for a foreigner, of training at the Hôtel-Dieu. There the midwives worked without male supervision or intervention, and from her observation of their successful practice she had concluded that instruments were seldom, if ever, necessary. On one occasion, she recalled, the Head Midwife, Madame Pour, had delivered a two-headed monster without recourse to instruments and with the help of no-one but a pupil midwife.[53]

Mrs Nihell's views on instruments were shared by Thicknesse and by other opponents of male practice. The man-midwife, they argued, was for 'dispatch'. He used instruments unnecessarily to hasten the birth and save his own time, as well as to impress the family with his dexterity and justify charging a higher fee.[54] Consequently more infants were lost than formerly, and if the mother did not die of the injuries she might sustain or of resulting childbed fever, she was frequently left with fearful and lasting disabilities.[55] Worse still, complained Mrs Nihell, the male practitioner, adding insult to injury, was so adept at concealing his errors with 'a cloud of hard words and scientific jargon', that the injured patient herself was convinced that she could not thank him enough for the mischief he had done.[56]

These onslaughts on man-midwifery did not pass without rebuttal from male practitioners, who could be as guilty of employing exaggeration and cheap sensationalism as their opponents. Midwives were 'ignorant cruel old beldames', alleged one, 'who crammed their patients with (alcoholic) cordials, and in order to hasten the birth drove them up and down stairs or subjected them to violent shakings, all the while ridiculing them and making fun of their distress'. These 'doting, dram-drinking matrons' wrote another, had lost every womanly quality but weakness of understanding and the wretched prejudices of the old wife. Many women suffering from incontinence, or from a fallen womb as a result of the incompetence and recklessness of midwives, had cause to regret their reliance on 'these worst of women'.[57]

However, the degree of truth in the charges and countercharges made by midwives and their detractors is, at this distance in time, impossible to determine. Educated midwives certainly possessed the anatomical knowledge essential to good practice. In general, the standard of the best London midwives is likely to have been higher than elsewhere, and some of them, as critical medical testimony indicates, were extremely well-qualified.[58] But the bulk of midwives were limited to lowly paid attendance on the poor. Such practice did not attract women with a good educational background who could afford to invest money in learning a profession. It followed therefore that the majority would be drawn from the lower classes in society. These women would have had little opportunity to acquire understanding of the physiological processes of childbirth and many of them would have been full of the ignorance which so often led to rash and fatal interference.

It is worth noting, however, that not everything the old 'beldames' were accused of was necessarily all bad. The practice, still common today in many parts of the world, of encouraging women in the first stage of labour to walk around the room, was recommended by eminent accoucheurs themselves as forwarding the birth, and has recently found renewed favour. Many accoucheurs, too, were discouraging the adoption of traditional upright positions for the second stage of labour, some condemning these as dangerous, cruel and indecent.[59] However, if the parturient delivered in bed she was usually propped up in a sitting position. However, Dr John Burton, (Sterne's Dr Slop) in his *Complete New System of Midwifery* (1751) argues for delivery lying on the back or side, as being easiest for the patient and most convenient for the operator.[60] This innovation ran counter to ancient wisdom (Soranus had stressed the importance of an upright position) denying the parturient the advantages of gravity and easier breathing. Yet by the nineteenth century the recumbent delivery position was to become the norm for civilised practice and to give birth out of bed was considered low-class, if not barbaric.

Nor is it true that all midwives indulged in alcohol. Yet the figure of the drinking midwife had long been part of traditional folklore—in Shakespeare's *Twelfth Night*, Maria's plot against Malvolio works 'like aqua vitae with a midwife'. Since most midwives were older working-class women, they could be expected to share the drinking habits usual in women of their age and station. At this time, too, drinking played a much larger part in the everyday life of all ranks of society than it does today, old customs requiring that many little occasions should be marked by drinking or treating. When a woman went into labour, her 'gossips' were sent for post-haste—day or night—and at the consequent gathering there was often more merriment than at a feast.

Better educated midwives prided themselves on maintaining high standards both in their professional and private lives. Advising midwives on their general conduct in her *Domestic Midwife* (1795), Margaret Stephen, a London midwife of long experience warned them never to accept cordials, 'though often invited to do so'. Nor would she allow these to be given to the parturient—a practice deplored by another educated midwife, Martha Mears, in her *Pupil of Nature* (1797) as still very prevalent, particularly among the lower classes. However, alcoholic cordials, whatever their possible disadvantages, would have a relaxing effect, helping to combat the tension and fear which together constitute one of the most formidable forces hindering the birth. At the same time, since alcohol was for long regarded by the general public and doctors alike as having great medicinal and strengthening properties,[61] it was judged especially beneficial in helping women to sustain the effort of labour.

But the midwife had a long-standing reputation of another kind—that of a manager of sexual intrigues—'truest friend to lechers',[62] as the seventeenth century poet Rochester put it. Some of their number, like 'the Amphibious Necessary, between Bawd and Midwife', in Ned Ward's *Rise and Fall of Madam Coming-Sir*, were procuresses, or worse.[63] Many, like the 'Mother Midnight' of Defoe's *Moll Flanders*, ran private lying-in homes (as, indeed, did some men-midwives) where 'ladies of pleasure', or others anxious to keep their pregnancy hidden, might be aborted, or await the birth of their child in secret. Here the proprietress' arrangements with the Overseers of the Poor would protect them from persecution or punishment by the parish officers—always anxious to prevent within their boundaries the birth of a child likely to become a charge on the rates. The child would then be disposed of, sometimes, as in *Madam Coming-Sir*, murdered on the premises, or, perhaps, put out to nurse. There were always women who for a down payment would take a child on the understanding that no questions would be asked about its welfare, and with whom its expectation of life was likely to be short. Then, if she had no protector, the young mother might be set to work as a prostitute for the proprietress for as long as she was useful.

However, Mrs Stephen was adamant that all these allegations did not apply to the generality of midwives:

> Those who have found it in their interest to bring midwives into disrepute, have charged them with intemperance, and even obscenity. How the being a midwife should make women possess such vices, is to me a mystery. I know no way of life in which a woman can be engaged, that is more calculated to fix sentiments of piety and morality upon the mind, nor have I ever been acquainted with any midwife who did not possess them.[64]

As far as relative safety between male and female practice was concerned there was insufficient information on which to base accurate comparisons. However, enough evidence existed to suggest to one thoughtful medical enquirer that common assumptions about the superior safety of male practice might be open to question. In his *Treatise on the Management of Pregnant and Lying-in Women*, Dr Charles White, himself a well-known man-midwife, pointed out that although the poor were often half-starved and diseased, and served only by ignorant midwives, their maternal death-rate might still be less than that of patients delivered in lying-in hospitals, or of the more affluent class attended by men.[65]

Whatever the rights and wrongs of the controversy, the growth in male practice continued unabated, increasingly taking the better paid work from midwives. To make matters worse, the old tradition that men should be paid at a higher rate for the same work applied in midwifery as in other spheres. In 1760, making an early protect against unequal pay, Elizabeth Nihell had condemned this devaluation of the midwife's work. No matter how expert or assiduous a midwife might be in her care of the mother before and after the lying-in, she declared, or how attentive to the welfare of the child, 'so seldom regarded by the men-midwives', many people felt they could never pay her too little, *'for no other reason on earth, but because she is not a man'.*[66]

Men-midwives, she complained, fanned these prejudices. Their arguments were that no-one could practise good midwifery without understanding anatomy, which science was the sole province of men-physicians or surgeons, that midwifery was a 'manual mechanical operation' and therefore better suited to men; furthermore, that it actually 'made the art cheap' to allow women to practise it. Yet the truth was the very opposite of this. Though a knowledge of the structure and disposition of women's reproductive organs was essential to the proper practice of midwifery, this was all the anatomy a midwife needed to know. In fact, nature had especially endowed women for this work. Not only did they have more compassion for their sex's sufferings, but their hands, being softer and more supple, were less likely to cause discomfort to women undergoing internal examinations than the 'boisterous grabbling and rummaging' by ignorant surgeon-apprentices with the 'delicate fist of a great horse-godmother of a he-midwife'. Moreover, women had patience to wait on Nature, whereas men were often precipitate, in breaking the membranes and in using instruments to save their time, frequently damaging the mother and killing the child. Yet although it was only because of this 'glorious privilege' of using instruments that men had attained to their 'usurped office', they now had the blasphemous effrontery to maintain that work which God himself had given to women was fitter for men.[67]

The jealousy of male competitors, alleged Mrs Nihell, was chiefly directed against the more successful midwives who represented the greatest threat to their advancement. There were many French surgeons who had been glad to take lessons from leading Parisian midwives, yet some of them, far from acknowledging their debt with respect and gratitude, had not scrupled to belittle female capacity and intellect. Even so, it had to be admitted that too few midwives were sufficiently mistresses of their profession. Some, like many men-midwives, were of a very low level of competence, but with the difference that they were incapable of doing as much actual mischief. All midwives, she stressed, should be thoroughly grounded in the anatomy relevant to their work and be able successfully to undergo the most rigorous examination in this subject. At the same time, the only way to exclude 'ignorant practitioners of either sex' was to subject both men and women practising midwifery to a system of governmental regulation such as obtained in Holland, with the prohibition of practice by all unqualified persons.

Mrs Nihell warned her readers that the future of the midwife was in real danger. Already 'false prejudices' against midwives were discouraging suitable women from taking up the work and replacing those good female practitioners who had 'gone off the stage'.[68] Thus the time might well come when, despite all the obvious objections to employing men, the public would be forced to this because there were no competent midwives to be had. However, it was not the only women's work at risk.

There had never been enough employment for women, declared Mrs Nihell, but now, as a result of the decrees of Fashion, occupations which had formerly belonged to them were increasingly invaded by men. But where would men stop? After the injustice of driving midwives out of their livelihood, what professions would they leave to women? If this trend continued, she protested, 'it will at last be discovered that men can spin, raise paste, cut out caps, pickle and preserve, better than we do'.[69] It was fortunate for women that there was no prospect of the occupation of dry-nurse becoming as lucrative as that of the man-midwife. Otherwise, Mrs Nihell concluded,

> I should not despair of seeing a great he-fellow flourishing a pap-spoon as well as a forceps, or of the public being enlightened by learned tracts and disputations, stuffed full of Greek and Latin technical terms, to prove, that water-gruel or scotch-porridge was a much more healthy aliment for newborn infants than the milk of the female breast, and that it was safer for a man to dandle a baby than for an insignificant women.[70]

Mrs Nihell's assessment of the market for women's labour was correct. In consequence of increasing industrialisation, which in many trades separated the workshop from the home, much gainful work was lost to the woman tied to her house and family. At the same time men were also invading other traditionally female employments. The fitting and making of women's stays had already gone to men, and ladies' hairdressing, which in the past had given many London women 'genteel bread', had now been taken over almost entirely by the fashionable, and more expensive, 'French Barber', or by men who, by speaking broken English, passed for such.[71] Moreover, as prosperity increased it was becoming less and less respectable for women to work outside the house, or even in the family business. More and more tradesmen sent their daughters to boarding schools to learn French and 'accomplishments' and, as Defoe had commented with disapproval in his *Compleat Tradesman*, kept their wives and daughters in the parlour rather than the shop. Such a climate did not encourage women of good educational background to take up work like midwifery.

Yet in the 1770s some London midwives were apparently making over £1,000 a year and keeping 'elegant' carriages.[72] However, as the *Gentleman's Magazine* pointed out, most of those recommended by the author of one of pro-midwife pamphlets lived in mean courts and lanes.[73] This may, as Mrs Nihell suggested, have been in part accounted for by the public's expectation that even highly skilled midwives should receive less than men, but was probably also due to their failure to attract a better-paying clientèle. Indeed, the advice given by Margaret Stephen to her pupils on fees to be charged might, if followed, have earned them the gratitude of the poor, but would certainly not have advanced their success in the eyes of the world. 'Be always ready', urged Mrs Stephen,

> to the calls of distress, and do not stand out because you do not know how you are to be paid. Never distress the distressed, nor turn your back upon a patient because she is become poor, and raise not your demands because you are come into great practice. If circumstances admit, people will be ready to put a proper value upon your time, and where you think they do not, you should be delicate in telling them of it, for some may think they have given as much as you should expect, though you are of a very different opinion. Avarice is a very bad qualification, or rather a bad vice, in those who have the health and life of their fellow creatures under their care.[74]

As the century wore on, so the decline of the midwife continued—a cumulative process accelerated by the interested propaganda of a section of the medical profession, and in particular, of younger men anxious to capture the midwifery which gave the entrée to general practice. Mrs Stephen relates how she herself had suffered from such calumny. In a case where the parturient's friends, impatient of the delays of a tedious but normal delivery, had demanded that a man be called in, it was not the experienced practitioner whom she recommended who was sent for, but a young, untried and *cheaper* man, whose clumsy efforts with the unnecessary forceps killed the child. Despite her tact in helping him conceal his error from the company, 'this perfect twig of the obstetric profession' had put the blame on her, and in consequence became the valued medical attendant of this 'little Plebeian family'.[75]

Midwives should therefore take care, warned Mrs Stephen, not to put their mothers, or their own reputation, at the mercy of young and inexperienced men;

> for had this affair happened in the earlier part of my practice, it might have hurt me very essentially, as then, like most of the *profession*, I was employed in the lower walks of life: and as the ignorant are always very credulous, the charge of having been the occasion of a child's death would in all probability have tript my heels.[76]

Leah Cousins, the successful and honoured village midwife described by George Crabbe in *The Parish Register* (1807), was not so lucky. Crabbe, who had himself trained as a surgeon, describes how the town-bred wife of a young farmer,

> A gay vain bride, who would example give,
> To that poor village where she deigned to live

engaged, in preference to the midwife, a newcomer to the village, 'young Dr Glibb'. Despite the fact that he lost the child, the wealthier part of the village were so impressed by his claim that it was only his skill that had saved the mother, that they left Leah and went over to him.[77]

The young doctor did his best to help on this process, sneering at Leah as 'Nature's Slave', who trusted only to luck, and in emergencies to prayer, while he, with his skill and courage, took pleasure in bending Nature to his will. In reply Leah pointed to her long record of success:

That I have luck must friend and foe confess,
And what's good judgement but a lucky guess?
He boasts, but what he can do: will you run
From me, your friend! Who, all he boasts, have done?
By proud and learned words his powers are known;
By healthy boys and handsome girls my own:
Wives! Fathers! Children! By my help you live;
Has this pale Doctor more than life to give?
No stunted cripple hops the village round;
Your hands are active and your heads are sound;
My lads are all your fields and flocks require;
My lasses all those sturdy lads admire
Can this proud leech, with all his boasted skill,
Amend the soul or body, wit or will?

But it was no use: her 'truth was vain', and gradually she declined and died, embittered and poor, deserted by those whom she had served so well.[78]

Most defenders of the midwife had always been aware of the need for adequate instruction for women, especially in anatomy, and midwives who put themselves under men teachers were warned to beware lest they were cheated. Male practitioners, it was alleged, anxious to suppress female practice among the rich, taught midwives less thoroughly than their male pupils, in order to foster their dependence on men, and so discredit them in the eyes of wealthy patients. In short, they trained midwives for their own service, not for that of the public.[79]

This warning was repeated by Margaret Stephen in her *Domestic Midwife*. She herself demanded high standards from her pupils, expecting them to consult the works of leading authorities like Smellie, Baudelocque, and others. Male teachers, she complained, took larger fees from women (the usual fee was ten guineas) yet taught them less, and then proclaimed to the world that women were ignorant and not to be trusted. For this reason she promised to continue with her own lectures to midwives 'until the men who teach that profession render them unnecessary by giving their female pupils as extensive instruction as they give the males'.[80]

The theoretical grounding which she gave her pupils was evidently very thorough. Her lectures included

the anatomy of the pelvis, &c and of the foetal skull, on preparations which I keep by me, with every thing else relative to practice in nature at labours, also turning, and the use of the forceps, and other obstetric instruments, on a machine which I believe few teachers can equal, together with the cases and proper seasons which justify such expedients, and I make them write whatever of my lectures may prove useful to them, in their future practice, for which they are as well qualified as men.[81]

But although she taught the use of forceps, she advised midwives always to send for a man when these were necessary, explaining that where the outcome was unfortunate, 'people are more reconciled to the event, because there is no appeal from what a doctor does, being granted he did all that could be done on the occasion'.[82]

Like many others who during the century had expressed their concern about the condition of midwives, Mrs Stephen urged the need for a public examination which would distinguish the qualified woman from the unqualified.[83] Most advocates of regulation, however, wished to go further than this and prohibit all unqualified practice, both male and female. Demands for such regulation had come alike from midwives, medical men, and members of the lay public. Significantly, medical advocates of regulation proposed that midwives should be placed under medical control through the London corporations of Physicians or Surgeons. Midwives and their supporters, on the other hand, with equal significance, proposed regulation by lay governmental authorities.

As far as the training of midwives was concerned, this was still left to voluntary charity or private endeavour, and in this field, as in others, charitable organisations multiplied during the second half of the century. Notable among these was the Manchester and Salford Charity, later St Mary's Hospital. Founded in 1790 by Dr Charles White, it aimed at creating a School or Nursery of Young Midwives for providing the town and surrounding counties with women of knowledge and experience. In contrast to the London lying-in hospitals, the charity provided free instruction to its own out-patient midwives and other pupils. In 1796 its example was followed by the Liverpool Ladies' Lying-in Charity, which appears to have been run on similar lines, though it was unusual among charities of this size in that its managing committee consisted entirely of women. England, however, compared unfavourably with Scotland, where in Edinburgh alone over a thousand midwives had been trained between 1780 and 1818,[84] or probably more than four times the number produced in the four London lying-in hospitals combined.[85]

Active steps were also being taken in Ireland for the improvement of midwife practice. In 1765 the Irish Parliament had empowered Grand Juries (the County authorities) to provide funds for the establishment of County Hospitals. Twenty years later, as part of its general policy of rate support for health care (Ireland had no Poor Law) the juries were empowered to raise a rate of £30 every five years to send a midwife for training at the Rotunda in Dublin.[86]

Yet despite the increasing emphasis on training midwives in Edinburgh, the regulation of midwife practice in both Edinburgh and Glasgow appears to have broken down by the end of the century, as had that established by some of the New England towns, a reflection of the increased popularity of Free Trade doctrines in Britain and America and the consequent reluctance of those in authority to meddle with the free working of market forces.[87]

The situation on the European Continent presented a sharp contrast to these 'laissez-faire' policies, as English midwives and their supporters did not fail to point out. Whereas England relied largely for its defence on the Channel and a volunteer navy, Continental countries depended for their protection on their ability to conscript large armies, and thus on the number of their able-bodied subjects. Pro-natalist policies (which Britain was not to embark on until after the humiliations of the Boer War) were actively pursued. Thus the need for improving standards of midwife practice and the distribution of skilled midwives led easily to free or subsidised provision of midwife instruction and services in many European countries, including Denmark, Austria, Russia and others. Many German cities had also appointed Hebammenmeister to teach local midwives, and set up midwives' schools. In France, where growing fears of a falling population had in 1728 led to a governmental enquiry into the skill of country midwives, steps were taken for their regulation by local Surgeons' Companies. In 1760 the King commissioned Mme DuCoudray, maîtresse sage-femme from the Auvergne, to tour the country giving lecture courses to both midwives and to surgeons (who were from then on, as surgeon-demonstrators, to teach midwives) and to establish lying-in hospitals—an office which she discharged for twenty years. The government also financed an issue throughout the land of midwifery manuals, including DuCoudray's own Abrégé de l'Art des Accouchements, which ran to five editions. Thus the official midwife in the French village was gradually becoming a subsidised public servant, gaining for her family the not inconsiderable privileges attendant on public office, such as exemption from the corvée and from military conscription.[88]

After the Revolution, the Government of Republican France was equally anxious to encourage population growth, and in 1803 embarked on determined measures to improve midwife practice in the country at large. Under a comprehensive national system of medical regulation set up that year, (also embracing medical practitioners, chemists and officers de santé, midwives were divided into two classes. The 'first class' who took longer training, might practise anywhere in France, while the 'second class' were licensed only for practice in their local department.

Minimum training was now at least six months and had been reorganised under Government regulations. At the same time, departmental prefects were required to finance local women as pupils in the Paris Maternité, the successor to the lying-in wards of the Hôtel-Dieu.[89] Over 100 women attended the first year's courses; that is, more than were being trained annually in the lying-in hospitals of the whole of the United Kingdom eighty years later.[90]

French and German midwives thus benefited from government recognition, government regulation, and government-provided and subsidised instruction, all lacking in England. Though the defenders of the English midwife recognized the need for better instruction, they cherished the unrealistic hope that this would be furnished either by midwives themselves, or by voluntary charity.[91] But, as Mrs Nihell had made clear, educated women would only invest in training for work which promised adequate rewards; once this prospect disappeared, recruitment from this class would fall off and ultimately cease. Nor was the continuance of a body of competent, educated midwives in itself a compelling enough object to attract charitable funds. This was to come only later, when the plight of the unsupported middle-class woman, no longer able to turn for a livelihood to midwifery and other dwindling employments, had become sufficiently acute to arouse public attention. Until that time, the decline of the English midwife would continue without interruption and male practice would become more general in England than anywhere else in Europe.

[1] Ivy Pinchbeck, Women Workers and the Industrial Revolution, 1750-1850, London, 1930, pp282-3, 304-6.

[2] W. Radcliffe, The Secret Instrument, London, 1947, pp38-39.

[3] Elizabeth Nihell, A Treatise on the Art of Midwifery, London 1760, p.xii. John Page, a Lutterworth practitioner, writes of the 'credit' he gained after his first forceps delivery, and the resultant increase in his practice. E. Chapman, A Treatise on the Improvement of Midwifery, London, 1735, pp23-4.

[4] J. Maubray, The Female Physician, London: 1724, p181; P. Thicknesse Man-Midwifery Analysed: and the Tendency of that Practice Detected and Exposed, London, 1765 pp4, 22.

[5] Nihell p204; letter to the London Gazetteer & Daily Advertiser, June 1772, Royal College of Surgeons Library.

[6] The last midwife's licence appears to have been granted in the Diocese of Peterborough in 1818. Peterborough Diocesan Administrative Papers.

[7] L. Sterne, The Life & Opinions of Tristram Shandy, Gentlemen, London, 1760-7, Bk.I, Ch.VII.

[8] J. Donegan, Women and Men-Midwives: Medicine, Morality & Misogyny in Early America, Westport (Conn.), 1978, p91.

[9] A Vindication of Man-Midwifery, London, 1752, p6.

[10] F Nicholls, College of Physicians, Annals, 23 Mar 1752; G. Counsell, The Art of Midwifery, London, 1752, p.xv.

[11] Chapman, 1735, preface.

[12] S. Stone, A Complete Practice of Midwifery, London, 1737, pp.x-xi, xvi, xix.

[13] Ibid., pp.xv-xvii

[14] Douglas, A Short Account of the State of Midwifery in London & Westminster etc..., London, 1736.pp2,66-7

[15] T. Dawkes, pp88-9

[16] Douglas, The Midwife Rightly Instructed, London, 1736, p47. The book was Instruction Familière et très-simple, faite par questions et réponses touchant toutes les choses principales, qu'une sage-femme doit sçavoir pour l'Exercice de son art, Paris, 1677. For an assessment of this work, see H. Fasbender, Geschichte der Geburtshülfe, Jena,1906, pp177-8.

[17] Douglas, pp71-4.

[18] R. Manningham, The Institution and Oeconomy of the Charitable Infirmary for the Relief of Poor Women in Labour of Child and during their Lying-in, London, 1739.

[19] It has been suggested that Manningham's Infirmary later became Queen Charlotte's Hospital (G.C. Peachey, Proc. R. Soc. Med. (Epidemiology), 1924, 17, pp72-6) but a recently discovered contemporary publication disproves this. See An Account of the Rise, Progress and State of the General Lying-in Hospital, London, 1768, and Jean Donnison, 'Note on the Foundation of Queen Charlotte's Hospital', Medical History, 1971, pp398-400.

[20] Carrier, pp48-9. The average number of women delivered in the City of London Hospital between March 1750 and January 1827 was 383 p.a.; between 1749 and 1813 the British Lying-in Hospital averaged 487 cases p.a. (Account of the City of London Lying-in Hospital, from March 1750-1 January 1827, London, 1827; Account of the British Lying-in Hospital, London, 1814). It is doubtful if either of the other two London lying-in hospitals exceeded these figures during this period.

[21] An Account of the Rise and Progress of the Lying-in Hospital for Married Women in Brownlow Street, 1752; British Lying-in Hospital, Minutes, 9 Feb.1787; Account of the City of London Lying-in Hospital, London, 1763.

[22] See, for example, Marylebone Overseers of the Poor, Accounts, 24 April 1730, 'Paid Pitham to get a woman in Labr out of the Parish & Relived her 3s 6d.'

[23] See Hendon Overseers of the Poor, Accounts, 5 Jan. 1717, 'Paid the Man-Midwife for laying Elizabeth Williams, £3.4.6d.'

[24] An Account of the Rise and Progress of the Lying-in Hospital for Married Women in Brownlow Street, London, 1752.

[25] Nihell, pp44-5.

[26] This could be as much as £30-£50 for a five to seven year apprenticeship. J. Collyer, The Parent's and Guardian's Directory, London, 1761, p196.

[27] Sterne, Bk.I, Ch.VII.

[28] Between 1754 and 1807 there are nine pupils recorded in this category, though these become less frequent towards the end of the period.

[29] For a list of these outdoor medical charities in London and dates of foundation see A.B. Granville, A Report of the Practice of Midwifery at the Westminster General Dispensary for 1818, London, 1819, pp3-4. The Middlesex Hospital started an out-patient department in November 1785. St Mary's Hospital, Manchester, founded 1790, also had such a department, and by 1793 so had the Westminster Lying-in Hospital. The Queen's Lying-in Hospital (previously the General Lying-in Hospital), had one at least by 1809, when existing records begin.

[30] Lying-in Charity, Minutes, 25 July 1766; Westminster General Dispensary, Minutes, 6 June 1774.

[31] On average the number delivered in the four Lying-in Hospitals was about 1,400 p.a. (A.B. Granville, A Report of the Practice of Midwifery at the Westminster General Dispensary for 1818, p16). Between 1767 and 1819 the Lying-in Charity alone averaged 4,000 cases a year (Account of the Lying-in Charity, London, 1820); the

Benevolent Institution for the Sole Purpose of Delivering Poor Married Women in their own Habitations, another of the larger London midwifery charities, had over 1,100 patients p.a. between 1780 and 1814 (A. Highmore, Pietas Londoniensis; The History, Design and Present State of the Various Public Charities in and near London, London, 1814, p381). By 1818 the Westminster General Dispensary had averaged 656 p.a. since its institution in 1774 (Granville, A Report on the Practice of Midwifery at the Westminster General Dispensary, p19).

[32] Maternal mortality in the practice of the Westminster General Dispensary for 1774-81 was 1 in 271 deliveries, whereas the rate in the lying-in hospitals was at least five times as much. (R. Bland, Some Calculations of the Number of Accidents or Deaths which happen in consequence of Parturition taken from the Midwifery Reports of the Westminster General Dispensary, London, 1781, pp6-7; C.White, A Treatise on the Management of Pregnant and Lying-in Women, London, 1773, pp332-5).

[33] A Plain Account of the Advantages of the Lying-in Charity for Delivering Poor Married Women at their own Habitations, London, 1767.

[34] G.E. Mingay, English Landed Society in the Eighteenth Century, London, 1963, p243.

[35] In the space of ten years (1741-51) Smellie took over 900 male pupils. Smellie, The Theory and Practice of Midwifery, London, 1752-63, p.v.

[36] Thicknesse, Man-Midwifery Analysed, 1765,p4.

[37] At the birth of at least three of her children she was attended by Mrs Draper, and Dr William Hunter waited in an adjoining room in case he should be needed, but he was not summoned. 'An Obstetric Diary of William Hunter, 1762-1765', J.M. Stark (Ed.) reprinted from the Glasgow Medical Journal, 1908, pp5, 10, 12.

[38] Thicknesse, Man-Midwifery Analysed, 1765, p39. To 'touch' was to perform a vaginal examination for the signs of pregnancy.

[39] Thickness, A Letter to a Young Lady, London, 1764, p11; F.Foster, Thoughts on the Times but chiefly on the Profligacy of our Women, London, 1779, pp4-5.

[40] O.R. MacGregor, Divorce in England, London, 1957, p11.

[41] Foster, pp6, 17-24, 31, 79.

[42] Thicknesse, Man-Midwifery Analysed, p25; Foster, p196.

[43] Thicknesse, A Letter to a Young Lady, 1764, p11; Man-Midwifery Analysed, 1765, pp10, 21.

[44] Thicknesse, Man-Midwifery Analysed, 1765, p15.

[45] Anon., The Trial of a Cause between Richard Maddox, Gent., Plaintiff, and Dr M..., London, 1754.

[46] Nihell, pp80-6.

[47] Maubray, pp181-2.

[48] Quoted in H.R. Spencer, The History of British Midwifery, from 1650-1800, London, 1927, P73.

[49] Stone, pp.xi-xii.

[50] F. Nicholls, A Petition of the Unborn Babes to the Censors of the Royal College of Physicians, London, 1751, pp8-11.

[51] Quoted in Spencer, History of British Midwifery, p55.

[52] College of Physicians, Annals, 23 Mar. 1752.

[53] Nihell, pp44-9

[54] Thicknesse, Man-Midwifery Analysed, 1765, p28; Anon., The Danger and Immodesty of the Present too General Custom of Unnecessarily Employing Men-Midwives in the Business of Midwifery, London, 1772, Letter II.

[55] Nihell, pp92-5; Thicknesse, Man-Midwifery Analysed, 1765, p22; The Danger and Immodesty, Letter II.

[56] Nihell, pp158-9.

[57] 'Old Chiron', Gazetteer and New Daily Advertiser, 17 April 1772; L. Lapeyre, An Enquiry into the Merits of these Two Important Questions..., London, 1772, pp27,35.

[58] E. Chapman, A Treatise on the Improvement of Midwifery, London, 1753, preface.

[59] J. Gélis et al., Entrer dans la Vie: Naissances et Enfances dans la France Traditionelle, Paris, 1978, pp.83-4; M. Laget, Naissances: l'Accouchement avant l'Age de la Clinique, Paris, 1982, pp.150-4.

[60] Emphasis mine.

[61] In his diary for 29 Mar. 1797, Parson Woodforde recorded that his apothecary, Mr Thorne, had prescribed for his niece Nancy large quantities of port. 'She has not drank less than a Pint for many Days. 'Diary of a Country Parson, J. Beresford (Ed.), London, 1924-31, Vol.V, p22.

[62] J. Adlard (Ed), The Debt to Pleasure, Cheadle, 1974, p92.

[63] Ward, The London Spy Compleat, 1794, Vol.2, pp396-9.

[64] M. Stephen, Domestic Midwife, 1795, p105.

[65] White, pp338-41.

[66] Nihell, p70, (emphasis added). The Poor Law records for Marylebone and Islington bear this out. In 1731, Mrs Fletcher, a Marylebone midwife, received 7s 6d. (2s 6d. More than the normal fee of 5s.), for 'an extraordinary case'. Marylebone Overseers of the Poor, Accounts, 19 Nov.1731. However, where the man-midwife was called in

to such cases, as he was in Islington, he received a guinea. Islington Overseers of the Poor, Accounts, 26 Mar. 1756, 5 July 1756, 26 Aug.1757.

[67] Nihell, pp.xii, 28-36, 317-25.

[68] Ibid., pp217-18. The case of Elizabeth Blackwell, wife of Alexander Blackwell, a Scots physician, illustrates this well. Mrs Blackwell took up midwifery at her husband's suggestion in order to retrieve the family fortunes, but gave it up because she could not bear the low conditions in which she had to begin practice. Instead she compiled her Curious Herbal (1737) for which she is justly remembered.

[69] Ibid., p65.

[70] Ibid., p190.

[71] Collyer, pp278-9

[72] Foster, p95

[73] Gentlemen's Magazine, May 1772, p234.

[74] Stephen, pp104-5.

[75] Ibid., pp55-63.

[76] Ibid., p62.

[77] G. Crabbe, The Parish Register, 1807, Pt III, in Poems, London, 1886.

[78] Ibid.

[79] Nihell, p469; S Fores ('John Blunt'), Man-Midwifery Dissected, London 1793, p180.

[80] Stephen, pp5-6, 20.

[81] Ibid., p4.

[82] Ibid., p43.

[83] Ibid., p19.

[84] J. Hamilton, A Letter to Sir William G..., Edinburgh, 1817.

[85] The records of the British Lying-in Hospital show only sixty or so midwife pupils as having trained there during this period. Records of the City of London Lying-in Hospital and the Westminster Lying-in Hospital do not contain this information, and those of Queen Charlotte's, which exist from 1809, indicate that only a handful were trained there during the following decades.

[86] J.D.H. Widdess, A History of the Royal College of Physicians of Ireland, 1654-1963, Edinburgh, 1963, p198; T.P. Kirkpatrick, The Book of the Rotunda Hospital, London, 1913, pp98-9.

[87] Donegan, p148

[88] J. Gélis, Sages-Femmes et Accoucheurs; l'Obstetrique Populaire aux XVIIe et XVIIIe Siècles, Annales, Economies, Societés et Civilisations, Oct-Nov 1977; Delacoux, pp71-2.

[89] H. Carrier, Origines de la Maternité de Paris, Paris, 1888, pp237-59.

[90] See Ch.5 in J. Donnison's book Midwives & Medical Men: A History of the Struggle for the Control of Childbirth, London, 1988, p111, below.

[91] Nihell, pp217-18; Fores, pp182-7.

THE DIFFERENT STAGES OF THE ELIMINATION OF MIDWIVES IN QUÉBEC

Hélène Laforce[†]

ABSTRACT

To establish that a profession has been eliminated, one must first ascertain that the profession did indeed exist. The profession also has to have been sufficiently well established and structured to withstand the normal interplay of supply and demand without being doomed to disappearance. The first part of this chapter contains a brief presentation of the practice of midwives in Québec up until their actual elimination. In the second part, we will study obstetrics by the medical profession. In the third part we will examine the doctors' motives for proceeding with the elimination of midwives.

THE MIDWIFE IN NEW FRANCE: 1650-1760

It is interesting to note that the country that colonised Québec in the seventeenth century was the most advanced in the field of obstetrics. French obstetrics had already gained international renown in the two previous centuries because of its unique maternity schools and the discoveries of its doctors and midwives.

The theorizations of these early French researchers were the first steps in the infant science of obstetrics. They proved to be fundamental to the understanding of the physical phenomena associated with childbirth and later to new teaching methods in the art of obstetrics. An example of this is that, by comparing the functioning of the uterus to a machine in the shape of a pump,[1] the French scientists were better able to prevent possible complications by using manual procedures. The purpose of the techniques developed during this period was to preserve the normal process of childbirth, while minimising risks, rather than to intervene with instruments. The ideology that supported the superiority of instrumental intervention over all other techniques was therefore not the fruit of French thinking, even though it was easily adopted by the French.

Obstetrics was not the only field in which the French were pioneers. They were also the first to produce innovative medical treatises in which the art of medicine was divided into three distinctive branches: the domain of the doctors, that of the surgeons, and that of the midwives. Within this tripartite division, doctors occupied a position of importance and controlled the generation of medical knowledge and the arts of diagnosis, and treatment. The domain of surgeons was more technical: they were called upon each time an incision or a dressing was needed. The matrons or midwives were called upon whenever, for the sake of modesty, their eyes and their hands were needed to carry out examination of intimate parts.[2] This division of tasks was clear and precise. Each group was governed by rights and obligations and structured according to a strict hierarchy. Within the hierarchical structure of midwifery the *maîtres* and *maîtresses* were responsible for quality control; the *entretenus* and *entretenues* were paid by the King; the

---

[†] In: Arnup, K., Levesque, A. & R.R. Pierson (eds.), *Delivering Motherhood*. With permission Routledge, London.

ordinaires and the *jurés* alone were allowed to give expect opinions in court and the *approuvés* enjoyed local privileges.

This professional infrastructure, with all its complexity, was transplanted to New France with the creation of French colonies in North America. By 1740, a network of midwives served the French colonists from Louisiana to Isle Royale (Nova Scotia). Each city (Québec, Montréal, Louisbourg, Nouvelle-Orléans) had its own *entretenue* midwife and its *matrones*, *maîtresses-sages-femmes* or *jurés*, each with a well-defined territory. Each village was proud to have an *approuvée* midwife around whom gravitated assistant-midwives and *accoucheuses* representing the new generation of obstetrical practitioners. The hierarchy was strict and well observed.

The profession of midwifery assembled under a single name a heterogeneous group of practitioners with very different economic and cultural backgrounds. The higher up the practitioners were in the hierarchy, the richer and more cultured they were. The *entretenues* midwives were trained at the *Hôtel-Dieu de Paris* which was, at the time, the best maternity school in Europe, and their salaries were almost the same as that given the King's surgeon.[3] Country midwives inherited their knowledge from their mothers, aunts or grandmothers according to family tradition. Apprenticeship was practised everywhere and the records often contain the mention of an assistant-midwife. In the villages, midwifery was part of a self-help system, even though in the cities it was becoming a habit to pay for the service.

Despite their diversity, the midwives knew each other and worked together within charity organisations such as confraternities or poor relief bureaux. Though corporative groups were forbidden in the colony, the midwives succeeded in establishing a network of practitioners who placed abandoned children and put city children out to nurse in the country. Midwives seemed to have played as much of a social role as a medical one. In the villages, they were recognised as moral and public advisers. In the cities, the midwife who was paid by the King had to be available at all times, and even free of charge, to meet the needs of the poor.[4] This was a kind of pregnancy insurance in keeping with the social welfare policies of enlightened monarchies.

All things being equal, the small French colony overseas seems to have been better provided with midwives than the mother country which suffered a midwife shortage in the seventeenth and eighteenth centuries. The luxury of established civil servants, a very costly system overall, was characteristic of an absolutist regime that wanted every French subject, wherever he/she might be, to enjoy the same privileges. This beneficent attitude on the part of the mother country toward the colony was far from completely disinterested. Since Colbert's introduction of childbearing subsidies in the 1660s, it had been realised that the best way to populate a colony, without draining France, was to endow the colony with a good obstetrical system. The gamble seems to have paid off. The newborn and maternal mortality rates for this period prove that not only did women in New France bear more children, they also lost fewer babies than their counterparts in France.[5]

Adapting French customs to be new geographical and social environment created a unique situation. During the century of colonisation, women of New France gained rights that were almost unknown to their European counterparts since it was no longer magistrates, lords or parish priests but women themselves who elected their midwives.[6] This was a privilege that gave women of New France real decision-making power in the field of childbirth.

Around 1720 a merciless war between surgeons and midwives began in France that was to last to 1760. In the small colonies of New France, meanwhile, both professions continued to practise without any conflict and with mutual respect. Far from denigrating midwives, surgeons and doctors on the contrary supported them, lodging a request with the authorities to send more. In practice, the midwives' territory seemed to be well respected. In 1730, a surgeon even refused to give a medical opinion in the area of childbirth because "that comes under the services of the midwives." It was not unusual for midwives to deliver the wives of surgeons. This cohesion was further reinforced in their private lives, especially if both surgeons and midwives belonged to the same socio-economic class. Working side by side, surgeons and midwives intermarried and their children married each other. The families of midwives and surgeons called on one another to share in godparenting, thereby strengthening the ties linking these two professional groups.[7]

Structured and organised into a hierarchy, well established in their community, efficient and highly skilled, midwives, unsurprisingly, were the ones to demand of the Minister of Colonies the creation of a school of midwifery in 1755.[8] This was an ambitious project that would have placed them in the forefront of the Canadian system, ready to be part of the quasi-technological change in European obstetrical knowledge during the eighteenth century. How then can one explain the ensuing disappearance of the profession? Could it have been one of the effects of the Conquest?

MIDWIVES DURING THE CONQUEST OF LOWER CANADA (1760-1840): A WELL-ADAPTED PROFESSION

With the arrival of a new master, the context for the development of the system of obstetrics in the colony began to change. A detailed analysis, however, reveals that the old customs survived. These customs, nevertheless, had to conform to the new rules of the game introduced by the English conqueror.

England at the end of the eighteenth century brought more than new administration to the colony. England also brought a new way of looking at political and economic realities as influenced by developing liberalism, industrialisation and the parliamentary system. English puritanism also introduced another way of viewing morality, the role of women in society and even science. The impact of protestantism, which favoured man's intervention in nature, had a significant effect on medicine and obstetrics.

In the England of the early eighteenth century, deliveries were performed within a kind of unregulated free market in which doctors and surgeons battled fiercely. Deliveries were still the midwives' domain but the introduction of forceps, invented by the barber-surgeon Chamberlen,[9] raised the stakes in the obstetrical field.

In 1760, at a time when the English were settling in Canada, the first debate over interventionism had just ended in Great Britain. For a few decades, in the maternity schools of London, Glasgow and Edinburgh, doctors and midwives pondered an important problem. What kind of knowledge was necessary to intervene in the normal process of childbirth? How and when should forceps be used? Since the use of forceps seemed to present real danger, even more so because the surgeons who used them tended to abuse them, the doctors of university faculties in agreement with an elite group of midwives concluded that the course of nature was usually adequate and that any intervention was liable to endanger women.[10]

It is on the basis of this consensus that doctors organised, at the end of the eighteenth century, a new legal framework for their system of obstetrics. The art of delivering babies became, to the detriment of surgeons, an enterprise shared by doctors, that is, learned men not much inclined to use their hands, and certified midwives.

This favourable prejudice towards midwives was no doubt the reason why the surgeons Blake and Fisher, who were consulted during the drafting of the first Act governing the practice of medicine in 1788, were in favour of the survival of midwives in the colony. Reflecting the values of their time, Blake and Fisher simply were giving, as were their colleagues in New England, the English doctors' point of view. Furthermore, would it not have seemed unfair to British midwives not to enjoy in an English colony the same privileges they had just acquired in their homeland? There are, however, other possible explanations, especially in Québec, for them to have been favourable considered, an important one being the verdict of incompetency rendered on Canadian practitioners by English surgeons as soon as they arrived on Canadian soil.[11] This controversial Durham Report of 1839, must be viewed with caution because of the generally disdainful attitude of the British towards the colonials.

The assessment of incompetency likely underlay the investigator-surgeons' recommendation in 1775 and in 1776 that city midwives be certified by the same authority that certified and granted legal recognition to doctors. They also proposed the creation of a school for midwives.[12] The school was never established but the profession of midwife was legalised by the Medical Act of 1788. Midwives were thus recognised as public officers by the Lieutenant-Governor and entered in the official gazette. They also had a specific place, in the official directory, in the medical practitioners' section. In the villages, midwives continued to be approved and controlled by the Church as well as recommended by doctors.

As far as the acquisition of knowledge is concerned, in the cities, midwives could enrol in courses given by obstetricians or continue their apprenticeship, as doctors did, with a doctor or a midwife. One can suppose that the knowledge of midwives who graduated from the new British schools surpassed that of Québec doctors who did not have access to specialised places of learning. This supposition is confirmed by the rather summary papers that Québec doctors presented from 1820 to 1822 at lectures of the Québec Medical Society.[13]

As far as efficiency and patient satisfaction are concerned the historical records offer, in fact, the best verdict one can find: that given by the patients themselves. Around 1820, two private institutions were founded in Québec City in order to help and assist poor women during childbirth. They are the *Dispensaire de Québec*, created in 1818 by doctors with a clinical approach, and the *Société compatissante de Québec* (Female Compassionate Society of Québec), headed, as early as 1819, by women who paid for the services rendered by midwives. These two organisations operated according to the same model. The practitioners made house calls and offered their services free of charge, as long as the women were recommended by the sponsors of the organisation. When the *Dispensaire* closed its doors a year later in 1819, its founder remarked that it was a pity that not a single pregnant woman had called on them for help. The *Société compatissante*, on the other hand, was swamped with requests from the first year of operation. In 1862, forty-two years after its inauguration, it still employed four midwives. The facts speak for themselves![14]

The profession of midwife, which was legalised, structured and competent, was therefore well established when the Corporation of Physicians was created in 1847. At this point, nothing seemed to forecast the subsequent disappearance of midwifery. Yet, the mechanisms that were to lead to its elimination were already in place.

THE DISAPPEARANCE OF MIDWIVES IN QUÉBEC

It seems as though the various interventions of doctors with regard to midwives were influenced by two major factors: periodic surpluses of doctors and the influence of the various types of international medicine. The interaction of these factors can be applied to Québec during two major phases. From 1760 to 1870, doctors attempted to share the field of obstetrics with midwives whose training they controlled as was the case in Europe. Then, from 1870 on, a new trend appeared which aimed at removing them completely from this field.

Firstly, a group of doctors, under the leadership of the doctor and Member of Parliament Pierre de Sales Laterrière, tried to establish a system to control midwives which would ensure their survival yet keep them under the supervision of doctors. This group of doctors tabled from 1790 to 1840 three bills that proposed the certification of country midwives by doctors who would see to their training, and the publication of handbooks aimed at their education. In 1818, the group attempted to organise courses for midwives at the *Dispensaire de Québec*.[15]

Although a textbook for country midwives was published and midwives were legally required to obtain certification from a doctor after 1800, these measures had little practical effect. After 1820, a new group of young doctors became increasingly influential and demanded more restrictive measures toward midwives. This development did not, however, prevent F.X. Trudel at the Ste-Pélagie (Montréal) Maternity Hospital and Dr Trestler at the McGill Maternity Hospital from training many midwives. It was nevertheless a bad omen for the future of this female profession.[16]

It is difficult to imagine what would have become of midwives if the group of doctors that supported them (the traditionalists) had won the struggle with their opponents (the radical doctors). Could midwives, put under the supervision of the traditionalists, have gained their independence as did dentists in 1870, veterinarians in 1905, homeopathic doctors in 1865 and pharmacists in 1870? No one knows for sure. We can nevertheless suppose that such supervision would have enabled these women to get together, organise and thus offer a legal alternative to the growing influence of medical knowledge in obstetrics.

Why, then, was not an association of midwives created in the middle of the nineteenth century? Two major reasons may explain this. Firstly, the socio-economic conditions of women deteriorated in the middle of the nineteenth century, causing women to be excluded from institutions of higher learning. They, therefore, did not have any way of grouping together to create a common front and defend their rights. Secondly, and without doubt most importantly, the surplus of doctors took on alarming proportions just when their field of practice was being eroded by the emergence of other healing professions. For example, doctors who had obtained a monopoly on the sale of drugs in 1863, lost it two years later with the legalisation of the Association of Pharmacists. Consequently, they could not afford to let the obstetrical field elude them, for it had become more and more vital to their profession. This would have indeed happened if midwifery had become a profession.

If, from 1847 to 1870, doctors seemed tolerant, occupied as they were with firmly establishing their teaching institutions and forming a united profession, in 1870 they were solidly established and ready for action. From this moment on, practitioners were everywhere and at all levels making sure they were gaining ground. This included the surveillance and harassment of country midwives (1890-1980) as well as the control of midwives holding a diploma, be they midwives (1870-1920), midwife-nurses (1920-1980) or immigrant midwives (1920-1986). The doctors' control was the most tenacious and vigorous with respect to midwives holding a diploma, who were surely the most threatening.

Firstly, the Corporation of Doctors let self-educated midwives continue practising in the country, hoping that this group would disappear on its own with the coming of 'progress' and 'civilisation'— progress meaning doctors and civilisation meaning hospitals. In fact, in the beginning, the Corporation attempted to have these women fined but was forced to show tolerance when the population came to the midwives' defence. In 1919, this is what happened in the village of Sacré-Coeur in the Saguenay region. The Corporation settled out of court so as not to establish any precedent.[17]

Secondly, a decision favourable to midwives in a trial, which took place in 1879, spurred the doctors into taking action to limit the field of practice of midwives holding a diploma. The trial came at a time when doctors were so preoccupied with the surplus of doctors in cities that a midwife was able to achieve, through the courts, a significant gain for her profession. Basing his verdict on the deposition of Dr. Hingston, then president of the Corporation, the judge ruled:

> that the plaintiff has the right to give the care she has given, that the word "midwife" must be taken in its general sense, that midwives can practise during and before pregnancy and therefore they can see to it that a woman's organs are in a state conducive to conception and a normal pregnancy.[18]

Since this decision was an important one, "for it established a precedent that tended to broaden the privileges and rights of midwives,"[19] the Corporation acted swiftly. In an article published in 1880, Dr. Hingston declared that he had had no choice in his testimony since "the Bureau of Medicine had just given a definition of the term 'midwife' during its last meeting in May 1879"[20] which he had felt he could not deviate from in court. To counteract the 1879 court decision, the Bureau simply called another meeting in April of 1880 and amended the regulations to read as follows: "the midwife licence shall only give her the right to deliver babies and not to practise medicine even in cases resulting from childbirth."[21]

Thus restricted, the expansion of the profession proved to be impossible. The massive arrival of foreign midwives, better informed and better organised, could have brought new leadership to the profession. But here, too, the Corporation was vigilant.

To illustrate the power gained by doctors over immigrant midwives, we will use a fairly contemporary example, that of Anna Farina Colantini, an Italian midwife.[22] In 1961, this graduate of one of the best maternity hospitals in Italy, after having been assured by the Canadian Embassy in Rome that she would be able to practise the profession she had been practising for over fifteen years, was refused a certificate on the pretext that she had not completed six months of courses in a Canadian university as was required by Section 33 of the Medical Act. Sponsored by a doctor friend who came to her defence and hired a lawyer for her, this woman finally agreed to take the courses, but the courses in question were only given at the *Hôpital St-Sacrement de Québec* and reserved exclusively for missionary nuns. The case of immigrant midwives is a good example of the way doctors determined the fate of midwives in general.

The fact that such cases tended to be settled out of court gives us indirect insight into the nature of the process. In a letter to the registrar of the Corporation in 1963, Dr. Augustin Roy summarised the attitude of the Corporation:

> It seems as though the present policy of the College is not to give licences to midwives. In this case, I wonder if it would not be wise to eliminate the controversial Section 33 from our regulations. This section is time-worn and goes against present-day customs. I think that such an action would spare the College future problems.[23]

Is it not significant that the Corporation never felt compelled to ask, at least not officially, to have Section 33 of the Medical Act repealed?

While the law continued to recognise the midwives' right to practise, insurmountable obstacles were systematically placed in their way. This process could never have become a reality without its institutional counterpart: the control of teaching institutions by doctors.

From 1840 to 1870 is the crucial period during which doctors asserted control over medical knowledge. It is a time when university faculties of medicine were created. Rejecting the U.S. model of competing private schools which were riddled with conflicts and often not very viable because more concerned with making money than offering serious courses, the Québec legislators chose centralisation. All schools of medicine had to be affiliated with a university which awarded the diplomas. Since there were few universities there were few faculties of medicine. In 1829, the Montreal Lying-In Hospital joined with the McGill Faculty of Medicine. L'Ecole de chirurgie et de médecine de Montréal united in 1845 with what was later to become the University de Montreal. The Ecole de Québec opened its own Faculty of Medicine at Laval University in 1848. Bishops University did the same in 1871. Still today, there are only four faculties of medicine in Québec, at the Université de Montréal, McGill University, Université Laval and the Université de Sherbrooke.

This concentration is very important for it allowed for better control by the government as well as by the Corporation of these institutions and of their curricula. Although midwives still retained their place within this infrastructure—it was still a mistress midwife who taught the interns at the McGill Maternity Hospital until 1880 and interns could take courses at Ste-Pélagie up until 1920—they, nevertheless, slowly lost the administrative and official control of these same institutions.[24] If women in general, midwives and nuns in particular, had not been ousted from the real centres of decision making, the story that follows would no doubt have been a different one.

The influence of university faculties made itself felt as soon as these institutions got a foothold within maternity hostels headed by nuns, where, since 1840, unwed mothers had found refuge to give birth. First introduced as volunteers, French-speaking doctors gradually imposed their directives and their way of thinking through contracts they negotiated with the religious congregations. The nuns did not have much choice in the matter since they needed university funding. As for the doctors, they needed to make use of these maternity hospitals in order to provide teaching opportunities, as improvement in practical teaching became more and more important and the number of medical students grew.[25]

In the English-speaking community, the process was simpler. The doctors simply took over the Board of Directors of the McGill Maternity Hospital and caused the teaching midwife to resign in 1880. In the French-speaking community, the gradual gaining of control by doctors proved just as efficient. This resulted, after 1920, in the abolition of courses in midwifery and their replacement by courses in nursing.[26]

In fact, one cannot really use the term 'abolition'. The process was more subtle. In 1913 and then again in 1915, the mother superior of Ste-Pélagie asked the Corporation's permission to extend the training courses for midwives so that they would be in conformity with the legal requirements. "This (was) in order to train more competent midwives who could administer quality care and neither put public safety nor the school's reputation in danger."[27] In an important brief, a group of nuns proposed the creation of an independent midwifery course that could serve as a retraining course for nurses. Since doctors were also asking for more hours of practical training in this same period, the Corporation never complied with the nuns' request. There was only room for one category of practitioner in obstetrics and it was decided that it would be that of the doctors.

The creation of university faculties had another less perceptible impact on the evolution of obstetrical knowledge. By gaining the right to control the admission of medical students, the doctors excluded women from francophone faculties of medicine until 1920. Women, therefore, had no say in these institutions of higher learning where gynaecology became firmly rooted after 1930. As in faculties of medicine, courses in midwifery were replaced by those in gynaecology.[28]

It was under the influence of gynaecology that the modern concept of "female nature" was shaped, that childbirth was defined as a pathological and dangerous event and that the interventionist approach—anaesthesia, forceps, Caesarean section, pubiotomy and so on—was favoured and became the basis for the dehumanisation of care.

Gaining wide circulation in the 1920s was the belief of Dr. DeLee, one of the renowned gynaecologists of the time, "That modern women were the nervous inefficient product of modern civilization."[29] According to that gynaecologist, the twentieth century, with its environment and education, had increased women's hypersensitivity—especially upper-middle-class women who were the target clientele of doctors of the time—causing the atrophy of their physical and emotional capacity. Women's worsened condition justified the growth of the specialisation of gynaecology and, in the name of protection, the increasing intervention by doctors into childbirth.

This thesis, disputed in Europe by midwives who managed to retain a more normal approach to pregnancy by limiting the intervention of gynaecologists to high-risk cases, was also debated in Québec by the traditionalists in the profession. The triumph of the radicals had great repercussions for women. Coincident with the rise of gynaecology occurred a widespread publicity campaign aimed at attracting women to hospitals thought to be safer than home delivery. Gynaecology's increasing ascendance furthered the hospitalisation of birthing women which, after 1960, became the norm. At the same time, the modern concept of female nature kept women doctors away from the practice of obstetrics. Their "physical weakness" and "tender hearts" would not allow them to face a sight so difficult for their sensitivity to endure. It is this same view of "female nature" that would be used as an argument to limit the field of practice of nurses specialising in obstetrics.

Nurses too became concerned with the field of practice of midwifery. The possibility of specialised training in obstetrics, which was offered to them sporadically from 1940 to 1972 at the Hôpital St-Sacrement in Québec City, made them available if ever the profession of midwife regained legitimacy. What was the nurses' position in this debate?

From 1897 to 1920, the superintendent of the Victorian Order of Nurses, Charlotte Hanington, tried to convince nurses to become midwives. The Nurses Association of Canada refused to get involved because the housework included among the midwives' tasks, as outlined by Hanington, seemed irreconcilable with the Florence Nightingale mystique. Fearing competition to their own profession, nurses opposed the importation of British midwives, as proposed by Hanington in 1917.[30] The midwife was a potential competitor to the nursing profession still not well established, judging from the reaction of a group of nurses from Québec that requested the abolition of midwifery courses given by the Institut technique de Québec in 1930.[31]

On the whole, it is mostly because the nurses generally endorsed the idea that the doctor is best suited to intervene in obstetrical cases that they refused to back a profession that might have insured them a path to new independence. The debate is still alive today between the Victorian Order of Nurses and the different nurses' unions.

THE REASONS AND PURPOSE OF THE INTERVENTION OF DOCTORS IN OBSTETRICS

The elimination of the profession of midwife by doctors thus took place from 1840 to 1960. The reasons and mechanisms involved have been studied by researchers worldwide. Many historians, American, Australian and Canadian, have observed the same basic scenario in their own countries, and have all come to similar conclusions.[32]

Doctors ousted midwives from obstetrics because this field of practice became, as the surplus of doctors increased competition, the basis for establishing a clientele. This elimination did not depend on the superior efficiency of obstetrical practice compared to midwifery even though the criterion of efficiency was used after the fact to justify the process. On the contrary, rigorous studies have shown that the massive intrusion of doctors in obstetrics between 1990 and 1930, the period of the elimination of midwives, did not decrease the peri-natal mortality rate.[33] It seems, in fact, as though the mortality rate increased because of the type of intervention often practised by doctors. According to a 1983 American report, from 1915 to 1929 a 40 to 50 per cent increase in the number of infants who died because of injuries sustained in delivery and half the maternal deaths of women in childbirth were attributable to incompetent interventions.[34]

Furthermore, it would be incorrect to assume that the elimination of midwives was based on the unanimous agreement of practitioners of the healing arts. The positions of health practitioners with respect to midwives during the past hundred years have been very diverse and contradictory. Québec historians Jean-Marie Fecteau and Jacques Bernier and the American historian Howard S. Berliner have shown that one particular group of doctors, the *réguliers*, gained ascendancy within the field of medicine.[35] As seen above, these 'regulers' were dominated by the radical faction, as opposed to the traditionalist, within the Corporation of Doctors. The members of this particular group, by gaining influence within the legislature and other powerful social/political institutions,[36] succeeded in securing for the Corporation the power of regulation it enjoys today.

---

[1] This mechanistic model could have proved to be wrong. It happened to be right. Richard W. Wertz & Dorothy C. Wertz, Lying-In: *A History of Childbirth in America* (New York: Schocken, 1979), pp. 32-3.

[2] Claude de Ferrière, *Dictionnaire de la pratique de la médecine en France*, t. II (Paris: Delegrange, 1773), p.222.

[3] 600 French pounds for the highest ranking surgeon in the colony; 400 French pounds for the *entretenue* midwife. At a time when a practitioner's expert opinion in court was paid according to the person's quality, a surgeon received 20

sols and a 'midwife 15 sols. Hélène Laforce, *Histoire de la sage-femme dans la région de Québec* (Québec: Institut québécois de recherche sur la culture, 1985), pp. 195-6.

[4] See Hubert Charbonneau, *Vie et mort de nos ancêtres* (Montréal: Boréal Express, 1973), p.210.

[5] Archives Nationales du Québec à Québec, Archives des colonies, série B, 25 janvier 1721, "Conditions de la dame Dorille, maîtresse sage-femme pour passer à la Louisiane," folio 403, p.2.

[6] The parish priest called a meeting of women for the purpose of electing midwives. This election took place according to the *Québec Ritual* in effect from 1713 until, in some places like Rimouski, 1930.

[7] Archives Nationales du Québec, Archives judiciaires, Inventaire d'une collection, 12 avril 1730. There was a case of a surgeon from Chateau Richer and his wife, the midwife of the area, who married their daughter, who was also a midwife, to a physician from Champlain and that couple inturn arranged a marriage of their daughter to another physician from Champlain.

[8] Archives des colonies, série B, 2 mars 1755.

[9] *Le Petit Robert 2*, 1981 edition, has no entry under Chamberlen and that is unfortunate. If the forceps used at this time were an instrument that both saved and took lives, it remains certain that they were useful in difficult cases when used correctly. It is the way forceps were used more than the instrument itself that was deplorable. The premature use of forceps could cause damage, infection and hemorrhaging and very often crushed the infant's head. It does not seem that the use of forceps by midwives was illegal during this period as was the case in France, for we know that several famous midwives used them in Britain. The reluctance demonstrated by the majority of midwives towards this instrument can no doubt be explained by: (1) the cost and the physical strength needed to use the original instruments, (2) the real dangers involved and the anxiety suffered by women giving birth who had been warned against the destructive use of the instrument; (3) the fact that surgeons refused to sell forceps to midwives and that the midwifery tradition knew other methods anyway.

[10] This does not stop the surgeons from using forceps as often as possible, whether the delivery was a normal one or not. This practice reduced the length of labour and gave them a clear advantage over midwives. The instrument made the reputation of the obstetrician and in France surgeons were encouraged to display it. Jacques Gélis, "Sages-femmes et accoucheuses. L'obstétrique populaire aux XVIIe et XVIIIe siècles," Annales ESC 32, 15 (septembre-octobre 1977), 929-52.

[11] Surveys found in "Rapport du Comité concernant la population, l'agriculture et la colonisation, part no. 18." Archives publiques du Canada, *Documents constitutionnels* 1759-1791, p.918.1

[12] Archives publiques du Canada, Documents constitutionnels 1759-1791. "Rapport du Comité concernant la population, l'agriculture et la colonisation," Rapport Fisher 1775, pp.918, 919.

[13] Laforce, p.94.

[14] Archives de la paroisse de Notre-Dame-de-Québec, *42e procès-verbal de la Société compatissante de Québec*, 1862.

[15] Archives publiques du Canada, Legislative Council Papers, 22 mars 1791, folio 483, p.2. Archives de la Bibliothèque municipale de Montréal (Salle Gagnon), *Rapport du Comité special formé pour amender la loi relative a la pratique et de l'art obstétrique dans le Bas-Canada*, Québec, Assemblée législative (25 octobre 1852), 20. Von Iffland, *La Gazette de Québec* (5 novembre 1819), 15.

[16] Archives des Soeurs de la Miséricorde de Montréal, *Chroniques de Soeurs de la Miséricorde, papiers privés*, 68. Dr. Trestler, "University Lying-in Hospital," *Montreal Medical Gazette* 1 (1844), 223.

[17] Montréal, Archives de la Corporation des Médicins, dossier sage-femme (privé), Procès des Dames du Sacré-Coeur, correspondance, 1920.

[18] "Des sages-femmes," *L'Union médicale du Canada* 9 (1880), 275.

[19] *Ibid.*, p.277.

[20] "Des sages-femmes," *L'abeille médicale* 2 (1880), 255.

[21] "Des sages-femmes," L'Union médicale du Canada 9 (1880), 277.

[22] Archives de la Corporation des médecins, Correspondance, "Dossier sages-femmes," cas de Anna Farina Colanti, 1961.

[23] *Ibid.*, letter written by Augustin Roy to J.-B Jobin, April 1963.

[24] Archives of the Bibliothèque municipale de Montréal (Salle Gagnon), fonds de l'Ecole de chirurgie et de médecine de Montréal, Soeur Marie Saint-Hilaire to Mgr. Georges Gauthier, Vice-Rector, Université Laval (October 1917).

[25] *Ibid.*, Dr. René de Cotret to Mgr. Georges Gauthier, 5 October 1917, 1-4.

[26] This question is dealt with in Rhona Kenneally, "The Montreal Maternity, 1849-1926; Evolution of a Hospital," unpublished M.A. thesis, McGill University, 1983.

[27] Archives de la Miséricorde, letter written by the mother superior to the secretary of the Corporation of doctors, May 8, 1915.

[28] Judith Walzer Leavitt, "Science Enters the Birthing Room: Obstetrics in America since the Eighteenth Century," *Journal of American History* 70 (September 1970), 281-304. According to Summey & Hurst: "The first period, from 1920-1944, marks the formal alliance of obstetrics and gynaecology in the United States and the formation of its

ideology." Pamela S. Summey & Marsha Hurst, "Ob/gyn. on the Rise: the evolution of professional ideology in the 20th century," Part One, *Women & Health* **2**, 1 (Spring 1986):133.

[29] Summey & Hurst, 140.

[30] Suzann Buckley, "Ladies or Midwives? Efforts to Reduce Infant and Maternal Mortality," in Linda Kealey, ed., *A Not Unreasonable Claim: Women and Reform in Canada, 1880s-1920s* (Toronto: The Women's Press 1979), pp.144-7

[31] Archives de l'Université Laval, lettre de Mgr. Camille Roy à M. Jean Bruchési, Université 500 no 153, 10 fébrier, 1938. "Je viens de recevoir une delegation de l'Association des gardes ou infirmières diplômées de l'Université Laval. Les gardes me prient d'intervenir auprès de l'honorable Secrétaire de la Province au sujet des cours de sage-femme et de garde-malades qui se donnent à l'ecole technique de Québec aux jeunes chômeuses en vertu du plan Rogers-Bilodeau, ce, afin de les faire cesser, car ils font une concurrence déloyale aux infirmières."

[32] For Australia, see Evan Willis, *Medical Dominance: The Division of Labour in Australian Health Care* (George Allen & Unwin Australia Pty. Ltd., 1983). In the United States the bibliography on midwives contains numerous titles. We particularly recommend the excellent synthesis by Richard W. Wertz & Dorothy C. Wertz, *Lying-In: A History of Childbirth in America* (New York: Schocken, 1979) as well as that by Judith Walzer Leavitt, *Brought to Bed: Child-Bearing in America, 1750-1950* (New York & Oxford: Oxford University Press, 1986). Two classic articles in the field are Judith Walzer Leavitt, "Science Enters the Birthing Room: Obstetrics in America since the Eighteenth Century," *Journal of American History* **70** (September 1970), 281-304, and Frances Kobrin, "The American Midwife Controversy," *Bulletin of the History of Medicine* **40** (July-August 1966), 350-63. For Great Britain see Jean Donnison, Midwives and Medical Men: *A History of Inter-Professional Rivalries and Women's Rights* (London: Heinemann, 1977), and Jean Towler & Joan Bramall, *Midwives in History and Society* (London: Croom Helm, 1986). See also chapters by Jane Lewis, Lesley Biggs and Jo Oppenheimer in *Delivering motherhood*, Arnup, Levesque & Pierson (eds), London: Routledge.

[33] Oppenheimer, pp.51-74. Wertz & Wertz, p.260.

[34] *Foetal, Newborn and Maternal Morality and Morbidity* cited in Wertz and Wertz, p.161.

[35] Jean-Marie Fecteau, "Pauvres, indigents et assistés au Québec: modes successifs d'insertion de l'Etat dans le processus de réduction des discordances sociales," unpublished M.A. thesis, Université Laval, 1976; Jacques Bernier, "Les praticiens de la santé au Québec, 1871-1921, quelques données statistiques," *Recherches sociographiques* **20**, 1 (janvier-avril), 41-58; Howard S. Berliner, "La consolidation du pouvour médical au début du siècle: une nouvelle interprétation du rapport Flexner," in *Médecine et société. Les annees 80* (Montréal: Les Editions Saint-Martin, 4e édition, 1985).

[36] For the influence of the College of Physicians on the Québec Legislature and on the Legislative Council, see Hélène Laforce, p.110.

MIDWIFERY REGULATION, EDUCATION, AND PRACTICE IN THE NETHERLANDS DURING THE NINETEENTH CENTURY[1]

M. J. van Lieburg & Hilary Marland[*]

Although within the Netherlands, there is a growing interest in the history of midwifery and its practitioners,[2] publications in languages other than Dutch have been few and far between.[3] Consequently, little is known internationally about the development of midwifery and, obstetrics in Holland. In stark contrast, in other European countries and, more particularly, America, there is a large literature on midwifery and obstetrics, including studies by feminist historians, sociologists, and historians of the professions, as well as medical historians. It seems paradoxical that the United States, one of the nations where the role of the midwife has declined most significantly in the twentieth century, has also produced the largest number of major studies on midwifery and its practitioners;[4] the Netherlands recognized as one of the few wealthy Western countries where midwives still play a major role in childbirth, has produced little historical analysis.

Present-day midwives in Holland hold a position of relative autonomy *vis-à-vis* obstetricians. They attend and supervise single-handedly such a large proportion of births, including many home deliveries, as to indicate that the specialty evolved In a way very different from many other European countries and America. In 1910, about 60% of all deliveries in the Netherlands were performed by midwives. This percentage gradually fell to 48% in 1940, 41% in 1950, 37% in 1960, and 36.7% in 1970. By 1977 there had been a small increase: out of 175,000 babies born, 37.8% were delivered by midwives (an average of 84 per midwife per annum, and a total of 66,000 deliveries). By 1983 the proportion of births attended by midwives had again risen. 57.7% of the 171,000 deliveries in Holland in 1983 were attended by doctors, and 41.6% by midwives.[5]

In Holland, as, elsewhere, the nineteenth century was a crucial period. In many countries this was an era of decline for the midwife, in terms of both status and the tasks she performed, in part due to pressure from male competitors.[6] But in the Netherlands this was also, in a number of ways, a period of consolidation for the midwife. Early in the century, midwives were already included in legislation to control medical practice, and facilities were established for their training examination, and regulation. As the century progressed, the tasks of the various professional groups, including the obstetric specialist and general practitioners, were clearly delineated, leaving large numbers of trained midwives opportunities to practice in an independent way. By the end of the century, midwives had set up their own professional organization and journal.

In the absence of accessible secondary literature, this article will outline the main developments in midwife practice and education during the nineteenth century. The term "midwife" will be applied here in

[*] Professor M. J. van Lieburg M.D. and Hilary Marland Ph.D., Vakgroep Metamedica. Instituut Medische Geschiedenis, Vrije Universiteit, Van der Boechorststraat 7,1081 BT Amsterdam, the Netherlands; and Instituut Medische Geschiedenis, Erasmus Universiteit Rotterdam, Postbus 1738, 3000 DR Rotterdam, the Netherlands. In 1996 Hilary Marland moved to the Centre for Social History, University of Warwick, UK.

Medical History, 1989, **33**: 296-317. Copyright The Trustee, The Wellcome Trust, reproduced with permission.

its narrowest sense, referring to those receiving a school or apprenticeship training and a licence to practice. Those practicing outside these boundaries, untrained or informally trained, unlicensed and unregulated, will not be considered, nor will the yet more informal childbirth assistance offered by female family members, friends, and neighbours. This is by no means to deny the significant role played by these informal practitioners, but merely to limit the scope of this survey. A thumbnail sketch will delineate the main legislative developments affecting the medical profession in general and midwives in particular during the nineteenth century. An outline will also be given of changes in the numbers of midwives and other obstetric practitioners during this period, of how midwives were selected, trained, and examined, their practices and incomes, and their relationship with male medical practitioners.

Primary sources for the Netherlands, particularly numerical evidence, are far richer than for nineteenth century England or America, due to legislative developments and the introduction or regulation, and the early institutionalization of midwife training.[7] For the period up to the late nineteenth century, largely unworked and unpublished statistical material, chiefly in the form of the provincial and state medical registers, has been drawn upon. Around the turn of the century, medical practitioners drew up a number of reports on midwife practice, and these, despite their built-in biases, have also been utilized in this analysis, particularly their numerical data.

THE ORGANIZATION OF THE MEDICAL PROFESSION IN HOLLAND AT THE BEGINNING OF THE NINETEENTH CENTURY

The first enactment's to affect midwifery practice, as indeed, all medical practice, in the Netherlands were passed following the occupation of the country by the French in 1795.[8] After the conclusion of peace that year, the old Republic of the Seven united Netherlands was replaced by the legislatively active Batavian Republic. In 1798, eight ministries were set up, including a Ministry for National Education (Agentschap van Nationale Opvoeding), which implemented laws applying to the medical profession. In 1810, the Netherlands was absorbed into France, and for the next few years was directly under French legislative and executive control.

From 1798 onwards, the various groups practising medicine came to be regulated, including the non-academically-trained practitioners who played an important role in Dutch medical care for much of the nineteenth century. The institutions which had formerly regulated the medical profession, including the Collegia Medica, a municipal supervisory committee, consisting of a select group of physicians and surgeons, and the surgeons' guilds, made way for provincial (or departmental) committees, composed of the "most skilled and experienced men": medical doctors, surgeons, man-midwives, and pharmacists. The provincial committees were to maintain standards of medical practice, and to supervise the local committees, which were to be established in districts with at least four practicing doctors.[9]

Eighteen years of political subservience to France ended in 1813, and in 1818 an enactment re-organized the medical acts passed during the "French period".[10] The new act, firstly, confirmed the precedence of national over local regulation and control, established during the French period. Secondly, the division within the medical profession between academic and non-academic practitioners, or university and non-university educated, was more clearly defined. The university-trained doctors were to receive a largely theoretical training, while the non-graduates were trained by apprenticeship. The two groups were separately licensed, medical doctors by the universities, and the non-academic group by the provincial committees. However, both groups fell under the control of the thirteen provincial medical committees. Thirdly, the spheres of practice of medical doctors, surgeons, and obstetric practitioners were defined, the law also differentiating between urban and rural medical practitioners.

The law of 1818 referred to three groups of obstetric practitioners: the doctor of obstetrics (who was also qualified as a medical doctor), the man-midwife, and the midwife. Instructions for each category of medical practitioner were drawn up, including special instructions for midwives. Obstetric doctors and man-midwives differed in their methods of training and examination. But, with respect to his practice, the obstetric doctor had to follow the instructions laid down for the man-midwife.

After 1818, the midwife continued to supervise most normal deliveries. According to the law of 1818, a midwife laid to be examined by a provincial committee before she could practice, and had to confine her practice to those births "which were natural processes or could be delivered manually, so that the midwife may never use any instruments for this purpose". She was, however, permitted to administer enemas and catheters. The midwife was instructed "to treat the woman gently and carefully", and to call in an obstetric doctor or man-midwife in difficult or dangerous cases; and she was obliged annually to report to the provincial committees on the complicated deliveries she had attended. The examination of the midwife concluded with the administration of an oath, in which she swore to maintain professional secrecy, and conduct all her affairs "as a good-natured and humane midwife was supposed to do".[11]

As a result of the law of 1818, fees for all categories of medical intervention were fixed by many of the provincial committees. Fees for obstetric cases varied between the groups of obstetric practitioners. In South Holland, the fee for a normal delivery in large towns was fixed at a maximum of 63 guilders and a 6 minimum of guilders for man-midwives, and 25 and 3 guilders for midwives. In the countryside, the corresponding charges ranged from 30 to 3 guilders, and 15 to 2.10 guilders. Special tariffs were also fixed for the giving of enemas and introducing of catheters by midwives.[12] While scales of charges were carefully detailed, little is known of the total incomes of midwives during this period. Those employed by the town councils as midwives to the poor were paid a fixed allowance of two to three hundred guilders per annum (about equivalent to the earnings of a labourer), but they were able to supplement this with fees from private practice.

THE TRAINING OF MIDWIVES BEFORE 1860

According to the law of 1818, midwives were to be trained by apprenticeship to a licensed midwife, but only after they had been educated for at least one year in the "theory of midwifery". The law referred implicitly here to the municipal courses in anatomy and obstetrics that had been given by medical doctors in the bigger Dutch towns since the end of the seventeenth century. The law also anticipated the setting up of special schools for the non-academic training of surgeons, man-midwives, pharmacists, and midwives. Before 1798, such training had been regulated by the surgeons' or pharmacists' guilds, but after this date no formal provision existed. A decree of 1823, however, provided for the foundation of provincial or municipal schools in those towns where a hospital could facilitate clinical training. Between 1824 and 1828 six such "clinical schools" were established in Middelburg, Haarlem, Hoorn, Alkmaar, Amsterdam, and Rotterdam. The Amsterdam and Rotterdam schools, with the highest numbers of pupils, came to be the most important.

Admission to the schools was confined to women, aged between twenty and thirty, who were healthy and capable of carrying out the work of a midwife, literate, and of "irreproachable character". Some of the pupil midwives were sent by local authorities for a small fee of 20 guilders per annum; other were admitted on a private basis. The course, which lasted for two years, was both theoretical and practical, although only three hours per week were devoted to theory. During the remaining time, the pupil midwife accompanied a trained midwife to both hospital and domiciliary deliveries.

Table 1: Numbers of pupil midwives attending the clinical schools of the Netherlands, 1824-67

	Amsterdam	Rotterdam	Middelburg	Haarlem	Hoorn	Alkmaar	Total
1820-9	2	29	9	7	8	8	38
1830-9	28	29	13	3	24	24	121
1840-9	34	24	9	6	14	16	103
1850-9	45	20	11	7	15	3	101
1860-7	24	14	1	3	5	6	53*
Total	133	91	43	26	66	57	416

*The substantial decline in the number of pupils in the years 1860-7 was due to the opening of the state school for midwives in Amsterdam in 1861, which was followed by the winding up of training for midwives in clinical schools.

Source: M. J. van Lieburg, *De studenten aan de geneeskundige scholen in Nederland (1824-1867). Een reconstructie van het Album Studiosorum*, Amsterdam, Rodopi, 1989.

Table 1 shows the number of pupil midwives attending the six clinical schools of the Netherlands between 1824 and 1867, broken down into ten-year periods. Of a total of 416 pupils admitted to the six schools, 321 (over 77%) passed the final examination, and qualified as midwives. The number of school-trained midwives, however, remained low, especially when compared with the number licensed following a period of apprenticeship on a private basis with a trained midwife. Both paths led to examination by the provincial medical committees. Between 1824 and 1867 an average of only eight women graduated from the six clinical schools each year by 1850 as shown in table 2, then were 811 licensed midwives in the Netherlands, of whom fewer than a third had received training in the clinical schools. In the province of South Holland, 59 trainee midwives were examined by the provincial medical committee between 1828 and 1841. Of these, only 19 (32%) had graduated from the local clinical school in Rotterdam.[13] There was a distinct contrast between school and non-school training for midwives, graduates from the schools receiving a more systematic and theoretical (but not necessarily more thorough or useful) education.

Table 2: Numbers of licensed midwives in the Netherlands during the nineteenth century

Year	Midwives	Trained (%)	
		Before 1865	After 1865
1820	819		
1830	820*		
1840	811		
1850	811		
1860	725		
1865 medical act			
1875	767	596 (78)	171 (12)
1885	764	383 (50)	381 (50)
1895	830	238 (29)	592 (71)
1905	849	--	--

* Estimate *Source*: Provincial and state medical registers.

THE MEDICAL AND OBSTETRIC PROFESSIONS
IN THE MID-NINETEENTH CENTURY

The position of midwives during the mid-nineteenth century should also be considered against the background of the general development of the medical profession in the Netherlands. 1838 marked an important turning point in intraprofessional relationships and the division of medical tasks. The ban on combined pratice fir medical doctors was then revoked, giving them the right to attend at obstetric cases, not only as consultants to man midwives and midwives but also as normal birth attendants. As a result, there was a massive increase in the number of medical doctors acquiring a second degree in obstetrics, as illustrated in table 3. In 1820, only 4.4% of medical doctors also held an obstetric degree; by 1866 this percentage had increased to 59.2%.[14] As a consequence, academic training in obstetrics became much extended. In Leiden, Abraham Simon Thomas (1820-86) was appointed Professor Extraordinary of obstetrics and gynecology in 1848;[15] this was the first, and for sixteen years the only, chair of obstetrics and gynecology in the Netherlands. At other universities, chairs of obstetrics and surgery were combined.

This development coincided with a debate on the unity of the medical profession, initiated by a group of young, progressive medical practitioners. As a prelude to new legislation, in 1849 the Dutch Society for the Promotion of Medicine (Nederlandsche Maatschappij tot Bevordering der Geneeskunst, NMG) was founded, the first national professional organization of doctors in Holland.[16] The NMG's primary aim was to change the medical law of 1818 according to the ideal of a profession unified in terms of education and licensing. As a pressure group, it was far from representative. For many years dominated by medical doctors and town surgeons, it attracted little support from the countryside: 32% of the medical profession had joined by 1850, and by 1865 this had only increased to 37%. After 1876 the NMG's membership finally included more than half of the profession.[17] However, pressure from the NMG did contribute towards the patient of the medical set of 1865, which created a new category of medical practitioner, the *arts* (pl. *artsen*), who was permitted to practice internal medicine, surgery, and obstetrics. The necessity of providing training for this large new group practitioners led to the establishment of academic hospitals, and to the appointment of professors in clinical subjects, including obstetrics, at all Dutch universities.[18]

Table 3 shows the changes in the numbers of each category of medical practitioner, including those involved in midwifery, before and after the medical law of 1865. Through the century, man midwives were forced to defend their positions vigorously in the face of growing numbers of academically-trained obstetric practitioners, both obstetric doctors and, after 1865, the *artsen* (general practitioners). The growth in the number of *artsen* resulted in increased competition between all categories of obstetric practitioners, and a further polarization between graduates and non-graduates. Meanwhile, elements in each category of male obstetric practitioner continued to depict midwives in largely negative terms.

Table 3: Numbers of medical practitioners in the Netherlands, 1820-95

Date	Population	MD	OD	OD/MD%	S	MM	GP	MW
*c.*1820	2,109,069	637	28	4.4	1081	540	--	819
*c.*1840	2,705,620	841	268	31.9	1453	1102	--	811
1855	3,183,003	1022	457	44.7	1422	1268	--	837
1866	3,444,328	990	586	59.2	1639	1302	8	692*
1875	3,769,111	875	?	?	1010	?	132	767
1885	4262,054	563	?	?	622	?	556	764
1895	4,807,776	384	?	?	408	?	1009	830

MD   medical doctor (*medicinae doctor*)
OD   obstetric doctor (*obstetriae doctor*)
S   surgeon (*heelmeester*)
MM   man midwife (*vroedmeester*)
GP   general practitioner of medicine (*arts*)
MW   midwife (*vroedvrouw*)

* All medical personnel were instructed to re-register under the medical law of 1865. The fact that many midwives chose not to re-register perhaps best explains the low figure for 1866.
Sources: Arntzenius, op. cit., note 13 above, pp. 25-53; provincial and state medical registers.

THE PRACTICE OF VROUW WALTMAN OF DORDRECHT

The casebook of a mid-nineteenth-century midwife, Vrouw Waltman,[19] who practised in the town of Dordrecht,[20] just south or Rotterdam offers some insight into a domiciliary midwifery of this period. Willemina Waltman was born in 1802 into a working-class family, her father, Cornelis van Eysbergen, being a millwright in Dordrecht. Vrouw Waltman's education was confined to primary school attendance, a fact later reflected in her primitive handwriting and the simplicity of the casebook notes. In 1823, aged twenty-one, she married Dirk Waltman, a painter, and the son of a town beadle. Only nine years later, in 1832, she was left a widow with two young children to support. While far from well off, Vrouw Waltman was apparently not left penniless, and nine years passed before she began to practice midwifery. She took her midwifery examination before the provincial medical committee in Dordrecht in 1841, at the age of thirty-nine. It is not known where or with whom she trained, although it is likely that she was apprenticed to a local midwife or man-midwife.

After passing the examination, Vrouw Waltman soon built up a busy practice. In 1842 she delivered twenty-nine women, and in the following year this figure had increased to sixty-seven. Five years later she was attending twice as many cases, delivering 140 women in 1847. The number continued to increase until her peak year, 1857, when she attended 268 deliveries, an average of five a week. In 1860 Waltman was appointed as town midwife to Dordrecht. After 1865 the number of cases she attended began to decline, to 101 in 1868, thirty-one in 1870, and in 1872, four. In July 1873 Vrouw Whitman attended at what was to be her last delivery, the birth of a grandson. She died the following year, aged seventy-two.[21]

Vrouw Waltman appears to have been highly respected in the community, and her services were much in demand. An official inquiry made during the mid-nineteenth century revealed that there were in practice in Dordrecht one doctor of obstetrics, twelve man-midwives, and ten midwives, so Vrouw Waltman had no lack of competition. Yet out of the eight or nine hundred births in Dordrecht annually, Vrouw Waltman attended many more than her quota, in some years around a quarter of all births; during her thirty years in practice she delivered almost 5,000 children.[22] Vrouw Waltman's average fee per case was not high, approximately 2.50 guilders, but her annual income of up to five or six hundred guilders was respectable.[23]

In her casebook, Vrouw Waltman noted down whether deliveries were early or had gone to full term; the position of the child; if it had been necessary to call in a man-midwife or second midwife; whether the child was born alive or dead, or had died shortly after birth; details of the pregnancy and lying-in period; and any unusual occurrences during childbirth. Most deliveries were normal head presentations, but Waltman also recorded seven face presentations, thirty breech, eleven footling, and four knee presentations in her casebook. Thirty-six children presented in a transverse position; Vrouw Waltman included within this definition twenty arm and nine stomach presentations, and one back presentation. Of the fifty-three twins delivered by Waltman, twenty-nine presented abnormally.[24] Even in difficult deliveries, Vrouw Waltman seldom found it necessary to call for assistance: during her entire career, she mentioned summoning a man-midwife or another midwife on only twenty-nine occasions each. Her casebook demonstrates that she was familiar with the technique of version and extraction. In one case, instruments had to be employed to complete the delivery; in another, the mother had an abnormally narrow pelvis. A case of placenta praevia was also mentioned in the casebook. In all of these deliveries Vrouw Waltman summoned a man-midwife to assist. To judge from the mortality rates of the children she delivered, Vrouw Waltman's results were good by nineteenth-century standards, although, as always, such results should be taken with more than a pinch of salt, for the death of infants was normally recorded only at birth or directly afterwards. While Vrouw Waltman delivered 205 stillborn children, only six were recorded as dying shortly after birth, giving a total perinatal mortality rate of 4.27%.[25]

THE CONSEQUENCE OF THE LAWS OF 1860 AND 1865 FOR OBSTETRIC PRACTICE

The law of 1865 instituted a system whereby admission to the medical profession could *only* be achieved through the passing of a state examination for *artsen,* composed of theoretical and clinical parts. This gave successful candidates the authority to practise *all* branches of medicine. Although those already qualified as obstetric doctors could continue to practise midwifery after 1865, the degree of obstetric doctor, still possible to acquire, became irrelevant. Likewise, those qualified as man-midwives could also continue to practise. However, the provincial medical committees ceased to function as examining bodies in 1865, and the qualification of man-midwife was abolished; consequently, the number of man-midwives declined. Meanwhile, as table 3 demonstrates, the number *of artsen,* in effect a new group of obstetric practitioners, grew almost eightfold, from 132 in 1875 to over 1,000 in 1895.[26] The growth in the number of *artsen* was paralleled by a decline in the numbers of both medical doctors and pure surgeons after 1865. The relative decline of midwife numbers in the middle of the nineteenth century is also illustrated in table 3. In 1876, new legislation made university education, including training in obstetrics, uniform and, in practice, compulsory for *all* medical practitioners. In 1885 the state and universities combined to set up a state medical examination.

Obstetrics and gynaecology were included in the general rise of specialties towards the end of the nineteenth century in the Netherlands. In 1887 the Dutch Association of Gynaecologists (*Nederlandse Gynaecologische Vereniging,* NGV) was founded by a small gathering of Amsterdam surgeons, who, in 1889, initiated the *Dutch Journal of Gynaecology and Obstetrics (Nederlands Tijdschrift voor Verloskunde en Gynaecologie).* Through their association and journal, this group promoted the recognition of obstetrics and gynaecology, as a specialist subject and branch of practice. During the nineteenth century, this small collection of specialists tended not to come into conflict with general obstetric practitioners, including midwives, because they normally confined themselves to consulting practices.

As far as midwives were concerned, the law of 1865 merely confirmed an enactment of 1860 which had been motivated by the belief that, as one minister stated, the "class of midwives is, to the damage of society, sinking more and more in general esteem".[27] The law of 1865 restated a clause of the act of 1818, that midwives were "only to attend such deliveries, that were the work of nature, or which could be executed by hand".[28] In some respects, this nineteenth century legislation marked a step backwards from the former situation of the midwife, in which, despite the lack of organized, systematic training, she sometimes attended at complicated deliveries, and, more rarely, practised gynaecology and surgery. Vrouw Catharina Schrader, the widow of a provincial surgeon, who practised midwifery in Friesland in the north of Holland during the late seventeenth century and first half of the eighteenth, provides an outstanding example of a midwife who was able to acquire much experience and skill, partly through assisting her husband in his practice. Vrouw Schrader became a specialist in emergency deliveries, and there is evidence to suggest that she picked up some surgical knowledge from her husband, and also had skills in nursing and the compounding and dispensing of medicines.[29] The wife of Hendrik van Deventer (1651-1724),[30] the famous Dutch obstetrician and author of midwifery texts, similarly acquired a knowledge of obstetrics, which she applied in her midwifery practice, from assisting her husband. This may well have been a two-way process as Van Deventer acquired from his wife more knowledge of normal childbirth than most male practitioners had. While these women were exceptional in terms of both their knowledge and specialized practices, before the nineteenth century the possibility existed, despite some restrictive local acts, of midwives going beyond attendance at normal deliveries.

The legislation of the nineteenth century, which applied to the whole of the Netherlands, thus forbade midwives from attending at abnormal deliveries. If complications arose during a birth, the midwife was to summon an obstetric or medical doctor, a man-midwife, or, after 1865, an *arts*. If there were none to be had in the neighbourhood, she was to call for the assistance of a second midwife. Clearly, in some situations a midwife, either unable or unwilling to ask for help, would have decided to continue with the delivery on her own, but the extent to which this took place is uncertain. A report on the status of midwives made in 1897 by the Dutch Society for the Promotion of Medicine, however, stated that, out of 196 midwives sampled, almost 80% called for assistance in good time.[31] A similar report, drawn up in 1911, also gave a percentage of 80%.[32]

The law of 1860, recognizing the shortage of well-trained, especially school trained, midwives in the rural districts established a new training system through the founding, in 1861, of a state school for midwives *(Rijkskweekschool voor Vroedvrouwen)* in Amsterdam.[33] Following the implementation of the medical law of 1865, the clinical schools were closed, except for the Amsterdam school, enabled to continue due to its special relationship with the Amsterdam Atheneum.[34] The provincial medical committees were also dissolved, and a state commission took over responsibility for the examination of midwives. The sole alteration to the new state school system after 1865 was an expansion of the midwife training program, through the establishment of a second school for midwives in Rotterdam in 1882.[35] The municipal school of Groningen offered the only other institutional facility for training: since 1851, midwives had been taught by the professor of obstetrics of the town's university.[36]

Training in the state schools for midwives was free, but the schools' graduates were obliged to practise for a number of years as midwife to the poor. There was a maximum number of pupils admitted each year in Amsterdam twenty-six, and in Rotterdam thirty-two. Each Dutch province could send two women annually to train as midwives gratis; the selection of candidates rested with provincial inspectors of public health. Private pupils were also admitted. Those admitted to the course had to be aged between twenty and thirty-five, preferably unmarried women or widows, and as far as possible "respectable citizens, and gifted with such knowledge and reason needed for a thorough scientific training".[37] The course lasted for two years, during which time pupils boarded in the schools, under the supervision of a "midwife-mistress". Training covered general anatomy and physiology, special knowledge of the female parts, the care of infants and sick women, and both theoretical and practical midwifery. Pupil midwives attended at deliveries in the associated clinics. Training in the state schools was recognized as being of a high standard, with a larger theoretical component than the clinical schools, but the general education of entrants was poor. To remedy this a teacher, who also functioned as matron and supervisor of the pupils, was appointed to teach the "three Rs". Finally, in 1902 an entrance examination was instituted.

Between 1861 and 1900 the total number of pupils trained at the Amsterdam state school was 1,143 (an average of 29 per annum); in Rotterdam, between 1882 and 1900, 628 (or 35 per annum). These figures represented a major increase on the numbers passing through the six clinical schools, which between 1824 and 1867 together trained only 416 women (approximately 10 per annum). However, while most of those trained in the clinical schools passed the final examination (almost 80%), fewer than half of the women educated in the state schools graduated at the end of the course. Of the Amsterdam pupils admitted to the course, only 462 (40%) passed the examination between 1861 and 1900. In Rotterdam the pass rate was similar, with 239 pupils (38%) graduating between 1882 and 1900. In Amsterdam the failure rate in the examination itself was high; in Rotterdam there was a system of continuous assessment and poorer candidates were weeded out before they sat the examinations.

The personalities and scientific background of the directors had a major impact upon the standard of education provided by the Amsterdam and Rotterdam schools. Perhaps the best example of this link is provided by Leopold Lehmann's directorship of the Amsterdam school, during the 1860s and 1870s. Lehmann (1817-80),[38] a dedicated follower of Virchow, had rejected the new theories of infectious diseases and bacteriology. Most significantly, he failed to recognize the link between puerperal fever and septic infection, and refused to introduce antiseptic techniques into the maternity ward. Complaints concerning the high mortality rate prompted the Amsterdam town council to appoint a committee to examine the maternity ward, but Lehmann died in 1880 before its report was completed. His successor, Professor G. H. van der Mey (1851-95),[39] introduced antisepsis to the maternity ward, thus reducing the maternal mortality rate from around 4% to 0.88%.[40] Lehmann's stand also brought him into conflict with the state examination committee, who refused to license many of the Amsterdam pupils. This helps account for the low number of midwives graduating from the Amsterdam school during the 1860s and 1870s.

Table 4: Pupil numbers at the state schools for midwives in Amsterdam and Rotterdam

	Amsterdam				Rotterdam			
	No of Pupils	Examined	Passed Exam	(%)	No of Pupils	Examined	Passed Exam	(%)
1861-65	107	?	30	(-)	-	-	-	
1865-70	125	?	62	(-)	-	-	-	
1870-75	129	?	51	(-)	-	-	-	
1875-80	130	60	50	(83)	-	-	-	
1880-85	174	101	76	(75)	89	20	19	(95)
1885-90	174	97	73	(75)	176	84	66	(79)
1890-95	176	95	68	(72)	177	75	75	(100)
1895-1900	128	62	52	(84)	186	82	79	(96)

Source: Van Tussenbroek, op. cit., note 36 above, pp.150, 170.

Table 5a shows the occupations of entrants to the Rotterdam state school between 1883 and 1909. The most striking numbers are those for domestic servants, who made up around 20% of entrants, and the 57% with no occupation. Midwives in Holland during this period came largely from lower middle class backgrounds, as can be seen from the small sample of the mothers of pupil midwives given in table 5b. There was little middle-or upper class input. Of the 432 cases where the occupation of the pupils' fathers is known, 63 (14.6%) were farmers, 20 (4.6%) shopkeepers, 16 (3.7%) each were teachers, carpenters or tailors, 13 (3%) each police constables or sailors, and 12 (2.8%) shoemakers. Most of the rest were tradesmen, clerks, or minor civil servants.[41]

Table 5a: Occupations of pupils admitted to the state school for midwives in Rotterdam 1883-1909

Occupations	Years			Total	(%)
	1883-89	1890-99	1900-09		
Domestic servant	33	33	24	90	(19.3)
Children's nanny	6	5	0	11	(2.4)
Nurse (without diploma)	2	3	7	12	(2.6)
Nurse (with diploma)	0	2	2	4	(0.9)
Assistant teacher	1	2	3	6	(1.3)
Pupil teacher	3	7	8	18	(3.9)
Nursery school teacher	4	2	2	8	(1.7)
Dressmaker	6	9	13	28	(6.0)
Shop assistant	4	5	3	12	(2.6)
Clerk	1	0	2	3	(0.4)
Pharmacist's assistant	0	1	1	2	(0.4)
Handicraft	1	2	2	5	(1.1)
No occupation	67 (52%)	110 (61%)	91 (58%)	268	(57.4)
Total registering	128	181	158	467	
Left school without diploma	18 (14%)	26 (14%)	15 (9.5%)	59	(13%)

Average number of pupils registering per annum 17
Source. 'Report', op. cit.. note 32 above, p. 1117.

**Table 5b: Occupations of mothers of pupils admitted to
state school for midwives Rotterdam, 1883-1909***

Dressmaker	4	Mangle woman	1
Midwife	27	Draper	1
Baker	2	Shopkeeper	2
Washerwoman	2	Landlady	2
Landlady of public house	1	Greengrocer	1

* Most pupils' mothers either had no occupation or it was not recorded.
Source: as table 5a, p.1119.

LATE NINETEENTH AND EARLY TWENTIETH CENTURY OBSTETRIC PRACTICE

While population[42] and birth figures are readily available for the nineteenth century, there is little statistical information concerning obstetric attendance in the Netherlands during this period. The first reliable figures on obstetric attendance are for 1906, when just over 170.000 children were born in Holland. Of these, 61,000, that is 36%, were delivered by medical men, and 101,000, or 59%, by midwives. The remaining 5% were delivered without obstetric assistance.[43] In 1910 there were almost 176,000 births, of which 58% were delivered by midwives, with an average of 110 attendances per midwife.[44]

In Holland, by the turn of the twentieth century, the urban/rural divide was still of little significance, with a low level of industrialization and few major cities, yet there were still noticeable regional differences in obstetric attendance. In the densely-populated and urbanized province of South Holland, out of a total of 41,500 births in 1906, 61.5% were attended by midwives, and 38.2% by doctors. Meanwhile, in less populous North Holland, the proportions were 71.6% and 28.2% respectively, out of a total of almost 28,000 confinements.[45]

Figures are also available on the numbers of stillborn children delivered by midwives and doctors in 1906. Of the 61,000 children delivered under the direction of a medical man, just over 3,000 were born dead (5%), compared with 1,775 out of the 101,000 children delivered by midwives (1.8%). Some 255 (2.9%) of the 8,712 children born without obstetric assistance were stillborn. In some regions the differences between the figures for midwives and medical men were more striking. In Limburg, for example, out of the total of 1,481 children delivered by medical men in 1906, 173 or 11.7% were born dead; out of the 8,843 children delivered by midwives, 153 or 1.7%.[46] Male obstetric practitioners were called in to attend at a higher proportion of pathological and protracted deliveries, and this goes a long way towards explaining the differences in the stillbirth rates. However, the regional variations need to he explained by other factors, be they economic, social, or related to the skills of the obstetric attendants.[47]

During the nineteenth century, as illustrated in table 2, the number of midwives in the Netherlands remained roughly constant, with a slight decline in the middle of the century. Their numbers, then, did not keep pace with the rise in population and births. Table 3 indicates that the total number of male obstetric practitioners also did not alter much during the century; and this suggests that numerical evidence is not the key to explaining changes in the division of labour. Rather, such changes can perhaps best be explained by alterations in the tasks, or in the size or duration, of the average midwifery practice. During this period, significant adjustments took place in the character of obstetric practices, including the medical man's takeover of much of the midwife's practice, and a likely increase in the average number of births attended by midwives.

As the male medical profession became increasingly overstocked during the mid- to late nineteenth century, midwives faced a growing tide of competition from, and, especially after 1865, undercutting by, newly-qualified doctor intent on building up a general practice. Because the competence of midwives failed to be extended during the nineteenth century, it is possible that women turned more frequently to male obstetric practitioners to attend them in deliveries, rather than face the risk, having already paid for a midwife, of having to pay a second fee in the case of complications. As in other European countries and America, the "midwife question" came to the fore in Holland during the late nineteenth century. Dutch midwives were portrayed, both professionally and socially, in a negative light by many members of the medical profession during this period. A. Geyl (1853-1914),[48] surgeon, gynecologist, and medical historian, was one of the midwife's most formidable opponents. In a series of articles published in the *Medical Weekly (Medisch Weekblad)* in 1897 and 1911,[49] Geyl concluded that seventeenth- and eighteenth century midwives were, on the whole, unskilled, careless, and lacking in a sense of duty and professional integrity. By the nineteenth century their position had *been* much improved, but they were still, according to Geyl, inadequately trained and unfit for obstetric work. Midwives did, however, have patrons amongst the medical profession, including Meinart Niemeyer (1861-1934),[50] a provincial general practitioner and medical journalist, and G. C. Nijhoff (1857-1932),[51] professor of obstetrics and gynecology, medical historian and a founder of the Dutch Association of Gynecologists. Both men lent much support to late nineteenth-century midwife organizations and journals.

In 1897 the Dutch Society for the Promotion of Medicine drew up a report seeking ways to improve the position of midwives, through raising levels of practice, fees, and status.[52] Although, one suspects, it reflects biases against midwives and their practices on the part of their male competitors, the report was fairly positive about the professional qualities of midwives; 60% of the medical practitioners responding to a questionnaire described the skills and theoretical knowledge of midwives as "good" or "very good".[53] The report also analysed the incomes of midwives. Generally, these were made up of payments by a town or region for attendance on the poor, which could take the form of a fixed payment or fee per case, and the fees of private patients, although occasionally medical men also paid midwives a fixed amount for attendance at deliveries.

The incomes of midwives, whatever their source, were subject to great variation. Before 1865 their fees were set in accordance with tariffs drawn up for all medical practitioners, guaranteeing some uniformity. After 1865 they fell outside of this scale of tariffs and midwives in effect entered the "free market", which helps explain the growing variation in incomes. The fees paid to town midwives, for example, bore little relation to the number of deliveries attended, and ranged from the 150 guilders paid by the Amsterdam town council for attendance at more than one hundred deliveries per annum (less than 1.50 guilder per case), to the 400 guilders paid to the town midwife of 's Hertogenbosch in the east of the Netherlands, for an unknown, but presumably much smaller, number of deliveries.[54] Private fees also varied greatly, according to the wealth of the town or region, and the availability of obstetric assistance. The report calculated that the fees paid by labourers and lower middle-class groups to midwives averaged 2.50 to 5 guilders, but the range could be much wider in either direction. In the province of North Holland the most usual fee was between 4 and 5 guilders for a normal delivery; in North Brabant 2.50 to 4 guilders was the average, but fees as low as half a guilder were also recorded.[55] Yearly incomes were also subject to great variation. They could be less than three hundred guilders or more than eight hundred, but an average for the country as a whole was given as five to six hundred guilders per annum,[56] an increase on the two to three hundred guilders cited in the early nineteenth century.

The report recommended that medical men offer more support to midwives and avoid direct competition with them, thus enabling them to extend their practices. In practical terms, little was achieved. One of the few concrete results of the report was the founding of a journal for midwives in 1897, the *Journal of Practical Midwifery (Maandblad voor Praktische Verloskunde,* and from 1899, *Tijdschrift voor Praktische Verloskunde),* by Niemeyer and Nijhoff, two members of the committee of inquiry, which came to cover medical issues, and information on the position of midwives in Holland and abroad. In the same year, the Dutch Society of Midwives *(Bond van Nederlandse Vroedvrouwen)* was founded; by 1898 it had around three hundred members.[57]

The general lack of progress in improving the quality of midwives and their practices resulted in the compilation of another, substantially more detailed, report in 1911. This report also offers evidence about male medical practitioners' perceptions of midwives, including an analysis of the opinions of general practitioners on midwife practice. The main elements of the questionnaire are shown in table 6. About the midwives' knowledge and skills, the respondents were remarkably positive, much more so than in the 1897 report; more than 80% described the obstetric skills of midwives as "good" or "satisfactory". Almost 80% of the doctors participating in the survey believed that midwives called for assistance in difficult cases in good time; over 70% claimed that midwives were familiar with aseptic techniques. However, 61% of the respondents concluded that midwives did not conduct proper examinations of pregnant women, and 63% claimed that urine examinations were not made. While most of the respondents believed that a refresher course for midwives would be of value, 84% also believed that their competence should not be extended.[58]

Table 6: Summary of answers received from GPs concerning the practices of Dutch midwives in 1911

	Good	Satisfactory	Moderate	Bad	No answer	
General knowledge	59	178	112	84	47	+
Theoretical knowledge	92	214	61	66	47	+
Midwifery skills	197	199	17	23	45	+
Practices of midwives-did they include?	Yes	No				
Pregnancy examination	131	291			58	-
Urine examination	141	303			46	-
Correct diagnosis	377	64			39	+
Calling timely assistance	380	70			30	+
Supervision of nursing	216	218			46	=
Use of aseptic techniques	342	107			31	+
Birth control advice	63*	381			36	-
Refresher course necessary	291	103			86	-
Extension of competence recommended	53	402			25	-

+ Generally positive response
- Generally negative response
= Response evenly divided
* The low figure was largely due to a misunderstanding of the questionnaire on the part of the respondents, who equated birth control with assistance in abortions.
Number of doctors responding: 480.
Source: 'Report', op. cit., note 32 above, pp. 1130- 1.

The character of obstetric practices in the Netherlands was very much related to the low level of institutional care for lying-in women, in either special or general hospitals. Until the beginning of the twentieth century, Dutch women regarded the lying-in hospital as the last resort, not least because of the poor conditions prevailing in these institutions (particularly in the Amsterdam clinic under Lehmann). There was a rigid division between home deliveries and hospital practice, which made no provision, as did British lying-in and general hospitals for example, for out-patient deliveries. The chief motive behind the establishment of lying-in hospitals in Holland was to provide facilities for clinical education. The Amsterdam lying-in hospital, a department within the general hospital, and the Rotterdam lying-in hospital (founded in 1831) were attached to the clinical and state schools, and were utilized in midwife training. By 1867 the Amsterdam lying-in clinic had over one hundred beds. However, generally, only a quarter of these were occupied by parturient women; the rest were taken up by sick children, patients suffering from eye diseases, and surgical cases.[59] Leiden's university hospital was the first to establish lying-in facilities, following the appointment of Simon Thomas as professor in 1848.

By the 1880s Holland still had only four lying-in clinics, connected to the universities of Amsterdam, Utrecht, Leiden, and Groningen. Together these catered for approximately 600 deliveries per annum, a number which rose to 850 between 1880 and the end of the century.[60] The number of deliveries taking place within all institutions in the Netherlands per annum around this time must have been well under a thousand.[61] By the final decade of the nineteenth century, the Amsterdam clinic was dealing with approximately 450 to 550 deliveries each year, by far the highest number of institutional deliveries in Holland;[62] midwife pupils at the Amsterdam school attended at well over one hundred deliveries per annum.[63] The lack of institutional facilities in Holland ensured that most women, rich or poor, had their babies at home. It also limited the research possibilities of obstetricians, and meant that training facilities for medical students in midwifery remained inadequate.[64] Institutional obstetrics in the Netherlands only began to play a significant role after World War II, and as late as 1955, 76.1% of deliveries took place at home.[65]

The practice of midwifery and obstetrics in the Netherlands incorporated a number of features which set it apart from other European countries and the United States. Perhaps the most striking divergence's were the early introduction of legislative control and licensing for both male and female obstetric practitioners, the institutionalization of midwife training, and the very low incidence of hospital births. There are obvious attractions in drawing up comparisons between the development of midwifery in the Netherlands and other nations, in particular England and the United States, where the fortunes of midwives took very different, and well documented, turns in the late nineteenth and twentieth centuries. However, the problems of drawing such comparisons are considerable. The Netherlands differed enormously from other countries, not only in its institution of regulation, formal educational arrangements and licensing, but also in its arrangements for childbirth (the sketchiness of the institutional facilities for lying-in women has been described above), and in the way legislation was achieved (that is, it was initiated chiefly by the government, not the midwives, medical profession or other concerned pressure groups). It is difficult, given these factors, to find bases for comparison. In attempting to explain such differences, we are also drawn inevitably into an analysis of Dutch society and economy, educational provisions, population distribution and changes, the role of women in the work-force and professions, and the culture surrounding childbirth, a task which falls beyond the scope of this paper.

Only the simplest and briefest illustration of differences in midwifery practice in various European countries will be presented here, in the form of a table, reproduced largely from an article published by Dr. S. Josephine Baker in 1912, which called for the better training and regulation of midwives in the United States.[66] This table demonstrates the varying roles of midwives in providing childbirth attendance by the end of the nineteenth century, and perhaps also indicates the way the wind was blowing for the midwife in the countries represented.

Table 7: Number of midwives in selected European countries in the late 19th and early 20th centuries

Country	Number of midwives	Year	Midwives: 10,000 inhabitants	Births: midwife pa. (average)
Germany	37,025	1898	6.8	55
Prussia	20,878	1907	5.7	63
Austria	20,000	1909	7.3	51
Switzerland	3,305	1903	10.1	29
Norway	*	*	5.5	53
France	*	*	3.4	67
Italy (active practice)	15,000	*	4.3	81
Russia	14,000	*	0.9	550?
England	12,500	(est. 1892)	2.6	36-52
	27,238	(reg. 1909)	7.3	38
Netherlands**	830	(lic. 1895)	5.8	unknown
	849	(lic. 1905)	6.5	119
	924	(lic. 1910)	5.9	110

* Data not supplied in Baker.
? This questionably high figure is taken from Baker.
** The figures for The Netherlands refer to trained and licensed midwives only.
Source: Baker, op. cit., note 66 below, cited in Litoff, op. cit., note 6 above, p.156; 'Report', op. cit., note 61 abobe, app. 6, p.144; Klinkert, op. cit., note 2 above, p.72; state medical registers.

At first glance, the midwife numbers for the Netherlands seem low, but the 830 midwives trained and licensed in the Netherlands by the early 1890s[67] compare with 1,200 trained midwives in England, as estimated in the 1892 Parliamentary inquiry on midwife registration.[68] In relation to the total population, there were approximately twice as many *licensed* midwives in Holland as *all* midwives in England. In terms of births attended, by 1910 each midwife in the Netherlands attended an average of 110 births per annum:[69] in England, in 1909, the corresponding figure was a remarkably low 38 per annum.[70]

The scope of this paper has of necessity been confined to a discussion of regulated midwives. In Holland, as elsewhere, we are to a large extent prisoners of data which concentrate on trained and licensed midwives. Yet, in Holland, some women, often of the poorer classes, and almost certainly a much smaller number than in North America and other European nations, practised midwifery uncontrolled, often on an irregular basis, without formal education, but not necessarily without informal training or inexpertly. Midwives practising without a formal education and license, and thus in effect outside of the law, remain in just as much obscurity in Holland as in other countries, though the lack of concrete data on this group should not discourage some future analysis of their role in providing obstetric attendance and shaping childbirth practices. There is also an obvious necessity, again despite the difficulties of sources, for learning more about midwives' day-to-day lives and work. It seems likely, especially given her case load, that the Dutch midwife devoted less time to individual cases than her counterpart in other countries, confining her services to the delivery of the infant and post-natal check-ups.

Throughout the nineteenth century, Dutch midwives came largely from the lower middle- or artisan classes. The fees demanded by the midwifery schools, of 60 guilders for a two-year training course (roughly equivalent to one-tenth of a year's earnings in a good practice), ensured that the profession was accessible to members of lower social strata.[71] Few middle- or upper-class women were attracted to midwifery in Holland during this period. This meant, on the one hand, that there was an absence of the tension which occurred, say, in England, between the "traditional" midwife, practising in her local community on an untrained and unlicensed basis, and the middle-class ladies, who from the late nineteenth century came to take advantage of the limited number of training courses in midwifery, and to dominate midwife societies and campaigns for legislation. On the other hand, the absence of a middle- or upper-class leadership group partly accounts, perhaps, for the comparative slowness of Dutch midwives in setting up midwifery societies and journals, and the domination of these organizations by male obstetric practitioners.

The low social status of midwives also served to isolate them from other female health professionals. The nursing profession, late to develop in Holland, tended, unlike midwifery, to be dominated by women of high social status; their perception of nursing was shaped largely by religious and charitable impulses, not financial need or the desire for occupational satisfaction and mobility.[72] The aims and practices of Dutch midwives had little in common with those of nurses; the two professions developed separately and remain distinct today. Meanwhile, women were slow to take up medical practice in Holland, the first female doctor, Aletta Jacobs, qualifying only in 1878; by 1900 only eleven women had qualified in medicine.[73] Dutch midwives, also for social reasons, lacked the allegiance of aspiring female medical practitioners, often so important in other countries.

The story of Dutch midwives in the nineteenth century is one of pluses and minuses. Legislative developments laid the foundations for the future evolution of midwifery practice. It seems likely that without the early establishment of licensing, training facilities, codes of practice and divisions of labour, midwifery and the fortunes of midwives as a professional group would have taken very different courses. But midwives paid a price for this security, in the form of a more rigid definition of their roles in the delivery room. The legislation of 1818, 1860, and 1865 stated categorically that midwives were only to attend at normal deliveries: all difficult cases were to be turned over to or supervised by a male medical attendant.[74]

Encroachment upon midwife's practice by male obstetric practitioners, both obstetric specialists and general practitioners, was not eliminated by regulation. Nor did the report' drawn up around the turn of the century by male practitioners, with the intention of improving the status and practice opportunities of midwives, do much to reduce competition. Midwives in Holland fell increasingly under the control of male medical practitioners during the nineteenth century. The teaching of midwives in the clinical and state schools was undertaken largely by obstetricians; training was followed by examination by the medical men who made up the provincial and state medical committees. The domination of midwife organizations and journals by male obstetricians has already been referred to. The incomes of midwives, although apparently creeping up towards the end of the nineteenth century, remained significantly lower than those of male obstetric practitioners, even for attendance at normal deliveries. However, the early establishment of formal systems of training, examination and control in the Netherlands, while closely defining the sphere and practice limits of midwives, also enabled them to consolidate their positions as attendants in normal childbirth, and to operate with a higher level of autonomy than in many other countries.

[1] This article is based on a paper presented at the conference 'Obstetric Problems, Past and Present', celebrating the fiftieth anniversary or the Nuffield Department of Obstetrics and Gynaecology, held in Oxford 10 October 1987. (Organized by the Wellcome Unit for the History of Medicine. Oxford, in association with the Nuffield Department of Obstetrics and Gynaecology.)

[2] For example J.J. Klinkert. *Verloskundigen en artsen, verleden en heden van enkele professionele beroepen in de gezondheidszorg*. Alphen aan den Rijn & Brussels, Stafleu, 1980; E. Scholte, M.J. Van Lieburg & R.O. Aalberberg. *Rijkskweekschool voor Vroedvrouwen te Rotterdam*, Leidschendam, Ministerie van Volksgezondheid en Milieuhygiene, 1982; Floor van Gilder, 'Is dat nu typies vrouwenwerk? De maatschappelijke positie van vroedvrouwen', *Tijdschr. Vrouwenstud*. 1982. 3:5-33; H. M. Dupuis *et al.., Een kind onder het hart. Verloskunde, volksgeloof, gezin, seksualiteit en moraal vroeger en nu*. Amsterdam, Amsterdams Historisch Museum and Meulenhoff Informatief. 1987; M.J.van Lieburg &Hilary Marland (eds.), *Midwifery in the Dutch Republic*. Amsterdam. Rodopi. [1990] a collection of English-language essays on midwifery during the seventeenth & eighteenth centuries.

[3] With the exception of the recent paper by Anja Hiddinga, 'Obstetrical research in the Netherlands in the nineteenth century', *Med. Hist.*, 1987, **31**:281-305

[4] Jane B. Donegan, *Women and men midwives. Medicine, morality, and misogyny in early America*, Westport, Conn. & London, Greenwood Press, 1978; Judy Barrett Litoff, *American midwives 1860 to the present*, Westport. Conn. & London, Greenwood Press, 1978; Richard W. & Dorothy C. Wertz, *Lying-in a history of childbirth in America*. New York, Scholten. 1979; Catherine M. Scholten, *Childbearing in American society, 1650-1850*, ed. Lynne Withey. New York & London, New York University Press. 1985; Judith Walzer Leavitt. *Brought to bed: Childbearing in America 1750 to 1950*. New York & Oxford, Oxford University Press, 1986, and the essays in *idem* (ed.), *Woman and health in America*. Madison, University of Wisconsin Press, 1984.

[5] I. Snapper, 'Midwifery: past and present', *Bull. NY Acad. Med.*, 1963, **39**: 526; Klinkert, op.cit., note 2 above, p. 72; Centraal bureau voor de statistiek, *1899-1979, Tachtig jaren statistiek in tijdreeksen*. The Hague, Staatsuitgeverij, 1979, and *Statistisch zakboek 1985*, The Hague, CBS publikaties, 1985.

[6] For England. Jean Donnison's study, *Midwives and medical men. A history of inter-professional rivalries and women's rights*, London. Heinemann, 1977, remains the standard on the changing relationship between male and female midwifery practitioners in the nineteenth century. For the United States see especially Donegan op cit., note 4 above, and Litoff, op. cit., note 4 above; and, for the early twentieth century, Neal Devitt. The statistical ease for elimination of the midwife: fact versus prejudice 1890-1935', *Women and Health*, 1979, **4**: 81-96, 169-86. Frances E. Kobrin. 'The American midwife controversy: a crisis of professionalization', *Bull. Hist. Med.*, 1966, **40**: 350-63. Judy Barrett Litoff, *The American midwife debate. A sourcebook on its modern origins*, Westport, Conn. & London, Greenwood Press, 1986. and *idem*. 'Forgotten women: American midwives at the turn of the twentieth century', *Historian*, 1978, **40**: 235-51.

[7] For example, records are extant for the six clinical schools on midwife training, dating from 1824 until their closure in the 1860s; for the lying-in hospitals of several major towns from the early nineteenth century; and for the state schools for midwives in Amsterdam and Rotterdam from 1861 and 1882 respectively. The records of the provincial and state medical committees provide information on medical practice in nineteenth-century Holland; annual provincial and state medical registers list all officially recognized medical practitioners, including licensed midwives.

[8] The most thorough guide in English to the political situation in the Netherlands during the nineteenth century is E.H. Kossmann, *The low countries, 1780-1940*. Oxford University Press. 1978.

[9] M. J. van Lieburg, 'De tweede geneeskundige stand (1818-1865). Een bijdrage tot de geschiedenis van het medisch beroep in Nederland', *Tijdschr. Gesch.*, 1983, **96**: 434.

[10] For a detailed account of Dutch medical legislation during the nineteenth century, see ibid.. pp. 43-53. For a summary in English, see Hiddinga, op. cit., note 3 above, pp. 283-7. For a description of the Belgian medical profession during the nineteenth century, with its sometimes parallel development, see Rita Schepers, 'The legal and institutional development of the Belgian medical profession in the nineteenth century'. *Soc. Health & Illness*, 1985. **7**: 314-41.

[11] *Verzameling van wetten, besluiten en reglementen, betrekkelijk de burgerlijke geneeskundige dienst in het Koninkrijk der Nederlanden*, The Hague, J. P. Beekman, 1836, p. 197.

[12] Ibid., pp.150-3.

[13] D. J. A. Arntzenius, 'Statistieke opgaven omtrent de geneeskundige bevolking in Nederland', *Bijdragen tot de Geneeskundige Staatsregeling*. 1845, **3**: 324.

[14] Ibid.; state medical registers. Arntzenius took most of his data from the provincial medical registers. See also M. J. van Lieburg, 'De medische promoties aan de Nederlandse universiteiten (1815-1899)', *Batavia Academia*, 1987, **5**:1-17, for the overall number of doctorates conferred by Dutch universities.

[15] Simon Thomas was appointed to a full professorship in 1857, which he retained until his death in 1866. He also taught obstetrics to the Leiden midwives from 1863. See Hiddinga, op. cit., note 2 above, p.292, and G.A. Lindeboom, *Dutch medical biographies. A biographical dictionary of Dutch physicians and surgeons 1475-1975*, Amsterdam, Ropodi, 1984, pp.1815-16. For Simon Thomas and other eminent obstetric practitioners in the nineteenth century, see P.H. Simon Thomas, *Het onderwijs in de verloskunde aan de Leidsche Hoogeschool gedurende het tijdvak 1791-1900*. Leiden, S.C. van Doesburgh, 1909; G.C. Nijhoff, 'Bijdrage tot de geschiedenis der practische verloskunde en gynaecologie in Nederland (1850-1860)', *Ned. Tijdschr.Genees.*, 1907, **51**, IA: 36-47 and *idem*., 'Het onderwijs in de verloskunde en de uitoefening der verloskunst in Nederland gedurende de laatste 75 jaren', ibid., 1924, **68**, IIA, 25-32; Hector Treub, 'Verloskunde en gynaecologie in de laatste 50 jaaren', ibid, 1899, **35**, II, 123-37; and for a more recent assessment H. Beukers, 'De opkomst van het universitair onderwijs in verloskunde en gynaecologie in Nederland', in F.J.J. van Assen (ed.) *Een eeuw vrouwenarts*, Amsterdam, Ropodi, 1987, pp.241-57.

[16] On medical societies before 1849, see M.J. van Lieburg, 'Geneeskunde en medische professie in het genootschapswezen van Nederland in de eerste helft van de negentiende eeuw', *De Negentiende Eeuw*, 1983; **7**:123-45. For the period after 1849, see C.C. Delprat, 'Het ontstaan der Nederlandse Maatschappij tot Bevordering der

Geneeskunst en haar rol bij de herziening der geneeskundige staatsregeling van 1818', in *Gedenkboek der Nederlandse Maatschappij tot Bevordering der Geneeskunst*, privately printed, 1924, pp.19-109. The mid-nineteenth century also witnessed the establishment of a number of medical periodicals. In 1857 several of these amalgamated to become the *Dutch Journal of Medicine (Nederlands Tijdschrift voor Geneeskunde)*, the organ of the NMG. For pre-1857 medical journals, see *idem*, 'De geschiedenis der Nederlandse geneeskundige tijdschriften van 1680 tot 1857', *Bijdr. Gesch. Geneesk.*, 1927, 7:1-114, 201-314, 417-90. For medical journals in de period 1840-70, see M.J. van Lieburg. 'De Nederlandse medische tijdschriften en de wetenschappelijke geneeskunde 1840-1870', in D. de Moulin (ed.), *Kracht en stof. De introductie van moderne natuurwetenschappelijke denkwijzen in de geneeskunde, zoals blijkt uit Nederlandse medische vakbladen, 1840-1870*, Amsterdam, Ropodi, 1985:pp.1-18.

[17] Van Lieburg, op. cit., note 9 above, p.448.

[18] *Idem*, 'Municipal hospitals and non-academic medical teaching in the Netherlands in the nineteenth century', *Clio Medica*, 1989, **21**.

[19] A.C. Drogendijk. 'Het dagboek van Vrouw Waltman', *Ned. Tijdschr. Geneesk.*, 1936, **80**, I:981-8.

[20] For midwifery and childbirth in Dordrecht, see also *idem, De verloskundige voorzieningen in Dordrecht from 1500 tot heden*, Amsterdam, H. J. Paris, 1935. The 1930s saw the publication of a number of regional histories of midwifery practices and practitioners, infant and maternal mortality, and the folk traditions surrounding childbirth. For example, J.H. Hagenbeek, *Het moederschap in Overijssel. Een onderzoek naar de verloskundige en de zuigelingenzorg in de provincie Overijssel*, Zwolle, H. Tulp, 1936; P.E.G. van der Heijden, *De zorg voor moeder en kind in Noord-Brabant*, diss., University of Amsterdam, 1934; J.H. Starmans, *Verloskunde en kindersterfte in Limburg. Folklore, geschiedenis, heden*, Maastricht, Van Aelst, 1930.

[21] Drogendijk, op. cit., note 19 above, pp. 982, 984.

[22] Ibid., pp. 982-3, 985.

[23] Ibid., p. 984.

[24] Ibid., p. 986.

[25] Ibid., p. 987.

[26] By 1910 there were 925 midwives in the Netherlands; between 1910 and 1960 the number decreased to 850. Meanwhile, the number of doctors more than tripled during this period, from 4.000 to over 13,000. By 1983 the total number of doctors had increased to 31,185 (one to every 463 inhabitants); midwives numbered 950 (1 : 15,215). Snapper, op. cit., note 5 above, p.527; *Statistisch zakboek 1985*, op. cit., note 5 above, p. 63.

[27] Scholte, Van Lieburg, and Aalbersberg, op. cit., note 2 above, pp.35-6

[28] Klinkert, op. cit., note 2 above, p.40.

[29] For Vrouw Schrader, see H. Marland, M.J. van Lieburg & G. J. Kloosterman, *"Mother and child were saved". The memoirs (1693-1740) of the Frisian midwife Catharina Schrader*, Amsterdam, Rodopi, 1987, and, for a summary of her life and work Simon Schama, *The embarrassment of riches. An interpretation of Dutch culture in the Golden Age*, London, William Collins, 1987, pp.525-35. In Dutch: see also, the fuller transcription of Vrouw Schrader's notebook with introductory essays, M. J. van Lieburg (ed.), *C. G. Schrader's memoryboeck van de vrouwens. Het notitieboek van een Friese vroedvrouw 1693-1745*, with an obstetric commentary by G.J. Kloosterman, Amsterdam, Rodopi, 1984; B. W. Th. Nuyens. 'Het dagboek van Vrouw Schraders', *Ned. Tijdschr. Geneesk*, 1926, **70**,II, 51:1790-1801; and for a commentary on the Dutch edition of the notebook, Willem Frijhoff, 'Vrouw Schrader's beroepsjournal: overwegingen bij een publikatie over arheidspraktijk in het verleden' *Tijdschr. Gesch. Geneesk. Natuurw. Wisk. Techn.*, 1985, **8**: 27-38.

[30] A.J.M. Lamers, *Hendrik van Deventer medicinae doctor 1651-1724. Leven en werken.* Assen, Van Gorcum, 1946.

[31] 'Dutch Society for the Promotion of Medicine. Report of the committee to investigate the means by which medical men can improve the standard and status of midwives in the Netherlands' ('Nederlandsche Maatschappij tot Bevordering der Geneeskunst. Rapport der commissie ter onderzoek naar de wijze waarop door geneeskundigen, verbetering gebracht kan worden in het gehalte en positie der vroedvrouwen in Nederland'), March 1897. In *Ned. Tijdschr. Geneesk.*, 1897, **33**, I: 610-28.

[32] 'Report of the commission selected by the Dutch Society for the Promotion of Medicine and the Dutch Association of Gynaecologists on midwifery practice in the Netherlands' ('Nederlandsche Maatschappij tot Bevordering der Geneeskunst. Rapport der commissie in zake het vroedvrouwenvraagstuk hier te lande, benoemd door het Hoofdbestuur der Nederlandsche Maatschaprij tot Bevordering der Geneeskunst in samenwerking met het Bestuur der Nederlandsche Gynaecologische Vereeniging'), February 1911. In ibid., 1911, **55**, IA (Supplement): 1105-32.

[33] On the Amsterdam school, see S. Sièvertsen Buvig, *Geschiedenis van de Rijks-Kweekschool voor Vroedvrouwen te Amsterdam, van 1861 tot 1921.* Amsterdam. 1921; the essays in *Bij het honderdjarig bestaan van de Kweekschool voor Vroedvrouwen te Amsterdam*, reprinted from *Tijdschr. Soc.Geneesk.*, 1961,**39**; 609-50; J. Klomp, 'De "Camperstraat" verhuisd-na 75 jaar. Ontwikkeling van de opleiding tot vroedvrouw in Amsterdam', *Ons Amsterdam*, 1976, **28**: 2-11; H.J. Versteeg, *85 jaar Amsterdamse vrouwenkliniek*, privately printed, with the support of the Stichting Wetenschapsfonds Verloskunde Gynaecologie, A.M.C., Amsterdam, 1986.

[34] After 1818, prospective doctors could train either for four years at a university or for two years each at an atheneum and university. The second option was cheaper. There were four athenea in the Netherlands, at Harderwijk (1815-18), Franeker (1815-43), Deventer (1815-76) and Amsterdam (1815-77). In 1876 the status of the Amsterdam Atheneum was raised to that of town university.

[35] On the Rotterdam school, see Scholte, Van Lieburg, en Aalsterberg, op. cit., note 2 above; M.J. van Lieburg, 'Uit de medische stadsgeschiedenis van Rotterdam: IV. Vroedvrouwen, verlosmeesters en doctoran', *Monitor*, 1975, **4**: 77-80; K. de Snoo, *De ontwikkeling van het vroedvrouwenonderwijs to Rotterdam*, Rotterdam, W.L. en J, Brusse, 1914.

[36] On the Groningen School, see Catherine van Tussenbroek, *De ontwikkeling der aseptische verloskunde in Nederland*, Haarlem, De Erven F.Bohn, 1911, pp.173-7.

[37] M.J. van Lieburg, 'De Rijkskweekschool voor Vroedvouwen (1882-1926)', in Scholte, Van Lieburg, and Aalsterberg, op. cit., note 2 above, p.5.

[38] For Lehmann, see Lindeboom, op. cit., note 15 above, pp.1165-6.

[39] For Van der Mey, see ibid., pp.1321-2.

[40] A. H.M. J. van Rooy, 'Drie kwart eeuw universitair verloskundig onderwijs te Amsterdam', in Gedenkboek uitgegeven ter gelegenheid van de viering van het vijf en zeventig-jarig bestaan van den Geneeskundigen Kring te Amsterdam. Privately printed. 1923, pp 105-6.

[41] Report, op. cit., note 32 above, pp.1118-19

[42] The population fluctuated around the two million mark between 1795 and 1815, but from 1815 to 1830 it grew at an average annual rate of approximately 40,000. Between 1850 and 1870 the population rose by almost 17% to reach 3,600,000 in 1870. By 1913 the population of the Netherlands had reached six million. Kossmann, op. cit., note 8 above, pp. 66, 215, 265, 419.

[43] Van Tussenbroek, op. cit., note 36 above, p.183.

[44] Klinkert, op. cit., note 2 above, p.72.

[45] Van Tussenbroek, op. cit., note 36 above, p.183.

[46] Ibid., pp.187, 189.

[47] Changes in maternal and infant mortality rates in Holland, and comparisons between the success rates of different groups of obstetric practitioners, and between the Netherlands and other countries, have been left out of consideration in this paper. For infant and maternal mortality, see, for example, ibid., and *idem*, 'Kraambedsterfte in Nederland', *Ned. Tijdschr. Verlosk. Gynaec.*, 1912, **21**: 1-37; the essays in *Feestbundel opgedragen aan Hector Truub bij de feestelijke herdenking van zijn vijfentwintig-jarig professoraat*. Leiden, S.C van Doesburgh, 1912; James Young, 'Maternal mortality and maternal mortality rates' *Am. J. Obst. & Gynec.*, 1936, **31**: 198-212, and Chr. Vanderbroeke *et al.*, 'De zuigelingen- en kindersterfte in Belgie en Nederland in seculair perspectief', *Tijdschr. Gesch.*, 1981, **94**: 461-91. For comparison of maternal mortality in various countries, including the Netherlands, see Irvine Loudon, 'Maternal mortality: 1880-1950. Some regional and international comparisons', *J. soc. Hist. Med.* 1988, **1**: 183-228.

[48] For Geyl, see Lindeboom, op. cit., note 15 above, pp 674-5.

[49] A. Geyl, 'Over de opleiding en maatschappelijke positie der vroedvrouwen in de 17de en 18de eeuw', *Med. Weekbl'.* 1897-8, **4**: 6-10, 18-26, 35-41, 53-62, 67-73, 86-90, 115-17, and *idem*, 'Beschouwingen en mededelingen over vroedvrouwen uit de 15de tot en met de 18de eeuw', ibid., 1911-12, **18**: 227-31, 266-70, 279-83. 318-22, 341-5, 353-7, 368-9, 377-81, 401-6, 414-17, 425-30.

[50] For Niemeyer, see Lindeboom, op. cit., note 15 above, pp. 1419-20.

[51] For Nijhoff, see ibid., pp.1427-8.

[52] 'Report', op. cit. Note 31 above.

[53] Ibid., p.162.

[54] Ibid., p.615.

[55] Ibid., p.616.

[56] Ibid., p.617. In general the salaries of nurses during this period were much lower. During the late nineteenth century, nurses in the Buitengasthuis, Amsterdam were earning only 15o to 200 guilders per annum. Van Tussenbroek, op. cit., note 36 above, p.94.

[57] Floor van Gelder, 'The case of the midwives, a forgotten profession social consciousness, of working women in the Dutch public health care, 1900', unpublished paper presented at 3rd Anglo-Dutch Labour History Conference, Maastricht, 1-3 April 1982, pp. 10-1. See also Van Gelder, op. cit., note 2 above.

[58] 'Report', op. cit., note 32 above, pp.1130-1.

[59] A. W. C. Berns, *De opheffing van de Amsterdamse kraaminrichting nader besproken*. Amsterdam, 1881. Cited in Hiddinga, op. cit., note 3 above, p.296.

[60] Van Tussenbroek, op. cit., note 36 above, tables pp. 136, 86

[61] This compared dramatically with the situation in England, where, by the end of the nineteenth century, numerous lying-in and general hospitals and workhouses had made provision for the delivery of poor women, albeit not always on a large scale. In 1889, 2,234 in-patients, and almost 25,000 out-patients were delivered in twenty-seven London

medical charities alone. Between 1871 and 1880 an average of 2,300 women per annum were said to have been confined in thirty metropolitan Poor Law infirmaries. Report from the Select Committee on midwives' registration. PP, 1892, XIV (289), app 4.p.136.

[62] Van Tussenbroek, op. cit., note 36 above, table p. 86.

[63] Ibid., p.170.

[64] After the passing of the 1865 medical act, for example, facilities for the training of medical students were so inadequate in the university clinics that the university professors of Leiden, Utrecht, and Groningen had to arrange for the practical training of students by having them assist with home births under the supervision of midwives. Hiddinga, op. cit., note 3 above, p. 291.

[65] In 1960 only 26% of the 242,407 deliveries in Holland took place in a hospital; the other 74% were home deliveries. Physicians conducted 63% of the total deliveries (152,753), 65% of them at home; midwives attended at 37% of deliveries (89,504), 80% of them at home. Meanwhile, in the United States in 1957, 96% of deliveries took place in hospital. By 1965 the proportion of home deliveries in Holland had been reduced to 68.6%, by 1975, 44.4%. In 1983 only 35.1% of babies in the Netherlands were born at home. Snapper, op. cit., note 5 above, p.526: Klinkert, op. cit., note 2 above. p.66; *Statistisch zakboek 1985.* op. cit., note 5 above, p. 52.

[66] S. Josephine Baker. 'Schools for midwives', *A. J. Obst. & Diseases of Women and Children*, 1912, **65**. Cited in Litoff, *The American Midwives debate*, op. cit., note 6 above, p.156.

[67] State medical registers, 1895.

[68] 'Report', op. cit., note 61 above, app., no6, pp.144, 148.

[69] Klinkert, op. cit., note 2 above, p.72

[70] Baker, op. cit., note 66 above, p.156.

[71] This compared with the much larger fees demanded for English midwifery courses, charges which were prohibitive for many women. A short course in the prestigious London lying-in hospitals could cost as much as £30 to £40 (equivalent to a year's earnings in a successful practice); even in workhouse infirmaries the fee for a three-month 0course could be £10. Donnison. op. cit., note 6 above, p.59.

[72] Cora Bakker-van der Kooy. 'Nurses and social consciousness', unpublished paper presented at the third Anglo-Dutch Labour History Conference, Maastricht, 1-3 April 1982; Truus Spijker. *Mooi en beschaafd verplegen. Een historische analyse van een vrouwenberoep.* Lochem, De Tijdstroom, 1979.

[73] Hilary Marland, 'Women doctors in the Netherlands 1878-1920', unpublished paper presented at the Deutsch-Niederlandisches Medizinhistorikertreffen, Amersfoort, 11 June 1988; Mineke Bosch, 'Blauwkousen en hobbezakken in een witte jas: De eerste vrouwelijke artsen in Nederland, 1872-1913', in Josine Blok *et al.* (eds.), *Jaarboek voor vrouwengeschiedenis 1982.* Nijmegen, SUN, 1982, pp. 63-97.

[74] See especially articles by Van Gelder, op cit., notes 2 & 57, on the cutting back of midwife's role in 19th century.

The Midwife in Contemporary Industrialised Society

Maureen Porter

Introduction

In the foregoing sections it has become apparent that midwives have struggled throughout history to overcome the medical profession's dominance and encroachment on their domain, which continues to this day. It was seen how technology effectively undermined the midwife, doing away with the need for her special skills. The various roles performed by midwives and traditional birth attendants in contemporary, non-industrialised societies have been examined, highlighting the diverse forms which exist but which are threatened by the trend to improve midwives' competence by formalising and standardising education and training. This section will show that the midwifery profession in many developed nations today is also undergoing major changes in education, role and status. These changes are partly the result of economic and political considerations imposed by various national governments and partly the result of ideological changes. The main change in ideology involves questioning the validity of a system of health care based on the traditional medical model and an openness towards one based on a midwifery model. In the former, authority rests with the physician and attention is focused on the patient's medical condition whereas it is focused on the whole woman and her needs in the latter model of care provision.

The Contemporary Situation

Reviewing the state of midwifery at the present time, Malin and Herminski (1992) argue that in the USA and many other Western nations, care in pregnancy and childbirth is largely given by physicians, often aided by midwives acting as obstetric nurses.[1] They suggest that countries such as Finland and the Netherlands, where midwives practise independently or provide the bulk of care, are exceptions, having followed a different historical course. Abraham-van der Mark (1993) says "Although midwives lost ground in the twentieth century in other Western countries, Dutch midwifery was characterised by growing professionalisation: midwives' qualifications were increased, standards for recruitment and training were made more rigorous, and their organization gained power".

Countries where midwives practise more autonomously generally enjoy lower rates of perinatal mortality than those where physicians predominate. This has resulted in other Western nations seeking to emulate them, although they themselves are under threat as a result of the demanding nature of one-to-one midwifery care and lack of appropriate political support (Abraham-van der Mark 1993). Thus in many Western industrialised nations at the present time midwifery and childbirth are issues of topical concern, reflecting political and economic difficulties. Most countries want to maintain or improve their rates of perinatal morbidity and mortality but aim to achieve this against a background of economic restraint. Western nations face rapidly rising costs of providing health care for an ageing population (Raleigh 1997). As these costs cannot be supported by economic growth, economies are sought elsewhere in health and social services.

So far, the provision of maternity services has not been greatly reduced although some have become more geographically concentrated as a result of smaller units closing. Also the numbers of obstetricians and midwives continues to grow throughout the West, despite steady or declining birth rates. Other changes are evident however. The policy of almost total hospitalisation for childbirth is under review in many European countries and the accompanying trend towards increased use of technology and intervention in childbirth which started in the 1960s has been slowed. Questions are being asked about what form maternity services should take, who should provide them and how they should be funded (Allison & Pascall 1994; Wagner 1996, Graham 1997). These changes are the result of public opinion as much as economic considerations (Michaelson & Alvin 1988; DeVries 1993). In the 1970s a movement towards more natural forms of birth flourished on both sides of the Atlantic and culminated in the official questioning of the routine use of technology and interventions. This has resulted in many obstetric practices and procedures which were taken for granted by midwives and physicians in the past, recently coming under scrutiny (Chalmers *et al.* 1989). Although some former obstetric practices such as routine use of enemas, shaving and episiotomies have been eliminated as a consequence of research questioning their validity, the use of intervention and technology remains an issue (Allison & Pascal 1994: Machover 1995). Episiotomy, for example, has remained popular although a trial by Sleep (1984) showed that it had no advantage over a second-degree tear. Furthermore, untested and unproven procedures are still being introduced without proper evaluation, as is the case with ultrasound screening and waterbirth (Wise 1993).

Given their history, it might have been expected that midwives would welcome debates about the provision of maternity care and their role and responsibilities within it, but midwifery itself is in a state of flux or crisis in many developed countries. Since the mid-1970s midwives have been concerned with the erosion of their role by the medical profession, resulting in a loss of confidence and competence to manage normal pregnancy and childbirth (Flint 1991; Robinson 1996). In the USA midwifery has almost vanished and is now trying to make a comeback against heavy opposition from a politically and economically dominant medical profession. In the UK there are problems recruiting new midwives whilst those who are trained and experienced are leaving the profession in droves (Mander 1993; Robinson 1996). On both sides of the Atlantic there is concern about whether training prepares the midwife for the role she is likely to perform. At issue are the independence, role and responsibilities of the midwife in the hospital and in the community (Askham & Barbour 1987 and this volume). This section contains descriptions of the work actually done by midwives in hospitals, clinics and home births in Europe and USA. Unfortunately space does not permit the inclusion of papers on other aspects of their work such as antenatal preparation for pregnancy and childbirth (Walsh 1993), postnatal care and breastfeeding support (Murphy-Black 1994; Parker 1994) though these topics are mentioned.

In the USA certified nurse midwives practice in publicly funded hospitals, private practice—independently and in partnership with physicians, birth centres and home births. In Britain such alternatives for normal women with unproblematic pregnancies have only become available in the last 10-15 years. Midwife-only units have arisen in many specialist obstetric hospitals. Patients are encouraged to complete birth plans—a list of their requirements for the birth—and midwives to meet these needs even if it means delivering a baby at home, under water, on all fours, or on the floor. "Domino" deliveries have enabled women to be delivered by a community midwife known to them in a local hospital and discharged home after six or less hours (see Beck 1989 and this volume). Independent midwives have provided all of women's care in their own homes without recourse to medical professionals. Team midwifery and "know your midwife" schemes have made it possible for midwives to use their traditional skills and look after women throughout their antenatal, intra-partum and postnatal periods. According to many reports such schemes improve continuity of care, are preferred by women, lead to fewer medical interventions and have no adverse neonatal outcomes (Flint *et al.* 1989; Butler *et al.* 1993; Turnbull *et al.* 1996). Now the British Government, apparently under the influence of consumer and midwives groups, has legitimised the midwives' stance with two reports (House of Commons 1992; Department of Health 1993) affirming the central role of midwives in normal childbirth and acknowledging women's needs for continuity of care and alternative methods of management.

However, most of these innovations sprang from a desire to give women a better birth experience rather than midwives' need for greater satisfaction in their work. Indeed the two aspects may be incompatible as such changes—often necessitating longer hours and more time "on call"—take their toll on the practitioners. DeVries (1993: 170) suggests making a distinction between the different interests at stake:

- those of midwives as persons
- those of midwifery as a profession
- those of midwifery as a service (interested in the health and well-being of women and babies)

These differences are apparent in the paper by Porter (this volume pp. 000-000) where the political changes in Britain leading to a totally new approach to the provision of maternity services are examined. She argues that this change in ethos is partially the result of a change in perspective within the health service to a more research or evidence-based approach to care. It is also partly a result of pressure from the consumer movement, feminism and more radical midwives; Porter suggests that it is a change for which the majority of midwives are perhaps ill prepared. She draws on empirical research completed in Scotland in the early 1980s to highlight the different concerns found among different types of midwives.

MODELS OF CARE

Among contemporary critics of maternity care it is generally believed that two conflicting models of care operate (Rooks 1983; Garcia et al. 1990; Schuman & Marteau 1993; Van Teijlingen & Bryar 1996). One of these two schools of thought emphasises that pregnancy is a normal life event, and the other stresses the possible risks related to pregnancy. The first school is founded on the idea that "normal" childbirth is a "natural" physiological event, i.e. that the overwhelming majority of pregnant women will have a normal and safe childbirth with little or no medical intervention, and that those women who are not expected to have a "normal" childbirth can be predicted and selected out. The second school is founded on the idea that "normal" childbirth requires medical control over the situation in order to guarantee safety, and monitoring which will enable intervention at the earliest sign of pathology, since risk selection is not really possible. Kirkham (1986), famously and controversially, said that in this view pregnancy could only be defined as normal in retrospect. The latter approach, which is dominant in industrial society, is perhaps implicitly seen as part of a wider civilising process (Elias 1978; 1982): gaining control over nature is part of this process. However, it is arguable that the more "civilised" humans become, the more they move away from nature. The American obstetrician Englemann, for example, argued in 1882 that in contrast to native Americans "modern, civilized, American white women were no longer capable of standing the pain and stress of labour" (Loudon 1992). Englemann spoke of "the deleterious effect of civilization on labour and its complications".

The majority of writers assume that midwives adhere to the natural, physiological model of childbirth and doctors to the medical model[2]. Midwives are held to see pregnancy and childbirth in the context of the family and as normal parts of the life process, preferring to wait and watch rather than actively intervening (Peterson 1983; Brooks et al. 1987; Lichtman 1988 and this volume). Physicians, adhering to the view that pregnancy and childbirth are potentially pathological, prefer to intervene (Barrett 1979). Graham and Oakley (1986) point out that doctors prefer to diagnose illness where it is not present rather than not to diagnose illness where it is present. This perspective, it is argued, explains why midwife-led care has lower rates of obstetric intervention and why the medicalisation of pregnancy and childbirth has occurred (Michaelson & Alvin 1988). Although they apparently agree over their respective domains—the midwife looks after normal women, physicians after "at-risk" cases—they do not agree on the criteria for "at-risk" cases or who should decide where women should be booked to deliver their babies. Although Beck (this volume) suggests that midwives, GPs and consultants "work together assessing the suitability of the mother and her family as well as her home circumstances..." this is not usually the case. Van Teijlingen & Bryar (1996) showed that the selection criteria for distinguishing normal from abnormal cases are set by obstetricians in Britain and most other developed countries and by midwives, doctors, health administrators and politicians collectively in the Netherlands (cf. Abraham-van der Mark 1993). Allison & Pascall (1994) analysed historical maternity records and demonstrated that midwives were good at judging who is likely to have a non-problem pregnancy. They conclude that the argument that pregnancies are only normal in retrospect is not well founded.

There is some evidence that these contrasting models may underlie the practical care that is provided for women on wards and in clinics as well as at home births (Peterson 1983). Sakala (1988) showed that independent midwives in Utah used pre-natal preparation, physical manipulation, herbs, hydrotherapy and breathing and relaxation exercises as alternatives to conventional methods i.e. analgesics and anaesthetic drugs. Annandale (1988) showed that midwives in a U.S. birth centre encouraged ambulation, hot baths, family support and squatting specifically to prevent women from being transferred to hospital "unnecessarily" in their view. Michaelson and Alvin (1988) finding that physicians used more technology on low risk women than did midwives, suggest that they use it because they fear litigation, experience pressure from colleagues and sincerely believe it is better to treat all women as "at risk" (cf. Graham 1991). Although Aaronson (1987) found physicians used more interventions than midwives, they were less likely to be chosen by women who believed in their own internal powers and more likely to provide care for women who believe in the influence of "powerful others". Yankou and colleagues (1993) found that although certified nurse midwives (CNM) and physicians apparently espoused the same philosophy, CNMs spent more time with mothers and talked to them more.

These models may account for conflicts which are reported on the hospital floor, as it were, over who carries out certain tasks, who makes decisions and who carries responsibility. Askham and Barbour's paper (this volume) points to areas where the division of responsibility between midwives and doctors was unclear or problematic. Sullivan and Weitz (1988), describing how midwives (licensed and unlicensed) in the USA manage the transfer of difficult cases into hospital, document examples of obstetric specialists being unkind to patients in labour as well as to their midwives. Kitzinger *et al.* (1990) describe rivalry in a British hospital and Graham (1991) in an American hospital between residents and midwives, each believing their knowledge and care to be superior. On the other hand, Barrett (1979) found that CNMs and physicians in the USA worked well at their allotted tasks but only because the CNMs accepted the physicians' authority and had less independence than they would wish. Weitz and Sulllivan (1985) suggested that lay midwives working in Arizona (USA) moved towards embracing the medical model as licensing increased their exposure to medical definitions of childbirth, a greater diversity of patients and the risk of being held legally accountable.[3] Lichtman (this volume) highlights the difficulty of retaining one world view or conceptual model whilst working in an institution which embodies its opposite.

Clearly not all midwives adhere to one perspective or physicians to the other. Flint (1991) for example, suggests that senior midwives may be out of touch with mother's needs for a normal delivery and prefer to defer to medical authorities. The British obstetrician Wendy Savage who was suspended from duty over alleged anomalies in her practice, adhered to the midwifery model of care (Savage 1986). Abraham-van der Mark (1993) suggests that many obstetricians in the Netherlands adhere to the midwifery model. Furthermore, conflicting models do not necessarily lead to conflicts in practice. Rooks (1983: 4) argues the professions are complementary. "Collegiality, cooperation, communication, and complementarity—not competition—are the characteristics we should strive for in our collaboration with physicians." Similarly, some mothers will welcome taking an active role whilst others will prefer to be passive and to leave decision-making to the experts (Too 1996). Annandale (1988) showed that some women resisted midwives' attempts to ensure they had a natural, intervention-free birth. Chamberlain and colleagues (1991) showed that although a majority of Canadian women interviewed were interested in alternative forms of birth and in midwifery care, 53% would choose to give birth in a hospital largely because of the availability of epidural anaesthesia. Australian author Andrea Robertson (1994) whose courses teach midwives to empower women to labour and give birth themselves argues that "We live in a society where women have little trust that their bodies are capable of giving birth safely, and fear pain in labour." She says that women are demanding epidurals, elective caesarians and inductions because they believe they are safe for themselves and their babies.

As their differing perspectives result in different emphases on care, it is perhaps surprising that a point of agreement cannot be found. The midwife offers support to healthy women whom she sees as active participants in a normal biological process. The physician is concerned with different women i.e. "at risk" cases and so is more likely to see a woman in terms of her statistical risk and to make her a passive participant in his care or "risk reduction strategies". Rothman (1982) says that midwives and physicians in the USA are antagonistic and it is impossible to combine and reconcile their roles. Page (1988), a British professor of midwifery, believes that they can be reconciled, and sets out five principles which both doctors and midwives should follow in modern maternity care: (a) continuity of care (b) respect for the normal (c) enabling informed choice (d) recognition of birth as more than a medical event and (e) family centred care. It is easy to imagine midwives accepting these strictures and physicians rejecting them. But it is not certain that the models which apparently underlie practice actually inform the majority of practitioners. The paper by Lichtman (this volume) further examines medical models and midwifery. Lichtman is a CNM who used participant observation of care to illustrate childbirth in two different types of US hospital—one staffed largely by nurse-midwives and the other by residents—and the effects of their different "structure, policies and power relationships on the midwife/researcher's ability to practice".

THE SOCIAL AND POLITICAL CONTEXT

Much of what is happening in contemporary midwifery and obstetrics depends upon the social context of care provision and the structure of health service delivery in a particular country. Torres and Reich (1989) explained the difference in home birth rates between the UK and Netherlands in terms of "the centralized planning apparatus of the National Health Service" (NHS) among other factors. In his international comparison of the status of midwives, DeVries (1993) argues that the enormous variations worldwide in the status accorded to women who assist at childbirth are influenced by four inter-related factors: geography, technology, social structure and culture. Examining the role of the structural arrangements for payment of services he shows that where a nationalised system of health care exists and midwives and physicians compete for clients, midwifery fails to prosper. In the USA midwives who were not granted licenses could not be paid and lost credibility with clients. On the other hand, Michaelson and Alvin (1988) show that US hospitals competing for clients (and their fees) were forced to provide alternative forms of childbirth such as family birthing rooms and to employ nurse-midwives. In Sweden midwifery has not been diminished by nationalised health care because of decentralised maternity care where most women are delivered by midwives in "low-tech" units (DeVries 1993; McKay 1993 and this volume).

It has been argued already that the government of the Netherlands encouraged home births and the development of maternity home care assistants at a time when most nations had a policy of total hospitalisation, Midwives there are paid on a fee for service basis and encouraged to supervise normal deliveries at home and in hospitals. Despite this policy of non-medicalised birth the country has, until recently, continued to enjoy good rates of perinatal mortality. It is for this reason, rather than the role of midwives or maternity home care assistants or the satisfaction of clients, that the Netherlands is often held up as the model which other European countries wishing to improve their maternity care provision might follow.

Several authors attribute the enhanced role and status of midwives in the Netherlands to this official patronage (DeVries 1993, Van Teijlingen & Van der Hulst 1995), some even going so far as to suggest that the government holds a midwifery model of health care provision rather than a medical one (Benoit 1991: DeVries 1993; Torres & Reich 1989). These issues are examined by McKay (1993 and this volume), an American nurse who, intrigued by differing rates of home birth, intervention, perinatal mortality etc in many European countries, observed maternity care in Denmark, Sweden and the Netherlands. She describes the system in each country, inter-relationships between midwives and physicians, their ideology of pregnancy/childbirth, and future prospects and makes comparisons with the USA.

That many countries' policy-making bodies are guided by the beliefs and ideology of the medical profession cannot be doubted. Writing in the *British Medical Journal*, Wagner (1996) says that in France, Germany, Spain, Italy and Greece doctors have promoted themselves as the best providers of maternity care[4]. Despite all the money spent on health care in the USA, rates of maternal and perinatal morbidity are the worst in the developed world and rates of surgical intervention such as caesarian section are second to none. It has been acknowledged that rates of intervention are too high but there has been no suggestion that increased use of nurse-midwives or change of venue for delivery might improve these rates (Declercq 1992; Sakala 1993). Though the number of CNMs is rising steadily, the number of lay midwives—the role of which was a major issue in the 1980s—has declined or stabilised. This is largely because of the power of the medical profession and, it has been suggested, to their greed (Wagner 1996). In this litigious country physicians are reported to be increasingly reluctant to permit natural vaginal birth, even in a hospital environment (Sakala 1993).

If the majority of governments do hold this model, that would provide an answer to a question raised by Van Teijlingen & Bryar (1996) i.e. "Why there are uniformly few home births when the systems of care are so different in Great Britain, France, USA, and Sweden?" The question then becomes how have physicians managed to make their view dominant? Wagner (1986) distinguishes seven ways in which the medical profession managed to gain control over childbirth. First, birth was redefined as (potentially) pathological; and "whoever defines a problem controls the solutions". DeVries (1993) similarly argues that midwifery has been marginalised by the language of risk. He suggests that professions gain power by redefining life events as risky and presenting themselves as having the means to control that risk. This thesis, he says, creates problems for midwives who present themselves as experts in managing normal i.e. low-risk pregnancy and therefore leave themselves without access to power. The second method of obtaining power was by concentrating births in hospital, the doctor's territory. Despite the recommendations of the aforementioned official reports in Britain, home births still accounted for less that 2% of all births in England and less than 1% in Scotland (Table 1). Thirdly, doctors increased their control over the education of midwives, thus institutionalising the latter's subordinate position. The Central Midwives Board established in 1902 consisted largely of doctors and was not chaired by a midwife until 1973. Fourthly, doctors obtained a monopoly over the prescription of drugs and the use of certain apparatus and procedures. This monopoly is being broken, however, as midwives take on more medical and surgical procedures such as suturing. Fifthly, they gained access to the research funds and control over the generation of new knowledge in obstetrics and midwifery, as well as the means of making new knowledge available to the scientific community and the general public. However, as Porter mentions in her paper (this volume), midwives are doing more and more research and are being encouraged to implement relevant research findings. Sixthly, doctors have come to control the development of official government guidelines for the organisation of maternity care. With the exception of countries such as Sweden and the Netherlands that has been true until recently. The British Government's Winterton Committee now appears to have rejected the medical model and physician's arguments in favour of a consumer/midwifery perspective. "We made the normal birth of healthy babies to healthy women the starting point and focus of our enquiry" (House of Commons 1992). Finally, over time the medical profession has been able to convince society that doctors and they alone are capable of evaluating their own activities. Again this is an area which has been contested for some years but came to a head in 1989 with the publication of the scholarly volume *Effective Care in Pregnancy and Childbirth*, a multi-authored work which listed the many procedures doctors used which might be unjustified (Chalmers *et al*. 1989). It was this work and its spirit which gave rise to the current NHS philosophy of "evidence-based practice" Porter argues in this volume.

Table 1 Percentage home births in England and Scotland 1994/95

Country:	1994	1995
England	1.8	1.9
Scotland	0.7	0.9

Source: Information & Statistics Division 1996:Table 1.4 p.: 6

However, it is possible to detect the continuing power and authority of the medical profession in the evaluation of the alternative systems of maternity care currently offered. Almost invariably these evaluations compare the new forms of care with the old in terms of intervention rates or perinatal mortality e.g. Turnbull *et al*. 1996; Biro & Lumley 1991; Butler *et al*. 1993. Flint *et al*. 1989 whilst acknowledging that the numbers are too small to show significant differences. One typical example is that published by Hundley and colleagues (1994) entitled, 'Midwife managed delivery unit: a randomised comparison with consultant led care'. Biro and Lumley (1991) looked at the safety of team midwifery in Monash birth centre. Their extremely cautious conclusion is typical of the genre: "Within this setting, with explicit criteria for booking and referral and a framework for consultation, team midwifery care is as safe as the standard maternity care provided within the State". Having established that their system is satisfactory by these "legitimate" standards, most authors add on a section about women's views and experiences. In most cases women find the midwife-led care more satisfactory. They do not usually study the providers' views. In one of the few papers addressing the views of service providers, Sakala (1993) examined the effect of home setting and midwifery care on caesarian section rates using interviews and prior observation with 15 independent midwives in Utah USA.

THE MIDWIFERY PROFESSION

Generally speaking, midwives appear to see themselves as belonging to a profession, older even than the medical profession. There are many and frequent arguments as to whether midwifery in developed countries constitutes a profession, a semi-profession or merely an occupation. Arguing that it is more than a semi-profession Van Teijlingen and Van der Hulst (1995) review Greenwood's (1957) criteria for a profession, i.e. it should have:

- systematic theory (gained through prolonged training)
- authority recognized by its clientele
- broader community sanction
- code of ethic
- professional culture sustained by formal professional associations

Semi-professions have been defined as lacking one or two of these criteria and applied to midwifery (Reid 1989). Defining a semi-profession as an occupation, which is less powerful and has less control than a profession but more than a trade, Van Teijlingen and Van der Hulst argue that midwifery, at least in the Netherlands is more than this. Van Teijlingen describes in this volume how maternity home care assistants help the midwife at home births and perform menial tasks around the home shows how midwives gain in status as well as work satisfaction as a result of the existence of this more lowly occupation.

Whether or not midwifery is a profession, the fact is that midwives have not achieved the same degree of status, power or economic reward as members of the medical profession. Radosh (1986) describing how physicians gained control of childbirth from midwives in the USA and how the CNM emerged, argues that women could not organize resistance to powerful medical men because they were too firmly and narrowly situated in the female role. In other words, they were too busy fitting their work around their homes and families! Klinkert similarly argues that Dutch midwives lacked the assertiveness and organizational skills necessary to defend their professional interests against increasing competition from doctors (Abraham-van der Mark 1993). However, the strictures of gender roles have not stopped midwives retaining control at the top of their profession unlike nursing (and teaching) despite a small but growing number of male midwives (Allison & Pascall 1994).

Problems arising out of gender roles also beset the working life of midwives in developed countries, leading to problems for the profession as a whole. There are difficulties recruiting new midwives in many countries and retaining trained midwives (Brooks et al. 1987). Partly this is because of poor pay, long hours in understaffed units, and the inflexibility of most hospital shift systems and partly because of disillusionment with the role and its lack of power, autonomy and job satisfaction (Robinson 1993). The system whereby midwives act merely as "obstetric nurses" is perceived as unendurable and a deterrent to practice (Brooks et al. 1987; Flint 1991). However, as mentioned earlier, the practical side of the new forms of maternity care are not easy to fit around a family. Those who have assessed these alternatives have often stressed the need for "commitment" or dedication on the part of the midwives concerned (Flint 1992). This situation is perhaps analogous to the notion of midwives being "called to the profession".

In an attempt to improve their position relative to physicians, midwives have sought to embrace the trappings of professionalism, ensuring that all midwives meet specific criteria of education, training and competence and now moving towards university/degree entry to the profession. Some argue that a university degree is no guarantee of competence and may attract the "wrong" sort of applicants, i.e. those with academic skills but no practical ability (Rooks 1983; Hicks 1995). Training is another area rife with contradictions. There are debates as to the appropriate length of midwifery training as well as its content. It is acknowledged that many train merely to enhance their job prospects, with no intention to practise midwifery. Robinson (1996) shows that a longer (18 months) midwifery course, intended to discourage such "careerists", has not had the desired effect. Some argue that midwives should be nurses first as they need nursing skills on occasion such as when a medical emergency arises (Rooks 1983). Others argue that midwives should go straight into midwifery training as the skills needed to practise midwifery independently are very different from those needed to assist doctors or to nurse the sick (Flint 1991; Robinson 1996). Abraham-van der Mark (1993: 151) quotes a midwife on this topic:

"The professions of nursing and midwifery are direct opposites. While one is devoted to care for the sick, injured and dying within a hospital, the other assumes care of the normal, healthy woman and her infant at home".

A further argument exists as to whether midwifery training is appropriate and prepares midwives for the work they will be doing. Robinson (1996) found students did not feel they had enough time in clinical areas such as the labour ward and Special Care Baby Unit. Whether they had trained for one year or 18 months they did not feel their training had prepared them for their role as assistants to physicians or independent, evidence-based practitioners. Furthermore some have fled from professionalisation fearing that it would change their view of pregnancy and childbirth and ultimately increase medicalisation of maternity care. Studies of lay midwives show that this appears to have happened to them (Butter & Kay 1990; Reid 1989). Butter and Kay (1990) showed that lay midwives eventually used self-certification in order to pre-empt certification by another body such as physicians. As mentioned earlier, the more midwives work within existing, doctor-centred health care systems, the harder it is for them to retain their different world view. In her article on Canadian midwives at work, Benoit (this volume) uses an interactionist approach to observational and interview data with retired and practising midwives. She puts the issue of midwives' professionalism into the relevant geographical, historical and socio-political context.

REFERENCES

Aaronson, L. (1987) Nurse-midwives and obstetricians: alternative models of care and client fit. *Research in Nursing and Health*, 10, 217-226.

Abraham-Van der Mark, E. (ed.) (1993) Dutch midwifery, past & present: an overview. *Successful Home Birth & Midwifery: the Dutch model* (pp. 141-60) London: Bergin & Garvey

Allison, J. & Pascall, G. (1994) Midwifery: a career for women? In J. Evetts (Ed.) *Women & Career: themes and issues in advanced industrial societies* (pp. 203-217) London: Longman

Annandale, E. (1988) How midwives accomplish natural birth: managing risk and balancing expectations. *Social Problems*, 35:2, 95-110.

Askham, J. & Barbour, R. (1987) The role and responsibilities of the midwife in Scotland. *Health Bulletin*, 45:3, 153-159.

Barrett, P. (1979) *The legitimation of an occupational role: the case of the nurse-midwife.* PhD dissertation University of Florida.

Benoit, C. (1991) *Midwives in Passage.* St Johns Newfoundland: ISER Books.

Biro, M. & Lumley, J. (1991) The safety of team midwifery: the first decade of the Monash Birth Centre. *Medical Journal of Australia*, 155:7, 478-480.

Brooks, F., Long, A. & Rathwell, T. (1987) *Midwives' perceptions of the state of midwifery.* University of Leeds: Nuffield Centre for Health Services Research.

Butler, J., Adams, B., Parker, J., & et al., (1993) Supportive nurse midwifery care is associated with a reduced incidence of caesarian section. *American Journal of Obstetrics and Gynaecology*, 168, 5.

Butter, I. & Kay, B. (1990) Self certification in lay midwives' organizations: a vehicle for professional autonomy. *Social Science and Medicine*, 30:12, 1329-1339.

Carveth, J. (1987) Conceptual models in nurse-midwifery. *Journal of Nurse-midwifery*, 32:1, 20-25.

Chalmers, I., Enkin, M. & Keirse, M. (1989) *Effective care in pregnancy and childbirth.* Oxford: Oxford University Press.

Chamberlain, M., Soderstrom, B., Kaitell, C., & Stewart, P. (1991) Consumer interest in alternatives to physician-centred hospital birth in Ottawa. *Midwifery*, 7, 74-81.

Declercq, E. (1992) The transformation of American midwifery. *American Journal of Public Health*, 82:5, 680-84.

Department of Health, (1993) *Changing childbirth: report of the expert maternity group.* London: HMSO.

DeVries, R. (1993) The midwife's place: an international comparison of the status of midwives. In E. Riska & E. Wegar (Eds.) *Gender, work & medicine* London: Sage

Elias, N. (1978) *The civilising process. The history of manners.* Oxford Basil Blackwell
Elias, N. (1982) *The civilising process: state formation and civilisation.* Oxford: Basil Blackwell.

Flint, C. (1991) On the brink: midwifery in Britain. In S. Kitzinger (Ed.) *The Midwife Challenge* (pp. 22-39) London: Pandora Press

Flint, C., Poulengeris, P., & Grant, A. (1989) The 'know your midwife' scheme—a randomised trial of continuity of care by a team of midwives. *Midwifery*, 5, 11-16.

Garcia, J., Kilpatrick, R. & Richards, M. (1990) *The politics of maternity care*. Oxford University Press.

Graham, H. & Oakley, A. (1986) Ideologies of reproduction. In C. Currer & M. Stacey (Eds.) *Concepts of health illness and disease: a comparative perspective* Leamington Spa: Berg

Graham, S. (1991) A structural analysis of physician-midwife interaction in an obstetrical training program. *Social Science and Medicine*, 32:8, 931-42.

Graham, W. (1997) Devolving Maternity Services—Recommendations for Research & Development. *Health Bulletin*, 55:8, 265-75

Greenwood, E. (1957) Attributes of a profession. *Social Work*, 2, 45-55.

Hicks, C. (1995) Good researcher, poor midwife: an investigation into the impact of central trait descriptions on assumptions of professional competencies. *Midwifery*, 11:2, 81-87.

Holland, B. & McKevitt, T. (1985) Maternity care in the Soviet Union. In B. Holland (Ed.) *Soviet sisterhood* Bloomington: Indiana University Press

House of Commons, (1992) *Health committee second report on the maternity services (Winterton Report)* London: HMSO.

Hundley, V., Cruickshank, F., Lang, G., & et al., (1994) Midwife managed delivery unit: a randomised controlled comparison with consultant led care. *British Medical Journal*. 309 1400-1404.

Information & Statistics Division, (1996), *Scottish Health Statistics 1996*, Edinburgh: Common Services Agency

Jabaaij, L. (1994) *The independent midwife in the Netherlands: work & workload*. Utrecht: Nivel.

Kirkham, M. (1986) A feminist perspective on midwifery. In C. Webb (Ed.) *Feminist practice in women's health care* New York: John Wiley

Kitzinger, J., Green, J. & Coupland, V. (1990) Labour relations: midwives and doctors on the labour ward. In J. Garcia, R. Kilpatrick & M. Richards (Eds.) *The politics of maternity care* (pp. 149-162) Oxford: Oxford University Press

Lichtman, R. (1988) Medical models and midwifery: the cultural experience of birth. In K. Michaelson & et al. (Eds.) *Childbirth in America: Anthropological Perspectives*. South Hadley MA: Bergin & Garvey

Loudon, I. (1992) *Death in childbirth*. Oxford: Clarendon Press.

Machover, I. (1995) The mobile epidural: is it such good news? *Associations for improvements in Maternity Services Journal*, 7:2, 10-11.

Mackay, S. & Yager-Smith, S. (1993) What are they talking about? Is something wrong? *Birth*, 2:3, 142-7.

Malin, M. & Hemminki, E. (1992) Midwives as providers of prenatal care in Finland—past and present. *Women & Health*, 18:4, 17-34.

Mander, R. (1993) Midwifery training and employment decisions. In S. Robinson & A. Thomson (Eds.) *Midwives, Research & Childbirth* Vol. 3 (pp. 233-229) London: Chapman Hall

McKay, S. (1993) Models of midwifery care: Denmark, Sweden and the Netherlands. *Journal of Nurse-midwifery*, 38:2, 114-20.

Michaelson, K. & Alvin, B. (1988) Technology and the context of childbirth: a comparison of two hospital settings. In K. Michaelson & et al. (Eds.) *Childbirth in America: anthropological perspectives* (pp. 142152) South Hadley MA: Bergin & Garvey

Murphy-Black, T. (1994) Care in the community during the postnatal period. In S. Robinson & A. Thomson (Eds.) *Midwives, Research and Childbirth: Volume 3* (pp. 120-146) London: Chapman & Hall

Page, L. (1988) The midwife's role in modern health care. In S. Kitzinger (Ed.) *The midwife challenge* London: Pandora

Parker, C. (1994) Breastfeeding: research & quality assurance issues. *British Journal of Midwifery*, 2:2, 56-60.

Peterson, K. (1983) Technology as a last resort in home birth: the work of lay midwives. *Social Problems*, 3, 272-283.

Radosh, P. (1986) Midwives in the US: past & present. *Population Research & Policy Review*, 5, 129-45.

Raleigh, V. (1997) Demographic Timebomb will not Explode in Britain for Foreseeable Future, *British Medical Journal*. 315, 442-3

Reid, M. (1989) Sisterhood and professionalisation: a case study of the American lay midwife. In C. McClain (Ed.) Women as healers: cross-cultural Perspectives New Brunswick: Rutgers University Press

Robertson, A. (1994) *Empowering women: teaching active birth in the 90s* Sevenoaks: Ace Graphics.

Robinson, S. (1993) Combining work with caring for children, findings from a longitudinal study of midwives' careers. *Midwifery*, 9, 183-196.

Robinson, S. (1996) Progress and problems in midwifery education: some conclusions from published research. In S. Robinson & A. Thomson (Eds.) *Midwives. Research & Childbirth* Vol. 4 (pp. 132-64) London: Chapman Hall

Rooks, J. (1983) The context of nurse-midwifery in the 1980s: our relationships with medicine, nursing, lay-midwives, consumers and health care economist. *Journal of Nurse-midwifery*, 28:5, 3-8.

Sakala, C. (1988) Content of care by independent midwives: assistance with pain in labor and birth. *Social Science & Medicine*, 26, 1141-1158.

Sakala, C. (1993) Midwifery care and out-of-hospital birth settings: how do they reduce unnecessary cesarian section births? *Social Science & Medicine*, 37:10, 1233-1250.

Savage, W. (1986) *A Savage enquiry: who controls childbirth?* London: Virago.

Schuman, A. & Marteau, T. (1993) Obstetricians' and midwives' contrasting perceptions of pregnancy. *Journal of Infant and Reproductive Psychology*, 11:2, 115-118.

Sleep, J. (1984) West Berkshire perineal management trial. *British Medical Journal*, 289, 507-590.

Sullivan, D. & Weitz, R. (1988) *Labor Pains: modern midwives and home birth*. New Haven Conn.: Yale University Press.

Too, S. (1996) Do birth plans empower women? A study of their views. *Nursing Standard*, 10:3, 33-7.

Torres, A. & Reich, M. (1989) The shift from home to institutional childbirth: a comparative study of the United Kingdom and the Netherlands. *International Journal of Health Services*, 19:3, 405-414.

Turnbull, D., Holmes, A., Shields, N., & et al., (1996) Randomised, controlled trial of efficacy of midwife-managed care. *British Medical Journal*, 348, 213-218.

Teijlingen van, E. (1990) The profession of maternity home care assistant and its significance for the Dutch midwifery profession. *International Journal of Nursing Studies*, 27:4, 355-366.

Teijlingen van, E. & Bryar, R. (1996) Selection guidelines for place of birth. *Modern Midwifery*, 6:8, 24-27.

Teijlingen van, E. & Van der Hulst, L. (1995) Midwifery in the Netherlands: more than a semi-profession? In T. Johnson, G. Larkin & M. Saks (Eds.) *Health professions & the state of Europe* (pp. 178-86) London: Routledge

Wagner, M. (1986) Birth and power. In J. Phaff (Ed.) *Perinatal health services in Europe* London: Croom Helm

Wagner, M. (1996) Midwife-managed care. *British Medical Journal*, 348, 208.

Walsh, D. (1993) Parenthood education & the politics of childbirth. *British Journal of Midwifery*, 1:3, 119-123.

Weitz, R. & Sullivan, D. (1985) Licensed lay midwifery and the medical model of childbirth. *Sociology of Health and Illness*, 7:1, 36-54.

Wise, J. (1993) Editorial: water birth: trial or error? *British Journal of Midwifery*, 1:6, 249-250.

Yankou, D., Peterson, B., Oakley, D., & Mayes, F. (1993) Philosophy of care: a pilot study comparing certified nurse midwives and physicians. *Journal of Nurse-midwifery*, 38:3, 159-64.

---

[1] In Britain most babies are delivered by midwives acting under the authority of physicians and following guidelines laid down by senior doctors.

[2] Exceptions to this generalisation are Carveth (1987) and Bryar (1988) who suggest that midwives have until recently borrowed the medical model or a social science model rather than developing their own specifically midwifery model.

[3] Reid (1989) similarly argues that the professionalisation of lay midwives resulting from their desire to progress, increase their services and be recognized has caused them to jettison their former identification with sisterhood and the women's movement.

[4] Though midwives in Germany are required to be present at every birth by law, they act merely as obstetric nurses.

MODELS OF MIDWIFERY CARE: DENMARK, SWEDEN, AND THE NETHERLANDS

Susan McKay[1]

ABSTRACT

The organization of maternity services in Denmark, Sweden, and the Netherlands was studied under the sponsorship of the World Health Organization European Headquarters Office of Maternal and Child Health. Midwifery care is highly respected and is a central feature of obstetric care in each of these countries. In Denmark and Sweden, almost all births are in the hospital, and autonomous midwives are employed by national health services. About three-quarters of Dutch midwives are in independent practice, and 34% of Dutch women give birth at home. In each country midwives provide "the first line" of care for normal pregnant women and are viewed as essential to the excellent perinatal outcomes these three countries enjoy.

Midwifery care in most European countries is respected, expected by childbearing women, and legislated as a right of pregnant women. The organization of midwifery and maternity care is, however, highly variable between countries. This article will discuss midwifery in three western European countries: Denmark, the Netherlands, and Sweden. These countries each have national systems of health care so that access to services is universal and paid for by the government.

Midwifery is a central feature of obstetric care in each of these three countries. Additionally, infant mortality rates in each country are lower than in the United States (see Table 1). Wagner[2] argued in testimony before the U.S. Commission to Prevent Infant Mortality that midwifery care is one of several essential elements contributing to the excellent perinatal outcomes these countries enjoy. He offered evidence that a strong independent midwifery profession is an important counterbalance to the obstetric profession in preventing excessive interventions in the normal birth process.

Table I Birth Rates and Infant Mortality Rates: Comparison with the United States

Country	n	Births* Rate per 1,000 Population	Infant Mortality Rate° 1990#	1989
Denmark	61,467	12.0	-	8.4
The Netherlands	188,999	12.7	7.1	6.8
Sweden	115,900	13.6	5.6	6.0
United States	4,021,000	16.2	-	9.7

* Data for 1989 or latest available year
° Infant mortality rate per 1,000 live births.
Provisional.
Adapted from Wegman, M. 'Annual summary of vital statistics-1990 *Pediatrics* (1991); 88:1081-92.

BACKGROUND OF THIS STUDY

From March to July 1991, I was affiliated with the World Health Organization European Headquarters Office of Maternal and Child Health, Copenhagen, Denmark. I studied the organization of maternity services in four western European countries with infant mortality rates lower than the United States (three of these countries will be described in this article). My interest was how countries such as Denmark and Sweden, with relatively small and homogenous populations (5 and 8 million respectively), a high proportion of hospital births (98% to 99%), and low infant mortality rates can offer models of care that can be used in the United States. Holland provided an opportunity to learn how home births (33.4%) with independent midwifery care can safely be offered as an option for childbearing women.

DENMARK

Health care in Denmark is considered a public responsibility, and there is equal and free access for the entire population to almost all health care services. Financing of health care services is through general taxation. The health care system is decentralized so that health care is the responsibility of politically elected regional and local government entities.

In Denmark, the word for midwife is "jordemoder," which means "earth mother." Danish midwives, of whom there are approximately 1,200, recently celebrated the 200th anniversary of the initiation of formal Danish professional education of midwives. All women see midwives during their pregnancies but approximately 10% to 20% of women receive "shared care" between midwives and specialists because of complications. Less than 1% of women only see a physician. Ninety-eight percent of women give birth in hospitals, with the remaining 2% having their babies either at home or in the country's one birth center, which is located in a Copenhagen hospital. Between 5% and 6% of live newborns are born to immigrants, and the same comprehensive maternity services are available at no cost to foreigners provided they are in the process of becoming citizens or are already citizens. Otherwise, foreigners pay for care.

The midwife's education consists of a three-year direct-entry midwifery program after completion of secondary education (which lasts until age 19); midwives are not nurses unless they have separately enrolled in a program of nursing education or have been educated in another country where nursing is a prerequisite to midwifery (i.e., Finland and Sweden). The Danish midwife's relationship with the general practitioner (GP) and obstetrician is collegial, and there is marked respect accorded to midwifery practice.

The organization of maternity care for women in Denmark is standardized, and 99% of women follow national guidelines for frequency of care and which care provider to see. This process unfolds as follows: When a woman first seeks prenatal care, it is usually with a GP in her community who does the pregnancy diagnosis. If pregnancy is normal, she is referred to community midwifery care where she will have at least five visits, although she will return to the GP for two more visits and to a specialist for one visit. The GP visits are widely acknowledged to be primarily for the purpose of cementing the woman's relationship with the GP who provides family medical care; it is freely acknowledged that GPs don't usually have the expertise required to provide the quality care that midwives and obstetricians do. If there are problems during pregnancy, the woman is referred to an obstetrician in the hospital. Prenatal education is offered by midwives and also may be available through adult education classes in the community. Women keep their maternity records, a practice that is common in Europe and in many other parts of the world.

Prior to the early 1970s, there was a mixture of independent midwives (private) and district midwives employed by the county health board. Now midwives are no longer in private practice but all are employees of their counties (which ultimately means the National Health Service). Therefore independent (private) midwifery practice is considered "experimental" and only one such practice (in Copenhagen) exists; one of its purposes in the severely strained economic conditions of the Danish health care system is to prove its cost-effectiveness while still providing high-quality care, continuity of providers, and home birth.

Midwives may do intrapartal, postpartal, or antenatal care or, usually, several of these, depending upon the organization of care in the county that is served by the hospital. Until recently, women had little choice but to go to the hospital designated by the county where they lived: this is changing, and hospitals are beginning to try to attract women by the services they offer—although not with the intensity of their American counterparts. Home births are rare even though women officially have this choice; however, there is an increased interest in this option. Several knowledgeable individuals maintained that women are usually "talked into" a hospital birth by midwives or doctors. Few contemporary midwives have experience in home birth, and I was told that women no longer have confidence in themselves to have their babies at home. Apparently this is also true for midwives. Further, the ever-present argument about safety of home birth is also heard in Denmark.

Women are only occasionally cared for during labor by the same midwives who followed them during pregnancy. Initiatives are now underway in Denmark to develop better continuity between antenatal and hospital care by organizing midwives into teams that provide total care to a group of women. In some districts, community health visitors (nurses with advanced education) see the mother-to-be one time during pregnancy. After birth and dismissal from the hospital, the woman is supposed to have one to two visits from a hospital midwife but, in reality, midwives usually do not have sufficient time to make visits.

Midwives are very attuned to the benefits of physiologic approaches to labor. Hospital labor units reflect this practice, and it is common to see pools for bathing during labor and other devices to facilitate the labor process, such as beanbags, padded platforms, a built-into-the-wall ladder so that women can hang onto a bar and squat and birth beds. Women are encouraged to develop a "list of wishes" to be shared with their birth attendants but they are not written into formalized birth plans. Because the national economy is considerably strained, few Danish hospitals have the beautifully decorated labor units that have become common in the United States. Nevertheless, a very humanized approach to the labor process can readily be seen in practice. For example, the following is a description of a normal birth observed in a large tertiary care hospital in Copenhagen:

Anne B., the midwife, stressed that she made decisions about care based upon each mother and not by routine. Maybe it is the luck of the draw that I have observed such flexible and woman-centered midwives (Anne being an outstanding example), but I have been tremendously impressed by how important they think the woman's experience is. There is minimal record keeping, which means that there is more attention paid to the mother. The mother, a gravida 2, para 1, was first seen in an admittance room for the fetal heart rate strip. She then went to the labor/birth room. All monitoring after the initial strip was manual. If the mother was leaning over and the midwife wanted to listen to the fetal heart, the midwife stooped down underneath the mother. The atmosphere was quiet and everyone was friendly. Tea was brought to the mother, which she occasionally sipped. She wore long "legging" stockings provided by the hospital and a front-open long shirt and moved freely into whatever position she wished. A midwife's helper came in and out of the room as needed; otherwise there was no outside interference. The membranes were ruptured because the woman's labor was not progressing after 8 cm (this also happened with her first labor). The delivery occurred with the mother in a semi-sitting position. The baby was put on the mother's skin and covered with a warm pillow and stayed there. The only intervention done was observing the baby and listening to the heartbeat. Eventually the baby's eyes opened and much later the baby began to lick the nipple and then to suck (about an hour after the birth). The unregulated awakening of the baby to her parents and surroundings and finally the baby's natural readiness to suck was something I had not previously observed without some kind of interference.

Self-regulated sucking has become common practice in Nordic countries, largely because of research conducted by Widstrom[3]. Her work demonstrated that babies have predictable feeding behaviors following birth and are not prepared to suck 30 minutes postpartum; instead prefeeding behavior seems to be fully developed at 45-60 minutes. Babies have been found to have the ability to crawl to the mother's breast after birth and attach to the nipple without help, this ability does not disappear during the maternity stay. Widstrom concluded that infants born to unsedated mothers seem prepared to suck about one hour after birth; to "force" the infant to the breast before sucking and rooting reflexes are developed seems to be a disadvantage with regard to the sucking performance.

There is serious discussion in Denmark about a number of maternity care issues. Denmark's infant mortality statistics, which are not as low as those of Sweden and Finland, are the focus of much of the debate about obstetric practice. One of these issues is whether highly technologic approaches, particularly for low birth weight infants, should be increasingly used as compared with the health promotion approach to birth; the latter emphasizes birth as a normal, woman-centered event. Much of this tension is apparently related to the "overabundance" of obstetricians in Denmark and their encroachment upon midwifery practice. More care provided by specialists has been promoted as a solution to reducing Denmark's infant mortality rate. There is also discussion about whether Danish midwives have sufficient practice in their educational program and whether they are as skilled as their Swedish counterparts in differentiating between normal and abnormal. Swedish midwives, who are also nurses, practice only in a hospital or an antenatal clinic so their skills may become more finely honed, and their nursing education may provide them with better preparation. Danish midwives with whom I spoke seemed mixed in their opinions about whether it would be better if they were also nurses. Some wished they had nursing skills; others felt that nursing education emphasized pathology instead of the normalcy that is the focus of direct-entry midwifery education.

SWEDEN

Like Denmark, Sweden's health care system provides universal access and is free to its people. Taxation provides for funding of health services. The oranization of health care services is similar throughout the country. Sweden is divided into 25 communes (counties), each of which has a certain number of districts organized for the distribution of health care. At least 99% of Swedish childbearing women receive maternity services vis-à-vis a highly coordinated network of clinics for prenatal and postpartal care (mothercare centers) and hospitals. Ninety-nine percent of women give birth in hospitals and are attended by midwives when labor and birth are normal. Home birth is legal but it is "hard to get." There are two birth centers in Sweden, one of which provides comprehensive (pregnancy through postpartum) services.

Sweden's infant mortality rate is third lowest in developed countries of the world[4], and is only slightly behind Finland, which is second (Japan is first). Sweden's outstanding infant mortality rate has occurred despite Sweden's childbearing population, which consists of an estimated 8% to 10% immigrant women. There is great interest in Sweden in social obstetrics—that is, social factors that affect obstetric outcomes— and interdisciplinary teamwork for better perinatal outcomes is highly valued.

Sweden's midwives are autonomous, collaborating with other Swedish care providers (i.e., physiotherapists, GPs, and obstetricians), who are employees of the national health service (government), within institutional settings. Midwives are pivotal in the delivery of maternity care services and receive much credit for Sweden's excellent perinatal outcomes. After upper secondary school (11-12 years), the Swedish midwife is educated for three years at the university level to become a registered nurse, followed by a course in midwifery for one and one-half years (four and one-half years total). Effective in 1993, if the last year at the upper secondary school is spent in nursing, only two years are necessary at the university to become a registered nurse.

The shortage of obstetricians requires these physicians to spend much of their time in the management of complicated pregnancies, so that care of normal childbearing women throughout pregnancy, labor, and postpartum is the responsibility of midwives. Obstetricians become involved for cesarean deliveries, vacuum extraction, and other complications.

Women receive prenatal care in their districts, usually at community maternal-child health (MCH) clinics, although there are a few private clinics. Clinics are modern, brightly decorated and comfortable. Women may have a pregnancy test at a pharmacy, do it themselves, or have a pregnancy test at the clinic. If the woman's pregnancy is normal, she begins care about the 10th week and will see a midwife 11 to 12 times (recently reduced from 14 visits) and an obstetrician once or twice, at 12 and 36 weeks. Like Danish and Dutch women, mothers-to-be carry their own maternity records. When there are pregnancy complications, referral is made to GPs and obstetricians.

Swedish midwives practice either in MCH clinics or in the hospital, but not in both. A pregnant woman usually sees the same midwife throughout pregnancy. When she goes to the hospital, she is cared for by hospital midwives unless there are obstetric factors that require specialist care. There is limited interaction between the antenatal and hospital midwives except when the antenatal midwife takes women to the hospital "on tour." Some hospital midwives expressed the belief that this lack of coordination means that women are not as well prepared for their labors as they might be because the antenatal midwives do not work with laboring women. On the positive side, there is continuity of antenatal care providers, and the antenatal midwives are highly skillful because they only do antenatal care. They also know their patients on a personal basis and are readily available to answer questions. One clinic in Lund had a "hotline" during special hours of the day; women could call the midwife directly with their questions, and the midwife's job during those hours was to be available to answer phone questions. Additionally, antenatal midwives offer childbirth education classes. Women return to the antenatal midwife six week's postpartally for a checkup and for contraceptive services. Often the child care clinic, staffed by nurses, is located in close proximity to the antenatal midwives so there is visiting back and forth when the mother takes her baby for well-child checkups. A network of MCH psychologists (200 in Sweden) works with the maternal and child care clinics, seeing women for individual appointments and also helping midwives and nurses to deal with difficult problems and to handle the emotional aspects of childbearing more effectively. Maternal-child health psychologists continue these activities until children reach school age.

Swedish obstetric practice has been influenced by the philosophy and practices of Michel Odent[5]; however, medical intervention in normal birth is typical, although at a lower level than in the United States. Swedish law guarantees women the right to pain relief in labor if needed, and the use of technology is standard. Electronic fetal monitoring is usual, epidurals, pudendal, and paracervical blocks are available, and pethidine is common for pain relief. In conjunction with the frequent use of technologic care is an integration of physiologic approaches and appropriate, not routine, use of medications and interventions. For example, laboring in a pool of water is common, and alternative laboring positions are normal practice. Breast-feeding is nearly universal both in Sweden and Denmark.

Nordic people are far more comfortable with their sexuality, including pregnant women's bodies, than is true in the United States. It is normal for women to expose their breasts during sunbathing, and this does not change during pregnancy or during breast-feeding. One Swedish prenatal book pictures a very pregnant woman playing on the beach, wearing only a bikini bottom.

As in Denmark, the economic situation in Sweden is strained, and there is increasing concern about the cost of health care. For three years, women in Stockholm were able to choose their hospital of delivery. This change set up an atmosphere of competition, resulting in some increase in choice for women. If a woman chose a hospital out of her district, the woman's own district had to pay the other hospital about $1,066 (in 1991 @ 6.1 SKr $1). This contrasted with the previous practice of not tracking health care costs. Since 1992, however, all the Departments of Obstetrics and Gynecology in Stockholm are on a DRG system of reimbursement.

One effort to provide continuity of midwifery care is occurring at the Stockholm Sodersjkuhuset Alternative Birth Center (ABC), founded by psychologist and midwife Ulla Waldenstrom, and run entirely by midwives with obstetric consultation. The ABC was set up as a randomized controlled trial of birth outcomes; half the women who choose the facility are not accepted for care, but their birth outcomes are followed and compared with those of the women accepted into the trial at the ABC. All aspects of maternity care, including education, are provided at the ABC by a group of eight highly experienced midwives. There is a strong emphasis upon psychological aspects of birth, learning more from laboring women about the process of labor and birth, and self-care during pregnancy and the postpartum. The midwives have observed that in the psychologically protected environment of the birth center, expectant parents feel psychologically safe and are much freer about their concerns. When women are in labor, nobody except the primary care midwife comes into the room. Early discharge with midwifery visitations is normal.

Swedish women, like their Danish neighbors, sometimes go home from the hospital early (in which case a hospital midwife visits her) but usually the stay is for four to five days. Babies remain with their mothers: Although in 1985, all babies spent the night in a nursery, central nursery care is now minimal in Sweden—this demonstrates how rapidly change in maternity practices can occur when there is consensus among practitioners. In one postpartal facility in Lund, family members stayed in a private room in an intermediate care facility, coming and going as they wished. Meals were in a large dining room where all ages and types of patients went through a cafeteria line. Newborn babies were brought in portable baby cribs to sleep at the tableside or breast-feed as needed. Family members were often joined by friends in a highly social atmosphere. In Stockholm, Karolinska Hospital has a postnatal unit that is run by midwives under the supervision of obstetricians who have medical responsibility: husbands and children stay up to 72 hours with baby and mother. A similar unit is at Huddinge Hospital in Stockholm.

Postgraduate education is very important for all levels of obstetric care providers, and, as is also true in Denmark, there is continuing countrywide dialogue about the best way to provide care. In Gothenburg commune, Sweden, members of the maternity and pediatric care team spoke of increasing recognition in Sweden that medical care has come as far as it can in improving perinatal outcomes and that attention to social problems is a priority if further advances are to be made. However, with the exception of the research unit at the ABC in Stockholm and the work of some behavioral scientists, research continues to focus upon medical aspects of maternity care.

In a visit to Sweden in June 1992, I met with Swedish midwives and heard about professional concerns that have arisen during the 1991-1992 year. Obstetricians are becoming more active in care practices that have been the province of midwives. For example, there is an increasing trend for obstetricians on the ward to "check" laboring women being cared for by midwives, a change from the past when the obstetrician did not "look over the midwife's shoulder" but was only involved when requested by the midwife. Midwives expressed their belief that their practice might quickly be usurped by obstetricians: further, the professional organization of midwives in Sweden has not been proactive in addressing changes. The midwives feared a decrease of their autonomy and scope of practice. An effort to address this concern occurred in a planned meeting in 1992 during which midwives and obstetricians discussed these practice issues.

THE NETHERLANDS

As in Denmark and Sweden, health care is free and access is universal for the people of Holland. Midwives, as are other obstetric care providers, are paid for their services by the government, whether they have a private (independent) practice or work in public facilities. Midwives can also be paid (indirectly) by private insurers, because 30% of the population (those with incomes over a certain level) carry private insurance. Holland's maternity system can be distinguished from other European countries because of its extensive use of independent midwives who own their own private practices in the community. Provided there are no medical contraindications, women are free to choose home or hospital birth[6]. There is one birth center in the Netherlands.

The policy of the Dutch government is to promote home births attended by midwives or GPs. More than a third of women (34%) give birth at home with midwives, who are helped by maternity home care assistants[7]. The maternity assistants, who complete a prescribed course of study, make one or two prenatal visits in the home, help during labor, and look after the mother and baby for approximately eight days or a maximum of 80 hours following birth. Seventy-three percent of childbearing women use the services of these maternity assistants[7]. I was told that the high level of support provided normal postpartal women by maternity home care assistants accounted for the low rate of postnatal depression in Dutch women, although data to validate this statement were not provided. Statistics are available, however, to demonstrate that perinatal mortality rates for babies of low-risk, home-delivered women are much lower than hospital births (the latter includes high-risk pregnancies delivered by obstetricians)[6]. In 1987 the perinatal mortality rate for home births attended by midwives and maternity nursing aides (92% of home births) was 0.14% compared with the national perinatal mortality rate in the same year of 0.94%[8]. It is noteworthy that a nationwide system of transfer to the hospital is available, and the rule is that this must occur in no longer than 15 minutes. Further, the midwife must be able to reach the home within 15 minutes or have another professional to stand in for her if it takes longer.

Midwives in the Netherlands, as in Denmark, complete five years of secondary schooling and then are educated over a three-year period in one of the three direct-entry midwifery colleges in the country; they are not nurses. Midwives represent a proud Dutch tradition and were given preferential treatment in 1941 by a Dutch law that said that midwives give the best obstetric care, and the system must pay midwives first. When problems arise, midwives refer women to the secondary level, which is the specialist and hospital.

Overall, midwives attend a little over 46% of Dutch births, which is markedly lower than in Denmark and Sweden. The number of midwives in Holland is close to that of Denmark, although the population of Holland is more than double. Almost 65% of Dutch births occur in the hospital, a little over half of which are births attended by obstetricians. The remainder of hospital births are under the sole care of the midwife unless complications require referral to an obstetrician for delivery. If a woman planning a home birth develops complications, the woman will be transferred to the hospital for care from an obstetrician, although her midwife may accompany her from home to hospital. About 11% of women are delivered by GPs, often in the remote areas where midwifery care may not be available. In 1988, 6.8% of women served were ethnic minorities.

In community-based midwifery practices, women have 13 to 15 prenatal visits, and they carry their own records. There are three to four home postnatal visits. At six weeks, the woman returns to the midwifery office for a checkup. Midwives "do not have time" to do childbirth education, but these classes are available in the community, and attendance is encouraged. However, during prenatal visits observed by the author, large amounts of time were devoted to answering questions and giving educational counseling. Continuity of care is an important feature of Dutch midwifery practice. Midwives may have solo practices or a group of midwives (for example, two to five) may share a practice; all will rotate in caring for pregnant women, and one will be present in the home or the hospital for birth, depending upon the woman's preference. If she decides on hospital care and all is normal, the community (private practice) midwife takes care of her there with the assistance of a hospital nurse. The midwife retains her independent status in the hospital and, in essence, the hospital room and nurse are "rented" until the woman goes home within a day after birth.

In a midwifery practice I visited in Amsterdam, three midwives cared for 300 women a year. These midwives work without supervision from doctors; they decide when high-risk referrals should be made and which doctors should receive the referrals. Van Teijlingen[7] observed that midwives in the Netherlands have invested so much money in their practices, thus having a vested interest, that there is very low turnover of Dutch community midwives. I was told that it was not unusual for the same midwife to provide care to several generations of mothers and daughters.

The belief in women's ability to give birth normally is a strong theme of Dutch midwifery care. The overriding emphasis is upon childbirth as a normal physiologic event which is why home birth is viewed as a safe option.

Pregnant Dutch women are not "patients" unless they are referred for high-risk obstetric care. It is deemed important to provide an extended period of postnatal support (90% paid by insurance) to all Dutch women whether or not there have been complications. When birth is in the hospital, if all is normal, women go home in less than a day and have maternity assistants care for them in their home. Astrid Limburg, a leading voice for maintaining independent midwifery practice in the Netherlands, told me that the midwife's pride is to let the woman "do it on her own with her eyes open ... Lots of pathology starts in the mind. Home birth is women." Almost all women give birth in a sitting position and episiotomies are rare. Limburg constantly strives to let women know they are in charge and believes the hospital undermines this ability. Further, she believes when the midwife goes to the hospital, she must be very alert not to change, because if she does, she is not protecting the woman as much from intervention, a role Limburg considers primary. Limburg characterizes the doctor's attitude as "trust me"—that is, for the woman to look to the doctor rather than her own ability to give birth, and women consequently lose their confidence. A comparative study that seems to support Limburg's assertions about intervention was carried out in 1986. Dutch and Danish intervention rates were compared during the period from 1960 to 1980. The results showed that after Denmark eliminated independent midwifery practice (by 1972), there was a considerable increase in instrumental deliveries; although in both countries perinatal mortality rates decreased continuously, there was a slightly faster improvement in early neonatal mortality in Denmark[9].

From the perspective of midwives, there are ominous signs of change and substantial problems for Dutch midwifery. Midwives are overworked and underpaid for their services (approximately $400 per birth, whereas specialists are paid far more), and midwives are struggling to support themselves and maintain their independent status in a climate where specialists are encroaching more and more upon obstetric practice. There seems to be a constant tension over territoriality, increased use of obstetric intervention, and questions about whether midwifery can hold its own. There is discussion in Holland of changing to a market system, and this would mean that midwives wouldn't receive automatic priority. There is also discussion of reducing the home stay benefit.

DISCUSSION

In Denmark, Sweden, and Holland midwives are autonomous (not supervised by physicians), although only in the Netherlands do midwives practice privately. In Denmark and the Netherlands, where obstetricians are in ample supply, there is sometimes tension between the two professional groups about the limits of practice and how much intervention is appropriate. Birth in each of these countries is viewed as a far more normal and physiologic event than is generally true in the United States; all three countries support a model of midwifery that is individualized according to the needs of the woman and her family. Self-regulation of the labor process is stressed, and keeping mothers and babies together is normal practice. Support after birth in the form of either home assistance or community-based nurse assistance is standard in each country. Families are always included in the pregnancy and birth process. Privacy is deeply valued, so strangers do not come and go during normal labor and birth as is common in U.S. hospitals. In each country, midwives are held in high esteem; they are "the first line" of care providers for normal pregnant and laboring women and are viewed as essential to the excellent perinatal outcomes that are achieved.

ACKNOWLEDGEMENTS

The research reported in this article was made possible through the assistance of Marsden Wagner, Office of Maternal Child Health, World Health Organization European Headquarters, Copenhagen. The University of Wyoming provided research leave and travel support. Simone Buitendijk (the Netherlands), Hanne Kjaergaard Nielsen (Denmark), and Ulla Waldenstrom (Sweden) reviewed the material in this article for accuracy in reporting about each of their country's maternity care systems. I am very grateful for their helpful comments and clarifications

[1] Susan McKay is Professor of Nursing, University of Wyoming, School of Nursing, PO Box 3065, Laramie, WY82071, USA. Affiliated with the WHO European Headquarters, Office of Maternal Child Health, Copenhagen, Denmark, from March to July 1991. Reprinted by permission of Elsevier Science from Models of Midwifery Care: Denmark, Sweden and the Netherlands, by S. McKay, Journal of Nurse-Midwifery, Vol. 38, 114-120. Copyright 1993 by the American College of Nurse-Midwives.

[2] Wagner M. Testimony before the U.S. Commission to Prevent Infant Mortality. Feb. 1, 1988:6-7.

[3] Widstrom AM. Studies on breast-feeding: behavior and peptide hormone release in mothers and infants. Stockholm: Karolinska Institute, 1988.

[4] Wegman, M., Annual summary of vital statistics—1990. *Pediatrics* 1991;88: 1081-92.

[5] Odent, M., *Birth reborn.* New York: Pantheon, 1984.

[6] Kleiverda, G, Steen, AM, Anderson, I, Treffers, PE, Everaerd, W. Place of delivery in the Netherlands: maternal motives and background variables related to preferences for home or hospital confinement *Eur J Obstet Gynecol Reprod Biol* 1990:36:1-9.

[7] Teijlingen van ER. The profession of maternity home assistant and its significance for the Dutch midwifery profession. *Int J Nurs Stud* 1990; 27:355-66.

[8] Treffers, PE, Eskes, M, Kleiverda, G, Alten, D. Home births and minimal medical interventions. *JAMA* 1990; 264:2203-8.

[9] Scherjon, S. A comparison between the organization of obstetrics in Denmark and the Netherlands. *Br J Obstet Gynaecol* 1986; 93:684-9.

MATERNITY HOME CARE ASSISTANTS IN THE NETHERLANDS

Edwin R. van Teijlingen [1]

INTRODUCTION

The Dutch system is often cited as an example of how the maternity services in other industrialized countries could be improved. One finds such comparisons in the English language, in a variety of writings referring to many different countries. For example, Australia, where: "Dutch midwifery is often held up as a beacon to Australian midwives as the perfect system of maternity care" (Belton, 1993); New Zealand, where Donley (1986:153-4) argued that the Netherlands "has a large rural population but does not have a 'flying squad' of obstetrically equipped ambulances" like New Zealand has. In the United States the argument is put forward that: "...aspects of the Netherlands' system could be used in the United States. For instance, nurses could investigate whether a maternity care helper program would help to lower the U.S. infant mortality rate" (Bradley & Bray, 1996); the United Kingdom: "The Dutch system of maternity care is occasionally held up as an example to be emulated by health care providers in the United Kingdom" (Mander, 1995); and industrialized countries in general: "The Dutch system of maternity care...receives much attention from other industrialized countries, where home births are often depicted in a negative light" (Wiegers *et al.*, 1998). Furthermore, campaigners for women-friendlier maternity services, such as obstetricians (Rickford, 1986), midwives (Newson, 1981; Beck, 1991), general practitioners (Cavenagh, 1968), childbirth activists (Arms, 1981), researchers (Jordan, 1978; Tew, 1998; Declercq, 1994; DeVries, 1996), consumers (Ashton, 1980; Borjars, 1993) and consumer-groups, such as the Association for the Improvement in the Maternity Services (AIMS, 1986), have all cited the Dutch model of maternity care as a better way of or even the ideal approach to providing maternity care for normal childbirth.

This paper outlines the unique characteristics that differentiate the Dutch maternity services from those of all other industrialized countries. These characteristics center on the specific organization of maternity services in the Netherlands and the position of the medical practitioners therein. Much emphasis is placed on continuity of care, not only during the period of the pregnancy, but also throughout the postnatal period. In addition, one key person in providing this desired continuity of care is the maternity home care assistant or 'kraamverzorgende'. Maternity home care assistants are engaged to look after the mother and baby for approximately eight days following the birth, if the postnatal period is spent at home. They look after the mother and new baby, provide health education, look after other children in the family, do the housework, contact the midwife or family doctor if necessary, and even walk the family's dog.

THE DUTCH IDEOLOGY OF MATERNITY CARE

The Dutch have a different approach to the care needed during and after a pregnancy than do many other industrialized nations (Haspels & Barentsen, 1986). Pregnant women in the Netherlands are not regarded as ill patients, unless something goes actually wrong or unless the delivery is expected to be difficult for previously assessed reasons. The principles underlying maternity care risk selection and referral policy in the Netherlands are that "pregnancy, labor and the postnatal period are in principle physiological events, and also that it is safe to have a home delivery, which is expected to proceed normally" (Ziekenfondsraad, 1987). Consequently, it is argued that medical intervention should be reduced to a minimum (Crébas, 1990). Regarding birth as a natural process also means that there is "in Dutch birth participants a deep-seated conviction that the woman's body knows best and that, given enough time, nature will take its course" (Jordan, 1978:37).

Many people in the Netherlands feel that the average healthy woman does not necessarily need a hospital delivery, let alone four or five days of nursing in hospital after the birth. On the other hand, the needs which do arise at this time go beyond the medical requirements of monitoring and the availability of emergency services when necessary. It is considered that a mother does need some practical help at home through the early days of the baby's life, together with information and advice about the new baby. Thus, attention is given to the practical needs of all pregnant women, as well as the medical needs of special cases, such as difficult deliveries and emergencies.

In some other industrialized countries a similar form of postnatal care is provided, but not for the majority of healthy new mothers. According to Garcia et al. (1989): "British women do receive 'home helps' in exceptional circumstances, such as multiple birth." This British approach contrasts with the Dutch ideology; help is available only in exceptional cases in Britain, whereas in the Netherlands this help is widely available for a normal healthy mother and baby.

HISTORICAL BACKGROUND TO MATERNITY HOME CARE ASSISTANTS

This paper thus focuses on maternity home care assistants, one important non-medical factor contributing to the unique Dutch way of organizing maternity care. The idea of professional care for the new mother and baby in their own home is not a recent one; as Kloosterman (1984) points out: "As early as 1902, in several cities and villages organizations were founded to train young girls to take care of a healthy woman and her baby during the lying-in period and to do her household chores". 1n 1926, the Ministry of Health laid the foundations of the current maternity home care organization by established training, introducing legislation to protect the occupation and licensing (Verbrugge 1968:9). The percentage of families who take a maternity home care assistant has increased steadily over the decades, and in the late 1980s stood at 73% of all births, that is to say, about 136,000 births (Nationale Kruisvereniging, 1989). The maternity home care assistant service is provided by 13 regional maternity centers and 19 regional centers providing a mixture of maternity and other home care services[2]. In 1995, 2,000 maternity home care assistants were employed by regional maternity centers, and 6,600 people by mixed service providers[3]. The overwhelming majority were female part-time workers.

THE TASKS OF MATERNITY HOME CARE ASSISTANTS

The duties of maternity home care assistants can be divided into five categories: (i) assisting a midwife or family doctor during a home birth or a short-stay hospital delivery; (ii) recognizing deviations from normality in mother and baby, i.e. symptoms that make it necessary to contact the midwife or GP at once; (iii) attending and nursing a healthy mother and her baby and looking after any older children in the family; (iv) housekeeping and doing other domestic tasks; (v) providing health education for parents: for example, guidance on how to establish breast-feeding or on how to bottle feed the baby, and how to change diapers, and information concerning the general health needs of babies.

A pregnant woman who wants to use the service of a maternity home care assistant has to apply at the local or regional maternity center. During her first antenatal visit to the midwife (or GP), she will be provided with information about this service (Bureau Obelon, 1986). Spanjer and colleagues (1986) stress that women have to book well in advance. It is virtually impossible to book a maternity home care assistant when you are more than three months pregnant.

When labor has begun, the midwife or GP attending the delivery will tell whoever is with the woman (usually the woman's partner) to phone the maternity center. The center will send a stand-by maternity home care assistant straight away. If labor progresses slowly the midwife or doctor may leave the maternity home care assistant with the laboring woman. This has considerable advantages for the pregnant woman as well as the midwife. The woman has somebody with her who offers emotional support to her (Jordan,

1978:46) and to make sure that the midwife is called neither too soon or too late. The maternity home care assistants are under medical supervision of a midwife or a GP.

TRAINING OF MATERNITY HOME CARE ASSISTANTS

The training of maternity home care assistants is combined with the training for a range of community-care work, including general home help, caring for old people, caring for children, and caring for mentally handicapped people (Kiers, 1986), which falls under the responsibility of the Ministry of Education (Seysener & Van Westering, 1986). Qualified maternity home care assistants are involved as supervisors of trainees—which adds extra responsibility to their post, but also makes it more difficult. Maternity centers are also finding it more and more difficult to find placements for trainee maternity home care assistants. They are meeting some resistance from mothers to trainee placements, stemming from a concern that they and their babies are becoming a means of training rather than the focus of care (De leidster-docenten, 1987).

TYPES AND FUNDING OF CARE PROVIDED

The maternity centers offer three possible arrangements for maternity care. The most favored service is full-time care; over two thirds (66.8%) of all customers use this type of care (Nationale Kruisvereniging, 1989). In this situation the maternity home care assistant stays with the family for up to ten days. The average, however, is eight days. In some regions the maternity home care assistant stays for about 12 hours on the day of delivery, and gradually over the following days the time spent with the family is reduced, giving an average of eight hours per day for eight days. In other regions she stays for eight hours during each day (Scheijmans, 1986). During this period of care a senior member of staff at the maternity center (a maternity home care assistant nurse) visits the mother twice to see if everything is going as planned.

The second type of care provided by the maternity centers is part-time help. Under this scheme the maternity home care assistant visits the mother and child twice a day, usually for an hour and a half in the morning and an hour in the afternoon. The maternity home care assistant's attention is focused on mother and child, and the family is expected to take care of the housework (Bureau Obelon, 1986).

Thirdly, a limited number of maternity centers offer a combination of the two types of care. In 1985 the National Cross Organization took the decision to supply more of this kind of flexible care. For example, starting with four days full-time care immediately after the delivery and part-time care for the remaining four days. The way in which flexible care is provided varies from maternity center to maternity center, because they are fairly autonomous (Nationale Kruisvereniging, 1987).

The maternity centers are financed by payments from clients and a supplement paid by the Sick Funds. The new parents have to pay a part of the total costs; this fee was $3 per hour in 1998 (6.30 guilders). The Sick Funds pay the remainder of the cost which is $21.75 per hour (50.25 guilders)[4]. Most private health insurance companies have similar arrangements for their clients. Special arrangements are made for people on state benefits/income support. They fall under an exemption, which limits payment for all medical costs to a maximum amount per year.

CONTINUITY OF CARE AND PLANNING

The maternity centers have a policy of ensuring that the same maternity home care assistant stays with the mother for the duration of the arrangement. Planning is of course difficult for the maternity centers, as it is impossible to predict the number of babies born in a certain area on a certain day. Only 4% of all babies are born on the day they are due. Dr. W van Santen, head of the care department of the National Cross Organization, stated: "Unfortunately care has to be refused now and again, but these are only incidental cases. We try to give everybody the necessary care" (Kiestra, 1987).

In 1986, 68% of all clients received full-time care, 18% received combined care, and 14% received part-time care (Samuël, 1988). Government cuts in spending on the maternity service mean that maternity centers have to budget for about 15% part-time care to reach the average of 64 hours of care per family.

According to a group of heads of maternity centers, the consequence of this will be that more families will be faced with a change of maternity home care assistant. Maternity home care assistants also miss out in this situation, being required to work with more families for a shorter period of time with each (De leidster-docenten, 1987). Ropping (1989) feels that they have less opportunity to get to know the parents than when they are with a family every day for over a week. Kerssens (1994) found in a study of 1,812 recently delivered women that almost one-third of the new mothers rated the availability as inadequate although the maternity home care assistant's expertise was rated positively. Moreover, increased part-time care also makes it more difficult for the maternity home care assistant to maintain an undisturbed social life and for the maternity center, woman-power planning becomes more difficult (De leidster-docenten, 1987).

THE SPECIFIC ORGANIZATION OF THE DUTCH MATERNITY SERVICES

In the Netherlands the Sick Fund, a state health insurance scheme, covers approximately 70% of the population; that is, those earning less than $30,600 per year[5]. People who earn more than this have to arrange cover through private health insurance companies. The Sick Funds (and many commercial health insurance companies) operate a selection system, distinguishing between high-risk and low-risk pregnancies. The present guidelines incorporate revisions made in 1987 by representatives of all Dutch professions involved in the maternity services (Ziekenfondsraad, 1987).

The selection is carried out by a midwife without intervention of an obstetrician or GP. In the case of low-risk pregnancies, the fee for a GP will be reimbursed only if there is no practicing midwife in the area, an arrangement, which favors the midwifery profession (Van Teijlingen & McCaffery, 1987). Only in instances of high-risk pregnancies will the Sick Fund reimburse the fee of an obstetrician.

This reimbursement system, together with the fact that Dutch midwives are autonomous obstetrical practitioners, facilitates a kind of organization of maternity services, which does not regard pregnancy as an illness. Dutch midwives used to spend three years in training (direct entry) at one of the three Colleges of Midwifery, however in 1994 training was increased to four years (Rooks, 1997: 414). Midwives are trained to identify high-risk women during antenatal care. Dutch midwives are not nurses like most of their colleagues in the industrialized world. Three-quarters of all midwives are self-employed community midwives, practicing solo or in small group practices. In 1987 they attended over two-thirds of the home deliveries and 31% of the hospital deliveries, together representing 44% of all deliveries (187,703 babies) in the Netherlands (CBS, 1989). They do their work without the supervision of a doctor. The average number of births attended by an independent midwife in the course of a year was 165 in 1986, but some of them attend over 200 deliveries a year (personal communication from a Dutch midwife in Vlaardingen, Province of South Holland).

Less than half of all GPs attend deliveries, representing approximately 15% of all deliveries in the Netherlands (Tweede Kamer der Staten-Generaal, 1990). Where GPs do attend deliveries, the individual doctor is quite likely to attend only a few each year. Three categories of normal deliveries are attended by GPs: deliveries of women whose private health insurance covers the GP's fee; those of women who will pay the fee personally; and those of women who live in remote rural areas where there is no practicing midwife. In addition, some births in cities are attended by GPs and/or midwives as an emergency measure when no previous arrangements have been made.

The midwife provides postnatal care for her own clients as well as for women who have delivered in hospital under the care of an obstetrician, and have been discharged early out of the hospital. Postnatal care is not as time consuming as it would be for British community midwives, since the maternity home care assistant spends some hours each day with the new mother and baby during the lying-in period. During these visits, she monitors the baby's progress, checks the temperature every day, and so on. The midwife calls in (briefly) every day after the delivery for four days and then every second day for the next week. Only in a case where the maternity home care assistant is not happy about the condition of baby and/or mother does she contact the midwife.

During a short-stay hospital delivery the midwife is assisted by nursing staff or occasionally by a maternity home care assistant, but the midwife is in charge. One Dutch midwife explained that she has access to both of the two municipal hospitals in her Sick Fund area. In one hospital, she would usually find one qualified nurse to assist with the delivery, in the other there would be a qualified nurse and a student nurse, but she stressed: "I am in command, and nobody looks over my shoulder," (personal communication from a Dutch midwife in Vlaardingen, Province of South Holland)

GOVERNMENT POLICY ON MATERNITY CARE

The Dutch Government supports the present organization of the maternity services and promotes home births and deliveries attended by midwives or GPs. The Dutch policy is to move care out of the hospital into the home. This policy is the main explanation for the rising percentage of mothers using the maternity home care assistant service in the 1970s and 1980s. For example, the Ministry of Welfare, Health & Culture (Adviescommissie Verloskunde, 1987) outlines the policy of "maintaining the quantity and quality of the maternity home care assistant service, which forms a cornerstone for the whole policy of maintaining or extending the number of home deliveries."

The Parliamentary Committee for Health Care met the Secretary of State for Welfare, Health and Culture in December 1989. At this meeting all the major political parties, from the Left to the Right on the political spectrum, agreed that the midwife was the obvious person to provide maternity care, and that deliveries should preferably take place at home (Tweede Kamer der Staten-Generaal, 1990).

DISCUSSION

The maternity home care assistant helps the midwife (and/or doctor) during a home delivery, or she arrives just before the mother returns home from a short-stay hospital delivery. After a home birth or short-stay hospital delivery, midwives (and GPs) are glad that they can leave the mother and the newborn baby in the experienced hands of a maternity home care assistant. "It relieves them of the post-delivery nursing activities" (Smulders & Limburg, 1988, community midwives in Amsterdam), or as Kitzinger (1980) puts it: "The midwife would be occupied with simple nursing tasks instead of concentrating on midwifery." These midwifery tasks are described elsewhere (e.g. Van Teijlingen & McCaffery, 1987; McKay 1993 and this volume; Van Lieburg & Marland 1989 and this volume; Tarharrofi, 1993).

The actual delivery can, of course, be time-consuming, but it does not necessarily mean that the midwife (or GP) has to be waiting for something to happen. A maternity home care assistant is often called just beforehand, to assist the midwife (or GP) during the delivery. In cases where the baby is taking its time, the midwife (or GP) can easily go out for a few postnatal visits or some sleep, while the maternity home care assistant stays with the mother to monitor progress. As long as the midwife can be contacted by telephone, this division of labor works well and it avoids the wasting of medical resources. Similarly, the midwife can leave the new mother and her child very soon after the birth, as the maternity home care assistant stays.

This brings out the fact that Dutch midwives are not regarded as nurses with an additional midwifery qualification. They have a separate direct-entry training course, and most of them operate as private independent community midwives, while somebody with fewer qualifications, less "professional" than they are, takes care of the postnatal nursing tasks.

The existence of maternity home care assistants strengthens the midwife's sense of professional autonomy. Another aspect of the Dutch way of organizing maternity care, which strengthens the professional autonomy of midwives, is the fact that it is they who decide which pregnant women are low-risk and which fall in the high-risk category. So not only can "a Dutch midwife legally practice obstetrics without the supervision of a doctor when pregnancies and deliveries show no indication of medical complications" (Smulders & Limburg, 1988), but it is also she who makes the high/low-risk selection of pregnant women.

CONTINUITY OF CARE

Continuity of care is seen as an important factor in the Dutch maternity services. Midwives operate alone or in small group practices. Their clients see them as individuals, in the same way that GPs or dentists in Britain are regarded as individuals. The same midwife, or perhaps two or three midwives in a group practice, will see the mother during antenatal visits, during the delivery, and during the postnatal visits. This continuity of care is regarded as a sign of good quality care. It is also important for the way Dutch mothers perceive their midwife, as a carer involved in their pregnancy and delivery.

In many countries midwives have become part of the hospital hierarchy and as such have blended in with the system. They are often not regarded as individuals by the pregnant women, but as part of the bigger hospital environment. The fact that many midwives wear uniforms symbolizes the hospital hierarchy. Most GPs in Britain do not wear a white coat during consultation. And in the Netherlands one finds that the community midwives do not wear a uniform either.

Midwives in the Netherlands are in many ways more like British GPs than the British midwives and nurses. They have professional independence, they work privately, alone or in a group practice, and as mentioned above, they do not wear uniforms. They have a vested interest in their private practice, because they have invested so much money in that practice, resulting in a very low turnover of Dutch community midwives. Therefore, woman can have the same midwife attending her for all her children. This is bound to improve the relationship between the midwife and her client, but it does not necessarily overcome the social distance that might exist between some women and their midwives.

INDICATORS OF SUCCESS: SOME STATISTICS

The perinatal mortality rate (PNMR = stillbirths plus deaths within seven days after the delivery) has declined over the past century. At present the perinatal mortality rates for Scotland, England and Wales, and the Netherlands (Table 1) are fairly low and fairly similar. Thus the Dutch system, with all its home births, does not "perform" worse than the British system.

Dutch birth statistics indicate that the stillbirth rates and PNMR for the mothers who used the service of maternity home care assistants are well below the equivalent overall national rates (Van Teijlingen, 1990:362-3). One explanation for this phenomenon is that the risk selection process works most of the time. Consequently low-risk pregnant women give birth at home or during a short-stay hospital delivery followed by the service of the maternity home care assistants at home during the postnatal period. Obstetricians in hospital attend the pregnant women who are at a higher risk, therefore their overall PNMRs are more than double the rates for mothers who use the service of a maternity home care assistant.

Table 1. Perinatal mortality rates (per 1,000 births) for 1985-1996
Scotland, England & Wales, and the Netherlands

Country	Scotland[+]	England & Wales	England only[+]	The Netherlands[*]
1985	9.8	9.8	-	9.8
1986	10.2	9.6	-	9.7
1987	8.9	8.9	-	9.4
1988	8.9	8.7	-	9.1
1989	8.7	-	8.1	9.6
1990	8.7	-	8.0	9.6
1991	8.6	-	7.6	9.1
1992	9.0 (8.5)	-	7.8	9.1
1993	9.6 (8.0)	-	8.9	9.1
1994	9.0 (7.4)	-	8.8	8.6
1995	9.6 (7.9)	-	8.8	7.6
1996	9.2 (7.9)	-	-	8.0

+ In the UK the Still-Birth (Definition) Act 1992 re-defined stillbirths, from 1 October 1992, to include losses between 24 and 27 weeks gestation. This table is based on all stillbirths registered during the year. The rates in brackets are based on stillbirths with a gestation period of 28 weeks and over.
* The stillbirth rate in the Netherlands is based on a gestation period of 28 weeks and over.
[Sources: Register General Scotland (1997), OPCS (1989), http:/statline.cbd.nl/witch/selned.htm]

The percentage of mothers breastfeeding can be regarded as one indicator of the effectiveness of the health education aspect of the work of maternity home care assistants. It may be significant that the proportion of those mothers using the service who were breastfeeding on the day the maternity home care assistant left showed an increase in the early 1980s, reaching a level of two out of every three mothers (Nationale Kruisvereniging, 1989). In other words, the increase in breastfeeding paralleled the increase in the number of families using the service of maternity home care assistants. However, a Dutch voluntary organization promoting breast-feeding has criticized the figures for breastfeeding mothers. Admittedly, the maternity home care assistant does a good job with regard to stimulating breast-feeding—but what happens when she leaves after eight or ten days? According to this organization: "Many women give up after the maternity home care assistant has left. A mother still needs support in her effort to breastfeed her baby after the lying-in period has finished" (Personal communication from a committee member of 'Borstvoeding Natuurlijk').

SOCIAL AND PROFESSIONAL DISTANCE

Most of the tasks performed by a maternity home care assistant are those that the family would normally be doing themselves. The kind of care that the maternity home care assistants provide, and the moment at which they enter the family—at a time when the family has a new member—together tend to reduce the social barrier between mother and maternity home care assistant. Reichardt (1980) suggests that this may be aided by the fact that many maternity home care assistants work in their own local regions.

At the same time being a maternity home care assistant is for most staff a job, not a career path, which is one of the reasons why maternity centers are finding it increasingly difficult to attract staff. Another reason is that maternity home care assistants find their irregular hours of work hard to combine with running their own households (Bureau Obelon, 1986). A further reason is the low status of the job. This is expressed in its low wages and the lack of credibility which maternity home care assistants have with some midwives and general practitioners.

Scheijmans (1986) notes that there are no career opportunities within the profession of maternity home care assistant, and the job itself is demanding. The demands it makes are perhaps increasing with the growing number of severe problems in families, the increase in the number of difficult cases caused by discharging some women from hospital before they are fit enough to go home (Roumen, 1987), and the added difficulties of dealing with larger numbers of foreign women: there is a language and culture barrier between maternity home care assistants and, for example, Turkish and Moroccan mothers. Several problems are mentioned by two maternity home care assistants from Rotterdam in an interview with a health union magazine: "You meet divorced people, people with all sorts of problems. Drink, drugs, run-away men. This sort of thing happened in the past too, but you did not get to hear about it. Now it all gets laid on the table. This makes the job a lot more stressful" (Leenders, 1988).

These factors also lead to an annual turnover amongst maternity home care assistants of some 15% (Roumen, 1987). Furthermore, Seysener and Van Westering (1986) point out that most maternity home care assistants still leave the job when they have their own children, although some may later return to work as stand-in help.

STAFFING DIFFICULTIES

The National Cross Organization finds it difficult to attract more people to take the training course, and more importantly, to start working as maternity home care assistants after they pass their exams. These problems experienced by the Dutch maternity centers in recruiting and keeping staff, complaints made by staff about low pay, the high turn-over rate of maternity home care assistants, especially in the big cities, must be familiar ones in the experience of British midwives. The midwifery profession in Britain faces exactly the same problems. It is therefore debatable whether the Dutch way of organizing the maternity services, at least as regards the people it employs, is structurally different. The Dutch midwives are indeed better off than their British counterparts in terms of professional autonomy, status and pay; but it seems as if another occupation in the Netherlands has taken the burden of being the lowest in the hierarchy.

FREEDOM OF CHOICE FOR PREGNANT WOMEN

The existence of a profession like that of maternity home care assistant enables a pregnant woman in the Netherlands to opt for a home birth or a short-stay hospital delivery without having to worry about the availability of sufficient help from family, friends, and neighbors when this help is most needed. This support at the mother's home turns home birth and short-stay hospital delivery into real options for the majority of Dutch pregnant women. The existence of a real choice for the low-risk pregnant woman as to where to give birth to her baby also has an impact on the relationship between the midwife and the woman. To put it simply: the midwife has more to offer. This aspect of freedom of choice is bound to improve the midwife/client relationship.

The system of parental financial contributions and Sick Funds' contributions makes the maternity home care assistant service available for everybody. It is relatively inexpensive and contributes to the satisfaction of recipients (Kerssens, 1994). This allows more women from all social classes to opt for home births and short-stay hospital deliveries, options which are sometimes regarded in Britain as open to middle-class women only. Wiegers and colleagues (1998:1511) argue that the social environment of wide acceptance of home deliveries for low-risk pregnant women, as perceived by the woman and her significant others, is "a precious commodity if the home birth option is to be sustained and preserved" in the Netherlands.

Finally, the question of the cost of providing postnatal care at home or in hospital is an increasingly important question in our overstressed health care systems. Fewer medical professionals attending births, and more deliveries and more postnatal care given at home, must be appealing to governments of industrialized countries trying to cut their spending on health care.

REFERENCES

Adviescommissie Verloskunde (1987) *Verloskundige Organisatie in Nederland: Uniek, bewonderd en verguisd* (final report), Rijswijk: Ministry of Welfare, Health & Culture.

Arms, S. (1981) *Immaculate Deception. A New Look at Women & Childbirth.* (3rd edn), New York: Bantam Books, 346-77

Ashton, K. (1980) Home delivery in Holland, *Nursing Times*: 1442-6

Association for the Improvement in the Maternity Services (1986) *Choosing a Home Birth.* (leaflet), London.

Beck, M. (1991) Independent midwifery in Amsterdam, *Midwives Chronicle & Nursing Notes*, 72-5

Belton, S. (1993) The Dutch model of maternity care, *Australian College of Midwives Incorporated* (Sept.):13-5

Borjars, K. (1993) Going Dutch, *New Generation* 12:46-7

Bradley, P.J. & Bray, K.H., 1996, The Netherlands' Maternal-Child Health Program: implications for the United States, *Journal of Obstetric, Gynecologic, & Neonatal Nursing,* 25:471-5.

Bureau Obelon (1986) Naar een klantgerichte kraamzorg, *Tijdschrift voor Verloskundigen.* 5, 141-54.

Cavenagh, A.J.M. (1968) Place of delivery: Dutch solution. *British Medical Journal*, ii:688-689

CBS (1986) *Compendium of Health Statistics of the Netherlands 1986.* The Hague: Staatsuitgeverij, 304 & 361

CBS (1987) Monthly / Demographic data. *Maandbericht Gezondheidsstatistiek.* The Hague: Staatsuitgeverij, 7, 22-3.

CBS (1988) Data on staff of maternity centres, 1987. *Maandbericht Gezondheidsstatistiek.* The Hague: Staatsuitgeverij, 6, 19-21.

CBS (1989) Births by obstetric assistance and place of delivery, 1987. *Maandbericht Gezondheidsstatistiek.* The Hague: Staatsuitgeverij, 8, 5-6.

CBS (1990) Monthly / Demographic data, *Maandbericht Gezondheidsstatistiek* The Hague: Staatsuitgeverij, 9: 22-3.

CBS (1998) Web page: http://statline.cbs.nl/witch/etc/scratch/1995411131/6363a05.html

Declercq, E.R. (1994) A cross-national analysis of midwifery politics: six lessons for midwives, *Midwifery*, 10:232-37

DeVries, R.G. (1996) The social and cultural context of birth: Lessons for health care reform from Dutch maternity care, *The Journal of Perinatal Education*, 5:25-28

Donley, J., 1986, *Save the Midwife*, Auckland: New Women's Press

Crébas, A. (1990) *Beroepsomschrijving Verloskundigen* (Dutch language publication), Bilthoven: NOV

Garcia, J., Blondel, B. & Saurel-Cubizolles, M.J. (1989) The needs of childbearing families: social policies and the organization of health care. In: *Effective Care in Pregnancy and Childbirth.* Vol.1., Chalmers, I., Enkin, M. & Keirse, M.J.N.C. (eds.), Oxford: Oxford University Press: 205-220

Haspels, A.A. & Barentsen, R. (1986) Overzicht organisatie verloskundige zorg en perinatale sterfte in verschillende Europese landen. In *Proceedings van symposium verloskundige zorg in Nederland*, Slager, E., Kloosterman, G.J. & Stolte, L.A.M. (eds.), Hoofddorp: Wyeth Lab. BV, 27-34

Jordan B. (1978), *Birth in Four Cultures: A Crosscultural Investigation of Childbirth in Yucatan, Holland, Sweden & the United States* (Series Editor: S. Clarkson), St. Albans, Vermont: Eden Press.

Kerssens, J.J. (1994) Patient satisfaction with home-birth care in The Netherlands, *Journal of Advanced Nursing*. 20:344-50

Kiers, J. (1986) Nieuwe opleiding MDGO-VZ is even wennen!, *MGZ*. 9, 18-9.

Kiestra, J. (1987) Kraamzorg flexibeler, *Inzet*. 1: 22-3.

Kitzinger, S. (1980) *Birth at home*, Oxford: Oxford University Press, 21 & 47.

Kloosterman, G.J. (1984) The Dutch Experience of Domiciliary Confinements. In *Pregnancy Care for the 1980s*. Zander, L. & Chamberlain, G. (Eds), London: Macmillan: 115-25,.

Leenders, P. (1988) Ook uit roze wolken valt wel eens regen, *Aaneén* 7 November, 10.

De leidster-docenten van kraamcentra in de Provincie Zuid-Holland (1987) *Een Zwartboek over de Kraamzorg* (unpublished), 16-23, 29-33.

Mander, R. (1995) The relevance of the Dutch system of maternity care to the United Kingdom, *Journal of Advanced Nursing* 22:1023-26.

Nationale Kruisvereniging (1987) *Evaluatie Voorbereiding en Invoering Flexibele Kraamzorg tot 1987*, Bunnik: Nationale Kruisvereniging: 3-11.

Newson, K. (1981) Direct Entry Method of Training Midwives in Three Countries: 1. The Netherlands, *Midwives Chronicle & Nursing Notes*. 2:39-43.

OPCS (Office of Population Censuses & Surveys) (1989) *Population Trends* Government Statistical Services, London: HMSO

Reichardt, A.G. (1980) Oudervragen bieden ingang voor preventief werken. *MGZ*. 5:11.

Registrar General Scotland (1997) *Annual Report of the Registrar General of Births, Deaths and Marriages for Scotland 1996*, Edinburgh: Registrar General Office for Scotland

Rickford, F. (1986) Deliverance, *Marxism Today*. 10:40.

Ropping, R. (1989) Kraamzorg Drenthe op de drempel van een nieuwe tijd, *MGZ*. 5:28-9.

Rooks, J.P. (1997) *Midwifery and Childbirth in America*, Philadelphia: Temple University Press.

Roumen, M. (1987) *Rotterdams Nieuwsblad*, (January 17th, Rotterdam, The Netherlands: 3

Samuël, A.C.M. (1988) *Kraamzorg verleend door de kraamcentra in het jaar 1986*, Leidschendam: Ministry of Welfare, Health & Culture: 2-3

Scheijmans, I. (1986) De positie van vrouwelijke werknemers in de kraamzorg. In: *Kenau of Nachtegaal, vrouwen in de verpleging en verzorgende beroepen*. M. Kroef *et al*. The Hague: Ministry Social Security & Employment: 67-77

Seysener, M. & Westering, J. van (1986) Kraamzorg in moeilijke hoek, maar situatie is niet zó alarmerend!, *MGZ* 9, 12-4.

Smulders, B. & Limburg, A. (1988) Obstetrics and midwifery in the Netherlands. In: *The Midwife Challenge*. S. Kitzinger (ed.), London: Pandora Press.

Spanjer, J. *et al.* (1986) *Bevallen en Opstaan.* (revised edn.), Amsterdam Uitgeverij Contact: 53.

SZ (1987) *Algemene Bijstandswet. Hoofdlijnen en bedragen.* (leaflet Dutch DHSS) p.10. The Hague: Ministry of Social Security & Employment 1 July 1987.

Tasharrofi, A. (1993), Midwifery in the Netherlands, *Midwives Chronicle & Nursing Notes*, 106, 286-8

Teijlingen van, E. & McCaffery, P. (1987) The profession of midwife in the Netherlands', *Midwifery*. 3: 179.

Teijlingen van, E.R. (1990) The profession of maternity home care assistant and its significance for the Dutch midwifery profession, *International Journal of Nursing Studies*, 27:355-66.

Teijlingen van, E.R. (1993) The occupation of maternity home care assistant In: Abraham-Van der Mark, E. (ed.), *Successful Home Birth and Midwifery: The Dutch model*, London: Bergin & Garvey, 161-71.

Tew, M. (1998) *Safer childbirth? A critical history of maternity care* (3rd Edn.), London: Free Associations Press

Tweede Kamer der Staten-Generall (1990) *Vaststelling van de begroting van de uitgaven & ontvangsten van hoofdstuk XVI (Ministerie van W.V.C.) voor het jaar 1990*. Parliamentary Hansard: 21 300 XVI, Nr.42, The Hague: SDU Uitgeverij

Verbrugge H.P (1968) *Kraamzorg bij huisbevallingen. Evaluatie van resultaten*, Groningen: Wolters-Noordhoff.

Wiegers,T.A., Zee van der, J., Kerssens, J.J. & Keirse, M.J.N.C. (1998) Home birth or short-stay hospital birth in a low risk population in the Netherlands, *Social Science & Medicine* 46: 1505-11

Ziekenfondsraad (1987) *De Verloskundige Indicatielijst,* Amstelveen. Ziekenfondsraad: 3-4

[1] This paper is an update of two previous publications (Van Teijlingen 1990; 1993) on Dutch maternity home care assistants. All translations from Dutch are my own.

[2] The following services could be provided: (i) district nursing: nursing and care of ill and infirm people at home; (ii) centres for infants and toddlers; (iii) the provision of health information and education; (iv) the loan of medical aids; (v) prenatal and postnatal care carried out by district nurses and antenatal teachers; (vi) maternity home care assistance (CBS, 1986; Kiestra, 1987).

[3] Data for 1995 from Dutch Governmental Statistics web page: http:/statline.cbd.nl/witch/selned.htm

[4] The consumers' contribution is the same throughout the country. The Sick Funds' share varies slightly from province to province, because the Sick Funds and the maternity centers negotiate provincial prices per day of caring (data for province of South Holland from Ms V/d Voorde, director of a maternity center).

[5] Figure refers to 1998 Sick Funds limit of Dutch Guilders fl.62,600 per year for people in paid employment (exchange rate one US dollar is approximately two Dutch Guilders).

THE ROLE AND RESPONSIBILITIES OF THE MIDWIFE IN SCOTLAND

*Janet Askham & Rosaline S Barbour**

INTRODUCTION

Concern has been expressed of late within the midwifery profession that the midwife's role and responsibilities are being eroded. This purported erosion is held to have three causes: the increased involvement of medical staff in duties traditionally part of the midwife's role; the increased use of technology in maternity care and the growing reliance on the establishment of rules or unit policies which undermine the midwife's decision-making power.

Our study set out to establish the extent of midwives' responsibilities in a variety of maternity care settings. We also sought to elicit midwives' own perceptions of their role and responsibilities and to examine how responsibility for maternity care duties and decisions is allocated in the work situation. Because of the nature of our research question we selected a combination of observational and interview techniques. We were thus able not only to see for ourselves which staff member was responsible for specific tasks and decisions but also to link our assessments as researchers with midwives' own opinions and feelings about their work.

The study had four main aims, to find out:

1. where the midwife's responsibility ends—i.e. where she hands over, or someone else takes over, tasks and decisions connected with the care of women during pregnancy, labour and delivery, and of mothers and their babies during the first days after delivery;
2. whether the extent of the midwife's responsibility varies from section to section or from one type of structure to another within Scotland;
3. what problems, if any, are perceived in areas where the work of other staff does impinge upon that of the midwife;
4. how midwives themselves view the situation.

The study was carried out in nine different locations throughout Scotland, chosen to reflect both the range of units (from large teaching hospitals to general practitioner units or health centres) and the range of maternity care settings (antenatal clinics; labour wards; post-natal wards and work in the community). Since the focus of this study was the extent to which midwives could function as 'practitioners in their own

---

* Janet Askham, Professor of Social Gerontology, Institute of Gerontology, King's College, London, Cornwall House, Waterloo Road, London, SE1 8WA; Rosaline S. Barbour, Senior lecturer, Department of General Practice, University of Glasgow, Lancaster Crescent, Glasgow, G12 0RR. Both formerly Researchers, Department of Obstetrics & Gynaecology, University of Aberdeen. Correspondence & reprint requests to: Professor Askham, Institute of Gerontology.
Health Bulletin 45 May (1987): 153-9. Crown Copyright is reproduced with the permission of the Controller of HMSO.

right', the two areas of midwifery concerned with the 'abnormal'—i.e. antenatal wards and special care baby units—were omitted from this part of the study.

THE ROLE OF THE MIDWIFE IN ANTENATAL CLINICS

A total of 42 midwives were observed at work in five different locations, ranging from a large teaching hospital to General Practitioners' (GPs') surgeries and at a variety of types of clinic, ranging from consultant clinics to midwives' clinics.

We found that there was considerable variation in the amount of responsibility accorded midwives working in different clinics, even when such factors as the purpose of the antenatal visit or the absence or presence of medical complications were taken into account. The widest variation occurred at GPs' clinics, some of which functioned as midwives' clinics with the midwife assuming full responsibility for examining pregnant women without complications, whilst others limited the midwife's involvement to that of non-clinical chaperone (with the GP carrying out the full examination). Moreover, it was not uncommon for an individual midwife to experience wide discrepancies in the amount of responsibility accorded her at different clinics or by different consultants or GPs.

Robinson *et al.* (1983) found that midwives working in antenatal clinics in consultant units were more likely than their counterparts in non-teaching and GP units to be dissatisfied with the amount of responsibility involved in their job. Our own findings, however, suggest that the picture is somewhat more complex. We found, overall, that there was a tendency for midwives to express satisfaction with the optimum amount of responsibility afforded as part of their current job. Dissatisfaction appeared to be related not to the type of unit in which a midwife worked but to her exposure to antenatal clinics where the midwife was accorded more responsibility. Where midwives did wish to see changes in the clinics in which they worked they wanted 'more of the same'—i.e. more midwives' clinics where these were already in operation: little enthusiasm, however, was expressed with regard to more radical changes, with midwives citing the constraints (either physical or organisational) of their particular setting in defence of the status quo.

Although most decision-making at clinics remained the final responsibility of the medical staff, our observations showed that midwives could and did exercise a great deal of influence over the decision-making process, often prompting more junior members of the medical staff and occasionally even appealing to the higher authority of the consultant when the well-being of a patient was felt to be at stake. This goes some way towards accounting for the high level of satisfaction expressed by midwives with regard to the way in which responsibility for decision-making was allocated in their units.

With regard to specific tasks midwives in most clinic settings were responsible for testing urine, weighing patients and taking blood pressure readings, being assisted by auxiliary nurses. Midwives reported themselves content with this division of labour and were happy to carry out these procedures but some resentment was expressed when the midwife's role was restricted to the performance of these routine tasks. Medical staff frequently assumed responsibility for taking samples of venous blood, even in situations where midwives had undergone specialised training to equip them for carrying out this procedure: few midwives, however, complained of this situation. Although midwives were observed to carry out vaginal examinations at one midwives' clinic their colleagues elsewhere were reluctant to add this task to their repertoire as clinic midwives.

Like Robinson *et al.* (1983) we too found that doctors frequently repeated examinations for oedema and abdominal palpations carried out by midwives. The midwives in the present study, however, did not complain about such repetition, and argued that their own performance of these tasks fulfilled a different purpose to that of medical staff: the midwife could provide a woman with more detailed information; her examination formed part of the midwife's overall assessment of the patient and thus afforded satisfaction in itself; the midwife's examination gave her the opportunity of gaining practice in these procedures. By contrast those situations where midwives were prevented from carrying out palpations aroused a great deal of criticism: palpation was a much-prized skill, which midwives feared could be lost through lack of practice.

In general midwives did not wish to take over the role or decision-making powers of medical staff at antenatal clinics, nor did they express much enthusiasm with regard to extending their own role to encompass additional tasks. The majority of midwives appeared, however, to respond positively to situations affording them considerable responsibility and were able to retain an appreciation of the differences in the respective contributions to be made by midwives and medical staff.

THE ROLE OF THE MIDWIFE IN THE LABOUR WARD

We observed 52 midwives going about their work in the labour wards of one large teaching hospital, two GP units and one maternity home attached to a consultant unit.

Obviously the content of the midwife's work varied considerably within and between these units, depending on the extent to which technology was employed and the absence or presence of medical complications in patients. However, even with regard to the management of 'normal' labours and deliveries the responsibility accorded the midwife was found to vary considerably depending on the unit and shift involved, Consultant unit policies, although sometimes relaxed on night duty, regulated and established medical staffs routine involvement in 'normal' labours. In GP units, by contrast, it was frequently the case—particularly at night-that a woman could be admitted and delivered without a doctor having been present at any stage.

We found, as did Robinson et al. (1983) that, even among midwives working in consultant units where medical staff were routinely involved in normal labours, the majority were content with the amount of responsibility accorded them.

The role of the midwife in the labour ward hinges around the detection of abnormality and the reporting of any such signs to the medical staff, who subsequently make the decisions about the further management of the patient concerned. Midwives were observed, however, to exert considerable influence over the decision-making process by virtue of their role as instigators of a sequence of events. Unit policies guided such decision-making in the consultant units, but there appeared to be general agreement within all the units studied as to the relative decision-making powers of doctor and midwife. Moreover, midwives could and did also employ tact in influencing doctors' decisions.

Although in consultant units some disagreement might arise between midwives and house officers or residents all participants bowed to the superior authority and knowledge of the consultant. In GP units, by contrast, relatively junior members of the medical staff might have final authority. In this setting midwives, as specialists with many years' experience, sometimes felt themselves better equipped to deal with the situations arising than were some GPs, as generalists with only a short experience of practice.

With the notable exception of suturing, midwives were happy to accept new responsibilities where these had already been introduced—e.g. topping tip epidurals and attaching scalp electrodes—but did not complain about doctors' continued involvement in these procedures, being content to share responsibility. Nor were they keen to further extend their role, expressing little enthusiasm for involvement in performing inductions, forceps or breech deliveries. Although midwives in each setting frequently considered themselves to be in a better position than doctors to judge the timing and quantity of intramuscular injections for pain relief, they were not keen to assume responsibility for prescribing sedatives: fear of litigation prevented midwives from pressing for more responsibility and affected their day-to-day behaviour in all units, with midwives being careful at all times to confirm by telephone doctors' instructions with regard to sedation.

Although just under half the midwives studied had been trained to suture perineums our observations established that it was quite rare for a midwife to perform this procedure in any of the units. Whilst staff shortages undoubtedly restricted midwives' involvement in this procedure their own ambivalence was also an important factor in inhibiting their involvement. Our observations suggested also that some midwives were employing standards higher than those of their superiors, being reluctant to carry out repairs unsupervised even after they had been certified competent. Like palpation, suturing was a skill which midwives felt could be lost through lack of practice, but, in this case, midwives did not seek to maximise their opportunities for gaining practice.

With regard to extending their role, however, several midwives working in GP units were keen to extend their repertoire to allow them to intubate babies in an emergency. This reflected their concern at the lack of paediatric cover: a concern about the overall quality of service rather than their own role as midwives.

The high level of satisfaction reported by midwives in all labour ward settings testifies both to their success in employing tact to maximise their responsibility and to their enjoyment of the actual work involved—delivering healthy babies to happy mothers. Midwives, like the mothers themselves, evaluate their role and experiences in the labour ward in a holistic manner, which transcends a formal consideration of the range of duties and responsibilities which constitute their role.

THE ROLE OF THE MIDWIFE IN THE POST-NATAL WARD

Forty midwives were observed at work in the post-natal wards of two hospitals (teaching and non-teaching) and two peripheral units (a separate GP unit and a unit attached to a consultant unit).

The content of a midwife's work on post-natal wards varied little between these different settings, except for the fact that midwives working in peripheral units tended to make more decisions autonomously. We found that in this area of work the involvement of medical staff was not great in terms of hours, being virtually confined to ward rounds. There was no overlap with regard to establishing infant feeding, keeping babies clean, warm, dry and adequately fed and the provision of advice on infant care and general maternal health: all of these tasks were regarded as the sole prerogative of the midwife. Some repetition did occur with regard to the examination of mothers or babies, but midwives were happy to share this responsibility with doctors: often the repeat examination was, in any case, carried out at the request of the midwife, who had detected some abnormality.

Overall, midwives in each setting expressed satisfaction with their current level of responsibility. Some dissatisfaction was evident, however, with regard to specific tasks. Many of the midwives thought that they should carry out venepuncture for routine haemoglobin checks on mothers, a responsibility at present restricted to medical staff in two of the units studied. The situation with regard to prescribing sedatives was seen by most midwives as illogical, but aroused relatively little conflict due to midwives' skill in prompting doctors towards certain decisions as, indeed, they did with regard also to the decision to carry out serum bilirubin tests on jaundiced babies. More senior midwives, particularly in peripheral units, might sometimes make such decisions themselves in the absence of a doctor.

The midwives in our study, like those studied by Robinson et al. (1983) said that the decision to discharge a mother and baby was always made by a doctor. However, our observations revealed that, even in consultant units where unit guidelines were established, midwives exerted considerable influence over this decision, which probably accounts for the low level of complaints recorded. Midwives were adept at prompting the decisions of the relatively junior members of the medical staff involved in the day-to-day work of post-natal wards. They could, if they wished, capitalise on their superior knowledge based on continuous observation of patients and also, in consultant units, on the fact that they were the only professionals with responsibility for both mother and baby.

Very little overt conflict or dissatisfaction was evident with regard to midwives' role in postnatal wards. Midwives were skilled in using tact to exert their influence; there was scope for a variety of different working arrangements with individual doctors and, for the most part, midwives were, in any case, left to get on with their work with medical staff being only sporadically involved.

THE ROLE OF THE MIDWIFE IN THE COMMUNITY

A total of 25 midwives were observed at work in the community. We studied the work of midwives based at a large teaching hospital, a GP unit within a non-teaching hospital and a health centre.

Midwives from all units visited mothers and babies at home until the tenth day following delivery (thirteenth day after a caesarian section). All midwives performed the same duties at these home visits, carrying out routine examinations to establish the progress of mother and baby. These responsibilities were accepted by all staff involved as the province of the midwife. Again her responsibility was to detect abnormalities and report these to the doctor involved, who thereafter was responsible for making decisions with regard to re-admissions to hospital and prescribing drugs.

Like the midwives studied by Robinson et al. (1983), the midwives we spoke to were not keen to extend their visiting period to the 28 days recommended by the Central Midwives' Board in 1977. Their contentment with the present situation is probably accounted for by the considerable freedom they enjoyed in extending visiting in individual cases where they felt this to be necessary. Nor were community midwives keen to extend the scope of their role to encompass home visits to monitor women's blood pressure readings.

We found, as did Robinson *et al.* (1983), that very few community midwives were involved in carrying out deliveries as part of their job. Despite the fact that all community midwives regarded delivering a baby as the core act of midwifery, lack of involvement in deliveries was not a major source of dissatisfaction. Only five of the midwives were involved in home confinement—a responsibility which afforded them much satisfaction, but which also caused them much anxiety. Like their colleagues in other settings, these midwives preferred to deliver babies in hospital, because of the complications which could arise; the difficulty in obtaining medical cover. The time lapse before the flying squad arrived and the inadequate equipment carried by community midwives. Domino deliveries (in hospital for delivery only, by community midwife) were seen as a compromise but midwives in all settings acknowledged the practical difficulties involved and did not see the introduction of domino deliveries as an immediate priority.

Community midwives did not spend much of their working lives in the close company of other members of the maternity care team and so opportunities for conflict were fairly limited. However, some conflict was seen to occur between midwives and health visitors: with regard, respectively, to midwives' involvement in visiting beyond the tenth/thirteenth day and health visitors' involvement in breast-feeding classes. Our observations revealed, however, that midwives who had regular informal contact with health visitors in health centres experienced less problematic working relationships. This also held true for relationships between midwives and GPs and between midwives and GPs' receptionists. Both these relationships could be problematic: GPs' knowledge of obstetrics might be considerably less or more out of date than that of an experienced practising midwife but they still held ultimate responsibility. Receptionists, although junior members of staff with no clinical knowledge or responsibilities, could and frequently did, restrict midwives' access to GPs—a situation which gave rise to considerable dissatisfaction on the part of the midwives involved.

In general, community midwives appeared very satisfied with the amount of responsibility accorded them at present. Again, midwives' use of tact enabled them to exert influence and maximise their responsibilities in many situations which might otherwise have been seen as unsatisfactory. There was considerable scope for midwives to negotiate with individual GPs and to develop relationships built on mutual trust and acknowledgement of expertise, which afforded midwives a great deal of professional satisfaction. Community midwives welcomed their responsibility as sole representatives of the maternity care team at this stage of care and derived a great deal of satisfaction from the special relationship which they felt they enjoyed with new and frequently anxious mothers during the first few days of their babies' lives at home.

CONCLUSIONS

Our study revealed a high level of general satisfaction on the part of midwives working in all four maternity care settings examined. This overall satisfaction, however, masked a considerable amount of dissatisfaction within specific areas and with regard to specific tasks or decisions.

Given that there were areas where the division of responsibility appeared to be unclear or problematic, one must address the question as to why there is not more general dissatisfaction or even militancy amongst midwives. The findings of the present study suggest several possible answers:

- Midwives may be ambivalent, wanting to take decisions but not to carry ultimate responsibility.
- Some midwives may want change whilst others wish to preserve the status quo.
- Midwives may already have a great deal of autonomy in that some responsibilities are accepted as their prerogative.
- Midwives may seize responsibility in some situations or may have responsibility thrust upon them.
- Midwives can make extensive and sophisticated use of tact in negotiating for responsibility in a wide range of settings.

ACKNOWLEDGEMENTS

The research on which this report is based was made possible by a grant from the Chief Scientist's Office of the Scottish Home and Health Department. We would also like to thank the Royal College of Midwives (Scottish Board) for their support and help in selecting locations for our study; the Department of Obstetrics and Gynaecology in Aberdeen, to which we were attached and the MRC Medical Sociology Unit which housed us.

[1] Central Midwives Board for Scotland, Annual Report 1977.

[2] Robinson S, Golden J, Bradley J. A study of the role and responsibilities of the midwife. London: London University, Chelsea College, Nursing Education Research Unit, 1983. (NERU Report No 1)

Domino Delivery: The Domino Delivery Scheme in Somerset Allows Community Midwives to Use Their Midwifery Skills to the Full

Maureen Beck[*]

I am a community midwife in Taunton, Somerset. The local maternity unit at Musgrove Park Hospital, Taunton, had 3,000 births in 1988, 90 of these were domino deliveries conducted by community midwives. This type of confinement is becoming increasingly popular amongst our clients and the community midwives in the area are enthusiastic about the scheme. Both consultant booked and GP booked clients are included in the scheme. The midwives, GPs and the consultants work together assessing the suitability of the mother and her family as well as her home circumstances for this type of delivery.

There are eight community midwives in the Taunton team covering the towns and suburbs of Wellington and Taunton, as well as the surrounding villages. We are all practice based and depending on the size of the practice work within between one and three practices each. We all carry two-way radios which are in contact with the ambulance control in Taunton.

We have midwives' antenatal clinics in all the practices as well as conducting parentcraft classes in conjunction with the health visitors who are also practice based.

All the mothers are visited at home antenatally by the community midwife and this is when the place of birth, length of stay, type of delivery etc. is discussed in detail. The parents and the midwife may have already had some discussion either in clinic or at parentcraft class. The parents are given all the options available and the midwife offers her help, support and advice, the parents then make their own choice.

If a mother chooses the domino scheme and she is booked under the consultant the community midwife writes to the consultant asking his/her opinion and agreement. If the consultant agrees then the mother is booked for a domino delivery. If a mother is booked under her GP then the GP's agreement is sought by the community midwife. Some GPs ask for a consultant's opinion before agreeing.

The community midwives do not actively encourage primigravidas to opt for the scheme but if a primigravida requests a domino birth and the appropriate doctor and midwife are in agreement then she may have this care. The main problem we have found with primigravidas having domino births is that they usually have a longer first stage of labour and due to pressure of work and shortage of staff it is sometimes difficult to give the continuity of care required. We would, however, like to make this service more available to primigravidas in the future. On the whole the initial request for a domino birth usually comes from the mother herself, either because she has had a domino birth before, known someone who has, or just because it appeals to her.

[*] Community Midwife, Taunton, Somerset, England

Midwife, Health Visitor and Community Nurse 1989; 25(11): 463-66. Reprinted by permission of Professional, Managerial and Healthcare Publications Ltd. Chichester, UK.

DOMINO DELIVERY IN SOMERSET

I would now like to concentrate on how the domino scheme operates in my own practice in conjunction with the rest of the team of midwives.

I work in a large practice with six GPs assisted by locums covering holidays, sickness etc. There is a high birth rate in the area as the practice covers a large council housing estate as well as a number of large new developments of private housing. The GPs in the practice no longer do GP maternity booking as a general rule, therefore nearly all the mothers are booked under a consultant. This group of GPs is now also very reluctant to take part in home confinements although they have done so in the past. Two of them will occasionally cover for a home confinement of their own patients. If a mother wishes to have a home confinement and stay with this practice we arrange to have two midwives present for the birth and emergency medical cover only.

All the mothers see a GP for their first antenatal appointment and myself (or deputy) for their second appointment. They then see either a GP or myself at appropriate intervals as well as their hospital appointments.

The GP usually discusses the consultant booking, shared care, etc. at the first appointment. Sometimes at this point the mother may request a domino delivery. If this happens the GP will inform me and if possible will introduce me to the mother at that time. (We have a midwives clinic being held at the same time as the GPs clinic).

If it is not possible for me to meet the mother on her visit the GP will let me know at the end of the session and I will meet the mother on her next visit. On the mother's second visit to the clinic she will see me and this is when parentcraft classes are discussed as well as breast examination and discussion about booking and home visits.

If the mother requests a domino booking and I am in agreement I then write to the consultant. When I have a reply I inform the GP and the rest of the team of community midwives. We have a file in our office at the hospital and about six weeks to one month before the expected delivery date I put the consultant's letter in this file. All the midwives check the file at regular intervals and we try to visit all the mothers booked for the scheme at home within the last month of pregnancy. I have to admit that because of pressure of work, distances and shortages of staff we do not always manage to do this but we do try and we do want to improve this part of our work.

When I visit the mother at home I give her the names of all the midwives and explain our on call rota so that she understands that if I am off duty she will be cared for by another community midwife. During this home visit I will also explain how the scheme operates and inform her who she has to contact when she thinks she is in labour. In this area it is the labour ward where they have a copy of our off duty and the on call rota. If a mother goes into labour during the day and her own midwife is on duty the labour ward staff will contact her via ambulance control on the two-way radio. If the mother starts labour at night or her midwife is off duty then the midwife first on call will be contacted. We always have two midwives on call, i.e. first and second.

LABOUR AND BIRTH

When I have been contacted about a domino client in labour I immediately contact her by telephone. If she is not on the phone I visit her. In phoning I assess the situation and arrange to visit her at home. At this home visit I take a history of the onset of labour, examine her, listen to the fetal heart and if appropriate perform a vaginal examination. It depends on the result of this assessment what my next actions are. If the mother is not in established labour she is reassured and informed whom to contact if she does progress or if concerned. If she is in early labour and I am able to leave her then I arrange when I will come back, carry on with my visits etc. and she can contact me via ambulance control. If she is in established labour or even in early labour and does not wish me to leave I then contact my colleagues on duty and delegate my outstanding visits and arrange cover for impending clinics or parentcraft classes.

Our aim is for the mother to stay at home as long as she is comfortable and wants to. We arrange transfer to hospital when she is in strong established labour making allowances for distance, traffic, family circumstance, etc. Obviously if the mother is already in strong established labour when I make the initial contact then I will arrange to meet her at the hospital providing I am sure she will get there! Occasionally women go straight to the hospital and the appropriate midwife is informed by the labour ward staff; the midwife then goes straight to the hospital.

I will keep the labour ward informed of the situation and inform them when I am transferring the mother to hospital. The mother usually goes to the hospital in her own car with her partner and I follow. If she hasn't any transport than an ambulance is used and I meet her there.

The central delivery suite at the hospital has ten delivery rooms and we usually use the family room. This room is not really very different to the other rooms, but we have tried to make it a little more homely with pictures, flowers, cushions and a bean bag. The parents are encouraged to bring with them a tape recorder, radio or anything else they wish which will help them in their labour. As we do not routinely use continuous monitoring we do not have a monitor in the room but there is one within easy reach. There is piped O_2 and Entonox.

When we arrive at the hospital the labour ward staff are welcoming and friendly and do not interfere with us at all. If it is at night and we have been on duty all day they are usually very helpful if they have time. We are always particularly grateful for their assistance with "The Computer" which we do not feel very friendly to after a long day and night. All our clients' notes are now on computer and this recording is done by the midwives themselves. As the community midwives are not using the computer every day we sometimes need assistance from staff who are more familiar with it. As I do not wish to leave the parents for any length of time during the labour I delay entering the records on the computer until after the delivery and record straight onto the written notes in the delivery room. This means that after the mother and baby are settled there is still quite a lot of work to be done by the midwife.

If the mother is a GP booking (i.e. not my own client) I will inform the GP on admission, the GP will then ask me to make contact again usually when the mother is fully dilated or before if necessary. If the mother is a consultant booking then the team "on take" will know of our arrival.

The mothers are free to move around as much as they wish, take up whatever position is comfortable and analgesia is available. If the mother wishes to be monitored she can be or if the consultant, GP or midwife considers it appropriate for any reason then it is done. If not continuously monitored then the observations are taken and recorded every 30 minutes. All the community midwives have fetal heart detectors (bought by fund raising events) and these are used to reassure the parents, otherwise pinards are used to hear the fetal heart.

Most of the mothers I have cared for with this scheme have needed very little analgesia, they are very relaxed and usually know me well. If the mother is not my own client we soon get to know each other because of the individual care given. The student midwives gain valuable experience of normal childbirth with the domino deliveries and really enjoy them. We have student midwives with us for three months at a time and they are on call when we are. If we haven't got a student with us then we work alone.

POST-NATAL CARE

Once the mother has delivered and the baby has been to the breast the parents are given a drink and then left on their own with their baby for a short time. After this time the mother and baby are bathed and taken to the ward until she goes home. Sometimes mothers wish to go home straight from the labour ward and provided the room is not needed she may do this. It really depends on what time of day the mother delivers and how she feels when she goes home. The baby is examined by either the GP or the paediatrician prior to discharge (depending on the booking). The mother may go home in her own car with another adult as well as the driver, or by ambulance. Most mothers stay in hospital between 6-24 hours after the birth. If she does not feel well enough to go home she may stay, of course. While she is in hospital her care is given by both the community and hospital staff who liaise together. Medical cover is always available during the labour either from the GP, duty doctor or the consultant team "on take". The mother's care may be transferred at any time from GP to consultant if any problems arise.

After the mother goes home she is visited accordingly by the community midwife, in this area twice a day for the first three days then once a day for a minimum of 10 days. She may be visited more often if the need arises. We encourage the student midwives to do 28-day follow-up visits on the clients they deliver. The midwife who starts to care for a mother in labour carries on except if she is in very early labour when her own midwife comes back on duty; if this happens then her own midwife may take over her care. If the duty midwife delivers a client from another practice she transfers the mother back to her own midwife after discharge from hospital.

LOOKING TO THE FUTURE

Women booked for the domino scheme are not booked just because they want to go home early, they are booked this way because they want a community midwife delivery and the type of care this involves.

We realise in Taunton that we do not always meet all the criteria or standards we would like to but we do feel the domino scheme is a good service, enjoyed by parents, their families, the student midwives and the community midwives. We would like to improve the service particularly in regard to visiting all the mothers involved in the scheme at home antenatally. The midwives keep their skills and confidence and this is most important now that sadly home confinements are becoming a rare event mainly because of lack of GP support. However busy we are or whatever cuts in the staffing rates we do not want to give up this service and the families who benefit from it certainly do not want us to. In fact more people wish to avail themselves of this service.

An interesting point to note, a number of GPs and GPs wives have chosen this scheme for themselves. This includes GPs who no longer do GP bookings for their patients choosing a GP booked domino birth for themselves!

Finally, in the Taunton and surrounding area the domino scheme is becoming more widely known as "A Community Midwife Delivery" either under the medical care of the obstetrician or the GP as appropriate. The community midwives in the area feel fortunate that we are able to utilise our midwifery skills to the full and we sincerely hope that we may continue to do so. We also hope that women who wish to have their babies at home may have home confinements without the battle that some women have to go through at the present time.

Changing Childbirth? The British Midwife's Role in Research and Innovation

Maureen Porter

In 1993 something quite astonishing happened to maternity services in Great Britain. The government published a report recommending that women should be the focus of maternity care, be fully informed and involved in decisions about their care, and that much of this care should be provided by a midwife known to them. These recommendations became government policy in 1993 when money and expertise were made available to ensure the policy was implemented. Women's organizations and consumer groups welcomed the change in philosophy and practice with enthusiasm (NCT 1994). It is not entirely clear whether health professionals were ready for the change as they received it cautiously or with open hostility (Allen 1993; Ilford 1993). This report was so radical, and its implications for midwives so enormous, it is necessary to examine it in more detail.

The Changing Childbirth Report

In March 1992 the all party House of Commons Select Committee on Health produced a report on maternity services, dubbed the Winterton Report after its chairman, which advocated changes in the maternity services involving the three Cs—Choice, Continuity and Control for women patients (House of Commons 1992). The 'Government Response' to the Winterton Report which was published in July 1992 set up an Expert Maternity Group chaired by Baroness Cumberlege, to make specific recommendations about the future of the maternity services (Cmnd 2018 1992). This group published its report *Changing Childbirth* in August 1993. The report acknowledged women's feelings about their maternity care, the poverty of communications between women patients and their medical/nursing attendants and the need to make maternity services locally available and responsive to all (Department of Health 1993). It advised that midwives can and should provide the continuity of care that women want. It outlined ten indicators of success to be achieved within five years of its publication:

1) All women should be entitled to carry their own notes.
2) Every woman should know one midwife who ensures continuity of her midwifery care—the named midwife.
3) At least 30% of women should have the midwife as the lead professional.
4) Every woman should know the lead professional who has a key role in the planning and provision of care.
5) At least 75% of women should know the person who cares for them during the delivery.
6) Midwives should have direct access to some beds in all maternity units.
7) At least 30% of women delivered in a maternity unit should be admitted under the management of the midwife.
8) Total number of antenatal visits for women with uncomplicated pregnancies should have been reviewed in the light of available evidence and the Royal College of Obstetrics & Gynaecology (RCOG) guidelines.

9) All front line ambulances should have a paramedic able to support the midwife who needs to transfer a woman to hospital in an emergency.

10) All women should have access to information about the services available in their locality.

These recommendations became government policy in 1994 with the setting up of a National Health Service Management Executive (NHSME) after a consultation period. Patients' existing rights and the improvements they could expect during the next five years were outlined in *The Patient's Charter: Maternity Services* published in April 1994. In England and Wales an advisory group was set up and money set aside to ensure the implementation of these policies and to publish a quarterly newsletter *Changing Childbirth Update*. In 1994 the Department of Health funded 14 projects designed to test and develop different aspects of woman-centred maternity care and a further 24 in 1995 which were intended to involve women more in the planning, development and monitoring of services. Scotland produced a 'Policy Review' (Scottish Office 1993) which embodied only some of these radical ideas and has been described as 'a pale imitation' of *Changing Childbirth* (NCT 1994). Northern Ireland, the fourth constituent of the United Kingdom, produced no response.

As a result of this policy, British midwives were expected for the first time in many years to carry their own case loads, work as independent practitioners and deliver women at home when that is what women wish. Placing the midwife at the centre of maternity care was an innovation, which was a surprise to many observers and meant the British government was out of step with many other developed countries. In France, for example, the trend was towards increased medicalization of maternity care with midwives remaining relatively unimportant. In the USA, midwives had yet to be recognized in many states but were trying to practise as something other than mere obstetric nurses. In some states, such as New York, certified nurse midwives (CNMs) were assuming more responsibility in the childbirth process, not as independent practitioners, however, but as 'employees' in the offices of traditional obstetricians or family doctors.

This paper will examine the background to the British decision and suggest that it was based not on scientific evidence but on pressure from midwives and consumer groups concerned with maternity care. It is not certain that women do want the kind of care being proposed or that midwives can provide it. There is little evidence of how effective midwives are as providers of maternity care as, until recently, there have been relatively few attempts to evaluate their practice. There is evidence of differences and divisions among British midwives and a general lack of confidence in their own abilities which does not augur well for the approach recommended by the British government.

BACKGROUND TO THE *CHANGING CHILDBIRTH* REPORT

Over the last 20 years in Britain many studies have elicited women's view of the maternity services. The majority has shown some degree of dissatisfaction with services, whether the focus was on antenatal (Hall *et al.* 1985), intrapartum (Mason 1989) or postnatal care (Murphy-Black 1994). Studies have shown repeatedly that women want a personal, friendly approach to care with continuity of care provider and that this is more important to them than technical competence. They want to be given information, the opportunity to ask questions and help to make decisions concerning their care (Hutton 1994).

Women's organizations have campaigned for a longer period for women's voices to be heard. The National Childbirth Trust (NCT) is perhaps the oldest and best known, celebrating its fortieth anniversary in 1996. It offers information and support in pregnancy, childbirth and early parenthood and aims to enable every parent to make informed choices. For the past ten years it has actively campaigned to make the maternity services more accessible and more responsive to women's needs. The same can be said of the Association for Improvements in the Maternity Services (AIMS) which was founded in 1960 and includes medical and non-medical members. Like the NCT it publishes a quarterly newsletter which 'spearheads discussion about change and development in the maternity services'. Among its objectives AIMS lists campaigning for an end to routine use of ultrasound scans, syntometrine in labour and rising caesarian section rates. Later organizations with similar aims include the Maternity Alliance founded in 1980, and the Society to Support Home Confinements and the Association for Community-Based Maternity Care founded in 1989[1].

During all these years there have been a number of government reports on various aspects of maternity services (e.g. Short 1980; Munro 1983). Many of these enquiries resulted from concern over the health of Britain's youth or rates of perinatal mortality. Many recommended that more money be spent on services, more care of one sort or another be provided or more doctors trained. The Short Report (1980) for example, examined Britain's performance in an international league table of perinatal and neonatal mortality and concluded that more care should be provided for pregnant women and babies. None of these reports was particularly radical and so none met the fate of the Black Report on inequalities in health. The findings of this committee—that poverty caused ill health—were so unpopular with the government of the day that publication of its report was limited to only 400 copies so that the results would not become widely known (Townsend & Davidson 1982). In most cases the reports on maternity care were welcomed by the medical and nursing professions and resulted in little change in the day to day experience of pregnant women. Scruggs (1983) compared three reports on antenatal care appearing after 1981/82 and found the NCT's was the only one to advocate a change in the emphasis of care; the RCOG's and Maternity Services Advisory Committee's first report both emphasising the need for intensive care and obstetric management.

Why the government should have taken the radical step of accepting the Cumberlege Committee report at this time is perhaps explained by a totally new culture to be found in the British National Health Service. This culture involves questioning the validity of many former medical and nursing procedures and using only effective treatments, giving only sound, proven advice and basing practice on research findings. This culture has pervaded the NHS, affecting all levels of staff who are now expected to find relevant research results, evaluate them and implement them if appropriate. It derived some of its momentum from the publication in 1989 by Chalmers, Keirse and Enkin of a two volume, 1,500 page tome entitled *Effective Care in Pregnancy and Childbirth*. The editors examined the effectiveness of virtually every aspect of routine antenatal, intrapartum and postnatal care and concluded with lists of forms of care that are of benefit, those with promising or unknown effects which require further evaluation and those which should be abandoned in the light of available evidence. Among the latter they included failing to involve women in decisions about their care, failing to provide continuity of care, involving obstetricians in the care of all pregnant women and insisting on universal institutional confinement.

The publication of this work marked a change in the philosophy underlying medical practice. It gave rise to the Cochrane Collaborative Pregnancy and Childbirth Database edited by Enkin, Keirse, Renfrew and Neilson which is issued on computer disk twice yearly by the BMJ Publishing Group and which means that access to published research by interested health professionals is relatively easy. Midwives had their own sources of information. The Midwives Information and Resource Service (MIDIRS) publishes a quarterly Digest which keeps midwives up to date with the latest research issues. The Royal College of Midwives and Health Visitors Association each produce current awareness bulletins and comprehensive reading lists. In 1988 MIRIAD (Midwifery Research Database) was established with the aim of publishing a directory of on-going and completed research related to midwifery and creating and maintaining a network of researchers working in the field of midwifery. From the early 1980s Sarah Robinson, an academic midwife based in London and colleagues, had set about making midwives more aware of research by holding annual conferences in which research findings were presented. She and Thomson also published a series of volumes of research conducted by midwives or concerning midwives' work (Robinson & Thomson 1989, 1991, 1994) and were on the editorial boards of midwifery journals which proliferated at this time and started to feature more articles on research activities and their implications for practice.

In such a context it may have been difficult for the British government to ignore the findings of so many research studies highlighting women's dissatisfactions with maternity care and questioning whether the longstanding policy of delivering all women in hospitals was justified (Campbell & MacFarlane 1987). What is perhaps surprising is that it chose to recommend that midwives be the lead professionals rather than family doctors (GPs). The funding of maternity services in Britain is such that it would have made more economic sense to use GPs rather than midwives to provide antenatal and postnatal care. Family doctors were paid by local health authorities out of monies raised locally whereas hospital doctors and midwives were paid out of central government funds. Moreover, it is widely reported that although family doctors prefer not to provide intrapartum care, they enjoy providing other aspects of maternity care, are liked by patients and generally succeed in providing continuity of care and contact well into the postnatal period (Flint 1992; Hall *et al.* 1985).

The explanation appears to lie in the apparent unwillingness of medical practitioners to provide intrapartum care in any setting other than a hospital which the profession continued to believe to be the only safe place (Smith 1996). The Winterton and Cumberlege Committees had embraced the well-documented argument that this was not true and also accepted the importance to the mother of having continuity of carer. They recommended midwives as the key professionals for normal women because they believed that midwives were willing to provide care from beginning to end. The Association of Radical

Midwives which was formed in 1976 had issued a statement in 1988, and which is reproduced in this volume.

We support any scheme in which a woman has the opportunity of getting to know a small number of midwives who will provide her care throughout pregnancy, labour and the postnatal period.

Whether this perception of midwives was justified and whether it was the view of the majority or a vocal few remains to be seen. Certainly a small number of pioneering midwives had shown their commitment to these ideals by choosing to work as independent practitioners, offering women complete continuity of care and experiencing the satisfaction of following them right through their birth experience into the postnatal period (Frohlich & Edwards 1989). Others tried to increase women's choices by offering domino deliveries (Beck this volume), water births or care in a midwife-only unit. Though much publicised in the early 1990s these schemes were not widely available.

It is conceivable that a further factor in the government decision was the perception of the relationship between midwives and patients and doctors and their patients. The relationship between a woman and her midwife was widely perceived as being superior to that between her and her doctor (Annandale 1987; Kitzinger 1988; Flint 1992). Why that is so will be explored in the next section.

PROVIDERS AND PATIENTS

Perhaps because of the influence of feminist historians or feminism in general, the history of obstetrics has come to be seen as a battle between male obstetricians and women midwives (Donnison 1977; Ehrenreich & English 1973; Radosh 1986; Rothwell 1995). In these and countless other texts, uncaring males are depicted as expropriating midwifery from caring women. Their motives apparently are not the welfare of women and babies but money and status (Oakley & Houd 1990; Wagner 1996). The willingness of midwives to risk prosecution and to work for little or no pay is treated as a testament to the purity of their motives. Around this notion has grown up what Macintyre (1977) calls 'the myth of a golden age' of obstetrics in which women gave birth to healthy, happy babies with very little intervention other than the support of a kind and trusted midwife. Even though some historians have cast doubt on this view of events (Shorter 1982), there is no doubt that there has been a change since the second world war from the majority of women giving birth at home attended by midwives to the majority giving birth in hospital. Though women in Britain are still largely attended by midwives, they are reported to feel powerless and alienated from their own process of reproduction by the decision making which goes on around them without truly involving them (Porter 1990).

The contemporary view, outlined in the introductory chapter, is that physicians whether family doctors or obstetricians, and midwives have competing ideologies of reproduction (Garcia et al. 1990; Graham & Oakley 1981; Schuman & Marteau 1993; Yankou et al. 1993). Whereas the midwife views pregnancy and childbirth as normal, physiological events which take place in the context of a family, physicians are held to view pregnancy and childbirth as potentially dangerous and largely unpredictable medical events which can be safely managed only in hospital. These differing ideologies result in different models of care or management. Physicians are seen as actively managing pregnancy and childbirth whereas the midwife prefers to wait and watch (Kirkham 1986). It can be argued that this philosophical and practical difference is reflected in different lengths of labour and different rates of augmentation and intervention as well as different feelings women have about labour and delivery (Flint 1992).

There is no doubt about which of these ideologies feminist commentators and the consumer movement favour. Because most doctors are men and most midwives women, there is a tendency to identify each contrasting ideology with the appropriate sex (Fraser 1995; Rothwell 1995). Doctors/men are definitely cast as the villains and women, whether providers or consumers, the victims (Oakley & Houd 1990; Beech 1994). There is a cavalier disregard for any competing ideologies among women and among doctors. Women are assumed to reject the more technological care provided by doctors in favour of natural, albeit painful labour and childbirth.[2] Yet several studies showed that women's views of the role of technology in childbirth varied with social class. Nelson (1983) found that working class women in the USA wanted a more passive birth with more medical intervention than did middle class women. McIntosh (1989) found a positive response to medical intervention among working class women in Glasgow in Scotland, as did Woollett (1983) among such women in London, though women's reaction changed according to the stage at which they were interviewed. Too (1996), looking at the use of birth plans by primiparous mothers concluded that some women wanted control of their labour but others wanted to leave that control in the hands of the midwife. Results such as these have been largely ignored and it has been assumed that what women 'really' want is non-technical, friendly, supportive care such as only other women can provide.

Yet there is no evidence that women are likely to provide better care just because they are women. Reid (1983) has called this approach 'sexual reductionist' and citing evidence of women health workers being as moralistic and condemnatory as any man, points out that it obscures the real issues. In a study of gynaecologists and family planning clinic staff, Porter (1990) found women staff could be less sympathetic with women's difficulties with family planning methods if they themselves found the methods satisfactory. The context in which health care is provided also has an important effect. Holland and McKevitt (1985) found that despite the predominantly female medical staff in health care settings in the former USSR, intervention was still routine and midwives were treated as obstetric nurses. Chalmers (1991) compared the information on breastfeeding given out by community midwives and health visitors and found that those who were following official guidelines issued to them were giving more accurate and up to date information. Clearly gender is not the most important variable at work here.

In some sociological and consumerist literature there is an assumption that midwives are uniformly excellent and could meet all women's needs for continuity, support, information and expertise (Kitzinger 1988). A similar stance was apparently taken in Canada in 1986 as Benoit, who rejects the argument, explains:

Midwives, they argue, are cheaper than doctors and will give 'personalized' service instead instead of the emotionally detached approach to which pregnant women are often subjected by doctors. Unlike doctors, furthermore, the new Canadian midwife will put her own self-interest second to the needs and wants of her clients. (Benoit 1986: 275)

This is not a view shared by the profession itself or the government committees involved in the changes. Both the Winterton Committee in 1991 and later the Expert Maternity Group which produced the Changing Childbirth Report took evidence from or directly involved members of a number of consumer groups and lay women as well as relevant health professionals, mainstream and radical. Unexpectedly, both committees went against the advice of the Royal Colleges of Obstetricians and Gynaecologists and of General Practitioners and embraced the approach of midwives' organizations and consumer groups. Midwives were seen as being the right people to deliver most babies and the people whom women wanted to provide with continuity of care. Nevertheless, the changes seem to have been recommended in a spirit of experiment as is apparent from the words of one member of the Expert Maternity Group:

We found that a number of midwifery units had tried to develop continuity through domino schemes, team midwifery or group practice. Some had achieved good results, but many had created teams that were too large, and some had lost continuity that had previously been there through the GP and midwife working in partnership. We recognised that making continuity of care a reality will require significant change in many services, and substantial flexibility on the part of both midwives and managers. But we saw sufficient examples of good practice to recommend a target that, within five years 75% of women should be cared for in labour by a midwife whom they have come to know during their pregnancy (Troop 1993).

MIDWIVES ON MIDWIVES

At present it is not clear whether the British Government's faith in the midwifery profession is echoed by its members. Within the midwifery profession there has been a lot of concern about the proposals contained in these two reports and the changing role of the midwife implied thereby (Page 1993b). Many members have publicly expressed doubts about the midwife's desire or ability to fulfil the role recommended by the report (Allen 1993; Fraser 1995). Page, for instance, says the new midwife is required to be 'a skilled companion' working with the mother where and when she is needed but that many midwives will not wish that. Powis (1993), reporting the birth of her sister's baby, described two community midwives reluctantly and incompetently attempting to deliver a baby at home.

There is relatively little evidence to suggest that the care currently provided by midwives is better than that provided by hospital or family doctors (Rogers 1991). As Oakley (1989) points out in this volume, little is known about the effectiveness or efficiency of midwifery practice because there is little research focusing on midwives or comparing their performance with that of other health care providers. In reviewing several small scale studies of midwifery care, Thomson (1994) reports that midwives were no better than obstetricians at explaining procedures to patients and Rogers (1991) that they were very poor at informing women, empowering them or accepting responsibility. Mackay and Yager-Smith (1993) video-recorded midwife-assisted births in the USA and found that communications between women and all their birth attendants were very poor. Comaroff (1977) compared midwives' and physiotherapists' perspectives of pregnancy and found that midwives had a more medical model of childbirth and were less open to questions and discussion than the physiotherapists. Rajan (1993) compared women's and providers' perceptions of pain relief in labour and found that midwives' and obstetricians' views were more likely to agree with each other than with those of the women concerned. Many existing studies can be criticised on methodological grounds. For example, Yankou and colleagues' (1993) conclusion that midwives spent more time with women at antenatal consultations, paid more attention to their home background and taught them more about caring for themselves was based on the results of questionnaires distributed to certified nurse midwives and physicians not on direct observation of practice.

For many years there have been problems within the midwifery profession in Britain which have led to poor recruitment and loss of midwives from the profession. Training, pay and prospects are acknowledged to be poor. Some have asked whether the changes proposed in *Changing Childbirth* will increase job satisfaction and autonomy and lead to an improvement in the recruiting situation (Le Febvre 1993). This seems unlikely as it appears not to be the poor prospects and lack of job satisfaction and autonomy which keeps women out of midwifery but the lack of part-time jobs compatible with family life (Robinson 1993). All the evidence suggests that providing the sort of care recommended in 'Changing Childbirth' is even less compatible with family life (Benoit 1986). Indeed, this inability to accommodate women's dual roles and the demands placed on midwives by unpredictable hours and caseloads are some of the problems currently facing the woman-centred Dutch maternity service (DeVries 1993; Jabaaij 1994).

A number of authors have examined *Changing Childbirth* in detail and enumerated the changes in midwifery training and practice required to meet their objectives. Among many others, Page (1993a) has argued the need for midwifery to become more evidence-based and reflective. But there is a question mark about how midwives are to become evidence-based practitioners when relatively few know how to conduct research, interpret findings or teach research methods (Robinson & Thomson 1991; Clark & Sleep 1991). According to several authors they lack confidence in their own abilities to conduct research, publish the results and implement others' findings (Phillips 1994; Hicks 1993; 1995). Their attitudes to research are not generally positive although those with a degree are more positive than those without (Bostrom *et al.* 1989; Hicks 1995). Relatively few midwives are actively involved in research though the number is increasing every year. The midwife research database report (Simms *et al.* 1994) lists 267 projects many of which are undertaken unpaid by midwives in their own time and more than half are concerned with breastfeeding and midwifery education. As a report funded by the Department of Health recently acknowledged, much of this research has been small-scale, a piece-meal response to local problems (Sleep & Clarke 1993).

If few midwives set the agenda for research, still fewer put research findings into practice. This may be because as Hunt's (1981) research on nurses suggests, midwives do not know about them, do not understand them, are unwilling to put them into practice or are not in a position to do so. On the other hand, it may be that midwives are 'their own worst enemies' and distrust the results of research done by other midwives more than that done by physicians (Hicks 1992). Evidence of doctors' attitudes towards research findings suggests there may be an unwillingness to accept results, which become available and affect practice. Paterson-Brown *et al.* (1993) found obstetricians were not interested in up-to-date research findings and did not refer to the research database when it was available. A Belgian study showed that awareness of rates of obstetric intervention had no effect on practice (Buekens 1993). On the other hand, there are several documented cases of midwives sabotaging research involving randomised controlled trials because they came to believe that giving or withholding a treatment was unethical (Thomson 1994). Oakley (1993), similarly reported that midwives were unwilling to randomise social support for pregnant women because they thought that the "wrong" women would get it. As their intuition often proved to be mistaken, Oakley argues that this gives scientific grounds for the randomised control trial.

Those few midwives who have innovated seem to have received a lot of criticism both within and outside the profession. As Flint (1991) shows, midwives have been widely criticised and disciplined by their own professional bodies for the way they have handled certain deliveries. Independent midwives have found it virtually impossible to obtain affordable insurance cover and have not been helped by their own professional body. Midwifery and medical journals in Britain contain many examples of articles criticising midwives' own attempts to improve care and suggesting that they do not have the intended effect (e.g. Lee 1995). Le Febvre (1993) and Walsh (1995) are typical in arguing that the team approach to midwifery sounds very laudable in theory but does not improve continuity of care for the woman or job satisfaction for the midwife. Walsh (1993), reporting on an experiment in team midwifery, suggests that the midwife's role in antenatal classes has changed as a result of government initiatives 'from teacher to resource person, from lecturer to facilitator, and from detached professional to skilled companion' and that few are prepared for this difficult challenge when they first encounter it. Floyd (1995) similarly reported a group of community midwives to be enthusiastic about home birth but untrained and inexperienced.

RESEARCH ON MIDWIVES

The difficulties which many individuals have when facing organizational change have been well documented (Flint 1992; Macintyre & Porter 1989; Hicks 1995). Flint (1992) who has been involved in establishing four midwifery teams lists among the factors militating against their success: inertia, sabotage and resistance from midwives not involved and from GPs, sabotage from hospital doctors and feeling threatened by the shifting of power from professional to mother. In the case of midwives it could also be argued that any lack of self-confidence and reluctance to innovate is a result of years of male/medical dominance. Dover and Guage (1995) for example in a study of 242 midwives' attitudes to fetal monitoring found a lack of confidence in the use and effectiveness of available technology. This uncertainty may also be a reflection of women's economic position in Western society. Whether or not they are the main wage earner in a household, midwives usually combine a job with raising a family and looking after a home. This is likely to make them reject change which involves a heavier work load even if there are compensatory factors in terms of job satisfaction (Fraser 1995). Team midwifery, domino deliveries and home births do not fit into the routine of family life. Some midwives may want simply to be obstetric nurses or to carry out discrete functions in an antenatal clinic or postnatal ward and fight shy of carrying responsibility for making decisions without clinical backing or supervisory support (Flint 1983; 1992).

In Aberdeen (Scotland) in the early 1980s a new system of antenatal care was imposed by medical staff on a compliant midwifery team (Hall et al. 1985). Evaluating this innovation researchers found significant differences in the attitudes and behaviour of midwives working in the community compared with those in the hospital antenatal clinic. The former welcomed the opportunity to work with family doctors running clinics of their own and visiting women with raised blood pressure at home. The latter, who had previously acted merely as assistants to obstetricians, were wary of running their own clinics and taking on new responsibilities for caring for pregnant women. They deferred to the doctor more often than necessary and found it hard to accept that women need not be undressed and examined at every visit. Indeed, a number of hospital midwives were so dissatisfied with the new system's recommendations for midwives' clinics that they failed to implement them, thereby undermining the new system and its evaluation.

Other midwives found in many cases that their misgivings were misplaced. They enjoyed working as independent practitioners and experienced an improvement in their relationships with doctors. Turnbull et al. (1995) similarly reported that those working in a Midwifery Development Unit experienced improvement in many aspects of professional practice including satisfaction, support and development of their role. The community midwives and family doctors in Aberdeen seemed to have been radicalised by the experience and became more critical of the system in general and hospital doctors in particular. Rothman (1983) similarly found that hospital midwives were radicalised by the experience of attending home births which challenged all their 'taken-for-granted assumptions' based on hospital timetables for labour and birth. The initial lack of self confidence among midwives may be a Scottish phenomenon as Askham and Barbour (this volume) also showed Scottish midwives reluctant to learn new skills or take on new responsibilities. Robinson and colleagues (1993) studying midwives in London, and Flint (1983) describing the development of a midwives' clinic there, did not report similar reluctance to innovate.

The point is that midwives, like doctors and patients, vary greatly. They vary according to whether they work in hospitals or in the community and in various parts of Britain or elsewhere in the developed world. They cannot be treated as an homogeneous group by those at the top of the midwifery profession who represent their interests in parliament and elsewhere. There may be many quiet members who want to be little more than obstetric nurses and get home to their families at night. Weitz's (1987) study of English midwives suggested that the majority did not see themselves as radical and their support for the more contentious midwifery ideas and proposals was limited.

CONCLUSION

Maternity care in England and Wales has changed greatly as a result of the 1993 Report 'Changing Childbirth' which recommended the provision of woman-centred maternity care, including an increased role for women in the management of their care and planning of care locally. In most cases these innovations are being evaluated to see whether they really do improve choice, continuity and control for the women concerned. Each edition of *Changing Childbirth Update* lists the projects underway and the successes achieved so far. For example, in June 1995 women were given 'Real choice regarding the place of birth' in London and June 1996 saw a reduction in the number of antenatal visits in London and improved communications with Asian parents in Birmingham. Unfortunately, reports are beginning to emerge of innovations which have failed, usually because of lack of funding or appropriate support. The problem is that changes which improve the service, benefit patients, or the profession of midwifery do not necessarily benefit individual midwives

In its recommendations for 'changing childbirth', the British government seems to have been swayed by the predominantly middle class voices of the consumer groups from which it took evidence. Inevitably, working class women, with their rather different ideologies, were not heard; nor perhaps were the less vocal and radical of the midwives. Among the ordinary membership of midwives there may be many who are unprepared for the changes and responsibilities that carrying their own caseload inevitably brings. Many may not have the time or commitment to learn research methods, undertake research studies or implement significant findings when they recognize them. Midwives who have followed a more academic course, an increasingly popular option in this country as in the USA, may find it easier to accept the call for evidence-based practice than do those who have trained on the ground. It is to be hoped that this will not result in a two-tier profession, which is unsatisfactory for all concerned.

ACKNOWLEDGEMENTS

I am grateful to my colleagues Edwin van Teijlingen, Peter McCaffery, George Lowis, Vanora Hundley and Sally Macintyre for commenting on earlier drafts of this paper.

REFERENCES

Allen, M.R. (1993). Midwives should welcome government initiatives. *British Journal of Midwifery*, 1:1, 25.

Annandale, E. (1987). Dimensions of patient control in a free-standing birth center. *Social Science & Medicine*, 25: 1235-48.

Association of Radical Midwives, (1988). *The Vision: proposal for the future of the maternity services*.

Benoit, C. (1986). Uneasy partners: midwives and their clients. *The Globe and Mail*, July 15, 275-84.

Bostrom, A., Malnight, M., Macdougall, J. & Harais D. (1989). Staff nurses attitudes towards nursing research: a descriptive survey. *Journal of Advanced Nursing*, 14, 915-922.

Buekens, P., Boutsen, M., Kittel, F., Vandenbussche, P. & Dramaix, M. (1993). Does awareness of rates of obstetric interventions change practice? *British Medical Journal*, 306, 623.

Campbell, R. & Macfarlane, A. (1987). *Where to be born? The debate and the evidence*. Oxford: National Perinatal Epidemiology Unit.

Chalmers, I., Enkin, M. & Keirse, M. (1989). *Effective care in pregnancy and childbirth*. Oxford: Oxford University Press.

Chalmers, J. (1991). Variations in breast feeding advice: a telephone survey of community midwives and health visitors. *Midwifery*, 7, 162-166.

Clark, E. & Sleep, J. (1991). Nurse education tomorrow conference 1990: the what and how of teaching research. *Nurse Education Today*, 11:3, 172-178.

Cmnd 2018, (1992) *Maternity services government response to the second report from the health select committee session 1991-1992*. London: HMSO

Comaroff, J. (1977). Conflicting paradigms of pregnancy: managing ambiguity in antenatal encounters. In A. Davis & G. Horobin (eds.). *Medical encounters: experience of illness & treatment* (pp. 115-34). London: Croom Helm

Department of health, (1993). *Changing childbirth: report of the expert maternity group.* London: HMSO.

DeVries, R. (1993). The midwife's place: an international comparison of the status of midwives. In E. Riska & E. Wegar (eds.). *Gender, work and medicine* London: Sage

Donnison, J. (1977). *Midwives and medical men: a history of interprofessional rivalries and women's rights.* London: Heinemann.

Dover, S. & Guage, S. (1995). Fetal monitoring—midwifery attitudes. *Midwifery*, 11:1, 18-27.

Ehrenreich, B. & English, D. (1973) *Witches, Midwives and Nurses: A History of Women Healers*, Glass Mountain Pamphlet No. 1, Old Westbury, New York: Feminist Press.

Flint, C. (1983). Growing in confidence. *Nursing Mirror*, January 19th, 22.

Flint, C. (1991). On the brink: midwifery in Britain. In S. Kitzinger (ed.). *The midwife challenge* (pp. 22-39). London: Pandora press

Flint, C. (1992). The basis of a midwifery team: continuity of carer. In G. Chamberlain & L. Zander (eds.). *Pregnancy care in the 1990s* (pp. 127-36). Carnforth: Parthenon

Floyd, L. (1995). Community midwives views and experiences of home birth. *Midwifery*, 11:1, 3-10.

Fraser, D. (1995). Client-centred care: fact or fiction? *Midwives*, 108: 1289, 174-177.

Frohlich, J. & Edwards, S. (1989). Team midwifery for everyone: building on the 'know your midwife' scheme. *Midwives chronicle and nursing notes*, March, 66-70.

Garcia, J., Kilpatrick, R. & Richards, M. (1990). *The politics of maternity care.* Oxford: Oxford University Press.

Graham, H. & Oakley, A. (1981). Competing ideologies of reproduction: medical and maternal perspectives on pregnancy and childcare. In h. Roberts (ed.). *Women health and reproduction* London: RKP

Hall, M., Macintyre, S. & Porter, M. (1985). *Antenatal care assessed.* Aberdeen: Aberdeen University Press.

Hicks, C. (1992). Research in midwifery: are midwives their own worst enemies? *Midwifery*, 8:1, 12-8.

Hicks, C. (1993). A survey of midwives' attitudes to, and involvement in, research: the first stage in identifying needs for a staff development programme. *Midwifery*, 9, 51-62.

Hicks, C. (1995). A factor analytic study of midwives' attitudes to research. *Midwifery*, 11, 11-17.

Holland, B. & McKevitt, Y. (1985). Maternity care in the Soviet Union. In B. Holland (ed.). *Soviet sisterhood* Bloomington: Indiana University Press

House of Commons, (1992). *Health committee second report on the maternity services (Winterton report).* London: HMSO

Hundley, V.A., Cruickshank, F.M., Lang, G.D., Glazener, C.M., Milne, J.M., Turner, M., Blyth, D., Mollison, J., Donaldson, D. (1994). Midwife managed delivery unit: a randomised controlled comparison with consultant led care. *British Medical Journal*, 309, 1400-04.

Hunt, J. (1981). Indicators for nursing practice: the use of research findings. *Journal of Advanced Nursing*, 6, 189-194.

Hutton, E. (1994). *What women want from midwives: obstetricians: general practitioners: health visitors.* London: NCT Maternity sales.

Ilford, R. (1993). Midwives to manage uncomplicated childbirth: a proposal worth supporting. *British Medical Journal*, 307, 339-340.

Jabaaij, L. (1994). *The independent midwife in the Netherlands: work and workload.* Utrecht: NIVEL

Johnson, M., Habbad, S., Smith, J., Walker, J., & Wong, A. (1992). Women prefer hospital births. *British Medical Journal*, 305, 255.

Kirkham, M. (1986). A feminist perspective on midwifery. In C. Webb (ed.). *Feminist practice in women's health care* New York: John Wiley

Kitzinger, S. (1988). Why women need midwives. In S. Kitzinger (ed.). *The midwife challenge* (pp. 1-20). London: Pandora

Le Febvre, J. (1993). Free speech: duo midwives. *Midwives Chronicle & Nursing Notes*, Dec., 508-9.

Lee, G. (1995). Free speech: the names woman? *Midwives*, 108:1288, 162.

Machover, I. (1995). The mobile epidural: is it such good news? *Associations for Improvements in Maternity Services Journal*, 7:2, 10-11.

Macintyre, S. (1977). The myth of the golden age. *World Medicine*, 12:18, 17-22.

Macintyre, S. & Porter, M. (1989). Prospects and problems in promoting effective care at the local level. In M. Enkin, I. Chalmers & P. Kierse (eds.). *Effective care in pregnancy & childbirth* (pp. 1458-1464). Oxford: Oxford University Press

Mackay, S. & Yager-Smith, s. (1993). 'What are they talking about? Is something wrong?'. *Birth*, 2:3, 142-147.

Mason, V. (1989). *Women's experience of maternity care—a survey manual*. London: HMSO

Mcintosh, J. (1989). Models of childbirth and social class: a study of 80 working class primigravidae. In s. Robinson & A. Thomson (eds.). *Midwives. Research & Childbirth*. vol. 1 (pp. 189-214). London: Chapman & Hall

Mead, S., Luker, K.A. & Cullum, N.A. (1996). An exploration of midwives' attitudes to research and perceived barriers to research utilisation. *Midwifery*, 12:12, 73-84

Munro Report (Maternity Services Advisory Committee), (1983). *Maternity care in action. Part 1—antenatal care*. London: HMSO

Murphy-Black, T. (1994). Care in the community during the postnatal period. In S. Robinson & A. Thomson (eds.). *Midwives. Research & Childbirth*. Vol. 3 (pp. 120-46). London: Chapman & Hall

National Childbirth Trust, (1994). *The challenge of change: helping lay representatives to work for change in childbirth*. London: NCT

Nelson, M. (1983). Working class women, middle class women and models of childbirth. *Social Problems*, 30:3, 284-297.

Oakley, A. (1989). Who cares for women? Science versus love in midwifery today. *Midwives Chronicle and Nursing Notes*, July, 214-221.

Oakley, A. (1993). Some problems of the scientific research method and feminist research practice. In A. Oakley (ed.). *Essays on women. Medicine and Health* (pp. 243-264). Edinburgh: Edinburgh University Press

Oakley, A. & Houd, S. (1990). *Helpers in childbirth: midwifery today*. WHO: Hemisphere Publishing corps

Page, L. (1993a). Education for practice. *Midwives index of research studies*, 3:3, 253-56.

Page, L (1993b). Redefining the midwife's role: changes needed in practice. *British Journal of Midwifery*, 1:1, 21-24.

Paterson-Brown, S., Wyatt, J., & Fisk, N. (1993). Are clinicians interested in up to date reviews of effective care? *British Medical Journal*, 307, 1464.

Phillips, R. (1994). The need for research-based midwifery practice. *British Journal of Midwifery*, 2:7, 335-338.

Porter, M. (1990). Professional-client relationships and women's reproductive health care. In S. Cunningham-Burley & N. Mckegany (eds.). *Readings in medical sociology* (pp. 182-210). London: Routledge

Powis, L. (1993). Do women really have a choice? *Midwives Chronicle & Nursing Notes*, Oct., 380-1.

Radosh, P. (1986). Midwives in the United States: past & present. *Population Research & Policy Review*, 5, 129-145.

Rajan, L. (1993). Perceptions of pain and pain relief in labour: the gulf between experience and observation. *Midwifery*, 9:3, 136-145.

Reid, M. (1983). Helping those mothers: antenatal care in a Scottish peripheral housing estate. In *Uncharted Lives: extracts from Scottish women's experiences* Glasgow: Pressgang

Robinson, S. (1993). Combining work with caring for children, findings from a longitudinal study of midwives' careers. *Midwifery*, 9, 183-196.

Robinson, S. & Thomson, A. (1989). *Midwives, Research & Childbirth* 1. London: Chapman & Hall.

Robinson, S. & Thomson, A. (1991a). *Midwives, Research & Childbirth* 2. London: Chapman & Hall.

Robinson, S. & Thomson, A. (1991b). Research and midwifery; moving into the 1990s. In S. Robinson & A. Thomson (eds.). *Midwives, Research & Childbirth* . 2. (pp. 1-15). London: Chapman & Hall

Robinson, S. & Thomson, A. (1994). *Midwives, Research & Childbirth* 3. London: Chapman & Hall.

Robinson, S. & Thomson, A. (1996). *Midwives, Research & Childbirth* 4. London: Chapman & Hall.

Rogers, J. (1991). Practitioner in your own right—myth or reality? *Midwives Chronicle & Nursing Notes*, May, 131-4.

Rothman, B. (1983). Midwives in transition: the structure of a clinical revolution. *Social Problems*, 30:3, 262-71.

Rothman, B.K. (1982). *In labor: women and power in the birthplace*. New York: Norton & Company.

Rothwell, H. (1995). Medicalisation of childbearing. *British Journal of Midwifery*, 3:6, 318-31.

Schuman, A. & Marteau, T. (1993). Obstetricians' and midwives' contrasting perceptions of pregnancy. *Journal of Infant & Reproductive Psychology*, 11:2, 115-8.

Scottish Office, (1993). *Provision of maternity services in Scotland: a policy review*. Edinburgh: HMSO.

Scruggs, M. (1983). Reform in antenatal care: a comparison of three reports. *Midwives Chronicle & Nursing Notes*, April, 110-11.

Short Report, (1980). *Second report from the social services committee session 1979-1980 on perinatal and neonatal mortality*. London: HMSO.

Shorter, E (1982). *A history of women's bodies*. London: Allan Lane.

Simms, C., McHaffie, H., Renfrew, M.J. & Ashurst, H. (eds.) (1994). *The Midwifery Research Database: MIRIAD a sourcebook of information about research in midwifery*. Hale: Books for Midwives Press.

Sleep, J. & Clark, E. (1993). Major new survey to identify and prioritise research issues for midwifery practice. *Midwives Chronicle & Nursing Notes*, June, 217-218.

Smith, L. (1996). Should general practitioners have any role in maternity care in the future? *British Journal General Practice*, 4:17, 16-18.

Thomson, A. (1994). Research into some aspects of care in labour. In s. Robinson & a. Thomson (eds.) *Midwives, Research & Childbirth* vol, 3 (pp. 293-324). London: Chapman & Hall

Too, S. (1996). Do birth plans empower women? A study of their views. *Nursing Standard*, 10:3, 33-7.

Townsend, P. & Davidson, H. (1982). *Inequalities in health* (Black Report). Harmondsworth: Penguin.

Troop, P. (1993). Birth rights. *Health Services Journal*, 11th November: 26.

Turnbull D., Reid M., McGinley M., Sheilds N.R. (1995) Changes in midwives' attitudes to their professional role following implementation of the midwifery development unit, *Midwifery* 11:110-9

Wagner, M. (1996). Midwife-managed care. *British Medical Journal*, 348, 208.

Walsh, D. (1993). Parenthood education and the politics of childbirth. *British Journal of Midwifery*, 1:3, 119-23.

Walsh, D. (1995). Continuity of carer: miracle or mirage? *British Journal of Midwifery*, 3:6, 336-38.

Weitz, R. (1987). English midwives and the association of radical midwives. *Women & Health*, 12:1, 79-89.

Weitz, R. & Sullivan, D. (1985). Licensed lay midwifery and the medical model of childbirth. *Sociology of Health and Illness*, 7:1, 36-54.

Wise, J. (1993). Editorial: water birth: trial or error? *British Journal of Midwifery*, 1:6, 249-50.

Woollett, A. (1983). The reactions of east London women to medical intervention in childbirth. *Journal of Infant and Reproductive Psychology*, 1, 37-46.

Yankou, D., Peterson, B., Oakley, D. & Mayes, F. (1993). Philosophy of care: a pilot study comparing certified nurse midwives and physicians. *Journal of Nurse-midwifery*, 38:3, 159-64.

[1] When it was founded in 1989 the Association for Community-Based Maternity Care was originally called 'The Association for General Practice Maternity Care'.

[2] Johnson *et al.* (1992) use the prediction that 8% women will demand home births as grounds for saying women prefer hospital births, but as so few women had experience of this option the argument is fallacious as most people prefer what they have experienced.

AN EXCEPTION TO THE CANADIAN CASE: AUTONOMOUS MIDWIFERY AT THE MARGINS

Cecilia Benoit[1]

INTRODUCTION

Reflecting their peers south of the national border (Conrad & Schneider, 1980; Freidson, 1986), over the past century Canadian physicians have claimed control over more and more aspects of the public's health and well-being, a process sociologists often refer to as *medicalization* (Coburn *et al.*, 1987; Riessman, 1983) While solving some problems, medicalization generates others of its own. When physicians are "gatekeepers" (Evans, 1984), patients/clients have restricted choice of alternative practitioners, of non-invasive medical procedures, and of out-of-hospital care (Clarke, 1990). Medicalization is, moreover, comparatively costly for individual citizens (in the U.S. case) and for society at large (in the Canadian case); the North American norm of fee-for-service physician reimbursement is prone to encourage medical interventions with the highest financial return, rather than cheaper options which often produce the best outcomes for patients (Light, 1986; The Report of the British Columbia (B.C.) Royal Commission on Health Care and Costs, 1991). Relatively high caesarean section rates are just one controversial case. The caesarean rate for Canada at present is between 21-25 percent, well above the 15 percent medically-justifiable caesarean rate set by the WHO, and substantially higher than the comparable figures for areas of the world where midwives are frontline workers for birthing families[2]. The various forces mentioned here, among others, have motivated Canadian health planners to question the status quo, in the hope of creating an economically-efficient and at the same time citizen-sensitive health care system (Coburn, 1993)

Maternity service reorganization is central to this new initiative. Canadian proponents of "woman-centred" maternity care maintain that alterations can be made in existing arrangements, in a way that enhances the physical, psychological and social well-being of birthing women, without jeopardizing their own health or that of their newborns (Barrington, 1985; Burtch, 1988). Pivotal to this programme for change is what some writers refer to as a "rise of midwifery" (Bourgeault & Fynes, 1997). Envisioned is a more personalized, and at the same time cost-efficient, maternity service with midwives "empowering women to take charge of their own health care and placing great value on social and emotional factors" (Rushing, 1993: 59).

Statistics support midwifery, Canadian advocates argue, giving evidence of comparatively low perinatal and infant mortality and .rates in both Continental Europe and the Nordic Countries, all of which employ midwives as primary attendants to normal birthing families (McKay, 1993; Phaff, 1986; Oakley & Houd, 1990). Canadian midwives from an assortment of social-cultural backgrounds and varying styles of training (like their U.S. counterparts (Reid, 1989), including those "helping out" at friends and neighbours' births and those holding college degrees in midwifery and/or nursing) have joined together under the banner of "community midwife", merged their prior separate interest groups and formed single provincial associations oriented towards achieving two main goals: 1) legal status for a unified midwifery as a self-regulating profession, distinct from both medicine and nursing; 2) inclusion within the publicly-funded Canadian health care system.

These dual goals—legal recognition and public funding—are in fact now realized by midwives in the central province of Ontario and the western province of British Columbia with a number of other provinces already or expected to follow suit in the not too distant future, at least in regard to granting legal status to midwives, if not public funding (Burtch, 1994; Benoit, 1997). Only recently Canada lost its dishonourable distinction of being among one of only nine countries belonging to the 210-member WHO that fail to recognize midwifery as a legitimate healing art (Phaff, 1986). Many birthing families from across the Canadian landscape appear eager to seek out the emerging community midwives promising to provide an economical, expert and compassionate style of practice which hitherto has been unavailable, not least because of shortage of midwives in most localities, as well as prohibitive out-of-pocket costs for many interested patrons (Task Force on the Implementation of Midwifery in Ontario, 1987; O'Reilly, 1989).

Sociological evidence indicates, however, that such health strategies as the Canadian maternity reform endeavour mentioned here are not easily implemented in practice (Hughes, 1958; Strauss, 1985; Roth, 1974). Because of mediating exogenous force[3], it is frequently a case of "strategy and muddling through" (Tsalikis, 1993), of "illusion" rather than true reform (Renauld, 1987). While there is little indication at present that such a bleak future is in store for emerging community midwifery in Canada, I believe it to be nevertheless helpful to step away from the limelight of urban Canada, caught in this fleeting moment, and to observe midwives at work in a less obvious area of the country—Newfoundland and Labrador (N&L)— across a stretch of time within living memory of three generations. For here, due to geographic isolation combined with economic disadvantage, medical dominance of maternity services even today is largely confined to regional hospitals in the province's southern pockets. It is thus possible to study midwifery practice in N&L in a way that is no longer the case (if ever so) in other areas of Canada. Among other findings, analysis of my data gathered during fieldwork in N&L indicate midwives' differential access to *occupational autonomy*, that is, capacity to organize care of birthing families free from external interference, be it pressure from hospital administrators, allied workers, government or business bureaucrats, the public at large or, indeed, from nature itself[4]. More on this below, after a brief discussion of my data collection procedures and research method.

DATA COLLECTION AND METHOD

The empirical data for this chapter are drawn from two main sources: 1) analysis of secondary writings on the past and present-day arrangements of maternity care across the industrialized world; 2) analysis of primary data on the historical transformation of maternity care in one geographic setting. My findings on three generations of N&L midwives practising three distinct styles of midwifery—traditional homebirth attendance, cottage hospital midwifery, and regional hospital midwifery—are drawn from a broader research project conducted in 1984, and later expanded and published in book form (comparing midwives' training, regulation, and work styles cross-nationally (Benoit, 1991, 1992))

I chose this particular fieldwork setting for multiple reasons: first, it is my province of birth and, until a decade ago, place of residence. This offered me many research advantages, not least among them familiarity with native landscape, socio-cultural traditions, and current customs of local inhabitants; secondly, unlike the situation in most other areas of Canada and many parts of the U.S., N&L midwives were never a rare or unusual sight to the province's birthing families. In fact, most middle-aged and older women delivered all of their babies (and they tended to have many) with a midwife standing by, and even younger counterparts now of childbearing age have often been "with midwife" when giving birth to their own children; thirdly, this area of Canada provides a rare opportunity to examine midwifery practice from its origin in the home, in the cottage hospital, and regional hospital. This research advantage is important not only to those of us interested in midwives' historical presence in North America (Mason, 1987; Benoit, 1991; Wertz & Wertz, 1977; 1990; Litoff, 1978, 1986; Leavitt, 1986; Laforce, 1990); it also holds relevance for present-day community midwives in Canada (and perhaps, too, their U.S. companions) grappling with how to design work settings that enhance their occupational autonomy (Barrington, 1985; Sullivan & Weitz, 1988; Bourgeault & Fynes, 1997). I return to this latter point in my conclusion.

By use of the "snowball technique" for finding potential respondents, I eventually carried out forty-five tape-recorded interviews with what has been described elsewhere as a "fortuitous sample" (Pickard, 1994) of N&L midwives: eight with traditional homebirth attendants; fourteen with retired and still employed cottage hospital midwives, and twenty-three with employed midwives in regional hospitals. The focus of my interviews was wide-ranging since my general aim at that point in the research project was to construct a composite picture of maternity care in one particular locality, as practised by three generations of N&L midwives. In order to carry out this task, I depended largely on the "life-history approach", or what is sometimes called the "biographical interview" (see Myerhoff & Simic (1978) for its use when interviewing the elderly). However, in my own case example I placed special emphasis on midwives' changing education styles, work patterns and regulatory standards, the three main themes emerging from the preliminary stage of my research[5]. The following pages outline aspects of N&L midwives' work; I call your attention, in particular, to their differential occupational autonomy.

MIDWIFERY IN TIME AND PLACE

Traditional Homebirth Attendance

As observed elsewhere in colonial North America regarding birthing in the home setting (Oppenheimer, 1983; Biggs, 1983; Sullivan & Weitz, 1988), most families in early N&L[6] had little contact with *learned physicians*—i.e., practitioners holding formal medical certificates. In my particular case study, these were either "company doctors" recruited by mining enterprises scattered around the province. These doctors provided emergency medical services for a fee to mine employees and their families (Neary & Hiller, 1980). A collection of physicians had also established private practices in the capital city of St. John's, where a small middle class existed with disposable income to pay out-of-pocket medical services. However, the vast majority of inhabitants largely relied upon their own healing cures or those of their close kin. In times of special concern, one of the many lay healers found in the 5,000 or so fishing communities dotting the province's coastline, in the scattered merchant trading towns, and capital city—bone setters, herbalists, horse doctors, among others—were secured. Women "in the family way" (Murray, 1979), regardless of economic standing and cultural background, would regularly pass the ten-day lying-in period (Nevitt, 1978) in their own homes with the aid of a birth attendant/midwife, locally referred to by affectionate kin terms of "auntie" or "grannie", no doubt reflecting the elderly status of most traditional N&L homebirth attendants (Benoit, 1989).

Yet traditional N&L homebirth attendants—indeed, any healer of the time, including the seldom seen learned physician —were limited in their capacity to provide a safe and happy birth experience. Some traditional homebirth attendants were dedicated to the task and appeared to enjoy their work. One of them spoke to me of some of the positive features of her service role:

"I first learned to 'doctor' the women and others in the village from my dear mother. I learned to give a newborn a steeped brew from weeds—caraway seeds perhaps. I was always present during birth, consoling and guiding the mother expecting. All the women used to help out; some cooked; others kept house; others washed and fed the children. Together we were a strong team."

Yet other N&L homebirth attendants were reluctant candidates for this line of service work. One respondent recalled the situation of her mother, a traditional homebirth attendant who entered the occupation without ambition, even with some fear:

"I can remember as a kid someone pounding on the door in the middle of the night and dad saying (later) that mom had gone to deliver a baby and would be back in two days. There was another older lady (but) she was probably in her seventies by that time. My mom was the only person available and she felt a certain responsibility. She couldn't bear the thought of somebody having to deliver on their own, and this would have happened, you know... But I think if she had a choice she probably would have never got into it... Now she has 'lost her nerve' and can't bear the thought of doing those things. Even the sight of blood bothers her."

Another traditional homebirth attendant related to me the strain that a 24-on call duty placed on her own health, and implicitly on that of birthing women themselves:

"I used to break a lot of rest. One time I was three weeks attending deliveries; never stopped. I went to one woman and was only there four hours before I had to go to another one. I'd just get my clothes off and get in bed when a knock come on the door: 'I wants you to come with me. My wife is sick.' I'd get up there and put on my clothes and go on. Every week like that. (In the end) it was getting too much for me. I was really beaten out."

In brief, while generally well respected, not least because of extensive socio-cultural knowledge of local birthing families—hence the close kinship terms of auntie and grannie mentioned above—it would be shortsighted to view traditional homebirth midwifery in the N&L context as patterned on occupational autonomy[7]. It is true that this first generation of provincial midwives enjoyed independence from physicians, who were rarely within reach of either midwife or birthing family. The same can be said in regard to hospital administrators and government health officials. However, traditional birth attendants enjoyed little autonomy in daily (and nightly) practice, not least because their work in the home environment placed them in a dependent position vis-à-vis birthing women and their kin; moreover, traditional birth attendant and birthing family, neither with access to the benefits of a welfare state, were under the control of nature. I will briefly speak of these two types of dependency below.

It is important to realize that the earliest N&L midwives were without either workplace or secure income. They were expected to "call" at the homes of birthing families, where norms and customs of the families themselves, in this particular, based largely on patriarchal descent systems[8], formed the organizing principles of the midwife's work. Local families, moreover, set the terms of payment for maternity services rendered. While sometimes reimbursed for their work—typically in kind (e.g. wild game, fresh vegetables), many traditional birth attendants were expected to perform their varied duties "out of the goodness of their hearts", as part of their "Christian duty". In this way they can be likened to lay midwives found in less-developed countries today (Laderman, 1983), providing a kind of "mutual aid" to local families in need, in the hope that someday other community members would practice "generalized reciprocity" towards them (Katz & O'Connell, 1983).

Of course, traditional homebirth attendants were advantaged in that they possessed what was locally referred to as *hands-on* know-how, what sociologists sometimes call *life world knowledge* (Böhme, 1984). Such know-how, in the traditional N&L midwife's case, might derive from informal apprenticeship to female kin or, less frequently, formal apprenticeship with female community elders; sometimes, as found in the Mother Country (Donnison, 1977), it was mainly based on the midwife's own personal passage(s) through pregnancy and childbirth. As one of the quotes above indicates, some traditional homebirth attendants were deemed highly knowledgeable, worthy of the status of "wise woman". Yet this situation was in no way universal. And even the wisest and most competent of them were often unable to deal with stressful problems sometimes accompanying childbirth, confounded in this historical instance by the poor general health status of birthing women, as well as virtual lack of access to any obstetrical aid[9]. During such times, traditional birth attendants found their "hands tied"; midwife and patient/client were left subservient to the "natural order of things" (Nevitt, 1978)

Cottage Hospital Midwifery

Traditional homebirth attendance held sway in N&L until the second decade of the twentieth century when, following the lead of Britain, the Mother Country (Lewis, 1990), state involvement in maternity care gathered momentum. Legislation was passed requiring the registration of all births, and public funds were made available to philanthropic associations to set up milk depots, health clinics, and other kinds of aid to birthing families of little means (Nevitt, 1978). In the early 1930s, a Cottage Hospital Plan (CHP) was initiated, patterned after analogous plans then underway in the Scottish Highlands and surrounding Islands and the western Canadian province of Saskatchewan. Despite disruption during the Great Depression and World War II, by the late 1940s the CHP was in full operation in N&L; it was based on eighteen community hospitals (and four outlying clinics/nursing stations), with referral of serious medical concerns to three regional hospitals and, in the capital city, to a base hospital operated by the Department of Health. Fourteen additional small community facilities, including a larger regional hospital, were established in the North of the province under the auspices of the religious-based International Grenfell Association, subsequently also placed under government direction. One eventual outcome, among others, was free universal access to maternity services co-ordinated by midwives working out of cottage hospitals.

Cottage hospitals were comparatively small 30-50 bed institutions employing a work team comprised of, depending on size, one or a few staff physicians, a number of nurses and midwives, and a small support staff. The community-based nature of these hospitals made it possible for midwives employed there to continue the personalized care characteristic of traditional homebirth attendance, yet at the same time to offer a level of comfort and safety for women in childbirth that was hitherto unavailable. According to my respondents, few local inhabitants were reluctant guests:

"After the granny midwife in our area, then the women were expected to come to the cottage hospital and they just came. I think many of them really liked to go to the cottage hospital because, you know, they were able to get away from a lot at home. Someone went in and took over their household when they were in; I guess then it was a holiday ... at least a rest."

At the same time, the internal organization of the cottage hospitals made it possible for midwives to work autonomously in daily practice. This was the case, according to my respondents, for at least two reasons. On the one hand, the cottage hospital provided midwives protection from the kind of direct family control mentioned above in reference to traditional homebirth attendance. Yet the cottage hospital never developed into a "health care bureaucracy" (Betz & O'Connell, 1983; McKinlay & Arches, 1985; McKinlay & Stoeckle, 1988), distinguished by tight medical and managerial authority, the not uncommon situation of the third generation of N&L midwives described below.

Cottage hospital midwives worked as first points of entry to the maternity care system. Following developments then under way in Britain (Robinson, 1990), this second generation of N&L midwives was instructed during formal midwifery training to care for the local women pre-natally; practitioner and patient/client met during weekly clinics held at the cottage hospital. Cottage hospital midwives were the main attendant during women's labours and deliveries as well; the staff physician was called upon by midwives on duty only when they suspected abnormality. Unlike traditional home birth attendants, cottage hospital midwives were therefore less often confronted with obstetrical complication during childbirth. Finally, cottage hospital midwives were available for birthing families with concerns during the postpartum period, including difficulties with breastfeeding. In cases when new mothers were unable to come to the hospital clinic, cottage hospital midwives would carry out home visits. In brief, "there was a great satisfaction with being a midwife in the cottage hospitals. (The) women seemed very relaxed too ... they wouldn't know about this uptightness you see today in the big hospitals".

Yet by the early 1980s, this work situation supportive of midwives' occupational autonomy was virtually obsolete, except in the northern area of the province where up to this day midwives in the few surviving cottage hospitals are commonly the senior person during normal pregnancy and childbirth. Developments elsewhere in the province, however, including decisions by subsequent provincial governments to promote policies of population resettlement into capital-designated growth areas, and regionalization of health services (both strategies well underway in most parts of North America by this time) led to a preference for large regional hospitals over the smaller cottage type, deemed by many local politicians as "backward" and "outdated" (House, 1978; Matthews, 1976). Among other staff, cottage hospital midwives found themselves without a means whereby to secure a livelihood. Some of them took early retirement; others, especially those who were younger and within travelling distance to a regional hospital, applied for the only position now available for non-medical trained maternity personnel: "obstetrical nurse". This new post, as I now describe, led to, among other things, a curtailing of midwives' freedom to exercise their own clinical judgement about maternity matters: in effect, to a demise of their occupational autonomy.

Regional Hospital Midwifery

On the outside, today's regional hospital midwives occupy an alluring work role. They serve a broad clientele drawn from a large catchment area, leading to a regular supply of pregnant women on the maternity ward. The regional hospital is equipped with up-to-date medical technology and a diverse maternity staff, including obstetrician/gynaecologists, pediatricians and anaesthetists, in addition to interns and residents handling obstetrical off-hours emergencies. The regional hospital's elaborate division of labour, in addition, makes it unnecessary for midwives there to perform general nursing duties commonly expected of N&L traditional birth attendants, and sometimes also expected of cottage hospital midwives. Because of the regional hospital's large size, more managerial positions are potentially available for aspiring experienced midwives than at smaller sites. Finally, the regional hospital attracts various types of students, conceivably placing midwifery employees in the role of teacher.

On closer view, however, many of these seemingly beneficial organisational features diminish rather than heighten regional hospital midwives' occupational autonomy. They often find themselves under close scrutiny of a hospital administration foremost concerned about rationalizing services and meeting budgetary limits. Regional hospital midwives, moreover, are frequently in rivalry in the performance of their maternity duties with attending physicians, obstetricians, staff nurses, and even medical students required to oversee a specified quota of labours and deliveries as part of degree requirements. Since N&L physicians, like their Canadian and U.S. counterparts, enjoy the legal right (until a few years ago in

Canada, the exclusive right (Blishen, 1991; Buckley, 1979) to oversee both normal and onerous childbirth, midwives working on regional hospital maternity wards work essentially as physicians' "handmaidens", performing obstetrical nursing duties which, while time-consuming and sometimes exacting, allow little room for independent clinical judgement. Prior to the moment of the newborn's arrival, regional hospital midwives are systematically shooed from the limelight while medical "experts" (often medical interns/junior doctors) "deliver the baby". This situation leads to increasing alienation between the regional hospital midwives and birthing women, who not surprisingly come to doubt the midwife's advice since apparently the "doctor knows best". Contributing further strain to the midwife-patient relationship is routine use of monitoring technology on regional hospital maternity wards. One regional hospital midwife was not alone in relating to me that a great deal of her work was "machine-minding":

"As far as I'm concerned, things right now are too mechanical in obstetrics. As soon as someone comes in, they're hooked up to what is called a "monitor", a great big thing by their bed showing the fetal heartbeat and all. There is a focus on the baby ... But, in my view, it is too mechanical. We have no opportunity to sit down and chat with our patients like you and I are doing now."

Many regional hospital midwives told me of how they had become "deskilled", that they no longer felt either "competent or confident" to be primary assistant to birthing women. Forced to work under conditions, which deny them occupational autonomy in crucial ways, many regional hospital midwives spoke of disillusionment with their declining status. One went so far as to describe herself as a "frustrated midwife" who is "stuck in a rut" work-wise. Another put it like this:

"I think that people tend to be forgotten—worker and patient—in a big facility. Nobody knows you. I think that is important: that you know people, know who they are, know something about them. I think a lot of things get lost in such a place. I'm inclined towards a smaller workplace."

SUMMARY AND CONCLUSION

Analysis of primary data gathered from three generations of N&L midwives points to variation in occupational autonomy. Genuine occupational autonomy was in many respects out of reach of traditional homebirth attendants; one contributing factor was the location of their work activities in birthing families' homes, where a system of patriarchal control held sway. In addition, like those they served, traditional homebirth attendants had virtually no access to the positive developments of modern obstetrics nor benefits of the welfare state; both practitioner and client were very much at the mercy of the "natural order of things". For different reasons, including control by medical and bureaucratic elites and fixation upon technology, present-day regional hospital midwives also have little freedom to exercise clinical judgement about maternity matters. By comparison, cottage hospital midwives enjoyed (and in northern regions, still enjoy) a fair degree of occupational autonomy, to the extent that they routinely drew upon their own expertise to organize care of birthing families, free of needless interference from external forces.

Is there a message here for emerging community midwives in Canada? A cautionary note is in order regarding generalizability from my single qualitative study confined to the poorest region of the country, with its own particular history and culture that no doubt has affected the shape of maternity services there. It should also be said that, despite comparative advantage in regard to midwives' occupational autonomy, cottage hospital midwifery was not without shortcomings from the perspective of some birthing families. Homebirth attendance, for one thing, was frowned upon by most cottage hospital midwives, who tended to equate safety of mother and newborn with (community) hospital confinement. In addition, short-term continuity of care was rarely practised by cottage hospital midwives; rather than a single midwife attending to the needs of individual birthing families from conception into the postnatal period, a midwifery team (albeit usually comprised of familiar faces) was the norm.

On the one hand, the "new midwifery" now underway in the Canadian provinces of Ontario and British Columbia is an attempt to remedy these shortcomings, by integrating a homebirth option, and short term continuity of care as cornerstones (Benoit, 1997). On the other hand, what is lost with the new midwifery system is the *long term* continuity of care, as well as the comprehensive reproductive services that cottage hospital midwives (and, e.g., present-day Swedish midwives (Benoit & Heitlinger, 1988) gave local clients, attending not only their frequently multiple pregnancies, but also giving them birth control and sexuality advice, and often attending to the reproductive concerns of their female relatives. Also unknown to date is whether the type of occupational autonomy, such as enjoyed by N&L cottage-hospital midwives in earlier decades, will be similarly enjoyed by late-twentieth century counterparts. This is a topic of much needed research as the new Canadian midwives attempt to meet public expectations, at a time when major health system restructuring is underway, and physicians are mobilizing to defend their traditional health care mandates, not least of all maternity care.

REFERENCES

Abbott, A. 1981 'Status and Status Strain in the Professions'. *American Journal of Sociology* 86 (4): 819-35.

Arber, S. & J. Ginn 1995 'The Mirage of Gender Equality: Occupational Success in the Labour Market and Within Marriage.' *British Journal of Sociology* 46(1): 21-43.

Barrington, E. 1985 *Midwifery is Catching*. Toronto: NC Press.

Benoit, C. 1989 'Traditional Midwifery Practice: The Limits of Occupational Control.' *Canadian Review of Sociology & Anthropology* 26(4): 633-49.

Benoit, C. 1991 *Midwives in Passage*. Memorial University of Newfoundland, ISER Press.

Benoit, C. 1992 'Midwives in Comparative Perspective: Professionalism in Small Organizations.' *Current Research on Occupations and Professions* 6: 199-216.

Benoit, C. 1994 'Paradigm Conflict in the Sociology of the Professions.' *Canadian Journal of Sociology* 19 (3): 303-29.

Benoit, C. 1995 'Midwives and Healers: The Newfoundland Experience' in E. Dua, M. FitzGerald, L. Gardner, D. Taylor & L. Wyndels (eds.), *On Women Healthsharing*. Toronto: Women's Press.

Benoit, C. 1997. 'Professionalizing Canadian Midwifery: Sociological Perspectives,' pp. 93-114 in F. Sharoff (ed.) *The New Midwifery: Reflections on Renaissance and Regulation*. Toronto: The Women's Press.

Benoit, C. & A. Heitlinger. 1998. 'Women's Health Caring Work in Comparative Perspective: Canada, Sweden & Czechoslovakia/Czech Republic as Case Examples.' *Social Science & Medicine,* 47(8):1101-11.

Betz, M. & L. O'Connell 1983 'Changing Doctor-Patient Relationships and the Rise of Concern for Accountability'. *Social Problems* 31: 84-95.

Biggs, L. 1983 'The Case of the Missing Midwives: A History of Midwifery in Ontario from 1795-1900,' *Ontario History*, 65 (1): 21-35.

Blishen, B. R. 1991 *Doctors in Canada*. Toronto: University of Toronto Press.

Bourgeault, I. & M. Fynes 1997. 'Integrating Lay and Nurse-Midwifery into the U.S. and Canadian Health Care Systems." *Social Science & Medicine* 44(7): 1051-63.

Böhme, G. 1984. 'Midwifery as Science: An Essay on the Relationship Between Scientific and Everyday Knowledge,' pp. 365-85 in N. Stehr and V. Meja (eds.) *Society & Knowledge*. New Brunswick, N. J.: Transaction Books.

Brier, L.M., 1987, *Sufferers and Healers: The experience of illness in 17th century England*, London: Routledge & Kegan Paul

Buckley, S. 1979. 'Ladies or Midwives' pp. 131-49 in L. Kealey (ed.), *A Not Unreasonable Claim*. Toronto: The Women's Press.

Burtch, B. 1988 'Midwifery and the State: The New Midwifery in Canada,' pp. 349-71 in A. McLaren (ed.), *Gender and Society*. Toronto: Pitman Ltd.

Burtch, B. 1994 *Trials of Labour: The Reemergence of Midwifery*. Montreal: Mc-Gill-Queen's Press.

Callaway, H. 1978 "The Most Essentially Female Thing of All': Giving Birth,' pp. 163-85 in S. Ardner (ed.), *Defining Females*. New York: Halstead Press.

Clarke, J. 1990 *Health, Illness and Medicine in Canada*. Toronto: McClelland & Stewart.

Coburn, D., C. D'Arcy, G.M. Torrance & P. New (eds.) 1987 *Health and Canadian Society*. Markham, Ontario: Fitzhenry & Whiteside.

Coburn, D.1993 'State Authority, Medical Dominance, and Trends in the Regulation of the Health Professions: The Ontario Case'. *Social Science & Medicine* 37 (2): 129-38.

Conrad, P. & J. Schneider 1980 *Deviance and Medicalization*. St. Louis: C.V. Mosby Co.

Donnison, J. 1977. *Midwives and Medical Men*. London: Heinemann.

Evans, R. 1984 *Strained Mercy: The Economics of Canadian Health Care*. Toronto: Butterworth.

Freidson, E. 1986 *Professional Powers*. Chicago: University of Chicago Press.

Hammersley, M. 1992 *What's Wrong with Ethnography?* London: Routledge.

House, J.D. 1978 *Newfoundland Society & Culture*. St. John's, Newfoundland: Memorial University of Newfoundland.

Hughes, E. C. 1958 *Men and Their Work*. New York: Free Press.

Jeffery, P., R. Jeffery & A. Lyon. 1989 *Labour Pains and Labour Power: Women and Childbearing in India*. London: Zed Books.

Jordan, B. 1978 *Birth in Four Cultures: A Cross-Cultural Investigation of Childbirth in Yucatan, Holland, Sweden and the United States*, St.Albans, Vermont: Eden Press

Kleinman, S., B. Stenross & M. McMahon 1994 'Privileging Fieldwork Over Interviews: Consequences for Identity and Practice.' *Symbolic Interaction* 17(1): 37-50.

Laderman, C. 1983 *Wives and Midwives: Childbirth and Nutrition in Rural Malaysia*. Berkeley, L.A.: University of California Press.

Laforce, H. 1990 'The Different Stages of the Elimination of the Midwife in Quebec,' pp. 36-50 in K. Arnup *et al.* (eds.) *Delivering Motherhood*. New York: Routledge.

Laget, M. 1977 'Childbirth in Seventeenth- and Eighteenth-Century France: Obstetrical Practices and Collective Practices.' *Annales E.S.C.*, 32: 958-92.

Leavitt, J. 1986 *Brought to Bed: Childbearing in America 1750 to 1950*. New York: Oxford University Press.

Lewis, J. 1990 'Mothers and Maternity Policies in the Twentieth Century,' pp. 15-29 in J. Garcia, R. Kilpatrick, & M. Richards (eds.) *The Politics of Maternity Care: Services for Childbearing Women in 20th Century Britain*. Oxford: Oxford University Press.

Light, D. 1986 'Corporate Medicine for Profit'. *Scientific American* 255: 38-45.

Litoff, J. 1978 *American Midwives*. Westport, Conn.: Greenview Press.

Litoff, J. (ed.)1986 *The American Midwife Debate*. New York: Greenwood Press.

Lorber, J. 1984 *Women Physicians: Careers, Status, and Power*. London: Tavistock.

Macintyre, S. 1977 'Childbirth: The Myth of the Golden Age.' *World Medicine* 15 (June): 17-22.

Matthews, R. 1976 *There's No Better Place Than Here: Social Change in Three Newfoundland Communities*. Toronto: Peter Martin Associates.

Mason, J. 1987 'A History of Midwifery in Canada.' *Report of the Task Force on the Implementation of Midwifery in Ontario*. Toronto, Ontario.

McKay, S. 1993 'Models of Care: Denmark, Sweden, and the Netherlands.' *Journal of Nurse-Midwifery* 38(2): 114-20.

McKinlay, J. & J. Arches. 1985 'Towards the Proletarianization of Physicians'. *International Journal of Health Services* 15: 161-95.

McKinlay, J. & J. Stoeckle. 1988 'Corporatization and the Social Transformation of Doctoring.' *International Journal of Health Services* 18: 191-205.

Mead, M. & N. Newton. 1967 'Cultural Patterning in Perinatal Behaviour', pp. 142-244 in S. Richardson & A. Guttmacher (eds.), *Childbearing: Its Social and Psychological Aspects*. Baltimore: Williams & Wilkins.

Murray, H.C. 1979 *More Than 50%: Woman's Life in a Newfoundland Outport 1900-1950*. St. John's, Newfoundland: Breakwater Books.

Myerhoff, B. & A. Simic 1978 *Life's Career—Aging: Cultural Variations on Growing Old*. Beverly Hills: Sage

Neary, P. & J. Hiller (eds.) 1980 *Newfoundland in the Nineteenth and Twentieth Centuries*. Toronto: University of Toronto Press.

Nevitt, J. 1978 *White Caps and Black Bands* St. John's, Nfld.: Jesperson Press.

Oakley, A. 1976 'Wise Woman and Medical Men: Changes in the Management of Childbirth,' pp. 17-58 in J. Mitchell & A. Oakley (eds.) *The Rights and Wrongs of Women*. Harmondsworth: Penguin.

Oakley, A. & S. Houd. 1990 *Helpers in Childbirth: Midwifery Today*. New York: Hemisphere Publishing.

Oppenheimer, J. 1983 'Childbirth in Ontario: The Transition from Home to Hospital in the Early Twentieth Century.' *Ontario History* 65 (1): 36-60.

O'Reilly. P. 1989 'Small 'p' Politics: The Midwifery Example', pp. 159-173 in C. Overall (ed.) *The Future of Human Reproduction*. Toronto: The Women's Press.

Phaff, J.M.L. (ed.) 1986 *Perinatal Health Services in Europe: Searching for Better Childbirth*. London: Croom Helm.

Pickard, S. 1994 'Life after a Death: The Experience of Bereavement in South Wales.' *Ageing and Society* 14: 191-217.

Reid, M. 1989 'Sisterhood and Professionalization: A Case Study of the American Lay Midwife', pp. 219-38 in C. Shepherd McClain (ed.), *Women Healers: Cross-Cultural Perspectives*. New Brunswick, N.J.: Rutgers University.

Renaud, M. 1987 'Reform or Illusion: An Analysis of the Quebec State Intervention in Health,' pp. 590-614 in D. Coburn, C. D'Arcy, G. M. Torrance & P. New (eds.) *Health and Canadian Society* (2nd edn.) Markham, Ontario: Fitzhenry & Whiteside.

Report of the British Columbia Royal Commission on Health Care and Costs 1991 *Closer to Home*. Victoria, B.C.

Riessman, C. 1983 'Women and Medicalization: A New Perspective'. *Social Policy* 14: 3-18.

Robinson, S. 1990 'Maintaining the Independence of the Midwifery Profession: A Continuing Struggle,' pp. 61-91 in J. Garcia, R. Kilpatrick, & M. Richards (eds.) *The Politics of Maternity Care: Services for Childbearing Women in 20th Century Britain*. Oxford: Oxford University Press.

Roth, J. A. 1974 'Professionalism: The Sociologist's Decoy' *Sociology of Work & Occupations* 1 (1): 6-23.

Rushing, B. 1993 'Ideology in the Reemergence of North American Midwifery' *Work & Occupations* 20(1): 46-63.

Starr, P. 1982 *The Social Transformation of American Medicine*. New York: Basic Books.

Strauss, A. 1985 *Social Organization of Medical Work*. Chicago: The University of Chicago Press.

Sullivan. D. & R. Weitz. 1988 *Labor Pains: Modern Midwives and Home Birth*. New Haven: Yale University Press.

Task Force on the Implementation of Midwifery in Ontario 1987 *Report on the Task Force on the Implementation of Midwifery in Ontario*. Toronto: Ontario.

Tsalikis, G. 1993 'Ontario's Health Strategy of 'Muddling Through' to the Millenium.' *Health & Canadian Society* 1(2): 395-413.

Wertz, R.W. & D.C. Wertz. 1977 *Lying-In: A History of Childbirth in America*. New York: Schocken Books.

Wertz, R.W. & D.C. Wertz. 1990 'Notes on the Decline of Midwives and the Rise of Medical Obstetricians', pp. 148-160 in P. Conrad & R. Kern (eds.), *The Sociology of Health & Illness: Critical Perspectives*. (3rd ed.) New York: St. Martin's Press.

---

[1] Segments of the data section cited in this chapter have previously appeared in *Midwives in Passage* (Benoit 1991). Address for correspondence: Department of Sociology, University of Victoria, Victoria, B.C., Canada, V8W 3P5

[2] As a case in point, a figure of 10-11 percent national caesarean rate for Sweden is reported by Anita Karlsson, Secretary of the Swedish Midwives Association, Personal communication, April, 1995.

[3] Due to space considerations, I omit discussion of various intervening personal factors, including frequent conflict between familial and occupational roles of service workers, that may impede easy realization of aspired service goals (Arber & Ginn, 1995) I am also unable to discuss here how individual career ambitions of service workers are often antithetic to what the public deems as quality care (Abbott, 1981).

[4] Sociologists widely disagree about the prospects of occupational autonomy for today's health workers, physicians included (see especially *The Millbank Quarterly* 66, Suppl. 2 (1988). Yet most would agree, I suggest, with my own definition of the concept.

[5] For discussion of the main advantages of the qualitative interview method, see Kleinman, Stenross & McMahon, 1994. For discussion of some of its pitfalls, see Hammersley, 1992.

[6] The province has a settler time-line of a half millennium. Most immigrants originated from the British Isles, initially to work in the local fishery which was until the 1930s an economic jewel of the Mother Country, Britain, and after 1949 until its virtual collapse in the last decade due to overfishing, a prized natural resource capitalized on by the Canadian Government (Neary & Hiller, 1980).

[7] Although for different reasons, my findings parallel those of Callaway (1978), Jeffery, Jeffery & Lyon (1989) and Macintyre (1977) regarding shortcomings of traditional homebirth attendance. Like these authors, I too take exception to the majority anthropological and feminist position (Laderman, 1983; Jordan, 1983; Oakley, 1976) that tends to celebrate indigenous midwives and original birthing systems.

[8] Shortage of space does not allow for discussion of this topic (Benoit, 1995) But here is how one elderly N&L midwife put it to me: "Women were told that 'once you find a man to take you to be his wife, you made your bed and now you lay in it'. Well, let me tell you this much, the women from around here didn't have any soft beds to choose from."

[9] For description of parallel historical circumstances in pre-modern England see Brier (1987), and pre-modern France see Laget (1977).

MEDICAL MODELS AND MIDWIFERY:
THE CULTURAL EXPERIENCE OF BIRTH

Ronnie Lichtman [†]

All participant observation is colored by the researcher's prior experiences and by her or his attitudes and beliefs. In this case, the observer's bias is clear. I am a certified nurse-midwife and as such have a deep commitment to practicing according to what I will call the 'midwifery model' of obstetric care rather than what is usually termed the 'medical model'. Although there is no universally accepted theory of midwifery, most practitioners would agree that there are several differences between midwifery and the medical model of birth as practiced by most physicians. The most widely accepted distinction is that midwives see pregnancy and birth as normal processes, as part of the life cycle, not as illnesses or disease states. In practice, midwives allow nature to run its course unless intervention becomes a necessity. Most midwives consider psychological, emotional, interpersonal, family and spiritual needs as essential parts of health care. Finally, most believe in each woman's right to maintain control of her body and of her care. This is accomplished through informed decision making, which mandates a great deal of teaching and information giving by midwives.

The data for this article were gathered by participant observation (as care provider, birth attendant and instructor of midwifery) in two distinct hospital settings. Despite a consistent belief in these principles, in the two settings in which I have been a birth attendant I have had profoundly different relationships to my work and to childbirth. The structure, policies and power relationships within these two settings have affected and, in fact, determined, the way I have been able to practice and my perception of myself as a practitioner, as well as the way that the women and families in my care have experienced their births.

TERMINOLOGY

Before describing the two hospitals in which I worked, it is important to discuss terminology. Vocabulary choice can reflect attitudes toward pregnancy or toward women. I have heard the words 'patient', 'client', 'consumer', 'woman', 'lady', 'girl' and 'mother' used to refer to pregnant persons. The word patient usually refers to someone who is sick. In the American medical system, this often implies dependency. Client is usually associated with a more equal relationship between a professional (e.g. a lawyer) and a recipient of her or his services. The professional is, in a sense, the employee of the client; a contractual relationship exists between them. This latter term has come into use by nurse-midwives (and some physicians) to express their belief that pregnant women are not ill and not dependent or powerless. It rings, however, of a somewhat impersonal relationship and overlooks the difference in the quality of emotional content of health care as compared to other services. The word consumer implies a buying and selling relationship—which only represents a part of what is involved in heath care interactions. Moreover,

[†] Chapter 8 in *Childbirth in America: Anthropological Perspectives* (pages 130-41)

Karen L. Michaelson & contributors (eds.), Bergin & Garvey Publ. Inc. Massachusetts, 1988. Reprinted with permission of Greenwood Publishing Group, Inc., Westport, CT.

in municipal hospitals women (and men) do not really have consumer power, and contracts with providers are at best verbal, more often unspoken or nonexistent. None of these terms is really adequate. I will, however, use the word patient rather than client or consumer, despite its unpopularity in progressive childbirth movements. I will use the term woman rather than lady or girl.

INSTITUTIONAL DIFFERENCES

Institutional characteristics affect the experience of birthing women in a number of ways. They affect the subjective perception of pregnancy and birth and, in a more total sense, of self, of control over one's body. The two institutions are both municipal hospitals. The women presenting themselves for care at both North and South Hospitals accept the needs for medical supervision during pregnancy. Therefore, to a large extent the association of pregnancy with illness is unavoidable, despite most midwives' firm conviction that pregnancy is a normal event, an event whose deep personal connotations far exceed its medical impact. Yet the vast majority of patients at North Hospital never see a physician during their pregnancy, while physician care is the norm at South Hospital.[1]

Most women who come for care at these institutions are poor, from an ethnic minority, and likely to have no more than a high-school education—frequently they have less. Many speak little or no English. Although in modern-day obstetrical thinking there is an assumption that all women of such 'low' socioeconomic status have greater risk in childbirth, in North Hospital the implementation of high-risk procedures must be based on an individualised assessment of such risk; in South Hospital high-risk procedures are routine. These procedures include uncomfortable but rarely dangerous interventions, such as enemas, pubic shaves and intravenous feedings, as well as those that are more invasive, such as the insertion of electronic monitors directly onto the fetal scalp, artificial rupture of membranes and lithotomy position for birth using high, widely spaced stirrups—any of which can potentially lead to complications.

The major difference between the two hospitals is that North Hospital's labor and delivery units are staffed by obstetrical resident physicians. Both services have attending obstetricians as back up. Although South Hospital does have a small staff of midwives, they see a relatively small number of pregnant women and do not provide 24-hour, seven-day-a-week coverage in labor and delivery as do the midwives at North Hospital. The midwives at North Hospital have some responsibility for all women in the obstetrical service, functioning with physicians as co-managers of care when a medical problem arises or is anticipated. Thus, midwifery philosophy permeates the care of every pregnant woman—healthy or ill, with or without problems—at North Hospital. At South Hospital, the midwives' presence has not significantly influenced the overall experience of childbirth except perhaps for the few women they attend.

Management choices and treatment of women at the two institutions reflect the different training, philosophies, and personal characteristics of care providers and the power relationships among them, as well as institutional goals secondary to health care. Although the main purpose of both hospitals is to provide direct patient care, South Hospital is also a training center for medical-school graduates who wish to specialise in obstetrics, while North Hospital is a demonstration project utilizing nurse-midwives as primary care providers.

DIFFERENCES IN PATIENT CARE

Prenatal Care

Pregnant women at North Hospital see the same midwife in clinic throughout their pregnancy, generally establishing relationships with their midwives on a first name basis. The midwives value the personal components of interaction with patients and emphasize health maintenance. Nevertheless, many women view hospital-based midwives as very much part of the medical system. When I was a staff midwife at North Hospital, I had several patients who consistently called me 'Dr Ronnie' regardless of my careful and repeated explanation that I was not a doctor and my assurance that they could see a doctor if they preferred (an option rarely exercised at North Hospital). Still, any cursory review of prenatal charts at the two hospitals attests to differences that begin in the prenatal period—despite the system recently established at South Hospital in which a consistent caregiver is provided for all prenatal visits. Most physician notes are short and refer only to the woman's physical condition: "23 weeks by size and dates, no problems" is a typical sort of entry. Midwifery notes tend to be more detailed and include references not only to physical but also to psychological and personal concerns, such as family relationships, childbirth class registration, and preparation for labor and delivery. Even notes about the physical aspects of pregnancy refer to topics such as nutritional intake and common discomforts of pregnancy often ignored or devalued by physicians. From such notes one can infer a very different focus at prenatal visits. Although two conference nurses are on staff at South Hospital, and a nurse-practitioner works as patient-care co-ordinator and counselor in the high-risk clinic, their care is not always ongoing, and since their responsibility is for all clinic patients, counseling is necessarily brief.

Such differences in prenatal care can certainly affect the cultural patterning of pregnancy. What happens at prenatal visits can determine how much attention is paid to diet, how involved other family members become with the actual processes of pregnancy and birth and with health maintenance in this period, how much time is devoted to preparation for the event of labor, and who participates directly in that event. This may be especially true for women such as those at North and South Hospital who do not, as a group, read extensively about pregnancy and birth and who do not come prepared to present caregivers with their own requirements.

Labor

In labor and delivery, differences are even more apparent. It is quite rare to see a woman laboring at North Hospital without the presence of a support person of her choice. It is a given policy, established by the director of midwifery when the service was opened several years ago, that every woman has the right to labor accompanied by a person of her own choosing—not necessarily her husband. Most North Hospital midwives believe that it is a woman's right to choose to have more than one person with her, including appropriately supervised siblings. Although opposition to that policy has come largely from nursing, individual nurses often support this more permissive approach. Two or three support persons are not uncommon at North Hospital, and occasionally, a child participates in labor and birth.

Conversely, until two years ago it was rare to see a woman at South Hospital who was not alone. The policy there required that in order to attend labor and delivery, a person had to have completed a series of childbirth-education classes and be able to produce a certificate as evidence of such completion. Many midwives (myself included) resorted to dishonesty in the face of powerlessness to change this policy by falsifying certificates for women who came into the labor unit with partners whom they wanted to remain with them. The rule was finally revoked at the insistence of a new director of midwifery, who has since left the service. Despite the policy, however, more pregnant women are alone in labor at South Hospital than at North Hospital; perhaps this is due to differences in prenatal teaching and preparation. Midwifery students are taught to discuss childbirth education classes with all women during prenatal visits and to encourage their attendance at such classes. Indeed, many midwives teach childbirth classes, and most midwifery schools offer teacher-training courses. This is not a part of medical education and is not stressed in obstetrical residence training programs.

An observant guest wandering through the labor units at these two hospitals would be struck by the contrast. At South Hospital, all laboring women are in bed with intravenous tubing and attached to fetal monitoring machines either externally via abdominal belts or internally via fetal scalp electrodes. I have witnessed scenes that, except for the human pain involved, would be comic: a woman comes to the labor floor fully dilated, almost ready to deliver, yet the intravenous is started before she is instructed to push. She may be told to stop her pushing efforts, which is not an easy task. This is all done without assessing the risk factors that might necessitate an intravenous, though most of these can be automatically ruled out just by the fact that the woman had gotten to this point in labor. Many women at South Hospital are medicated, though this in no way makes for painless childbirth; sounds of pain, varying in type and degree, often permeate the labor area.

At North Hospital there is greater diversity in the patterns of labor. Laboring women who have no complications often choose to walk around. Couples—composed of a pregnant woman and either her male partner or another, often older, woman—can be seen wandering about. Occasionally a group of three or more is encountered. Contractions are dealt with in a variety of ways. A woman may lean up against a wall, against her support person, or continue moving. Rocking back and forth is not uncommon. Some women spend part of their labors sitting in chairs. Others remain in bed, in semi-sitting positions, lying on their sides, or assuming a hands-and-knees position to relieve back pressure. Of those women in bed, some are connected to fetal monitors, others are not. Most commonly, the machine is used intermittently.

Another noticeable difference between North and South Hospitals is the amount of privacy afforded patients. In neither institution is privacy considered a priority. Staff members value their right to freely enter any room at any time. At North Hospital, however, there are attempts made to safeguard privacy. As a practitioner at North Hospital, I felt comfortable closing doors; at South Hospital I know that sooner or later someone—a nurse or a resident—would come in, not necessary to provide patient care but to check on what was going on 'behind closed doors'. I remember one day working in the admitting room at North Hospital when an older, well-dressed gentleman approached the door. I was with a woman whose legs were in stirrups on the exam table. The man started to enter, announcing, "It's all right; I'm a doctor". "I'm sorry", I told him, "there's a woman being examined in here. I'd like you to wait please". He did. I later found out that he was the service's newly appointed director of obstetrics. I was quite pleased with myself and never heard any more about the incident. I must admit that at South Hospital I would have been much more hesitant in the same situation, and I don't know what the reaction or repercussions would have been.

Seasoned practitioners, myself included, can easily lose sensitivity to the need for privacy. To understand how important it might be to a woman, I have to remember my own shock and outrage in my first obstetrical-nursing job at another city hospital—quite similar, in many aspects of its functioning, to South Hospital—at the complete inattention paid to the rights and needs of women for privacy. Over the years, my horror has diminished, much to my own chagrin. For each woman, the feeling of intrusion must be like my own initial reaction except that, in a very real sense, it is her body that is being assaulted.

Birth

Deliveries provide another area of contrast. With a few exceptions, births at South Hospital take place in the delivery room, which looks like a standard operating room with its steel tables and imposing lights. Women are moved from their beds to a narrow, flat table. Their legs are generally placed in stirrups and covered, along with their abdomens, with sterile towels. The women are told not to touch the towels. The baby is born into the hands of the obstetrician, held aloft so that the mother can identify its sex, and quickly placed in a warmer, which the mother, lying on her back, cannot see. Eventually, after the baby is footprinted, identified with wristbands, and has had medication placed in its eyes, she or he is given to the mother for a brief period. The newborn is soon transported to the nursery. It is several hours before the mother will see her child again.

This scenario is sometimes played out at North Hospital—in the event of a baby with a problem—although even then the delivery table is only used in the rare event that forceps are anticipated. Instead, most North Hospital births are done in the labor room, in the labor bed. Even when there is a problem that may require infant-resuscitation equipment, available only in the delivery room, the laboring woman usually remains in her bed, which is wheeled to the delivery room. This has several advantages: she need not move at a time when moving is awkward and uncomfortable; she need not have her legs in stirrups which puts undue pressure on the perineum (and may cause trauma to the legs, especially in heavy women); she can sit up or lie on her side. Both these positions facilitate pushing efforts far better than lying flat. In the sitting position, the woman can sometimes see her baby emerge or touch its head as it is crowning. Although some hospital delivery tables have elevated backrests and mirror arrangements to enable women to watch their babies emerging, South Hospital uses neither of these.

Many midwives place the baby on the mother's abdomen once it is born, if she wants this immediate contact. Although the North Hospital nurses will take the baby away for a while for identification and medications, the period of initial contact is much longer than at South Hospital. The mother is in a more comfortable position to hold, cuddle and often breastfeed her newborn.

PATIENTS AND STAFF

Another difference, perhaps not perceptible from casual observation, is the relation between staff and patients—the extent to which patient needs and desires are solicited and incorporated into the management plans for each individual labor. Management is a broad term which relates to the treatment of labor and birth: what is done for the woman and her baby. In midwifery practice, the management of labor involves several aspects: the physical care of the laboring and birthing woman and her newborn, her emotional care, and the involvement of her family and/or friends. In each of these areas, the input of the woman is implicit. Ideally, this input begins with pregnancy and continues during labor and through the actual birth. In North Hospital, this modified by the constraints of a busy service and by the fact that the birth attendant usually meets the woman and her support persons for the first time when they arrive in labor since the midwives work in scheduled shifts rather than on-call. In South Hospital, midwifery management is modified by rigid hospital protocols and hierarchical relationships among staff members that place the patient—along with the midwife—at the bottom of a long chain of command.

An anecdote involving my interaction with a resident at South Hospital well illustrates this relationship to patients. A midwifery student and I were caring for a woman who was quite uncomfortable and was having a long and difficult labor. During contractions she was loudly making her discomfort known, but between contractions she was alert and lucid. We discussed the possibility of medication with her, outlining its pros and cons. We explained that it might relax her and relieve some, but not all, of her pain and it would make her feel more distant from the pain. We told her that we would give her a dose that would not harm the fetus or, since it was early enough in her labor, produce a sleepy baby, though subtle effects on the newborn were possible. Although her labor was sufficiently established so that it would not be stopped entirely with medication, we presented the possibility that it might slow down. The woman asked a few questions and decided against the medication. She did not want to risk prolonging her labor at all. Shortly afterward, a senior resident entered the room. He checked the woman's monitor print-out and suggested that we consider medication. I told him that we had just discussed it with her and she had decided against it. "You discussed it with her?" he asked in a puzzled voice. "With whom? With Dr. M? She didn't want to prescribe medication?" (Dr M. was the junior resident who happened to be female) "No", I replied, "with the patient. The patient doesn't want medication". His face showed his clear surprise. It obviously had not occurred to him that we had negotiated our care with its recipient. I was not sure if he would order the medication anyway, but he did not.

I had a similar experience with a physician at North Hospital; the difference was not in the doctor's attitude, but in my own attitude and behavior. I was with another young woman, also vocal in her contractions, but relaxed, comfortable, and aware between them. We had a similar discussion about medication and she made the same choice—to get through labor without it. A few moments later, I overheard the attending physician ordering 50 milligrams of a narcotic commonly used in labor. I had a hunch it was intended for that patient. I knew she was the noisiest woman on the floor, and doctors (and midwives) are troubled by noisy patients. It makes us feel that we have somehow failed in making their labor comfortable. Anyway, I confronted the attending physician. I told him about my conversation with the woman and asked if he had discussed the order with her. He had not. I informed him that the patient was not to have medication at that time. He admitted that the need was more his own than hers. The crucial difference was that I know that my decision to accept the patient's wishes would not be superceded at North Hospital and that I could tell the physician my plan without being put in the position of needing his approval.

PROFESSIONAL IDENTITY

For me, working at these two institutions has been like having two professional identities—and at times, two selves. What I could offer to women in terms of their childbirth experience, how much decision-making power I had, how confident I was in my own abilities to make judgements and carry them out, how competent I felt as a teacher, and even how secure I felt in my hand skills have all been determined by the institutional settings in which I have had to function. At North Hospital I could work with women and with families to make childbirth humane and satisfying, even in the face of complications. There was the possibility of preserving dignity for birthing women and for myself as a birth attendant with knowledge and skills. I felt I could pass this sense on to students and teach them how to make safe judgments and to individualize labor and birth management in ways that they could carry with them wherever they worked.

At South Hospital I saw my role as an attempt to make the experience of childbirth as humane as possible given the circumstances and to teach as well as possible, helping students to see beyond the situation at hand. In my teaching I used the technique of creating fantasy situations. "Pretend you were free to use midwifery management for this woman", instructors might say to a student; "what would you do?" This is a poor substitute for reality since belief and philosophy in health care must be based on what is actually experienced, but it was the only way to educate students at South Hospital to be creative and flexible practitioners whose care would be based on the safest management for each woman, rather than on routines learned by rote.

Although the basis for routine care, especially in busy institutions, is to avoid danger through omission, the implementation of particular routines in certain situations can itself create problems. Whenever a student and I cared for a woman at South Hospital, I would make certain that one of us was in the room at all times so that the residents would not come in and change our management. We would devise strategies to avoid their intervention. For example, even in situations frequent vaginal exams are contraindicated, as in ruptured membranes, the routine at South Hospital is to examine everybody every two hours. The residents would insist on knowing how our patient was 'progressing'. They would not accept indicators other than pelvic findings, such as changes in contraction pattern or behavioral clues. We would thus anticipate their queries and come up with reasons to prolong the time between exams. "We were just about to examine her, but she needed to use the bedpan. We'll be examining her as soon as she's finished", would be a typical excuse. Such conniving was not needed at North Hospital, where midwife management and judgment were accepted.

CESAREAN RATES

The actual physical event of childbirth differs between these two institutions. At South Hospital, where birth is far more likely to become an operative procedure with its attendant risks. The published cesarean rate for North Hospital is below the national average (NICHD 1980:5), while staff report of South Hospital's cesarean rate indicates that it is generally above the national average. According to the *Draft Report on Cesarean Childbirth* (NICHD 1980) maternal mortality and morbidity rates are significantly higher following cesarean birth than after vaginal deliveries. Although there is no single reason for the difference in cesarean rates at the two hospitals, there are several possible explanations. Some involve factors that are institutionally determined, other explanations have to do with population variables independent of hospital control. All are speculative and until research demonstrates their relative worth, individuals will base their acceptance or rejection of each on personal values and beliefs.

One possibility is that because midwives do not perform cesareans, they have a vested interest in helping achieve vaginal birth. This attitude may lead to greater willingness to extend the time limits of what is medically considered normal in labor. At South Hospital, the residents need to learn to do cesareans. Although I have never seen a cesarean performed merely for a resident's education, there can be an unconscious desire for such experience that may subtly affect management. For example, the recommendation to perform a cesarean if the labor is longer than 'normal', even if there are no other problems, often feeds this need. Furthermore, high-risk procedures applied to low risk women have the potential to create risks. One example of this is the artificial rupture of membranes relatively early in labor to apply a monitor to the fetal scalp. Since such internal monitoring is the policy at South Hospital, membranes are generally ruptured by at least 4-5 centimeters or shortly after admission if a woman comes into the labor unit at a more advanced dilation. Such treatment forces women to stay in bed. This can slow labor and increase the likelihood that exogenous hormones will be needed to stimulate contractions. The result can be a labor so powerful that it leads to fetal distress. Another example is the more routine use of medication which may slow labor.

Looking at the situation from a different perspective, it can be claimed that South Hospital is located in a neighborhood whose population is less healthy than that of the community surrounding North Hospital and that this explains some of the disparity between cesarean rates in the two institutions. Another explanation is that a lack of prenatal care leads to increased risk necessitating operative deliveries. According to figures compiled by the state department of health, the proportion of women receiving late or no prenatal care in the area served by South Hospital is higher than that in the area served by North Hospital. Interestingly, it is not known how much of this difference in prenatal care is due to population characteristics and how much is due to institutional factors, such as the amount of time spent in and the quality of interaction during prenatal visits.

The differential education of practitioners may also play a role in accounting for cesarean rates. Medical education, and hence practice, differs greatly from midwifery education. There is often a value placed on aggressive action in modern medicine. This is particularly evident in surgical specialties, of which obstetrics is one. I have heard physicians at continuing education conferences declare that there is absolutely no reason to avoid gathering as much information as possible about labor if the technology is available. This translates into the use of electronic fetal monitors throughout labor for everybody. Such an attitude ignores the possible dangers of continuous monitoring for women who have no medical indication for the procedure. Midwives, however, are taught to watch nature work, to use non-invasive measures to observe progress in labor. Many midwives refer to themselves as guardians of nature's processes.

DISCUSSION

Education, and its attendant socialization, can only be a partial explanation of the many institutional differences described here. After all, there are physicians at North Hospital. Indeed, without medical support, the midwifery service could never have been established. Ultimately, the doctors control obstetric policy. Furthermore, some of the physicians at South Hospital are willing to step back so that the midwives can care for patients with little interference. Various human factors also have an impact on differences in care. Personal characteristics obviously play a role. Flexibility, security, ego strength, and a willingness to relinquish power are rarely found in new medical-school graduates. Attitudes toward women are also significant. Surprisingly, perhaps, this is not necessarily determined by sex. Women in obstetrics are, as a group, more in philosophic agreement with their male medical colleagues than with female midwives. They are not even necessarily more polite to patients or more willing to accept the patient's having an active role in her own care. This may be due to a number of factors: the selection process of medical schools; the socialization process during medical education; psychological factors related to the choice of obstetrics as a specialization; the stress inherent in obstetric residency programmes; and the fact that women in medicine comprise a small minority. Like other minorities, they may feel that in all aspects of achievement they have to outdo the dominant group—males—on male terms. It remains to be seen if obstetrics will change significantly if women become the majority of its practitioners.

The most compelling and pervasive explanation for the differences seems to be a structural one. The organization of South Hospital to achieve its secondary goal—physician training—is most responsible for the role delegated to its midwives. The organizational chart of that hospital's obstetric service presents a clear hierarchy. At the top are attending physicians—those who have already progressed through the various steps and are certified as obstetrical specialists. Beneath them are senior residents, those in their last year of post-medical-school training. Obstetrics is a four-year program so that the residents' hierarchy has four distinct categories. Each year is directly responsible to the ones above it, with the chief resident (chosen from among the seniors) directly responsible to the attending physicians on staff. Junior (first- and second-year) residents are subject to continual surveillance, though senior residents are not above supervision either. Yet, because this supervision is not always available on a one-to-one basis, even junior residents are often in a position to make important decisions. Such a system makes independence, flexibility, and creativity in management virtually impossible. Rules must be rigidly adhered to.

Theoretically, the midwives, who, unlike the residents, have completed their training, are not a part of this hierarchy; they are perceived as being on a level with the senior residents. And in theory, only the senior residents and attending physicians are consultants to the midwives. In fact, this does not always represent reality. The junior residents often regard the midwives as being on the bottom of the hierarchy and may take control of the supposed midwifery patients, especially if there is relatively little else for them to do at any particular time. Furthermore, the midwives must negotiate with the resident in charge for the right to take care of a given patient. In contrast, because the secondary function at North Hospital is to provide a model for midwife-based care, the personnel structure at that hospital is, in fact, quite different from that at South Hospital. In North Hospital the midwives assign patients to themselves or to co-management, if a problem arises or is anticipated. It is a rare doctor at North Hospital, who does not accept the midwives' word "She's normal" and refrain from actively involving himself or herself in that patient's direct care.

There are similarities, of course, between North and South hospitals. Both are busy municipal hospitals and share many of the same problems: there is a lack of calm and peace; practitioners are often harried; tempers can be short; women are frequently left too long without professional attention; and laboratory reports are often missing. In addition, South Hospital has made some changes in the seven years since I first worked there as a midwifery student. Support persons are no longer required to take educational classes to be with a woman in labor. Some midwives do bed deliveries, and some protocols—such as a two-hour limit on the pushing (or second) stage of labor—have been relaxed. Perinatologists have joined the staff, and the quality of medical care, as reflected in better statistics in important obstetrical indicators such as perinatal mortality, have improved.

CONCLUSIONS

For women who can afford private care, the childbirth of their choice can sometimes be purchased. Midwives need not be a part of this package; an increasing number of physicians in private practice are attempting to meet consumer demand by changing the patterns of childbirth to provide what has become known as 'family-centered' care.[2] But the care seen at North Hospital is rare in municipal hospitals where most poorer women must go. The quality of that care is directly related to the fact that midwives are responsible for the day-to-day running of the service.

There is a contradiction inherent in this model, however. Nurse midwifery as it exists today is dependent on medicine—its beneficence in 'allowing' midwives to practice or its acquiescence to consumer demand by including midwives for birth care. Rothman (1982) calls midwifery "almost a profession", because it does not adhere to the sociological definition of a profession as "an occupation that has social power and thereby social control". The midwifery model as practiced at North Hospital will thus not be widely accepted as the standard for municipal hospital obstetric services as long as those who espouse the medical model remain in power.

Remaining Questions

This chapter raises many issues that warrant further research. The impact of an alternative model for the delivery of maternity care in the public sector needs to be examined from the medical perspective in terms of maternal and newborn outcomes. But just as important, it must be examined from the perspective of social science. How, for example, do perceptions of the experience of childbirth differ between women delivering at a midwifery-model hospital and medical-model hospital? How do these hypothetically different perceptions affect other attitudes? How do they influence a woman's sense of control over her own body, her sense of self-respect? Do differing family roles in childbirth affect family roles in childrearing? How does the experience of childbirth relate to future health-related behaviors and interactions with the health care delivery system for the indigent? These questions have significant policy implications.

On a macro level, there are economic and political questions to be explored. What is the economic impact of midwifery-run services? Are they cost effective? If so, at what other cost is this economic benefit maintained? Why, for example, is one of North Hospital's perpetual problems a high turnover rate among midwives? Do midwives work too hard for too little money? In this era which espouses equal pay for equal or equivalent work, how can midwives, who are predominantly women, continue to accept salaries far lower than those paid to physicians, who are predominantly men? Could midwifery survive if midwife salary scales become equivalent to those of physicians? Would that be equitable? What political strategies can women and midwives use to change the power relationships in the health services? How can those women who are without economic purchasing power effect change in the health care systems that serve them? Can midwifery ever become a true profession? What can be done to make that happen, and what would be its effect on the overall structure of health care delivery? These compelling questions, which have potentially far reaching implications, must be explored by future investigators.

REFERENCES

NICHD (National Institute for Child Health & Human Development), 1980, *Draft Report of the Task Force on Cesarian Childbirth*, Bethseda, Maryland: National Institutes of Health

Rothman, Barbara Katz, 1982, *In Labor: Women and Power in the Birthplace*, New York W.W. Norton Reprinted as *Giving Birth: Alternatives in Childbirth* New York: Penguin

[1] North Hospital and South Hospital are fictitious names that indicate only a geographic relationship between the two hospitals.

[2] I would prefer woman-centered care with the family included to the extent that the woman chooses, but this is not what childbirth activists have been promoting.

THE TRADITIONAL MIDWIFE AND THE
MEDICALISATION OF MATERNITY CARE:
A "CROSS CULTURAL PERSPECTIVE"

George W. Lowis

Women in traditional society who become specialists in childbirth matters are most often referred to as traditional midwives (TM) or traditional birth attendants (TBA). Because of their esteemed status in most societies they tend to acquire respect from the community at large (Paul & Paul, 1975; Sargent, 1982; Recio, 1986; Maglacas & Simons, 1986), quite often because their position is considered "necessary" (Beeman, 1978; Peng, 1979; Oyebola, 1980a). In order to understand the significance of midwifery as a female occupational specialisation, it is necessary to consider the cultural implications of the statuses that midwives occupy, and the many variable roles they are expected to play as occupants of these statuses (Paul, 1975; Etzel, 1976, Cosminsky, 1977, Finerman, 1982; Morsy, 1982; Flint, 1982; Karim, 1984; Edwards, 1989; Vincent-Priya, 1991; Steinberg, 1996; Sich, 1988; O'Dempsey, 1988).

Contrary to the tendency of the biomedical profession to treat childbirth as a medical event, sociologists and anthropologists have focused on the cultural elaboration of this universal biological function. That is, birth is viewed as a biological event for which every society provides a means of management and control—including a system of values and practices concerning pregnancy, labor, delivery and post-natal care. Conversely, the study of childbirth may be regarded as a means of analysing the structure of socio-cultural systems.

SECTION ONE: SELECTED ETHNOGRAPHIC STUDIES

This part of the book focuses on midwifery and childbirth in non-western traditional societies, and is divided into two sections. In Section One, focus is on selected ethnographic studies and the importance of culture in the role played by the TM or TBA in the birthing and recovery process. Specifically, emphasis is on the duties and functions of midwives within the community as child care and ritual specialists in such diverse non-western traditional societies as Mexico (Jordan, 1993); Guatemala (Cosminsky, 1982); Malaysia (Laderman, 1983); Taiwan (Kang-Wang, 1980); and India (Jeffery & Jeffery, 1993). In an ethnographic account of two cases of childbirth, Laderman (1983) focuses on the norms associated with childbirth in rural Malaysia and on the culturally patterned behavior of the TM or *bidan*. In one birth, which was uncomplicated, the village midwife successfully delivered the child. In a second delivery, where the labor was difficult, and potentially dangerous, a government midwife was called to assist the village midwife. In both cases, the childbearing woman herself, not the practitioner was the ultimate arbiter of decisions taken during childbirth, unlike the relatively helpless Indian woman giving birth in Jeffery and Jeffery (1993). Importance of the role played by the TM is especially emphasised, however, in Jordan's (1993) ethnographic account of contemporary Maya Indian childbirth in Yucatan, Mexico. Although the people of this geographic area have been the object of anthropological and archaeological investigation for many years—beginning some eighty years ago with the Smithsonian (Gann, 1918) and the Carnegie Institutes of Washington studies (Shattuck, 1993; Steggerda, 1941; Villa Rojas, 1945)—it was not until

Jordan's (1993) empirically based study in the 1970s that a comprehensive and accurate account of childbirth practices appeared, based on participant observation by the author and information gained from a Maya midwife called Doña Doña Juana, who was the author's principal collaborator. Specifically, focus is on the status and roles played by Doña Juana, and on what the role expectations are in this community in regard to such matters as prenatal care, the birth event itself, and the postpartum period and how these expectations are translated into behavior for the midwife and expectant mother.

Doña Juana is about sixty years old, proud of her work, and head of an extended matrilocal family. She learned much of her midwifery duties from a Doctor Sanchez who provided her with instruments and equipment, and from her mother who was also a midwife. Doña Juana is generally considered the best midwife in town and is on mutually respectful terms with the medical doctors in the town's small hospital, although there is no particular deference exhibited in her interactions with the medical doctors. "She acknowledges their expertise in certain areas (e.g. manual removal of the placenta) but is also aware of her own special expertise, for example, in doing an external version of the baby if the baby is not in the proper position for birth" (Jordan, 1978:14). Births in this community typically take place at home, either in the woman's own home or if a first birth in her mother's; and a woman's husband is expected to be present during labor and birth, sometimes to assist the midwife and comfort his wife. During labor, arrangements are made to separate the birth area from public space, e.g. hanging a blanket from the rafters, thus screening the woman's hammock from the rest of the room, or the entire house may be placed off limits to all but the midwife and the expectant mother's helpers (ayudantes). By the time the family send for Doña Juana during the beginning stages of labor, she has already seen the expectant mother several times, most importantly in having performed prenatal and diagnostic massages. Occasionally, if the midwife determines in the course of a massage that the baby is in a breech (bottom-first) or transverse (side-lying) position, she will do an inversion; i.e., she will locate the baby's head and hip and apply strong, even pressure to these parts thereby shifting the baby's body into the more preferred head-down position. A day or two after birth, Doña Juana returns to check on mother and baby, typically to supervise the cleansing baths of mother and child and offer practical advice about nursing, even though breast feeding generally begins minutes after birth. Twenty days post-partum, she will administer one or more massages, as needed.

The indigenous birthing systems identified—and the role played by midwives as principal actors in the birthing process—present a sharp contrast to those prevalent in western societies, even as the indigenous systems undergo radical changes toward medicalization. One strong indicator of this trend toward medicalization is the co-existence of traditional native and modern medicine systems enabling patients to move from one system to the other or use the two systems simultaneously. This trend has been observed in Nigeria (Oyebola, 1980b); Zimbabwe (Mutambirwa, 1985); China (Lee, 1981; Rosenthal, 1981); Malaysia (Chen, 1973, 1981; Laderman, 1983); Mexico (McClain, 1975; Moser 1982); Taiwan (Kang-Wang, 1980, Lin, 1987); West Africa (Sargent, 1982); and India (Jeffery et al., 1989; Jeffery & Jeffery, 1993). In Malaysia, however, co-existence is threatened. Since only 38 per cent of the TBAs were under the age of 60, it is expected that these traditional midwives will ultimately be phased out and replaced by government midwives, as a result of recent legislation which requires the bidan to register as untrained midwives before they are allowed to practice (Laderman, 1983). In the ethnography of Cosminsky (1982) focus is on two Mayan areas in Guatemala where the beliefs and practices of childbirth are undergoing change under the impact of Western medicine. Birth is traditionally viewed as a ritualized process where one important agent in this process is the Mayan midwife who is regarded as an obstetrical and ritual specialist. Important components of this process are discussed by Cosminsky including, for example, how the midwife is recruited, what antenatal and postpartum care entails, and how labor and delivery are managed. In all regards, the concepts and practices of the indigenous birth system in Guatemala—which may be characterized as a holistic system—presents a sharp contrast to those promoted by Western medicine in the midwifery training programs, health care facilities, and prenatal clinics, which are based on the biomedical model of birth. Taiwan is a special case in that it still retains the traditional medical system co-existing with the modern (Kang-Wang, 1980), although midwifery is presently in decline (Lin, 1987). Kang-Wang (1980) offers a historical and comparative overview of the midwife in Taiwan including the network of relationships that currently exist between the midwife and client, midwife and obstetrician, and the role played by the midwife in the management of childbirth and postpartum care. The majority of Taiwanese babies are delivered by midwives, either professional midwives trained according to the Western model or TBA's or "granny midwives". Some of the better-educated, more affluent women follow the Western fashion of seeking a male obstetrician to deliver their babies in a hospital. Comparisons are also offered between the maternity care systems of Taiwan and the United States. The Taiwanese system is portrayed as a client or family centered care model with the midwife playing a constructive role in the birth process satisfying social, religious and medical needs, in contrast to the American system, where pregnant women tend to receive physician centered maternity care which almost always is a cold, sterile experience. In a more recent analysis, Lin (1987), on the other hand, hypothesizes that midwifery in Taiwan is in decline because of modernization of the country, development of medical insurance, and the transformation of attitudes towards hospital delivery. The trend begun in the early 1980s has recently been accelerated whereby the young, better educated and those living in cities, are increasingly expressing a preference for Western medical care—inclusive of the use of obstetricians and hospitals, since the latter have advanced technical equipment and reliable modern instruments for diagnosis such a fetal monitoring and supersonography.

SECTION TWO: MIDWIFERY TRAINING PROGRAMS

Many developing countries, which typically possess the world's highest infant mortality rates, are launching midwifery training programs. In the Sudan (Almasy, 1968) student midwives undergo a nine month course in which they are taught basic hygiene and how to cope with obstetrical problems and minor sickness in mothers and infants following delivery. However, the obstacles to any such reconciliation are considerable. They are discussed in the Guatemalan context by Jordan (1989 and the 1993 edition of *Birth in Four Cultures*), and in the context of Nepal by Pigg (1997), who points out that to speak of just two systems is already something of a distortion, for there are many different patterns of maternity care in different regions of Nepal.

In Algeria (Zemor, 1988), the importance of the midwife is illustrated by the fact that one out of every two deliveries is performed by a *matrone* (TBA) whose duty is also to teach the mother some of the rudiments of hygiene and nutrition. In the cluster of readings comprising Section Two the principal question addressed is whether the introduction of midwifery training programs has resulted in an improvement in the maternal and child health care in the region or country surveyed. In representative papers by Sparks (1990); Janowitz (1985); and Alto *et al.* (1991) a pattern emerges whereby introduction of new midwifery training programs has produced beneficial results. A contrary pattern is observed in contributions by Greenberg (1982); Justice (1984); Scheepers (1991); Jeffery & Jeffery (1993) and Pigg (1997)—which raises doubt about introducing such programs in the first place. Positive critiques are, however, offered in how such programs might be justified and/or achieve success in the future.

In northeast Brazil, TBAs were trained to refer women to the four obstetric units in rural areas, and to the hospital in the city of Fortaleza if they had certain pregnancy complications or were in a certain age group (Janowitz *et al.*, 1985). Generally—even though some women were inappropriately referred or others were not referred when they should have been—the system of referral that has developed in the hospital is working well in saving scarce hospital resources, and in treating only the most complicated cases. Mainly, however, it has allowed TBAs to attend uncomplicated deliveries and to refer only women with complications to hospitals. In another study, Alto and colleagues (1992) found that certain linguistic groups in the Southern Highlands of Papua New Guinea are unique in that there is no culturally established role for the TBA. Therefore, women deliver alone unattended. In one village (Angalheneng), 32 village midwives were trained in modern gynecological techniques to assist in childbirth—such training occurring at the local Government Health Center during the period 1981 to 1989. By 1989, their efforts had successfully contributed to lower infant and perinatal mortality rates in their community as compared with those of neighboring villages. Sparks (1990), on the other hand, undertook a study of the practices and attitudes of trained and untrained TBAs in Zimbabwe, a sub-Saharan African country with a population of 11.2 million people in 1995. The importance of TBAs is demonstrated in that they attend to more than 50 percent of all births, and are both health educators and health providers. Data obtained from midwives— through interviews and observation—reveal that those who attended the Government training course exhibit improved and safer practices (e.g. better hygiene), and refer more high-risk pregnant women to clinics or hospitals.

Problems faced by the Assistant Nurse-Midwife (ANM) program in Nepal are examined and some possible solutions offered (Justice, 1984; Pearson, 1987; Pigg, 1997). The program was initially instigated in response to national and international pressures to develop careers for Nepal's women, and was designed to train young women for service in rural areas. Traditional expectations of rural Nepalese concerning women, however, impaired the program's effectiveness. Specifically, it is culturally unacceptable in Nepal for females to travel and live alone as ANMs are expected to do. Implications for future planning issues in primary and health care are discussed. In particular, collaboration between anthropologists and planners could make programs such as ANM training successful if it were made more sensitive to local culture and social realities. In an interesting study of villages in the central highland (Anis) region of Yemen, Scheepers (1991) found no single term to indicate "midwife" or a category of women who had specialized knowledge and experience in assisting at childbirth. Instead, she found the term *jidda* was used as the appropriate Yemen Arabic referent for TBA. "*Jidda* literally means grandmother" (Scheepers, 1991: 959 and this volume). Apparently, any older woman who assists at deliveries—whether it be the mother or mother-in-law of the pregnant woman or an unrelated older woman—is referred to with the term *jidda*. It is important to recognize therefore, that if TBAs are to be trained in Yemen by the World Health Organization (WHO) or the Yemen Government, such training should not focus on one or two TBAs or *jidda*s in a village, but "perhaps a less sophisticated training should be directed to all women who have at least some experience in conducting deliveries" (Scheepers, 1991: 961 and this volume p.000-000). In an attempt to reduce the high incidence of infant mortality in the rural areas of Guatemala, the Guatemalan Ministry of Health has trained traditional midwives in the importance of accepting and adopting Western birthing practices as "scientific truths", and to dismissing indigenous beliefs and practices as "primitive superstitions" (Greenberg 1982). An examination of these midwife training programs in two rural areas of Guatemala revealed that the program has had difficulty in achieving this goal because it pays little attention to the Mayan traditional culture of childbirth, which is in some ways at odds with modern medical practices. Conflicts have, in fact, arisen—and many of the well intentioned health care programs have been ineffectual—because of the failure to reconcile the two co-existing but opposite systems: (1) the importation of Western medical techniques and knowledge in health care training programs; (2) the dismissal of indigenous beliefs and practices—involving such matters as herbs, baths, massage, cutting the umbilical cord and postpartum practices—as primitive superstitions. It is suggested that in order for any health intervention to be effective, a reconciliation between the two systems must be brought about.

Especially revealing in regard to the introduction of new midwifery training programs is the commentary by Jeffery *et al.* (1989) and Jeffery and Jeffery (1993) who focus on some of the negative assessments associated with current midwifery practices in the State of Uttar Pradesh in Northern India. These practices are considered to be responsible for the daily deaths of between 50 to 100 women from childbirth or related causes, and for the failure of 800 of 10,000 children born to survive one week. Furthermore, the mortality data serve as a justifiable argument for introducing training programs for TBAs. The authors, however, question the efficacy of this approach for this region. Their argument is culturally based. An examination of the statuses and roles of women in Northern India will reveal that they occupy subordinate and inferior positions in all institutionalized activities including property ownership, job function, marriage, and childbearing. Prior to childbirth, for example, the woman has little or no part in any discussion concerning the management of her pregnancy. During childbirth, crying out is considered shameful, and there are no remedies for reducing the experienced pain. After childbirth, the newly delivered mother is considered impure and must remain in the home of the in-laws untouched by her husband for several weeks. This subordination process is, however, best illustrated in the author's examination of the statuses and norms of the two females who play a role in the childbirth process. The overall management of the childbirth process is in the hands of the Senior Attendant (typically the mother-in-law or *sas*) who is represented in folklore as an "ogre" and is identified in ordinary conversation by the abusive term *susri*. The other assistant in childbirth is the *dai* who—even though called in 90 percent of the child delivery cases—is not regarded as a midwife in the Western sense, being regarded as a low-status, low-caste menial. The *dai* is called only when labor is well established. Overall, the *dai* has the demeaning task of internal examination to check dilation and the engagement of the head, and otherwise provide information about the progress of labor to the Senior Attendant—to whose authority the *dai* is always subject. The manner of payment further emphasizes their inferiority. Negotiations over fees are often abusive and promised payment is not always fulfilled. The typical *dai* is a landless, illiterate, and widowed older female who cannot support her children, and is untrained in midwifery. The authors argue that midwifery training programs are not the panacea for improving maternal and child mortality rates in this region, since the principal source of these problems can be found in the cultural norms associated with the subordinate status of women in general and childbearing women and those TBAs who serve them in particular. Specifically, since more *dai* are elderly any benefits from training them would be short-lived. Their low social standing, moreover, suggests they are not proper channels for the dissemination of general health information. Consequently, focusing on the *dai* represents an incorrect diagnosis of the problems to be remedied, as the main sources of maternal and child health inadequacies are not located here but in the lack of social and economic power that childbearing women have over their lives. Implicit in their conclusion is the assumption that unless there occurs a radical transformation and redefinition of the status system that Indian women occupy, introducing training programs for TBAs is futile and doomed to failure.

REFERENCES

Almasy, P. (1968), "Sudan's donkey-back midwives", *Today's Health* 46: 16-8 (January).

Alto, W.A., R.E. Alba & G. Irabo (1991), "An alternative to unattended delivery: training programme for village midwives in Papua New Guinea", *Social Science and Medicine* 32(5): 613-8.

Beeman, W.O., & A.K. Bhattacharyya (1978), "Toward an assessment of the social role of rural midwives and its implication for the family planning program: an Iranian case study", *Human Organization* 37(3): 295-300.

Chen, P.C.Y. (1973), "An analysis of customs related to childbirth in rural Malay culture" *Tropical & Geographic Medicine* 25: 197-204.

Chen, P.C.Y. (1981), "Traditional and modern medicine in Malaysia", *Social Science & Medicine* 15A: 127-36.

Cosminsky, S. (1977), "Childbirth and midwifery on a Guatemalan Finca", *Medical Anthropology* 1(3): 69-104.

Cosminsky, S.(1982), "Childbirth and change : A Guatemalan study", in C. MacCormack (ed.), *Ethnography of Fertility and Birth*, N.Y.: Academic Press, pp.205-29.

Edwards, N.C. (1989), "Traditional Mende society in Sierra Leone: a sociocultural basis for a quantitative research study", *Health Care for Women International* 10(1): 1-14.

Etzel, R.A. (1976, 1977), "The birth and development of midwifery, Liberian obstetrics" (two parts), *Journal of Nurse-Midwifery* 21(4): 24-37 and 22(1): 18-30.

Finerman, R. (1982), "Pregnancy and childbirth in Saraguro: implications for health care delivery in southern Ecuador", *Medical Anthropology* 6: 269-78 (Fall issue).

Flint, M. (1982), "Lockmi: An Indian midwife", in M.Kay (ed.), *Anthropology of Human Birth*, Philadelphia: F.A. Davis Co., pp.211-19.

Gann, T. (1918), *The Maya Indians of Southern Yucatan and Northern British Honduras*, Washington, D.C.: Smithsonian Institute, Bureau of American Ethnology, Bulletin No. 64.

Greenberg, L. (1982), "Midwife training programs in highland Guatemala", *Social Science & Medicine* 16: 1599-1609.

Janowitz, B. (1985), "Referrals by traditional birth attendants in Northeast Brazil" *American Journal of Public Health* 75: 745-48.

Jeffery, P., R. Jeffery & A. Lyon, eds. (1989), *Labour Pains and Labour Power: Women and Childbearing in India*, London: Zed Books.

Jeffery, R. & Jeffery, P. (1993), "Traditional birth attendants in rural north India", in S. Lindenbaum & M. Lock (eds.), *Knowledge, Power & Practice: the anthropology of medicine and everyday life*, Berkeley: University of California Press, pp.7-31.

Jordan B. (1978), *Birth in Four Cultures: A Crosscultural Investigation of Childbirth in Yucatan, Holland, Sweden and the United States*, (Series Editor: Sherri Clarkson), St. Albans, Vermont: EdenPress.

Jordan, B. (1989), Cosmopolitical obstetric: some insights from the training of traditional midwives, *Social Science & Medicine*, 28: 925-37

Jordan B. (1993), "Buscando la forma: an ethnography of contemporary Maya childbirth", pp.15-44 in *Birth in Four Cultures*, revised and expanded by Robbie Davis-Floyd, 4th edn, Prospect Heights, Illinois: Waveland Press.

Justice, J. (1984), "Can socio-cultural information improve health planning? A case study of Nepal's assistant nurse-midwife", *Social Science and Medicine* 19(3): 193-98.

Karim, W.J. (1984), "Malay midwives and witches", *Social Science & Medicine* 18(2): 159-66.

Laderman, C. (1982), "Giving birth in a Malay village", in M. Kay (ed.), *Anthropology of Human Birth*, Philadelphia: F.A. Davis Co., pp.81-99.

Laderman, C. (1983), "A baby is born in Merchang" pp.152-73 and 247-59 in *Wives and Midwives: Childbirth and Nutrition in Rural Malaysia*, Berkeley: University of California Press.

Kang-Wang, J.F. (1980), "The midwife in Taiwan: an alternative model for maternity care", *Human Organization* 39(1): 70-9.

Lee, R.P. (1981), "Chinese and western medical care in China's rural commune, a case study", *Social Science and Medicine* 15A: 137-48.

Lin, M.Y.W. (1987), "Will the role of the midwife disappear from Taiwan, Republic of China?" *Journal of Nurse-Midwifery* 32(1): 48-51.

Maglacas, A.M., & J.Simons (eds.) (1986), *The Potential of the Traditional Birth Attendant*, Geneva: World Health Organization.

McClain, C.S. (1975), "Ethno-obstetrics in Ajiic", *Anthropological Quarterly* 48(1): 38-56.

Morsy, S.A. (1982), "Childbirth in an Egyptian village", in M.Kay (ed.), *Anthropology of Human Birth*, Philadelphia: F.A. Davis Co., pp.147-74.

Moser, M.B. (1982), "Seri: From conception through infancy", in M. Kay (ed.), *Anthropology of Human Birth*, Philadelphia: F.A. Davis Co., pp.221-32.

Mutambirwa, J. (1985), "Pregnancy, childbirth, mother and child care among the indigenous people of Zimbabwe", *International Journal of Gynecology and Obstetrics* 23: 275-85.

O'Dempsey, T.J.D. (1988), "Traditional belief and practice among the Pokot people of Kenya with particular reference to mother and child health: 2. Mother and child health", *American Tropical Pediatrics* 8: 125.

Oyebola, D.D.O. (1980a), " The method of training traditional healers and midwives among the Yoruba of Nigeria", *Social Science & Medicine* 14A: 31-7.

Oyebola, D.D.O. (1980b), "Perinatal care by traditional healer-midwives of Nigeria", *International Journal of Gynecology and Obstetrics* 18(4): 295-9.

Paul, L. (1975), "Recruitment to a ritual role: the midwife in a Maya community", *Ethos* 3(3) 449-67.

Paul, L., & Paul, B. (1975), "The Maya midwife as sacred specialist", *American Ethnologist* 2: 707-26.

Pearson, M. (1987), "Old wives or young midwives? Women are caretakers of health: the case of Nepal", in J.H.Momsen & J.G.Townsend (eds), *Geography of Gender in the Third World*, Albany, N.Y.: State University of New York Press, pp.116-30.

Peng, J.Y. (1979), "The role of the traditional birth attendant in family planning in South-east Asia", *International Journal of Gynecology & Obstetrics*, 17: 108-13.

Pigg, S.L. (1997), "Authority in translation: finding, knowing, naming and training 'traditional birth attendants' in Nepal", in R.E.Davis-Floyd & C.F.Sargent (eds.), *Childbirth and Authoritative Knowledge: cross-cultural perspectives*, Berkeley CA: University of California Press, pp.233-262.

Reccio, D.M. (1986), "Birth traditions in the Philippines", pp. 66-74 in A.M. Maglacas & J. Simons (eds) *The Potential of the Traditional Birth Attendant* , Geneva: World Health Organization.

Rosenthal, M.M. (1981), "Political process and the integration of traditional and western medicine in the People's Republic of China", *Social Science & Medicine* 15A: 599-613.

Sargent, C. (1982), "Sociological and career attributes of midwives", pp. 56-85 and 175-85 in *The Cultural Context of Therapeutic Choice*, Dordrecht, Netherlands: D.Reidel Publishing Co.

Sargent, C. (1985), "Obstetrical choice among urban women in Benin", *Social Science & Medicine* 20(3): 287-92.

Schattuck, G.C. (1933), *The Peninsula of Yucatan : Medical, Biological, Meterological & Sociological Studies*, Washington, D.C.,: Carnegie Institute, Publication No.431.

Scheepers, L.M. (1991), "Jidda : the traditional midwife of Yemen", *Social Science & Medicine* 33(8): 959-62.

Sich, D. (1988), "Childbearing in Korea", *Social Science & Medicine* 27: 497.

Sparks, B. (1990), "A descriptive study of the changing roles and practices of traditional birth attendants in Zimbabwe", *Journal of Nurse-Midwifery* 35(3): 150-61.

Steggarda, M. (1941), *Mayan Indians of Yucatan*, Washington, D.C.: Carnegie Institute.

Steinberg, S. (1996), "Childbearing research: a transcultural review", *Social Science & Medicine* 43(12): 1765-84.

Villa Rojas, A. (1945), *The Maya of East Central Quintana Roo* (translated from Spanish), Washington D.C.: Carnegie Institute Publication No. 559.

Vincent-Priya, J. (1991), "A tradition of care: Traditional midwifery amongst the Minangkabau", pp.111-27 in *Birth Without Doctors, Conversations with Traditional Midwives*, London: Earthscan Publishing.

Zemor, O. (1988), "Midwives in Algeria", *World Health* (December issue), 15-6.

CHILDBIRTH AND CHANGE: A GUATEMALAN STUDY

S. Cosminsky [†]

As a life crisis, birth is not only a universal biological event, but also a culturally patterned process. Various rituals and symbols mark the transition from one phase of life to another for both mother and child. These birth practices are based on certain conceptions about the body and reflect values and themes of the culture. In many societies, a specialist or midwife is a pivotal figure in the birth system and serves as both a medical and a ritual specialist. The role of the midwife and many traditional birth-related practices are being influenced and changed in a variety of ways, especially through the spread of Western medicine, both through directed changes, such as midwifery training programmes, and undirected changes, as through radio advertisements.

This chapter will discuss the beliefs and practices surrounding childbirth in two areas of Guatemala, a highland village and a lowland plantation, and the changes that are occurring in them under the impact of Western medicine. As in many parts of the world, birth is a heavily ritualized process. Viewing ritual as a symbolic code communicating certain aspects of ideology and social structure (Douglas, 1966; Firth, 1973; Turner, 1967), some of the rituals and practices will be analysed in terms of the underlying values and social relationships that they symbolize.

RESEARCH SETTING

Data was collected through participant observation and interviewing in the community of Chuchexic, a rural district or *aldea* of the town of Santa Lucia Utatlán in the western highlands of Guatemala, and the surrounding hamlets, and on a lowland sugar and coffee *finca* (plantation), Finca San Felipe (a pseudonym) located on the Pacific lowlands of Guatemala.[1] Interviews and observations were with midwives and medical personnel conducting midwifery training programmes, as well as with mothers.

Chuchexic and its surrounding hamlets have a population of approximately 1600 and the whole town or *municipio* of Santa Lucia has a population of 7742 (1973 census). Approximately 96% of the inhabitants of Chuchexic are Quiché-speaking Mayan Indians; the rest are Ladinos.[2] The Indians are primarily subsistence farmers cultivating maize as the staple crop. They supplement their incomes by growing wheat as a cash crop and engaging in wage labour, especially on coastal plantations. The Ladinos are landowners, entrepreneurs, or wage labourers. The Indians live mainly in dispersed households in the rural *aldeas*, whereas the Ladinos mostly live in the town centre. The majority of Indians are Catholic. However, they are split into two groups: one is a reformed Catholicism which centres around the Catholic Action movement and the other is a syncretic form based on sixteenth century Catholicism and Mayan Indian influences. This latter includes the use of the Mayan ritual calendar and shamans, worship of *El Mundo*, the

[†] Department of Anthropology, Rutgers University, Camden College of Arts & Sciences, Camden, New Jersey, USA. Permission granted Harcourt Brace and Co. Ltd. Copyright S. Cosminsky (1982), "Childbirth and Change: A Guatemalan Study," In C. MacCormack (ed.) *Ethnography of Fertility and Birth*, New York, Academic Press: pp.205-29.

essence or spirit of the earth, and *Aire*, the air, combined with the worship of God, Jesus, Mary, and the Saints. There is also a handful of Protestant or Evangelical converts.

Finca San Felipe is a coffee and sugar plantation with a population of about 690. The adults and older children are wage labourers as well as landless agriculturalists. Men work for cash most of the year, in sugar or coffee production, and women and older children work seasonally at picking coffee and drying sugar cane. The entire family participates in the cultivation of corn and beans on small plots of land provided by the finca owner.

The finca population is of mixed heritage, consisting mainly of second or third generation Indian migrants from different towns in the Western highlands. Approximately two-thirds of the population classify themselves as Indians, the remainder as Ladinos, who originally came from the nearby coastal towns. Many of the Indians are "ladinoized"—i.e. speak Spanish and wear Western dress. Only a few older people still speak Quiché or one of the Indian languages, but many still wear the Indian skirt (*corte*) and retain various Indian cultural traits, including certain birth and curing practices.

In both locations, over 90% of the births take place at home, attended by a local indigenous or "empirical" midwife. There are several midwives in Chuchexic, but only one at present on the finca. A few women give birth in the hospital, those from Chuchexic going to the departmental capital of Sololá, and those from the finca going to Retalhuleu, but these are usually either for complications, for sterilisation, or they are women of higher socio-economic status. There is a Catholic mission clinic in Chuchexic run by nuns, at least one of whom is a nurse-midwife. They run a prenatal clinic and they have given a midwifery training course (Cosminsky, 1978). They also assist in cases of complications and drive emergencies to the hospital in Sololá.

The midwives represent varying degrees of traditionalism, acculturation and Western training, ranging from a traditional Mayan midwife with no Western training to those, both Indian and Ladino, who have attended a midwifery training course and received an official licence (Cosminsky, 1977, n.d.). Despite these differences between Ladino and Indian contexts and the lowland and highland environments, many basic concepts and practices concerning childbirth are shared. These concepts include: (a) the midwife as a ritual, as well as obstetrical specialist, (b) the location and movement of organs, (c) the hot-cold theory, and (d) the influence of emotions and social relations on the body. Differences will be indicated only when they are meaningful to this study.

THE MIDWIFE

The indigenous Mayan midwife is regarded as an obstetrical and ritual specialist (Paul, 1975). She is called an *iyom* or *ilonel* in Quiché and *comadrona* in Spanish. The traditional path of recruitment is through supernatural calling. This destiny or *mandado* is revealed in various ways, such as through birth signs and omens, dreams, illness and finding strange objects (shells, scissors, special shaped stones and mirrors). The dreams and signs are interpreted by a diviner or shaman as signifying her destiny as a midwife, and the objects are considered messages sent by the supernatural (God or the spirits). One midwife had found a red and white mirror when she was young, in which she saw the face of a white-haired woman. This was interpreted as being Santa Ana, the patronness of childbirth, and the red was said to symbolize the fire of the sweatbath. If a person does not follow one's calling, she shall suffer supernatural sanctions in the form of illness or death either to herself or members of her family (Cosminsky, n.d.).

Even midwives who do not subscribe to the belief of the supernatural or divine recruitment, such as the Ladino midwives, believe they receive supernatural assistance. They pray to God, to the spirits of the dead midwives (*Comadronas invisibles*), Mary and Saint Ann for the protection of their clients and for assistance. According to the midwives, these spirits tell them if the birth is normal or not, how to massage, what to do if the baby is not in a correct position and what herbs and medicines to use. During a birth, they are accompanied by these spirits.

As part of the process of becoming a midwife, she may have repetitive dreams, such as having babies in her arms and lap, which are interpreted by a shaman as being a sign of her calling. She continues to have special dreams throughout her practice. One midwife said that if she dreams that a man arrives and leaves money in her hand, a boy will be born, and if she finds a shawl or napkin, a girl will be born. Another midwife said she dreams that she is hurrying on a road out of breath, which portends an imminent birth.

Bodily movements, such as twitches or tremblings are also felt. Some midwives said they feel a movement, like air, in the hand or some other part of the body when someone is going to come to call for a birth. If it's in the left hand, the birth will be delayed, and if the right, it will be quick. These bodily manifestations, such as dreams, twitches, and sickness, are regarded as messages from God or the spirits. Supernatural forces are constantly manifested throughout the midwife's body. The body is sacred and is not separated by a boundary from the moral, social, and supernatural context, but is constantly permeated by these influences.

These signs validate the midwife's status as a ritual specialist. She can interpret various signs and omens and mediate between her client and the spiritual world for a safe birth. The supernatural validation also may increase her own confidence and consequently her patient's, and help allay anxieties about birth. In addition to the claim of a supernatural source of knowledge, several of the midwives had been apprenticed to other midwives.

The midwife both in Santa Lucia and on Finca San Felipe is usually an older woman (40 years of age or older) with much prestige and highly respected for her skills, which may be both obstetrical and ritual. In fact, in Santa Lucia, at least four midwives were over 70 years old. Respect is manifested in forms of deference, such as terms of address, kissing of the hand, formalised requests for her aid, godparent relationships and gifts of food and drink. There is also a special bond of respect between the midwife and the children whom she has delivered, who greet her with bowed head and kiss her hand.

Several of the traditional midwives have had training courses given by the Public Health Ministry. The courses were given in Spanish in the departmental capital with an interpreter to translate into Quiché. The success of these programmes and the communication problems involved remain to be evaluated. The training, whether in 1952, the year one of the midwives in Santa Lucia took the course or in 1978, stressed the same things: the importance of asepsis and washing the hands, disinfecting the instruments, the use of the horizontal delivery position, the limitations of the midwife and the recognition of complications which she should refer to the nearest doctor or hospital. Most of the traditional practices were condemned, including the use of herbs, the sweatbath and the kneeling or squatting delivery position (Cosminsky, 1978). The nurses in the mission clinic in Chuchexic have offered a course for new midwives (whereas the public health training course is mainly for already practicing midwives). The official licence and training is offered as an alternative to the divine mandate, opening up the role to others who want to practice. It also marks the increasing secularisation of the role. The acquisition of Western medical training and a licence raises one's status, especially if added to one's supernatural mandate. The licence seems to be more important for some of the younger mothers, who mentioned they chose one midwife over another because the former had her licence. It is not clear, however, to what extent the licence alone without supernatural validation confers status to a midwife.

The midwife provides antenatal care, management of labour, and postnatal care, for which she usually charges a $5 or $6 fee. The practices associated with each of these stages will now be described.

ANTENATAL CARE

Antenatal care begins when the mother-in-law or husband requests the midwife to visit the patient, usually between the fifth and seventh month, earlier if it is a primipara. Among the Mayans, the request is made in a formal ritualised language, presenting a gift of food for the midwife and 10¢ or 25¢ for candles and incense for Saint Ann and other saints and spirits to bless the client. The midwife visits and examines the client every 20 or 30 days during the early months and every week during the last month. Before each visit, the traditional midwife prays and burns incense in front of the sweatbath. She asks for help from God, the spirits of orphans, widows, doctors and midwives, and thanks El Mundo, the spirit of the Earth, Aire, the spirit of the wind, and Santa Ana, San Augustin and Santa Christina, all of whom aid her in making the patient's delivery successful. At the house of her client, she says an "Our Father", and "In the name of the Father, the Son and the Holy Ghost", making the sign of the cross. One of the Protestant Ladina midwives also stresses the importance of prayer. "I have to help a person because God helps me. I don't believe in anyone, only my God, no doctor, because God is my doctor ..."

The midwife first looks for bodily changes that signify pregnancy, including the colour of the nipples, the size and shape of the breast, and the swelling and height of the abdomen. One midwife said she can also tell by the woman's eyes, which have an empty (huero) or different look. The most important aspects of prenatal care are the examination for the foetal position, palpation and massage of the abdominal area. The midwife gently but firmly massages the abdominal area, moving her hands in opposite directions across the abdomen and along the sides. The massage is believed to help promote an easier birth. Sometimes she also massages the calves and thighs, which is supposed to prevent cramps or problems with the legs. It is believed that the foetus should be in an upright position until the last month, when it turns around. During the examination, she attempts to manipulate the foetus by external version if she feels the baby is not in a correct position. She also estimates when the baby is due. Some midwives say that they can tell whether the baby will be a boy or girl, depending on its position to the right or left side, the height of the abdomen and the pigmentation markings on the mother's face. If the woman gets dark markings on her face, which are considered to be caused by the strength of the baby's blood, the baby will be a boy. There is no internal examination nor listening to the baby's heartbeat.

Women continue working their daily chores throughout pregnancy. It is believed that if she exercises and works, the baby will not be too large, whereas if the mother sleeps too much, the baby may grow too big and cause a difficult delivery. However, she must take care while washing clothes and she should not lift heavy objects. She should not pass over a lasso or sew with a long thread, or the baby will be born with the cord over its neck.

Special care should be taken by the mother during pregnancy, since the woman and foetus are in a physically and spiritually weak state, and thus more susceptible to illness and evil forces. One of the most profound influences on the body is believed to be the degree of "hot" or "cold". As in many parts of Spanish America, foods, herbs, medicines, illnesses and bodily states are classified into categories of hot and cold. These are regarded as innate qualities of substances, often judged by the effect they have on the body or from exposure to sun, water, or physical temperature. A healthy body is one which is in balance; illness is due to excess of hot or cold within the body. Treatment is based on a principle of opposition (Cosminsky, 1975).

A pregnant woman is considered to be in a very hot state, partially because of the accumulated blood in her body. Blood is classified as hot. Therefore, care must be taken to avoid certain foods or medicines that might cause an excess of either quality, harming either her or the foetus. Her excess heat makes her vulnerable to attacks of cold, and too great a contrast, as well as too much of one quality, is considered dangerous. Very cold foods include beans, pork, avocados, certain greens, sodas (Coca Cola, Fanta) and sometimes includes eggs. One midwife said that if a pregnant woman eats eggs or "cold" greens, she would swell from *aire* (air or gas). Other midwives said that the restrictions really depend on the health of the mother and that prenatally, she can eat everything unless she is sick. For example, if a woman has colic or *aire*, which are cold illnesses, she should not eat greens, eggs, or beans since these cold foods will make her worse. She should eat and drink items considered as neutral or "hot", but also avoid very hot substances such as chilli). The midwives generally tell their clients they should eat "alimentos", which are locally defined as nourishing foods (Cosminsky, 1975), but also support the belief they should not eat very cold foods, especially if they have a cold illness. Other food proscriptions have a metaphorical or sympathetic basis, such as restrictions against eating "twinned" fruits, like the *chayote* (Sechium edule), to avoid having twins, or rabbit meat, to avoid having multiple births. There is a wide variation concerning the extent to which the restrictions are followed and they are more relevant if the mother is ill. Many of these restrictions remain ideal rules and are not actually followed by everyone. Dietary restrictions are emphasized more in the postpartum period.

Because poor nutritional status is a common problem among pregnant and lactating women (McGuire, 1976),[3] these dietary restrictions are attacked in the midwifery training programmes and midwives are told that the patient could and should eat everything. The programmes, however, could utilize the accepted practices and add foods that fit into the belief system, e.g. chicken soup and greens classified as hot, rather than try to change the beliefs. Furthermore, the principle of neutralization can be used as an accommodation, that is, mixing a cold food or medicine with a hot one or vice versa to make it more acceptable (Harwood, 1971). The medical personnel should determine the relevancy of the hot-cold classification. Treatment and advice will be more likely if it is communicated within the midwives and mothers' tradition and with respect for such beliefs.

Physical temperature is also considered critical in maintaining a hot-cold equilibrium state. A pregnant woman should not bathe in cold water late in the day or too often in one day, or else the baby will be born with a cold, or the mother might have pains. They also say that going in the river may cause knots in the legs, leg cramps, or rheumatism, and cold water may cause the mother to swell. The woman should also be careful when washing her hair that she does not get cold. This problem is more critical on the finca, where women wash themselves in the river and put their legs in the water when washing clothes, whereas in Santa Lucia, they usually bathe in the sweatbath and kneel on the riverbank or rocks when they wash clothes in the river.

People report having pregnancy cravings. If these are not satisfied, the child might be miscarried. Several mothers retroactively attributed the cause of their miscarriages to such unfulfilled cravings. Cravings are considered desires of the foetus and are usually for fruit or special meats, earth, salt, or special clay tablets called "Pan de Señor". Nevertheless, the midwives say that the pregnant woman should not eat salt or earth, since these will "cut the blood" and make the woman swell (cause edema). Earth eating, however, does seem to be a relatively common practice according to the midwives, although only a specific type of earth called *tashkal* is eaten. Since too much salt does cause water retention and edema, and the earth may contain parasites, this restriction is a beneficial one.

A pregnant woman must avoid exposure to eclipses, which is believed to cause cleft palate, harelip, other infant deformities or stillbirths. On the finca some anacephalic stillbirths were attributed to the mothers' exposure to an eclipse. It is believed that an eclipse results when the sun or moon is "eaten" and that a part of the foetus will similarly be eaten. For prevention, Mayan women are supposed to wear a piece of metal or iron nails in the form of a cross, or a red cloth around the stomach (Saquic, 1973: 101).

Although a pregnant woman is in a weak and vulnerable state, she is also a source of danger to others. Because of her heated state she can give the "evil eye" to infants and young animals (Cosminsky, 1976). In most cases, the evil eye is unintentional.

Children are highly valued and are a primary means of status and respect. According to some of the midwives, sterility may be caused by a "cold womb" which consequently does not receive the semen. One treatment is to warm the womb in the sweatbath and administer "hot" herbal teas. However, if the sterility is caused by God, the midwife cannot cure it.

Strong emotions, such as anger, fright and sadness can cause illness under ordinary circumstances, and should be particularly avoided during pregnancy and the postnatal period. Several types of complications were attributed by the midwives to the mother having suffered "anger" (*enojos* or *colera*). These problems included premature birth, miscarriage, stillbirths, retained placenta, cold or insufficient milk and a sickly baby. One midwife attributed her own sickly childhood and life to fright (*susto*) her mother had suffered during an earthquake while pregnant with her. Another woman said her baby was weak and sickly because of the fright and sadness she suffered from her father-in-law's death. He was run over by a car when she was three months pregnant. Other causes involve conflicts or beatings by a drunk or aggressive husband, which either cause the foetus to have fright (*susto*) and be stillborn, miscarried, or born prematurely (Cosminsky, 1977).

Emotions and the social relations they stem from can influence the body at any time. Anger is not supposed to be expressed openly. Excess bile is thought to be produced by anger and unless the emotion is resolved body functioning will be impaired. When a pregnant woman is frightened or angry she should go to the midwife for herbal teas with "hot" or "cold" properties, and be massaged to restore the body's equilibrium. Douglas has suggested that controlling the body is an expression of social control (1973: 70). In this case, the woman herself is to blame for being angry and endangering her unborn child, not her husband for abusing her. Because the unborn child is endangered by the mother's anger and fright—by her lack of self-control—the woman is socially subordinated to her husband who may lose self-control through drunkenness with relative impunity. These cultural definitions enlist the midwife as an unwitting agent of social control. By working to overcome the risk caused by a woman's emotions she acquiesces to the prevailing definitions of social roles. Not only is an imbalance of emotions and social relations expressed in definitions of dangerous body states, but the crisis of a state such as threatened miscarriage is a stimulus for restoring normal social relations (Manning and Fabrega, 1973: 269).

MANAGEMENT OF LABOUR AND DELIVERY

When labour begins, the midwife is summoned. Delivery takes place in the mother's home. The midwife says a prayer when she arrives, palpates the woman's abdomen, examines the position of the baby, and looks for the signs of imminent birth. These are the breaking of the sac, the intensity and frequency of contractions, the position of the baby's head, and the heat, flushing and sweating of the woman. Massaging may be done during labour if the woman is having much pain. This takes the form of downwards movement on the dorsal and frontal sides. According to the nurses in the clinic in Chuchexic, the midwives do not distinguish the different stages of labour and have the woman push too early.

The woman usually delivers in a kneeling position, with the midwife catching the baby from behind. Sometimes she may squat and hold on to a rope. If the husband is present, he is expected to help by holding and supporting the woman, a duty that is intended to teach him what women have to suffer through. The mother or mother-in-law or other female relatives may also be present. The midwifery training courses stress the horizontal (lithotomy or supine) delivery position, as based on American and European obstetrical practices, and discourage the traditional one. In one course, the trainees were told not to use the traditional position because the baby might hit its head on the floor possibly causing brain damage. The probability of this occurring should be questioned.

The manual for training midwives issued by the Guatemalan Ministry of Public Health advises the midwife to arrange the mother in a semi-sitting or physiological position that is most in agreement with the cultural patterns. However, when the dilation is complete, ask the woman to bend her legs, with feet resting on the bed, grasping her ankles, and to push softly. This is accompanied by a picture of a woman lying on her back with her shoulders slightly raised by a pillow, knees bent and feet on the bed—thus reinforcing the idea that the horizontal position is best. The use of the supine position has been recently questioned (Haire, 1972). Although it is easier for the obstetrician or midwife to see, it may be more difficult for the mother and child because it is against gravity and may promote interference. (For a more detailed discussion: cf. Cosminsky, 1977). Care should be taken in the programmes not to eliminate a beneficial practice in favour of one which may be less advantageous and even potentially harmful.

The midwife may also administer remedies—herbal teas if the labour is difficult or delayed. These teas include the root of the *acuzena* (Lilium longiflorum), or *kispar* (Petiveria allionacea), or *pimpinela* (Poterium sanguisorba) mixed with clove and cinnamon. The midwife on the finca also adds oregano, or nine leaves of *Flor de Pascuas* (poinsettias), nine avocado leaves, and 20 drops of *esencia maravillosa*, a liquid made from alcohol and extracts of several herbs sold in the pharmacies. All these herbs are classified as "hot" ones. According to Saquic (1973: 10) the Indians in Santa Lucia attribute difficult births to the misbehaviour of the wife, who has to confess. She is given a candle and asks the pardon of God. If this does not help, she is given a drink of oil or yolk of one or two eggs. If she still has trouble, the midwife tells the husband to take off a sandal or shoe and hit the woman three times with it on her back saying that she is forgiven for whatever bad she has done.

The umbilical cord is usually not cut until after the placenta is expelled. If the cord is cut before, it is believed that the child might die, and the placenta might rise up in the woman's body and cause her to choke. If the placenta is retained and the cord must be cut, it is tied to the woman's leg so it will not rise, until she is taken to the nearest doctor or hospital. Some midwives give the woman a little bit of cooking oil to drink which is to help the placenta slide out. Others put the woman's braid or two fingers in her mouth to make her gag and cause contractions to expel the delayed placenta. The body is perceived as a tube in which organs can be displaced or move up and down.

The placenta is thought to have a special relationship to the child and can affect its future. Consequently, proper disposal is necessary. In both Santa Lucia and on the finca, the placenta is burned and the ashes buried. Care must be taken so that dogs will not unearth it, as this will harm the child. Proper disposal is supposed to assure that the person will not wander from his village when an adult.

The courses for traditional midwives teach that one can cut the cord before the placenta is expelled. However, if the cord is cut before it stops pulsing, crucial blood is cut off from the baby, and thus the traditional practice is of some benefit. Medical personnel, however, feel that the midwives wait too long to cut the cord.

Some of the traditional methods for cutting and dressing the cord, such as cauterising the cord with a candle flame or hot blade have been criticised by medical personnel, who teach the midwives to disinfect the scissors and use alcohol on the cord. Since cauterising the cord also leaves it sterile, there is no reason why it should be condemned. One nurse said that the candle wax might be dirty, and that's why the practice was harmful. Some midwives have combined the practices, first cauterising the cord and then using the alcohol and mertiolate (Cosminsky, 1977).

The cord is examined for various signs, which the midwife, as a ritual specialist, has the knowledge and power to interpret. The number of lumps or markings symbolise how many children the woman will have. Round lumps signify girls and long ones males. The distance between the markings indicates the birth interval. For example, if the marks are two fingers apart, the interval will be two years. If the cord is short or smooth the mother will not have any more children. If a baby is born in a sac or with a caul, the child may become a transforming witch or *characotel* unless it is removed properly from behind and then burned. Pieces of the sac on the baby indicate certain types of predestined birth, including that of a midwife (Paul, 1975, reports similar beliefs in San Pedro la Laguna). The degree to which these beliefs are held vary among the midwives and mothers. Some maintain certain ones while doubting or being sceptical of others.

One midwife said that the pieces of the veil or sac are put there by the midwife herself. With more Western training and less belief in the supernatural power and destiny of the midwife, one can expect a decline in the persistence of these signs and omens, and thus attenuation in this aspect of the ritual role of the midwife.

On the finca, the midwife said that the stump of the cord should be put in a covered jar and saved after it falls off. If the baby is a male, sometimes the cord is put in a tree, so that he will be able to climb when he gets older; if a female, it is put under the hearth so she will do her household duties.

After the birth, the midwife on the finca washes the blood-stained clothes of the mother in the river. This was part of the traditional role of the midwife in some areas of Guatemala. The finca midwife said that she now washes the clothes only if the woman has no other female relatives to help her, because she feels sorry for her. In one of the observed review classes for midwives, the nurse told the midwives not to wash the clothes. She said that the *only* thing the midwife should do is assist with the birth. She should not wash clothes, nor help prepare meals (as some midwives do), nor give medicine. These should not be part of the midwives' duties. If she does such chores, she should charge extra. Some of the nurses complained that untrained midwives charge less and also wash the clothes, thus undercutting them. The nurse defined the midwife's role according to the Western biomedical system as a strictly obstetrical one, but the traditional role is an expanded role, part of a support system that includes social, ritual and psychological components.

POSTPARTUM CARE

In Santa Lucia, the postpartum confinement period is 20 days. The 20-day period is equal to one month of the ancient Mayan ritual calendar. Although the mother can work after 20 days, she should not have sexual relations for 40 days following the birth. This *cuarentena* probably derives from Spanish influence (Foster, 1960: 5). On Finca San Felipe, the confinement period is eight days, during which the woman must rest. In each case, the actual number of days and activities of the woman varies according to her physical and nutritional condition, the number of female relatives to assist her and her socio-economic status. The midwife visits the mother every few days during this confinement period to examine and change the dressing on the cord of the baby and to massage the mother. Usually warmed cooking oil or olive oil, or a commercial preparation such as Pomada Valencia is used. Medicated plaster, such as Hazel Menthol may be applied afterwards.

The body is perceived as a tube in which the various parts (organs, veins, bones etc.) may become displaced and lead to illness or complications. The massage is said to return the uterus to its proper place and size and relieve postpartum pains. Fallen uterus is considered by the midwives to be the most common postpartum problem. Some of the midwives also massage the legs, downwards from the thighs and upwards from the calves, for "distended nerves" which can cause pains in the mother's legs and to prevent problems with the veins. The bones of the birth canal are believed to open when the child is born. In order to close the bones, as well as to keep the womb in place, an abdominal binder is then tied below the navel, pushing the abdomen upwards. The physical contact and focus of attention involved in these practices also provides emotional and social support to the mother.

Medical personnel have expressed concern about the massaging being too hard and thus dangerous. They have also discouraged the use of the binder in the hospitals and the training programmes. An understanding of the way these practices are linked to perceptions of the body, as mentioned above, and of their possible beneficial effects (Harrison, 1977) might enable them to adapt the practices in a more compatible manner and thus be more effective. For example, gentle massage might be suggested rather than trying to persuade midwives to give up their practice of massage. The abdominal binder could still be used, but not tied too tightly, and be phrased in terms compatible with the midwives' beliefs.

The mother is in a cold state after the birth and must take proper precautions. Certain dietary restrictions are advised during the confinement period, the most common one being the avoidance of "cold" foods, similar to the restriction during pregnancy. However, they seem to be regarded as more important postnatally because they are thought to cut the mother's milk or make it cold and consequently make the nursing baby ill. Special foods are recommended such as chicken soup, bananas and *atole* (a maize gruel), and "hot" foods (but not too hot like chilli). Relatives, godparents and neighbours visit the woman during this transitional period and bring these foods which are considered good for giving strength and good for lactation. One midwife, however, said that if the woman or child does not have any illness, she can eat everything. "If she eats *alimentos*, she will have good milk and good health." If the child is sick, however, the mother should avoid eating cold things because they make the child worse. She must only wash in warm water and avoid cold baths and cold water, which will make the milk turn cold and watery. The mother's head should be covered with a scarf for 10-15 days and her shoulders covered with a shawl or sweater to prevent getting *aire* (air) and turning the milk cold. Some women expressed anxiety about hospital deliveries because they said they could not keep their head and shoulders covered the way they thought necessary and that the hospital food was not compatible with dietary restrictions.

The midwife administers herbal teas as remedies for postpartum pains, usually made from a mixture of "hot" herbs, such as *artemisia*, *pimpinela* (Poterium sanguisorba), oregano and white honey. One midwife said she no longer uses herbs since she had the training course, because she was told not to use them. The use of herbs at any state in the birth process is condemned by Western medical personnel, based on the assumption that the midwife is ignorant of the effects of the herbs, and some of them may be effective and therefore dangerous if given too large a dosage. However, since some of these plants may have beneficial effects, investigation and analyses should be made of these herbs. The herbal knowledge is being gradually lost and the newly trained midwives are more familiar with patent medicines instead. The traditional midwives say they learn the herbs through dreams or visions, although they may also learn through apprenticeship with another midwife. The decline in the use of herbs and the loss of this knowledge represents an attenuation of the midwife's role resulting from her attempt to adapt to modern medicine, on which she is becoming increasingly dependent.

The application of heat is emphasised, especially in the postnatal period. This may take the form of a sweatbath, among the Indians in Santa Lucia, a sitz bath (*bajo*) as among the Ladinos, or a herbal bath, as on the finca. The heat is believed to help restore the bodily balance. The midwives say that the bath increases the flow of milk, "lowers" the milk into the breasts, prevents it from becoming "cold", protects the woman from *aire*, eases afterbirth pains and promotes healing.

Traditionally, the woman takes a sweatbath every three or four days, during which she is massaged by the midwife. The sweatbath (Quiché: *tuj*; Spanish: *temascal*) is a small adobe structure located adjacent to the house. Inside, rocks are heated and water thrown on top to make steam. The person sits on a wooden board inside the *temascal*. Branches from the plant *kewuj* (*Corepsis mutica*) are used to beat and drive the steam towards the woman. The sweatbath usually lasts about a half hour. One midwife said she gives the first sweatbath on the third day, but not very hot and only for cleaning, not for a massage. On the eighth day, she takes the sweatbath again, making it hotter and massages the woman. She used to visit every 3 or 4 days, but now does it once a week during the 20-day period. The bath provides ritual as well as physical cleansing, since the blood from the birth is regarded as polluting. It also gives emotional and psychological support to the mother. However, the frequency and use of the sweatbath varies and is declining. One of the traditional Mayan midwives said "the sweatbath is my medicine", whereas others do not use it at all. One midwife takes the woman into the sweatbath but only bathes her. She massages her afterwards inside the house and bathes the child in warm water rather than in the sweatbath. Another midwife said that before she received the Public Health training course, she used to enter the sweatbath, but then she was told not to. When she first visits a pregnant woman now, she explains that she will not go into the sweatbath with the woman. Usually the woman will then take a sweatbath herself before the midwife's visit and the midwife will massage her in the home. One of the Ladino midwives also does not use the sweatbath because it gives her a headache and makes her legs bad, although the mothers want it. She said she is not used to it since it is an Indian rather than a Ladino custom. Instead, she uses a vapour bath in which the woman sits over a basin or bucket of hot water containing several herbs, covers herself and lets the steam enter from below.

The sweatbath has been discouraged by official medical personnel. In one observed review class, the nurse giving the course mentioned that some untrained midwives still used the sweatbath, but she did not believe that anyone in the room used if for their patients. The manner and tone of the statement was mocking and condemnatory. The nurse did not give any explanation at that point of why it should not be used, so I asked. The nurse in turn asked the midwives. One Ladino midwife who had never used it said she had heard about a midwife who had an attack and fainted inside the sweatbath with her patient, and that was why it was dangerous. The nurse then said that the sweating might cause dehydration and thus fainting. Other nurses told me they believed the sweatbath was debilitating and promoted hemorrhaging. How often such dehydration occurs is unknown. The nurse also said that the person might catch pneumonia from the sharp change in temperature if they go outside after the sweatbath. Ironically, the nurse is expressing agreement with the folk theory of illness causation, which attributes an illness like pneumonia to sharp or extreme contrasts of hot and cold. In actuality, people take great care to stay inside, covered up, after taking a sweatbath. To my knowledge, no studies have been made concerning these supposedly harmful effects of the sweatbath, nor of any possible beneficial effects, such as stimulation of blood circulation, milk flow, relaxing muscles, promotion of healing, preventing infection and easing soreness. The effects depend on the intensity, length and frequency of the sweatbaths, and the condition of the woman. Modifications could be suggested in these ways, rather than complete condemnation. Further research should be done in this area.

On the finca, a herbal bath is given on the third day and the eighth day. Until this bath, the woman is not supposed to do any household activities. The herbs used in the bath are "hot" herbs. These are Santa Maria (*Piper sp.*), *guaruma* (*Cercopia peltata*), *ciguapate* (*Pluchea odorata*) and *siguinai* (*Vernonia sp.*). The herbs are put in a bucket of hot water. A handful of the heated herbs are placed under the woman for her to sit on, some are placed in front of the vaginal area, and some under her feet. The feet are considered vulnerable points of entry for *aire* or wind. The midwife rubs the mother's back and breasts with a handful of the herbs as she is bathing her with the hot water. One of the main functions of the bath is to warm and lower the breast milk. One woman became quite anxious when the bath was delayed because the midwife had been called elsewhere. She was concerned about the condition of her milk and the restrictions on her activity. After she was bathed, the midwife made her squeeze out some of the milk first, saying that the milk would still be cold because the herbs had not yet taken effect.

After the bath, the midwife massages the woman and puts on an abdominal binder. On the finca, the bath is repeated on the eighth day, which marks the end of the midwife's duties and mother's seclusion. In Santa Lucia, the last sweatbath is on the twentieth day, at which time a special ritual feast is held, called *elesan xe ch'at* or "taking out from under the bed" (Saquic, 1973: 104).

ELESAN XE CH'AT—A POSTPARTUM RITUAL

At the end of the 20-day period of confinement, a ritual celebration and feast are held. Preparations usually begin the previous day and continue to the day of the celebration. The woman's female relatives (mother, mother-in-law, sisters, sisters-in-law, and some aunts and nieces) help grind the maize, make the *tamalitas* and cook the meat and soup. The male relatives (father, father-in-law, brothers and brothers-in-law) fetch the firewood, cover the floor with pine needles, set up the benches and tables and serve drinks. The couple is responsible for providing the food and drinks.

When the midwife arrives, she goes into the kitchen area and is served some bread and coffee. Later she is given drinks and a serving of the ritual meal. Sometimes the midwife gives the woman a sweatbath first, after which she massages the woman. In one case, the midwife massaged the woman "because she had heat in her stomach". Usually, the abdominal binder is removed at this time. Previously, all the garbage from whatever the woman ate during the twenty days, such as maize husks from the *tamalitas* and chicken bones, was thrown under the bed. One informant said this is no longer done because it is unhealthy and people know better today. They still observe the ritual cleaning and sweeping, however.

The midwife cleans out the sweatbath, removing the ashes and rubbish that have collected during the postpartum period, and puts them in a basket or bowl, lined with leaves. The husband buries this in the nearby maizefield. While cleaning out the sweatbath, the midwife crosses herself before and after. She lights two candles of wax or tallow on a piece of inverted clay tile, burns some incense and coral and sprinkles white roses on the place in the sweatbath where the fire is lit. She offers these in prayer to Santa Ana, patronness of the sweatbath and pregnant women, saying:

Now they have completed the twenty days, pardon me. I do not have anything to give you, only this bit of candle, this bit of incense. Make use of it, then pardon me. Perhaps I had it in garbage or filth, pardon me, señora, pardon me; it is my blame. You cleansed us. You polished us during the twenty days. You took away all dirtiness. Nothing happened to us. We are all well. The child is with good health and the mother is with good health. Thank you very much.

She also says two "Hail Mary's" and two "Our Fathers", crosses herself and kisses the ground to *El Mundo*, the spirit of the Earth, "who gives us food and life". One midwife who has converted to Protestantism does not make the offerings, but she does clean out the ashes from the sweatbath. The Ladino midwife does not perform the ceremony at all.

The midwife then goes into the room where the woman's bed is, takes off all the bed coverings and blankets and shakes them out. Meanwhile, she crosses herself, prays and says the name of the baby. She dusts off all the boards of the bed with some branches and leaves. She takes the middle board off, and taps the other bedboards with the edge, in the sign of a cross, repeating the name of the newborn baby. She then sweeps out all the pine needles and rubbish from under the bed. This is burned and buried together with the ashes from the sweatbath. Variation exists in the extent to which this ritual is carried out. One midwife reversed the order, cleaning the bed out first and then the sweatbath; another cleaned out the sweatbath, swept under the bed, but did not clean the bed or bedclothes. The Ladino midwife cleans neither the sweatbath, bed, or bedroom, instead, she gives the woman a purgative on the twentieth day.

As suggested in an earlier paper (Cosminsky, 1976), the ritual cleaning of the bed and the sweatbath may be a symbolic acting out of the cleaning referred to in the prayer. The ritual marks the status transition from an "unclean" state to a condition of "cleanliness". As the sweatbath and its patronness, Santa Ana, have "cleansed" the woman, so does the midwife clean the sweatbath and the bed. Blood (which is regarded as polluting), bodily wastes and left over wastes from food are separated out as dirt. As Douglas (1966) suggests, what is considered "dirt" symbolizes disorder. Elimination of it is an attempt to organize the environment. All this "dirt" is buried together in the fields, into the formlessness of garbage and earth, thus restoring order. Similarly, the ceremony marks the mother's and child's integration into the social order. Saquic, who is originally from Santa Lucia (1973: 104), says the ritual symbolizes a new life.

Drinks of rum are then passed around, first to the men, then to the midwife and lastly to the women, who stay in the kitchen. The meal of soup, meat and tamalitas is served, the men eating first, either in the main room or on tables set up in the patio, and the women in the kitchen. The children eat either in the main room or in the kitchen after the men have been served. After the meal, the women send baskets containing food to various relatives, neighbours and godparents, primarily people who had visited the woman during the 20-day period and with whom she has reciprocal obligations. The young girls and women carry the food to the various houses.

The midwife may also pierce the ears of a female child on this day. In one observed case, the midwife first rubbed the child's ear to make it numb. She threaded a needle with red thread (possibly because red is used against the evil eye), heated it, and pierced the baby's ears, tying the thread in a loop.

The *elesan ch'at* ceremony marks the end of the midwife's duties and obligations, and the end of the mother's seclusion, which was regarded as the most dangerous period for the mother and child. The joint participation of relatives from both sides of the family emphasizes the importance of the birth in continuing the family lines and cementing the bonds, as well as reinforcing family solidarity. This is also symbolized in the exchange of food mentioned above. The woman is reintegrated into her family role and both mother and infant are given social support and recognition of their new status. (Paul & Paul, 1975, describe a similar postnatal bath and ritual carried out on the eighth day among the Zutuhil Maya in San Pedro la Laguna.)

The frequency of this ritual is declining, despite its seeming importance. Several people mentioned that they have not given it or only gave it for some of their children. One person said that the only reason they gave it this time (August, 1974) was because the particular midwife would gossip about them to other people. Although this personality trait was criticized, it served as an effective mechanism of social control. The fear of social pressure indicates that probably the majority of people still regard the ceremony as necessary and critical. This particular family had not had the ceremony for their other two children (despite the fact that the paternal grandfather was a shaman); they had also used a different midwife then. Another person said she would have the midwife clean out the sweatbath and give her some food, but felt they could not afford the ritual meal with the relatives. The celebration is expensive relative to the material wealth of these families. Three people said they used about 40 lb. maize, 10 lb. meat, potatoes, chayotes and other vegetables, bread, rum, and coffee. Since the price of maize has tripled between 1968 and 1974, the economic factor will probably become increasingly important. However, the ritual's decline also marks a decreasing adherence to and sharing of certain symbols and beliefs associated with the ritual.

CONCLUSION

The concepts and practices of the indigenous birth system in Guatemala present a sharp contrast to those promoted by Western medicine in the health care facilities, prenatal clinics and midwifery training programmes, which are based on the biomedical model of birth. In this framework, pregnancy is viewed as a disease; it is a physical bodily disturbance and is medicalized. The birth specialist performs a medical or obstetrical role. The body is separated from the self and its social and physical environment. In contrast, the indigenous Mayan view of birth is part of a holistic and personalistic system, involving moral values, social relations and the environment, as well as physical aspects. Furthermore, as Manning and Fabrega have suggested, for the Maya of Chiapas, Mexico, the body is a sacred concept rather than a mechanistic one with a "machine-like instrumentality" (1973: 278).

One aspect of this holistic system is the maintaining of the hot-cold balance or equilibrium both within the body and with the environment. This is related to the importance of heat, which seems to be not only related to the hot-cold balance but also to the concept of cleansing of pollution. Heat has semantic associations with blood and fertility, both symbolic of women. Blood is usually considered "hot", although there are varying degrees of hotness. A pregnant woman is considered as being in an unusually hot condition, whereas after delivery, the woman is in a cold state, both from the loss of blood and the expulsion of the baby. Therefore, she needs heat, both with respect to qualitative and physical temperature. As mentioned earlier, she is given "hot" foods and herbal teas, hot postnatal baths or sweatbaths, and avoids cold foods and substances. During the massages, the midwife's hands and the oil she uses are warmed. Heat is nourishing for both the mother and child. Heat, either in the sweatbath or herbal bath, is cleansing and purifying, both physically and spiritually. This is elaborated in the 20-day postpartum ritual where the woman, the bed, the baby and the sweatbath are all cleansed.

Not only must a balance be maintained between the hot and cold states, but also of emotional states and social relations. The centrality of emotions and the equilibrium of social relations, especially within the family, is another aspect of the indigenous holistic model. Medical personnel should be made aware of the importance of emotions in the local belief system, in the management of pregnancy and childbirth, and their influence on the birth process.

The sacred and ritual aspects of the birth process, and the midwife's role, are being attenuated in the process of change (Landy, 1974). The concept of divine mandate is declining and the official licence and training is being offered as an alternative, primarily for younger women. The midwife's role as mediator between her client and the supernatural, including Santa Ana, the spirits of dead midwives, El Mundo, God, Jesus and Mary, is declining. This change can be seen especially in the decreasing practice of the 20-day postpartum ceremony with its prayers, cleaning and ritual meal. The midwife cannot perform certain rituals and interpret signs if she is not supernaturally validated and does not have the power or "call". The decrease in the sacred aspects of the midwife's role and increasing secularization also probably reflects a decrease in the extent to which some of these beliefs and symbols are shared among the client population, as a result of other changes in religion (the Catholic Action movement and Protestantism), in wage labour and in education, as well as from the spread of western medicine.

The midwife plays a role in social control and in maintaining the traditional system. She is a repository of traditional practices and beliefs, some of which she imparts to the mother in the form of advice and dietary and behavioral restrictions, and others which are incorporated into rituals and backed by supernatural sanctions. If a particular ritual is not held and Santa Ana not properly thanked, some misfortune may occur to either the child or mother.

The midwife is an agent of social control also through gossip and other informal sanctions. The woman who said she had held the *elesan xe ch'at* ceremony because the "midwife talks", was not worried about supernatural sanctions but about social pressures. The midwife exerts influence through her higher social status, and works towards maintaining the traditional role of the female and mother (although ironically her role violates many of the general female restrictions, cf. Paul, 1975). Although the midwife may actually increase the anxiety of the mother in this respect, much of her behaviour seems to allay the mother's fears. The midwife's visits, massages, advice, prayers and rituals provide the mother with social and emotional support, all of which can help reduce the anxieties associated with the life crisis of birth. However, the increasing secularization of her role represents a narrowing of her role to little more than an obstetrical one.

The midwife can also be an agent of change. Incorporation of certain practices and medicine, such as the use of alcohol and mertiolate on the umbilical cord, reflects an adaptive change, especially where midwives have added these practices to the beneficial traditional one of cauterizing the cord. At the same time that there is an expansion of the midwife's knowledge concerning aspects of biomedicine, there may be a curtailment of traditional knowledge. She is told in the training programmes not to use herbs, not to use the sweatbath, not to use the traditional delivery position, not to do household duties for the mother, not to massage and not to handle complications, but refer them to the doctor. If they accept this "modern" attenuated role, their knowledge will not be passed on to new midwives.

The general tone is strongly negative toward the traditional practices, condemning them and encouraging the imposition of Western ones. No attempt has been made at accommodating any possible beneficial aspects or of adding the Western practices, rather than substituting them. A number of practices are either positive or innocuous in their benefits and there are some about whose effects very little is known, "although they are prohibited or denounced in carte blanche fashion by the medical establishment" (Harrison, 1977: 31). Although programmatic statements have been made concerning the need for health programmes, including midwifery training programmes, to include anthropological concepts and consider the local beliefs, practices, social context and specialists (Kelly, 1956; Verderese & Turnbull, 1975; Cosminsky, 1978), this remains an ideal that has not yet been realized. Such considerations have rarely been incorporated in programmes in Guatemala. There seems to have been little attempt to understand, build on or incorporate these into the training or health programmes, but rather to eradicate them (Harrison, 1977). The birth concepts and practices of the midwives and the client population discussed in this paper are not merely "superstitions" or "problems" to be ignored or eliminated, they are ways people have devised to cope with the crisis of birth and are intimately related to other aspects of the social milieu.

Changes are occurring in the indigenous birth system. Attempts to make both these changes and the training and medical programmes that are promoting them more compatible with the sociocultural framework of the local population would also make for more effective programmes and, hopefully, improved maternal and child health.

REFERENCES

Cosminsky, S. (1976). "Birth Rituals & Symbolism: A Quiché Maya-Black Carib Comparison". In *Ritual & Symbol in Native Central America* (P. Young & J. Howe, eds.). University of Oregon, Anthropological Papers No. 9

Cosminsky, S. (1977). "Childbirth & Midwifery on a Guatemalan Finca". *Medical Anthropology* 1 (3), 69-104.

Cosminsky, S. (1978). "Midwifery and Medical Anthropology". In *Modern Medicine & Medical Anthropology in the United States-Mexico Border Population* (B. Velimirovic, ed.). Washington: Pan American Health Organization. Scientific Publ. No. 359.

Cosminsky, S. (n.d.). "Role Adaptation among Indigenous Midwives: A Case Study in a Guatemalan Mayan Community". To be published.

Douglas, M. (1966). *Purity and Danger*. New York: Praeger.

Douglas, M. (1970). *Natural Symbols*. New York: Pantheon Books.

Firth, R. (1973). *Symbols: Public and Private*. Ithaca: Cornell University Press.

Foster, G. (1960). *Culture & Conquest*. Viking Fund Publication in Anthropology No. 27. Chicago: Quadrangle Books.

Harrison, P. (1977). Adiestramiento de Comadronas Tradicionales. Report of Comadrona Section, Maternal-Child Health Study, Health Sector Assessment. Unpublished Draft. Guatemala, Academia de Ciencias.

Harwood, A. (1971). "The Hot-Cold Theory of Disease: Implications for Treatment of Puerto-Rican Patients". *The Journal of the American Medical Association* 216, 1153-1158.

Kelly, I. (1956). "An Anthropological Approach to Midwifery Training in Mexico". *Journal of Tropical Pediatrics* 1, 200-205.

Landy, D. (1974). "Role Adaptation: Traditional Curers under the Impact of Western Medicine". *American Ethnologist* 1, 103-127.

Manning, P. & Fabrega, H. (1973). "The Experience of Self and Body: Health and Illness in the Chiapas Highlands". In *Phenomenological Sociology* (G. Psathas, ed.), pp. 251-301. New York: John Wiley.

McGuire, J. (1976). A Dietary Survey of Guatemalan Women on the Finca San Luis. Unpublished manuscript.

Ministerio de Salud Publica y Asistencia Social, Guatemala. (1976*). Manual para adiestramiento de comadronas tradicionales*. 3ᵃ Revision.

Paul, L. (1975). "Recruitment to a Ritual Role: The Midwife in a Maya Community". *Ethos* 3, 449-467.

Paul, L. & Paul, B. (1975). "The Maya Midwife as a Sacred Specialist: A Guatemalan Case". *American Ethnologist* 2, 707-726.

Saquic, R. (1973). "La Mujer Indigena Guatemalteca". *Guatemala Indigena* 8, 81-116.

Turner, V. (1967). *The Forest of Symbols*. Ithaca: Cornell University Press.

Verderese, M. de Lourdes and Turnbull, L. (1975). *The Traditional Birth Attendant in Maternal and Child Health and Family Planning*. Geneva: WHO. Offset Publication No. 18.

World Health Organization (1979). *Traditional Birth Attendants*. Geneva: WHO. Offset Publication No. 44.

[1] Fieldwork in Santa Lucia was supported in 1968-1969 with a fellowship from the Institute of Nutrition of Central America and Panama (INCAP) and the National Institutes of Health, and in the summer of 1974 through a grant from the Rutgers University Research Council. Fieldwork on Finca San Felipe (pseudonym) has been carried on at different intervals in several trips from 1974-1978, and supported by grants from the Williams-Waterman Foundation, Massachusetts Institute of Technology and the Rutgers University Research Council. I would also like to express my appreciation to Dr Nevin Scrimshaw for his support and assistance and to Dr Lorin Nevling, Jr, of the Field Museum of Chicago for the plant identifications.

[2] The term "Ladino" refers both to descendants of former Spanish or mixed Spanish-Indian ancestry and to people oriented towards Spanish or Western culture in contrast to those oriented toward Indian culture.

[3] A study of dietary intake of a sample of the plantation women showed only eight percent of the pregnant and none of the lactating women were meeting the INCAP recommended dietary levels for calories, protein, riboflavin or niacin levels, 31% of the pregnant women and 12% of the lactating women were below 50% of the recommended protein level whereas none of the non-pregnant and non-lactating women were that low.

A BABY IS BORN IN MERCHANG

Carol Laderman [†]

I have, until now, described customs as a general script for the acting out of gestation and birth—a script learned from numerous observations and conversations. Since all learning is contextually specific, and since the particulars of each sequence of events require people to improvise their actions from the elements of these cultural scripts, I will recount two cases of childbirth to show how this is done. In both cases the patient, not the practitioner, is the protagonist in the drama of birth. Her wishes must be respected; she is the ultimate arbiter of decisions taken during childbirth. For the majority of births, producing a normal infant after an uncomplicated delivery, this preservation of female autonomy, so alien to most deliveries in America, is strongly conducive to the mother's well-being. Responsibility carries certain risks, however, particularly when the person in command does not have all the facts at her disposal. The first case, an uncomplicated birth attended by a village midwife, illustrates the positive aspects of the traditional medical system; the second, a difficult labor attended by both government midwife and bidan kampung, shows its dangers.

CASE NO. 1: SENANI HAS A SON

At about 8 A.M. Sapiah came to my house to tell me that a woman was in labor. She was a cousin of my assistant on her father's side and related to his wife on her mother's. She had given permission to Sapiah to invite me to be present at the delivery of her baby. She and her husband had come from Kuantan (in Pahang, the neighboring state to the south and west) so that she might give birth at her parents' home. She had already borne five children, including a pair of twins who had died in infancy. Senani's oldest child, Liza, a classmate of my son, had been given years ago to her grandparents to raise, since otherwise their house would have been empty of children and they would have been lonely. The doctor in Kuantan advised Senani to give birth in the hospital, but since he did not suspect a twin birth this time she thought it unnecessary. She had also been examined at the Health Center in Marang (the capital of the district which includes Merchang). The doctor at the Health Center told her that she was carrying twins, but Sapiah was convinced it was only one baby. Her opinion, added to that of the Kuantan doctor, strengthened Senani's resolve to deliver at home. She was having very mild contractions at irregular intervals when we arrived. Sapiah felt Senani's feet and said that she would not deliver very soon. She said that if the big toe was cold it was a sign of approaching childbirth, but the birth would not be imminent until the cold travelled up to the ankle. The extremities become cold, she explained, because much of the blood leaves them at that time and flows to the uterus. The heat collecting in the uterus, resulting from the unusual abundance of the "hot" body fluid, blood, makes the womb uncongenial to the baby, thus aiding in its expulsion.

Since the signs did not point to a quick delivery, and Senani was in no pain or need of moral support, Sapiah decided it would be safe to leave her patient and go to her morning's rubber tapping. We returned twice during the day to check on whether labor had begun in earnest, once at 3 P.M. and once at 7 P.M. I

[†] *Wives and midwives: childbirth and nutrition in rural Malaysia,* (Part of chapter 6) Berkeley: University of California Press. 1983: 152-73

noticed that Senani was wearing a bracelet of black twisted wood on her wrist. She said it was badur wood (*Amorphophallus campanulatus*), given to her by an Achenese friend to ensure her safety during childbirth. The tubers of badur are poisonous on account of their needle crystals of oxalate of lime, and its juice is used as a component of dart poison by the Semangs of Perak, one-tenth part making a poison strong enough to kill a rhinoceros or tiger (Burkill, 1966: 140-1). Senani said it was bisa, and so it is. Bisa can mean both poisonous and powerful, in the sense of a magically effective charm. The badur's empirically poisonous (bisa) qualities appear to have influenced its symbolically powerful (bisa) attributes.

At eleven thirty that night a child came to my assistant's house (next door to mine) to say that Senani was in labor. He awakened me. I put a sarong and blouse over my nightgown and hopped on the back of his bicycle. When we arrived, Sapiah was sitting alongside Senani, gently massaging her abdomen. She had been there since 11 P.M. She said that it would be some time yet before the birth. She could tell by feeling Senani's navel: "If it is hard and raised, birth is imminent." She asked me to touch the navel and see for myself. It was neither hard nor raised. Sapiah felt the pulse in Senani's wrist. "If the pulse is fast," she said, "it is a sign that labor is progressing." Senani's pulse was just a little faster than normal. Her older brother's wife sat behind her and cradled Senani's head in her lap. Senani's three-year-old daughter did not want to sleep and kept coming in and out of the screened-off room. She did not appear worried or frightened, just very interested in what was taking place. Her aunt told her that she would soon be the big sister of a new baby. Sapiah asked for the salt mixture, quietly recited a jampi, and threw it to the four directions and into the space between the floorboards to the ground below.

The floor on which Senani lay was covered with oilcloth, upon which newspapers had been laid. A pail of water stood in a corner of the room, with a cake of soap in a dish alongside, for the midwife to use when washing her hands. Nearby was an empty bucket, used as a receptacle for soiled and dirty cloths. Sapiah had brought along her kit, a covered wicker basket lined with white cloth, in which she kept small bottles filled with habitane-in-spirit for the umbilical stump, dettol (an antiseptic), flavine-in-spirit (in case there are small cuts or tears of the perineum), a pair of scissors, cord to tie the umbilical cord, and absorbent cotton.

Senani lay on her back with her knees flexed, feet close to her buttocks and legs apart. Her sister-in-law placed one hand on each side of Senani's abdomen, above the fundus of the uterus. Senani held her around the hips. She had tied a rolled up sarong above her uterus earlier in the day to keep the baby from rising.

At 12:55 Sapiah massaged Senani's abdomen, feeling the outline of the uterus. She lifted Senani's sarong to her knees in order to insert a finger into her vagina to ascertain whether the baby's head was already in the vestibule. The three-year-old finally decided to go to sleep on a mat near her mother. Senani began to pray whenever she felt a hard contraction. Between pains she carried on a conversation with the women in the room: Sapiah, her sister-in-law, her mother, and me. The room was lit with two lamps. The men slept in the outer room on mats that had been spread on the floor. From time to time we women could hear the men snoring and occasionally breaking wind, which always elicited comments and laughter from the women, even from Senani.

For the next two hours Sapiah alternately, massaged Senani's abdomen and looked at her vagina. She said that massaging the navel gently encourages the baby to descend. Senani, tiring of her supine position, turned on her side for awhile and then sat up, calling for some coffee. Although she yawned repeatedly, she was alert and in command of the situation.

At 2:45 a little bloody amniotic fluid escaped. Sapiah wiped it away and asked Senani to move so that her head faced southwest, the correct position for the day according to Sapiah's system. Senani complained of pain on the left side of the lower abdomen. Sapiah said it was because the baby was on the right side and would probably be a boy. She asked Senani to grasp her ankles and draw them up close to her buttocks, and encouraged her to bear down with her contractions. Senani's mother entered the room with a basket of baby clothes, and some soft clean old sarongs, which Sapiah tore up for rags. The men, Senani's father, husband, and brother, and my assistant woke up and began to talk in low voices in the outside room. Sapiah placed her finger up Senani's vagina and said that the baby's head was close. Senani's husband, upon hearing this, entered. Sapiah gave him a large piece of bamboo from which he cut a long sharp piece. Sapiah whispered a jampi over it and put it into the clothes basket. She dripped oil into the vaginal opening to make the passage more slippery and massaged Senani's abdomen gently with her oily hands.

By 3:10 Senani had become impatient. She asked Sapiah how much longer and was answered, "Just a little while more." Her father, who had been softly praying in the next room, entered and suggested that they call Pak Su Omar (a respected bomoh), but Sapiah said it would not be necessary. Senani's husband came back and stayed for a few moments, caressing his wife's shoulders. At 3:15 Senani asked her sister-in-law to hold tight over the fundus; at 3:30 there was a gush of amniotic fluid, and at 3:35 the baby's head crowned. Sapiah took it out in a way that reminded me of a head emerging through a turtleneck sweater. She protected the perineum against tearing by pressing a wad of clean cloth against it. She applied upward traction to deliver the posterior shoulder and downward to deliver the anterior shoulder. The baby slipped out easily. It was a boy. Sapiah pointed out to me that her prognosis had been correct.

Sapiah placed the baby on his back, wrapped in a cloth, upon a folded newspaper. She massaged Senani's abdomen to encourage expulsion of the afterbirth. As the cord begin to elongate, she gently pulled on it, wrapping it around her hand. When the placenta was delivered, she wrapped it in newspaper and turned her attention once more to the baby. She rubbed his body with coconut oil to remove the vernix caseosa. A heavy coating of vernix caseosa, she told me later, is a sure sign that the couple have been having intercourse during the latter part of pregnancy a practice she considers dangerous. She believes the white vernix caseosa to be an accumulation of semen.

Sapiah rubbed the umbilical cord with heated ashes wrapped in a little cloth bag. The cord is cold to the touch and must be heated before it is cut. She put a piece of turmeric under the cord, after tying, it in three places, cut the cord with the piece of sharp bamboo that had been prepared earlier, and put the end of the cord still attached to the placenta up to the baby's face for the first lepas[1]. Then she bathed the baby with soap and warm water in a basin, using a soft cloth. She rinsed his head with cold water, because the head is supposed to be naturally hotter than the body. If it is overheated, sickness or even madness may result. The baby enjoyed the warm bath but cried when the cold water was poured on his head. After bathing the baby, Sapiah applied a piece of absorbent cotton soaked in habitane-in-spirit to the umbilical stump and covered it with a piece of white cloth, held in place by an abdominal binder. The bidan dressed the baby in a shirt and diaper and then wrapped him in a swaddling cloth. Before being wrapped, the baby's arms and legs must be straightened. The cloth holds them in place and keeps the baby from exhibiting the (Moro) startle reaction, which might deplete his semangat.

The midwife handed the clean dressed baby to his grandmother, who touched him lightly with scissors. This was done to harden his semangat, newly received with the cutting of the umbilical cord. After the baby had been laid to rest on a small mattress placed upon a floor mat, covered with a pretty cloth and surrounded on either side by bolsters, the bidan prepared the afterbirth for burial. She washed it thoroughly in water into which lime juice had been squeezed. After the afterbirth was washed, it was placed inside a half coconut shell, lined with a piece of white cloth. Salt, tamarind, a small piece of absorbent cotton and a bit of white cloth were added. When the midwife had tied the ends of the cloth lining, the "corpse" was ready for burial. Some time within the next few hours the baby's father must bury it beneath a young palm tree, to the accompaniment of prayers for the dead. Salt and tamarind are preservatives and gatekeeping mechanisms, and the bits of cloth and cotton are symbolic representations of the afterbirth's status as semihuman. When Malays bury adult corpses, they use absorbent cotton to close up the orifices and to cover the face. The cotton covers a baby's entire body before it is wrapped in a white winding sheet. The afterbirth is entitled to a decent burial, too, as befits the baby's older sibling. The umbilical cord was not buried with the placenta, but kept for future use. After it has dried it can be ground up and added to water, to make a medicine with which to bathe the baby's eyes, should they become sore. Some people add a bit of dessicated cord to the older siblings' food in the hope that this will decrease family friction; however, the midwife told me that she had done it for her children with no success.

After the placenta had been prepared for burial, the midwife felt Senani's abdomen to see if the uterus was hard. A soft boggy uterus is a danger sign of postpartum hemorrhage, the contingency most feared following delivery. Sapiah massaged the abdomen with coconut oil to expel the "bad" blood of menstruation, accumulated during the many months of pregnancy during which the opening of the womb was glued shut. Senani smiled and held the midwife's ankle affectionately. She changed her sarong and moved to a clean mat and pillow. Her mother handed her a hot tungku stone, which she placed on her abdomen. The midwife cleaned up the debris of childbirth and washed her hands. The father busied himself setting up the "roasting" bed. The grandmother served coffee and steamed cakes. The long night was over. Sapiah, my assistant, and I left for our respective homes, and Senani's family settled down to sleep.

On the way home, my assistant told me that just before the birth took place he awoke to find the hairs on his arms standing on edge, a sign that hantu were about. He thought of telling people to throw rice to chase the spirits away, but decided it was none of his business—yet another example of Malay reluctance to offer advice unless it is specifically requested.

CASE NO. 2: THE BIRTH AND DEATH OF ASMAH'S FIRST CHILD

Asmah was a healthy, well-to-do woman in her early twenties. Her family owned a store and a coffee shop. I had visited her often during her pregnancy to collect blood samples and dietary information. Her husband woke me at five o'clock one morning to announce that his wife was in labor. He wanted me to inform the government midwife and drive her to their home. I woke Halimah and waited while she dressed in her white uniform and checked the contents of her delivery kit, an aluminum case. When we arrived, we found that Mak Wah, a bidan kampung, had been there since midnight. Halimah asked Asmah if the baby had moved recently. Asmah was unsure. She felt Asmah's abdomen to see if the head was presenting. She removed her fetal scope from her kit and listened for the baby's heartbeat. She called for hot water to wash her hands, which she scrubbed with her own soap and nail brush and dried on her own hand towel. She gave Asmah an enema, and told her that the baby would descend within an hour, if the birth were to take place that day. Asmah asked Mak Wah to tie a wrapped sarong around her waist to encourage the baby to descend. Mak Wah asked for the salt mixture, recited her jampi and threw it to the four directions and under the floorboards. She rubbed some minyak selusuh, which she had prepared at the occasion of Asmah's lenggang perut, on her hands and massaged Asmah's abdomen. Asmah's mother served coffee and cakes. Asmah drank some sweetened coffee but refused the food. Halimah examined Asmah's abdomen again at 7 A.M. and said that the baby would not come until the afternoon, at the earliest. She said she would return later that morning after visiting some nearby patients. Mak Wah, Asmah, and I lay down on mats and pillows to have a nap.

Halimah returned at 9:30. Asmah continued to have mild and irregular contractions. Both midwives sat and talked, occasionally massaging Asmah's abdomen, waiting for labor to begin in earnest. At about 1 P.M. Asmah's mother served lunch. Asmah again would only drink coffee. She felt nauseated. Mak Wah gave her some water with three drops of minyak selusuh to drink. She massaged Asmah's abdomen with some of the treated oil, moistened a cloth with some more, and rubbed it on her vulva. At 2:30, while she was examining Asmah, Halimah noticed meconium escaping from her vagina, a sign of fetal distress. She told Asmah and her husband that this was a bad sign, and recommended that she deliver at the hospital. The husband replied that his wife was perfectly healthy and he saw no reason for her to be moved. Halimah explained that it was the baby she was worried about, not the mother. Neither Asmah nor her husband considered that a valid argument. Halimah told the husband that he would have to sign a statement absolving her of responsibility, since she had recommended hospital delivery but he had not consented. After he signed, Halimah listened for the baby's heartbeat with her fetal scope. She scrubbed her hands again and examined Asmah internally. Her cervix was dilated two fingers. Mak Wah cradled Asmah's head on her lap, placed her hands on Asmah's abdomen, and prayed. Halimah massaged her abdomen, making circular rubbing motions over the navel exactly like those of Sapiah (who claimed to have taught her this technique). Asmah's mother prepared the keras. She and Mak Wah took turns supporting Asmah's head in their laps and pressing above the fundus of her uterus. At 4 P.M. Halimah listened again for the fetal heartbeat. She invited me to listen, too. Although she claimed to hear a beat, I could hear nothing. Asmah's cervix was still dilated only two fingers. At 4:30 Halimah asked me to drive her back to her clinic. She told the family to call her again when the pains were strong.

Asmah's husband came to my house at 9 P.M. that night and asked me to pick up Halimah. When we arrived, we found that Pak Cu, a bomoh who specializes in difficult labors, had been called. Pak Cu treats no other conditions. He uses Arabic sentences from the Koran in place of the usual Malay jampi. Asmah's head rested on his lap. She put her arms around his back with every contraction. Asmah's religion teacher, with whom she had studied Koran as a child in Kelantan, had sent her a bottle of air tawar to use during labor. She took sips from time to time during the next few hours and used it on a cloth to refresh her face. Halimah opened her delivery kit and spread the contents on a clean white towel. Her kit contained the following:

    1 kidney basin and 2 smaller bowls
    2 clamps for umbilical cord
    1 cord scissors
    1 syringe and 2 needles
    enema set
    mucus extractor

fetal scope
baby's spring balance scale
thermometer
urethral catheter
forceps for lifting bowls
sterilizer container
sterile cotton swabs, gauze
soap, nailbrush, and towel
plastic apron
plastic square
2 ampules of ergometrine
1 bottle of Panadol (analgesic)
1 bottle of Dettol (antiseptic)
1 bottle of flavine-in-spirit
1 bottle of habitane-in-spirit
1 bottle of cord ligatures
1 bottle of eyedrops

Halimah scrubbed her hands and cleaned Asmah's perineal area with dettol. She asked Asmah's mother to bring clothes in which to wrap the baby. Night was falling and little kerosene lamps were lit. Mak Wah took Pak Cu's place at Asmah's head. She moistened Asmah's long hair with the minyak selusuh and wiped her abdomen with the oiled hair. She took some lime from a box containing the ingredients for betel chewing and rubbed it on Asmah's abdomen. Halimah sat at one side of Asmah's flexed legs and I sat at the other. She dripped coconut oil into Asmah's vagina just as Sapiah had done. Mak Wah advised Asmah to move so that her head faced west.

Asmah was in pain, but she did not cry or scream. She said, "It's been going on for such a long time," and asked how much longer it would be. The women advised her to pray. She asked for Pak Cu, who had been sitting in the outside room. He massaged her abdomen with minyak selusuh and recited passages from the Koran. At 10:30 Asmah began to push every two minutes. She asked for her husband, who came into the room to sit by her side and hold her hand. Her mother served coffee again, but this time Asmah did not drink. By eleven, Asmah's contractions had once more become irregular. At 11:25 a second bomoh arrived. He recited a jampi and threw rice to repel any noxious spiritual presences. By now everyone was yawning. The children (Asmah's siblings and cousins) had already fallen asleep in the outside room. One woke up and cried and was quickly comforted by one of the women.

Mak Wah told Asmah's husband to step over his wife's body three times. Perhaps labor has been prolonged because of her behavior during pregnancy. Halimah did another internal examination and said that delivery would soon take place. The second bomoh came back into the room, said another jampi and threw some more rice. He gave Asmah a cloth which had been treated with benzoin fumes and incantations to tie around her left hand.

At 12:30 A.M. Halimah fell asleep. About 1 A.M., Mak Wah woke her up. She did a vaginal examination and asked Mak Wah to wake her again when she saw the baby's head crown. By 2A.M. the baby's black hair could be seen at the end of the birth passage, but then it withdrew from sight. Mak Wah woke Halimah and told Asmah's parents to open all the doors and windows. The second bomoh came in and recited another jampi. Halimah told Asmah to sit up and try to urinate. Mak Wah said it would be wise to move her into another room. She was beginning to feel the presence of hantu. I asked whether they would like me to call for an ambulance. Asmah's husband and mother wanted to wait a while longer. Halimah said that she thought an ambulance should be called if the baby was not delivered soon. It started to rain, a steady torrential downpour heralding the arrival of the monsoon season. Asmah was moved into another room near the kitchen. At 2:45 the family agreed that it was time to call for an ambulance. I went out to turn my car around, but when I re-entered the house, Halimah said, "Wait, the baby is ready to come out." For the last hour the top of its head could be seen, approaching the opening of the vagina and retreating. At 2:55 the baby was born. As its head emerged, we could see that the umbilical cord was looped three times around its neck. Halimah quickly unlooped the cord, clamped and cut it.

She lifted the baby out. It was painfully thin and dehydrated, its ribs were showing, its stomach was sunken, and its body was limp. Mak Wah spat several times in the baby's direction[2]. Halimah massaged the baby's back, but it did not respond. The afterbirth was delivered. The umbilical cord was green, the placenta green and black, the amniotic fluid had turned black. Asmah's mother said *"Tak apa-apa."* (It's nothing, it's all right). The phrase was repeated by almost everyone. Asmah echoed, *"Tak apa-apa."* No one cried. The only silent ones were myself and Halimah. Mak Wah said that she could feel the hantu pushing the baby back into Asmah's body for an hour before it finally emerged. She said that the hantu had been able to suck the baby's blood because its body had been weakened by the looped cord.

Asmah was very tired. She lay back and closed her eyes. Halimah washed the dead baby, wrapped it in cloth and laid it down on the small mattress which had been prepared to receive a live child. I placed mosquito netting over it. It was to remain there until the family had rested from its ordeal. The following day it was buried in the cemetery.

Halimah washed the afterbirth and prepared it for burial. Mak Wah prepared bath water with "hot" leaves for Asmah while her husband and stepfather got the "roasting bed" ready. Asmah's mother served more drinks. It was 5A.M., exactly twenty-four hours since we had first arrived. Halimah asked me to drive her home. Mak Wah stayed on to clean up the debris.

Certain norms guided the behavior of the actors in the two cases I have recounted: the wishes of the mother were a primary consideration, her feminine modesty was respected, and her emotions were not given free rein in the face of pain and even death. The bidan's ritual activities during the birth of Senani's child were the bare minimum necessary for a normal birth: she threw the salt mixture, prepared the afterbirth for burial, and performed a preliminary lepas for the baby. Ritual activities increase considerably when labor is protracted or when there are unusual circumstances connected with the birth, as in Asmah's case. In addition to the normal precautions, the bidan rubbed minyak selusuh on Asmah's stomach, hair, and vulva and gave her some to drink. She bathed her face with air tawar, which Asmah also drank. She rubbed lime on her abdomen to make her womb "hotter" and therefore less attractive to the baby, following humoral rather than magical theory. She advised Asmah's husband to step over his wife's body to reverse the negative effects of her behavior during pregnancy. Two bomoh were also called in on the case, one who specialized in childbirth and employed only Koranic sentences, and a second who uses Malay jampi and who prepared an amulet for the laboring woman. When none of these treatments had the desired effect, the midwife suggested that Asmah move to another room to escape the hantu's influence, and requested that all doors and windows be opened.

Invoking the laws of sympathetic magic by opening doors and cupboards, loosening the mother's hair, and leaving windows wide open (described as normal procedure in rural Malay births by Wylde, 1957: 131; Winstedt, 1951: 106; Chen, 1975: 105) is not a usual feature of childbirth in Merchang. When a sick woman is treated by a bomoh, her hair must hang down to allow the sickness to escape from her body, but while she is in the throes of labor her hair is swept up to keep her cool and comfortable. Neither cupboards nor doors are deliberately opened for normal births. Since few houses have internal doors, the room in which birth is to occur is partitioned off from the rest of the house by means of a cloth hung over a string. Windows in the delivery room are usually left closed to protect the mother's modesty, and mats or cloths are placed against walls that have spaces or chinks that might afford passersby a glimpse of the drama within. On stifling hot days, windows may be opened a crack, but the women make sure that the shutters or cloths are arranged so as to preserve decorum. Except in unusual and dangerous circumstances, considerations of feminine modesty outweigh the possible benefits that a magical correspondence between open windows and open wombs might confer. Asmah's ordeal was the only occasion on which I witnessed doors and windows opened to facilitate birth.

Malay women are encouraged to pray during labor and are strongly discouraged from crying or screaming. On one occasion a young woman giving birth to her first child was lightly slapped on the face when she cried out. The assembled women asked her if she had no shame, to act in that manner. In many respects this is a useful adat (custom in the widest sense of the word). Concentration on prayer rather than pain may lead a woman away from anxieties that can interfere with her uterine functions. If incipient hysteria is cut off in its beginnings, and a satisfactory alternative substituted, it may be beneficial for the outcome of labor. The prohibition against exhibiting strong emotions is a salient feature of rural Malay life.

During the course of a survey, I asked people whether they thought that strong emotions could affect physical health. I was almost invariably told, "I never have any strong emotions." At the funeral of Rohani's baby, I was the only person crying. My assistant told me that when his wife almost died bringing forth his firstborn, a stillbirth, he did not shed a single tear. The reaction to the tragic outcome of Asmah's protracted labor was, "It's all right, it's nothing." This denial of emotions takes its toll. Most of the conditions treated by Malay shamans are classified by them as sakit berangin, a disease whose etiology is the frustration of talent. character. and desires.

THE MIDWIFE AS MEDICAL PRACTITIONER

Although, in the cases presented above, the normal birth was attended only by a traditional midwife while the stillbirth was attended by both government midwife and bidan kampung, I in no way mean to suggest that the government midwife can he held responsible for the tragic outcome. She recognized the signs of fetal distress and recommended hospital delivery to the parents, but she was in no position to compel them to follow her recommendation. Her behavior was not only congruent with rural Malay standards of courtesy and noninterference but was also strategically correct, given her position within the community.

Had she insisted or tried to bully the family into following her suggestion, she would have encountered opposition which might easily have spread and generalized to other potential patients and their families. As I pointed out earlier, villagers do not consider the government midwife's services absolutely essential. A domineering government midwife might soon find herself persona non grata.

Ignoring the bidan's ritual function and considering her only in her role of medical practitioner, we find there are many points of similarity between the performance of the government midwife and that of the bidan kampung. Both provide moral support and encouragement to their patients, both deliver the baby in the same manner, both massage the woman's abdomen before delivery to soothe her and after the baby is born to facilitate expulsion of the placenta. Both know the signs of placental separation and are careful to note the elongation of the umbilical cord before they slowly and carefully pull it to assist in the delivery of the afterbirth. Both clean, bathe, and dress the baby.

Their differences seem primarily a matter of emphasis rather than true divergence. The point of difference stressed by the villagers credits the bidan kampung with always being available and staying with her patient from the onset of labor through its conclusion. They frequently criticized the government midwife for being unavailable during the night and while her clinic was in progress. They also complained that she would not stay with her patient for more than an hour or two, and accused her of trying to speed up her patient's delivery by putting her fingers up into the birth canal.

The last complaint has no basis whatever in reality. It is clear from my accounts of births attended by government and traditional midwives that both do several vaginal examinations during the course of labor. Halimah, being trained to gauge cervical dilatation, examines farther up the vestibule than Sapiah, who merely wants to ascertain whether the baby has begun its descent down the birth canal. Although the availability of the government midwife was a real problem, because she was afraid of going out alone at night, the villager's estimation of the bidan kampung's availability was somewhat illusory. As we have seen in chapter 5, village midwives do not make a conscious effort to be within constant reach of their clients, but go about their daily activities[3]. The difference between the relative unavailability of the government and traditional midwives is due primarily to the fact that there is only one of the former and many of the latter. If any particular bidan kampung is unavailable, another can be called. The government midwife, as the sole representative of her calling in the parish, is highly visible and her role cannot easily be carried out by a substitute.

Complaints about the government midwife's not seeing her patients through their entire labors and deliveries have two dimensions. The first is her time allocation. She must attend to many duties besides the one at hand. If, in her judgement, the patient will not deliver within the next couple of hours, she may decide that it is safe to leave her temporarily. This, as we have seen, was also true of Sapiah, yet no one complained about her. The reason for this difference in patients' attitudes is the second dimension of this problem. Sapiah, with her many years of experience, had extremely good judgment about the imminence of birth. In all the time I spent in Merchang, I never observed or heard of a case where she left her patient only to find upon her return that she had given birth unattended. This was not uncommon, however, in Halimah's case. On four occasions where I was present and several others that were reported to me, Halimah left her patient, assuring her that she would not deliver until much later, and the woman delivered within the following hour. This was not owing to any laziness or unconcern on Halimah's part, as villagers supposed. Where circumstances were clearly abnormal, as in the case of Asmah, Halimah spent as much as eight consecutive hours in attendance. The difference, then, was not so much in the length of time spent at the patient's side as it was in the judgment of when it was safe to leave her unattended.

The point of difference stressed by the medical establishment in Trengganu was the government midwife's sterile procedures and the traditional midwife's lack of them. As noted in the accounts above, both Sapiah and Halimah washed their hands before and after vaginal examinations. Halimah used hot boiled water and scrubbed with a nail brush, while Sapiah only used well water and soap. Both used cloths to protect the perineum against tearing, but Halimah used a sterile pad while Sapiah used clean old pieces of sarong. Halimah's instruments were sterilized, while Sapiah usually used a clean but unsterilized pair of scissors to cut the umbilical cord. Halimah used a bulb syringe to remove mucus from a baby's airways, while Sapiah used her own mouth. Halimah's sterile procedures broke down, however, during the last part of labor. Probably following Sapiah's example, she dripped ordinary coconut oil into her patient's vagina.

Both villagers and bidan kampung found Halimah's delivery kit impressive and enviable. She regularly gave her patient an enema if there was enough time before the delivery, thus obviating the frequent unaesthetic mess which the bidan kampung were accustomed to cleaning up during labor. However, the standard enema customarily given to women in labor by hospital-trained medical attendants has been shown to cause electrolyte imbalances (Birnbaum, 1978: 108). The bidan kampung admired the way Halimah clamped and cut the umbilical cord before the placenta was delivered, and they would have liked to have been able to copy her actions. Delay in cutting the cord, however, has been demonstrated to add an appreciable amount of iron to the baby's store by favoring maximal drainage of blood from the placenta into the baby's body (McLean, 1951: 136). Moreover, early clamping of the umbilical cord has been shown to lengthen the third stage of labor, and increase the likelihood of maternal hemorrhage, retained placenta, or the retention of placental fragments (Botha, 1968: 30-3).

On balance it appears that some of the newer procedures are conducive to the greater health and safety of the baby, that is, sterile scissors used to cut the cord, avoiding the threat of neonatal tetanus, while others introduce the possibility of iatrogenesis, for instance, cutting the cord before the end of the third stage of labor.

Halimah's strength lay in her recognition of danger signals during labor and her ability to summon help via the ambulance. Her professional strength, however, was turned to impotence in the face of her patients' refusal to heed her advice.

The most serious accusation made against bidan kampung by medical authorities is that they contribute to maternal death by attempting to expel the fetus forcibly if labor is prolonged (Chen, 1974-1975: 341; Siti Hasmah, 1968: 6; Sambhi, 1968: 347; Thambu, 1971: 294). This procedure will not rupture the uterus if the cervix has fully dilated. If prolongation of labor is, however, owing to obstruction, such as abnormal presentation of the baby, or disproportion, pressing down very strongly on the uterus can cause it to rupture, resulting in death for the mother and child unless emergency laparotomy is carried out. The pressure must be that of "extreme violence" (Thambu, 1971: 294) "so brutal as to cause bruising of the gut" (Sambhi, 1968: 348). Such strength is not usual in a Malay woman, so "a few strong men have (to be) called in by the Bomoh midwife to apply pressure on the abdomen and uterus with the view of pushing the baby out" (Sambhi, 1968: 347). Although Dr. Siti Hasmah says that obstructed labor, combined with pressure on the uterus exerted by bidan kampung "is frequently the cause of maternal death" (1968: 6), the figures from the General Hospital at Kuantan, covering all cases admitted to the Department of Obstetrics and Gynecology for the period January 1968 to December 1969, show four cases per year (Thambu, 1971: 293). On the basis of this data, Thambu concludes that "rupture of the uterus is a rare condition" (1971: 294).

None of the traditional midwives I observed pressed down violently on the parturient woman's uterus or called in strong men to do so for her, although I was present at several protracted labors. They did massage the abdomen, particularly the navel area, both in an effort to ease the woman's discomfort and in the belief that it would speed up delivery, but the massage was done gently and carefully. A woman in labor customarily lies with her head in the lap of a female relative, who presses on her diaphragm while she grasps her kin around the waist from behind, but the pressure exerted is not enough to cause damage. If the woman in labor objects to this procedure, it is not performed or is discontinued. No doubt such violent treatment and dire results can be attributed to some bidan kampung. There are levels of intelligence and competence in any field, and the lengthy training of a bidan is no more a guarantee of excellence in all midwives than a medical degree is an assurance that a particular physician possesses the competence that such a degree implies. Every group of medical practitioners provides its patients with both valuable care and a certain measure of iatrogenic harm. To characterize the entire group by the standards of its worst practitioners, however, would be grossly unfair.

A theme running through rural Malay beliefs and practices connected with childbirth is that of flexibility and accommodation. According to a popular saying, "If you are giving birth, you should listen to the midwife" (*Kalau kita beranak, ikut kata bidan*), but she is listened to because of her authority, accumulated over years of successful practice, and not because of any power to compel behavior. The mother's comfort and wishes must be respected. The bidan only assists; the mother has the final decision. If she wants to lie on her side or sit up, and the birth is not imminent, there is nothing to prevent her from doing so. If she wants to eat or drink during labor, she may. If she doesn't want to wear a sash during labor, she may discard it. If she objects to pressure being exerted on her abdomen, it will be stopped. The only rules she must follow are not to stand during the last phase of labor so as to avoid the possibility of the baby's emerging rapidly and dropping on its head, and to keep her legs spread during delivery, for obvious reasons.

Even in the case of protracted or abnormal labor, the role of the parturient woman is not usurped. Although one or more bomoh may be called in, they do not become hero shamans or physicians, but remain merely her assistants and attendants. Bomoh and bidan may be thanked for their efforts, and their assistance is highly valued, but parents, and not they, are congratulated on the birth of a child.

Malay treatment of abnormal labors, and the theory behind it, have both positive and negative aspects. The bidan's reassurances and use of magical paraphernalia, and the bomoh's incantations, may change the laboring woman's biochemical and physiological responses, aiding her in the successful completion of her task. However, lack of recognition of fetal distress on the part of bidan kampung, and Asmah's refusal to avail herself of the benefits of hospital delivery, illustrate a defect in Malay traditional childbirth practices. Had Asmah and her family understood the significance of escaping meconium and the necessity for immediate medical intervention, the baby's life might have been saved.

Every society has priorities that shape the ideology and conduct of childbirth. In America, mindful of possible dangers to the mother and child, we treat birth as a potentially life-threatening illness. For the mother's safety, she must be placed in the hands of an expert whose decisions, although they may be open to discussion along the way, are ultimately final. While this may minimize certain risks, it undoubtedly diminishes the mother's autonomy. Rural Malays view childbirth as a normal event in every woman's life which, however, may infrequently imperil her well-being. The dangers of childbirth are not allowed to erode her autonomy—her decisions are respected, even when they may lead to her death. On one occasion, a mother was told by the government midwife that she might die unless she delivered at the hospital.

Since she was living alone, her husband having gone to work outside the kampung and no other relative within easy reach, she said she preferred to die at home rather than go to the hospital by herself. None of her neighbors attempted to change her mind. When my assistant noticed my concern, he said it was nobody's business but her own: if she wanted to die, then let her die. Fortunately, she did not die, but if she had, the responsibility would have been entirely hers.

Whether one takes the view that traditional Malay childbirth practices foolishly expose the mother and child to unnecessary risks, or sees them as procedures that allow a woman to take command during the most important hours of her life, the essential difference between childbirth in America and childbirth in Merchang is clear: American women are delivered by obstetricians; Malay women give birth.

REFERENCES

Birnbaum, D.A., 1978, Iatrogenesis of damaged mothers and newborns, In: *21st Century Obstetrics Now*, vol.1, Edited by Lee Stewart and David Stewart, Marble Hill, Mo.: NAPSAC Inc.

Botha, M., 1968, The management of the umbilical cord in labour, *S.Afr.J. Obst. 6:30-33*

Burkill, I.H., 1966, *A Dictionary of Economic Products of the Malay Peninsula*, Kuala Lumpur: Ministry of Agriculture and Cooperatives

Chen, P.C.Y., 1974-5, The Malay Traditional Birth Attendant, *Ethnomedizin*, 3:335-352

Chen, P.C.Y., 1975, *Midwifery Services in a Rural Malay Community*, DM thesis, University of Malaya

McLean, E.B., 1951, Iron therapy in hypochromic anemia, *Paediatrics*, 7:136

Sambhi, J.S., 1968, Bomoh's abdomen, *Far East Med. J.*, 4:347-8

Siti Hasmah bt. Mohd. Ali, 1968, *The effect of Islam and Adat health attitudes*, paper presented at Malaysian Sociological Research Institute, Kelantan

Thambu, J.A.M., 1971, Rupture of the uterus, *Med. J. Malaysia*, 25(4):293-4

Winstedt, R.O., 1951, *The Malay Magic*, London: Routledge & Kegan Paul

Wylde, E.M., 1956, Some superstitious customs surrounded childbirth noted in Kuala Lumpur, In: *Applied Nutrition in Malaya*, Edited by I.A. Simpson, Kuala Lumpur: Institute for Medical Research.

[1] This was the only time I ever observed bamboo used to cut the umbilical cord. All other times scissors were employed. As the bidan kampung were not in the habit of sterilizing their scissors, a newly cut piece of bamboo might have been the better choice.

[2] Although Winstedt writes that for all births "the child is first spat upon by the midwife in order that he may be protected against the old Indonesian spirits of disease" (1951: 41) this was the only occasion at which I witnessed such behaviour.

[3] Chapter 5 of 'Government Midwife and Traditional Midwife' describes the training, ways of practicing and interaction between these two groups of midwives in Malaysia.

A Descriptive Study of the Changing Roles and Practices of Traditional Birth Attendants in Zimbabwe[*]

Barbara Taylor Sparks[†]

ABSTRACT

In Zimbabwe, traditional birth attendants (TBAs) attend more than 50% of the births. Training courses to improve their skills have been offered since 1983. Although there are many assumptions about the TBAs' work, there has been little formal investigation. This is a descriptive study of the practice and attitudes of trained and untrained TBAs in Zimbabwe. Seventy-one midwives were divided into groups according to geographic area and attendance at an upgrading course. Data were obtained through informal small group interviews and observation. Findings indicate that TBAs have traditionally been both health educators and health providers. Midwives who have attended the training course exhibit improved practices, refer more high-risk pregnant women to clinics, and perceive themselves to be attending fewer births. As a result of delivering fewer babies, the TBAs believe that they have lost credibility as health educators.

Zimbabwe is a country of 8½ million people in sub-Saharan Africa. After almost 100 years of colonialism, it gained independence in 1980. Before majority rule, an inadequate formal health care system was available to the indigenous people. Missionaries provided much of the care in the rural areas, and the quality of that care varied with their resources and training. In the urban areas poorly equipped segregated hospitals and clinics were the only formal health care available to most Zimbabweans. A mainstay of health care during the time of colonial rule had been the traditional system of beliefs and practices. This system included both traditional healers (*ngangas*) and traditional birth attendants. These providers, while lacking in formal training, incorporated into their practice the values and beliefs long held and valued by the people. So, at the time of independence in Zimbabwe a dual health-care system existed. One system, which was unavailable to many of the citizens, represented the formally trained doctors and nurses practising in clinics and hospitals. The other system involved deeply ingrained practices of health care provided by lay healers in the villages that incorporated traditional health practices and beliefs[1].

One of the highest priorities of the new Zimbabwean government has been to establish an adequate, new health care system for all. Public health measures are an essential component of this effort. Safe water was available to only 10% of the rural population at independence. Acceptable sewage systems, as well as public transportation, were also required. Large numbers of well-trained Zimbabwean doctors and nurses were

---

[*] Reprinted by permission of Elsevier Science from A descriptive study of the changing roles and practices of traditional birth attendants in Zimbabwe, by B. Sparks Journal of Nurse-Midwifery, Vol. 35: 150-161, Copyright 1990 by the American College of Nurse-Midwives.

[†] Barbara Taylor Sparks graduated from the University of Michigan with a BSN in Nursing, and from Michigan State University with an MSN in Nursing. She is an assistant professor at Michigan State University in the College of Osteopathic Medicine, Division of Obstetrics & Gynecology, and provides health care to women as an independent provider. Ms. Sparks was a visiting lecturer at the University of Zimbabwe, Department of Obstetrics & Gynecology in 1986-1987. She is currently investigating pregnancy-related hypertension in Zimbabwe.

Journal of Nurse-Midwifery, 35 (3), 1990: 150-60

Address correspondence to Barbara Taylor Sparks, MSN, Michigan State University. College of Osteopathic Medicine, 409 W. Fee Hall, East Lansing, MI 48824

needed to replace the many missionaries who had left Zimbabwe during the struggle for independence. This problem was especially acute in the rural areas, which were desperately short of providers and clinics, and where 90% of the population lived.

Training programs for Zimbabwean medical and nursing students have been greatly expanded since the time of independence. However, it will take many years to provide an adequate number of formally trained providers. Currently, traditional providers, including the TBAs, are widely used and it is expected that they will continue to practice for many years.

In 1982, the Ministry of Health in Zimbabwe formally acknowledged the importance of the TBAs to the MCH effort in the country. Pilot training courses were begun to upgrade the skills of the TBAs, to familiarize them with the procedures and personnel in rural clinics, and to encourage them to make appropriate referrals to the clinics. The formal acknowledgement of TBAs and development of a plan to improve their skills was appropriate in the early years after independence because TBAs were attending the births of at least 75% of the rural women[2]. There were many assumptions about their practices, but there was only one attempt to record and systematically analyze the methods these women use when they attend births[3]. The need to document further the practice and attitudes of TBAs was apparent.

Mutambirwa provided the first formal study of traditional pregnancy and childbirth in Zimbabwe[4]. Her work on Shona attitudes about childbirth has been important to both health planners and providers. The effort to learn about TBAs, provide training programs for them, and maintain data flow to government planners continues in 1990.

BACKGROUND

Traditional Shona society in Zimbabwe is both patriarchal and patrilineal. Property is handed down through the male's family and men make most of the important decisions, such as the number of children and allocation of family resources[5]. Under some circumstances, husbands will defer to an older woman, particularly if she is attending a birth and a decision must be made about transport or medications. It is not uncommon for women in their childbearing years to be advised by a physician not to have more children and for their husbands to insist that they become pregnant once again. Many times, particularly in the rural villages, women defer to their husbands' wishes even if this jeopardizes their own health. In the face of these cultural realities the role of the TBA as a grass roots health-care provider is vital. These midwives understand the cultural values of their patients and can reflect these values to formal health-care providers when a conflict occurs between beliefs and decisions about health.

PURPOSE

TBAs represent an important resource for primary health care in many developing countries[6]. Training programs to upgrade the midwives' skills are common and are strongly encouraged by the World Health Organization. These training programs vary with the resources of individual countries and with the health beliefs and practices of the local people.

In Zimbabwe, the training programs for the TBAs are organized at the provincial level and then taught at the rural clinic level. This is appropriate, because customs and beliefs vary from one province to another. The purpose of the training programs in Zimbabwe is to help the midwives achieve the following goals: (1) provide safe deliveries; (2) recognize high-risk pregnant women and refer them to the nearest clinic; and (3) to recognize complications of delivery and encourage transport of the laboring woman to the nearest clinic[7]. In addition to the goals mentioned above, these local training courses familiarize the midwives with the nursing staff of the rural clinics, thus encouraging exchange of ideas and mutual solving of obstetrical problems in the local communities.

Given the urgency of the situation, the training program was implemented without specific knowledge about the midwives' practice. Assumptions were made about the role of the TBAs, their delivery techniques, and their attitudes toward their clients. Formal study of the TBAs as well as the training program is warranted to expand the knowledge base about these health workers and also to evaluate the effect of the training program on the TBAs' attitudes and practices[7].

Expansion of the formal health-care system may directly and/or indirectly cause changes in local TBA practices in parallel with the training program. Knowledge of these changes is important for several reasons. First, new knowledge and skills are most effectively taught when the content is relevant to current practices and problems[8,9]. Ongoing research about the changing practice and attitudes of TBAs can provide a database with which to formulate new or revised relevant education programs. Second, TBAs are encouraged to refer their patients to providers in the formal health-care system if complications are anticipated or if they occur. It is helpful for these providers to have realistic expectations about the care their referred patients have received in the villages (T.H.K. Chimbira, personal communication, 1987). This knowledge of traditional practices may positively influence the outcome of both mother and infant once they reach the hospital. It is for these reasons that the current study was done to identify the practices and attitudes of trained and untrained TBAs in one area of Zimbabwe.

DEFINITIONS

Both trained and untrained midwives were studied. In accordance with the Zimbabwe Ministry of Health's definition, a woman is considered a TBA if she has delivered two or three babies in each of the last three years. Although this is a much smaller number of TBA deliveries than found in other developing countries such as Mexico[8] or Ghana[10] it is considered the norm in Zimbabwe. A TBA is considered "trained" if she has completed a 10 session course at a rural clinic and is awarded a pin and a certificate according her the title vanyamukuta (the aunt who delivers).

SAMPLE

Using grounded-theory methodology, a snowball sample of 71 TBAs was selected and interviewed. All midwives were members of the Shona ethnic group. Sixty-nine midwives were born in Zimbabwe, and two had immigrated from Mozambique more than 20 years ago. The midwives were selected from three geographic areas in Manicaland West and Mashonaland Central. Trained and untrained midwives were selected from three areas. These included a periurban area called Glen View/Glen Norah, a communal land 54 kilometers from Harare called Domboshawa, and a very remote communal land roughly 125 kilometers from the nearest town called Chidamoyo. In total, 31 TBAs had completed a training program and 40 had not. Trained and untrained midwives were found in both communal land areas. Only untrained midwives were found in the periurban areas.

The midwives were initially contacted to talk with me by friends, family members, and village elders. A few trained midwives were identified by the rural clinic nurses who worked with them in the training courses. These midwives then notified their colleagues. All volunteered to participate in the study. Although many women who aspired to be midwives requested that they be allowed to participate, only midwives who fit the definition mentioned above were included in the study. The wish to become involved in the health movement is so great that in the periurban area, when an inaccurate message was circulated, 70 women sought out the investigator because they thought an upgrading course for TBAs was being offered. The names and addresses of these women were submitted to nursing personnel in the Ministry of Health, to be used in the event that a TBA training course was instituted in the area in which they lived.

METHODS

At the first meeting with each TBA, the purpose of the study was explained. It was stressed that the researcher was not "from the Ministry" and was not sent to regulate or sanction aspects of their work in any official capacity.

Qualitative data were gathered from May to November 1987 by small group discussions (six or fewer midwives). Trained and untrained TBAs were interviewed separately. Each midwife was interviewed at least three times, and each interview lasted between 1 and 2½ hours. Three contacts were needed with each TBA group to gather adequate depth of information. Additionally, visits to midwives' homes and their patients' homes validated information and impressions obtained during the discussions. Constant comparative analysis stimulated increasing depth of information at subsequent interviews. When saturated, categories of data were further analyzed, reduced, and compared. This method resulted in the emergence of common themes within and across TBA groups.

A Shona woman, Grace Kamba, acted as translator. The accuracy of her translation during group discussions was validated three separate times by local nurse-midwives who were fluent in both English and Shona. During the discussions, interviews were tape-recorded and then transcribed within 24 hours by Mrs. Kamba. Tapes and transcriptions were also randomly selected twice and submitted to nurses for validation of accuracy. The nurses agreed that the transcriptions made from taped interviews were done with great accuracy.

The interviews took place in villages, on farms, and, in the case of some of the trained midwives, under a shade tree outside of a rural clinic. The interviews were loosely structured and guided by general categories of relevant information. General discussion consisted of stories of births that had recently occurred. Problem-solving was lively among the midwives. Formally trained providers (nurses at the local clinics) were not allowed to attend the discussions. If a curious man or adolescent wandered near the group, they were asked to leave by the midwives. In Zimbabwe, only women who have already given birth themselves may serve as a birth attendant to others or participate in discussions of such matters.

It was very difficult to observe the TBAs attending a birth. This was because of two factors. First, the midwives were called only when a woman was in advanced labor. Second, each midwife attended only a few births each year. Although the investigator was often based a short distance from the villages, the lack of telephone or transport with which to notify her, combined with the usually short time the TBA actually attended the laboring woman, created significant barriers to direct observation of birth. Three births were observed and many postpartum visits were made to women who had delivered within the previous 12 to 24 hours.

No formal payment was given to the subjects. Biscuits and soda were provided at the end of some group discussions. Occasionally a small gift, such as alcohol or string that would be of use during a delivery was offered to the subjects. The midwives frequently requested a special time period to problem-solve difficulties they encountered during births. Several midwives remarked that "we taught each other."

FINDINGS

Demographics

Attempts were made to identify trained and untrained midwives working in the periurban area around Harare, the capital of Zimbabwe. Eighteen untrained TBAs were interviewed and there were no trained midwives identified, as was anticipated. Although some women in the periurban areas deliver at home, attended by TBAs, it is believed by the Ministry of Health personnel that this is a small number and therefore no training programs for TBAs are offered in the urban areas (O.L. Mbengeranwa, personal communication, 1987). The untrained TBAs who worked in Harare had access to safe water that was close to most homes. They lived approximately 30 minutes from a clinic by foot and although telephones were not often available, transport for a laboring woman with complications could usually be mobilized within a few hours.

The rest of the TBAs, both trained (n = 31) and untrained (n = 18) were from the rural areas. These women had variable access to water (often a 20 or 30 minute walk to a well), no electricity, no telephones, and only occasional bus or automobile availability. Organizing transport to a clinic for a woman with labor complications was a lengthy and occasionally impossible situation. Oxcarts and wheelbarrows were occasionally used for transport when an emergency occurred.

Most of the midwives were unsure of their ages. Having been delivered themselves by TBAs, they did not have accurate documentation of specific birth dates. By estimates based on major life events (i.e., first child born at the time Kariba Dam was built), most were between 35 and 65 years old. All but one of the TBAs were illiterate.

Sixty-nine (97%) of the midwives were married, and two were widowed. Many of the rural women's husbands had migrated to the urban areas for employment and those midwives had total responsibility for childcare, house maintenance, and food production, as well as their delivery work. Several sold handmade crafts to supplement their meagre incomes.

All of the midwives had been pregnant. The mean gravity of the trained midwives was 7.7, while their mean parity was 5.8. In the untrained group, the gravity was 9.2 and the parity 6.6. It is noteworthy that almost all of these women had lost at least one child during pregnancy or in the first year of life.

Considering that the current infant mortality rate is approximately 76/1000 live births, this is not unusual in Zimbabwe and is probably similar to the general population in the same age group.

Training

Most TBAs were initially selected by an older female relative (herself a TBA) for apprenticeship. Some older TBAs expressed a wish to teach a young woman her skills to "carry on" when she died. Selection of an apprentice was based on interest or bravery, which implies a willingness to attend laboring women in isolated rural areas with few resources. Some women delivered themselves rather than call someone to attend them, and thus began their training in that way. The apprenticeships were informal and varied from watching or helping with two births to supervision of as many as fifteen. None of the midwives expressed a religious calling to their work, although many had religious affiliations. These affiliations varied from Catholicism to Protestantism to the Apostolic Faith. Interspersed among these religious ethics established during the time of colonialism is a deep and pervasive belief in powerful ancestor spirits, which are an integral part of the Shona health belief system[4,11].

The TBAs who were selected for the formal government upgrading course were chosen by their village communities. The basis for selection was experience and a reputation as a successful birth attendant. A practical attribute, mentioned several times, was the ability of a midwife to travel to the local clinic to attend the weekly classes. This implies the availability of money for bus fare, or the willingness to walk many kilometers to clinic. As stated by Maglacas and Simons: "The typical TBA is illiterate, believes in folk models of the human reproductive process, does other work besides midwifery, and has limited opportunities to attend training sessions"[12].

Payment

The tradition of payment for delivery services is deeply entrenched in this informal health-care system. Usually the untrained birth attendants do not arbitrarily set a fee for delivery assistance; rather there is some negotiation between the TBA and the family. After the birth, the family presents the midwife with goods such as a chicken, sugar, a dress, or a bowl. Sometimes $5 or $10 is substituted for the goods. This payment is presented to the TBA after the newborn's cord falls off, as this is the end of the midwife's formal responsibility to the mother and baby. If the baby dies or is ill when born, the midwives refuse payment. The payment is also waived if the TBA deems it a hardship for the family, or if she has a special relationship with the family. The amount of goods or money offered is not as important as the fact that payment was made.

Among the trained midwives, the issue of the fee for delivery was the cause of great controversy. This is the result of one of the training course policies. The TBAs were told that they should not charge, that they should provide their services free "for the Government" or "for Comrade Mugabe." All of the trained midwives felt this is unfair, because they incurred expenses attending the training course and must leave their other duties to attend a birth. They also stated they should be compensated because they must "touch blood," which is considered unclean in Shona culture. Three of the TBAs mentioned the need to purchase a special traditional medicine (*muti*) with which to cleanse themselves after attending a birth.

The trained TBAs have arrived at a compromise between the directive not to charge and their wish to be compensated for their work. If the family volunteers goods or money, they accept it. However, they neither request a fee nor negotiate for a certain amount. This is a subject that elicited long, emotional discussions whenever it was raised in the interviews. Although the *vanyamukuta* try very hard to comply with the economic directives of their training course, they do not agree with the government directive about payment and circumvent this suggestion whenever possible.

Role

The TBAs have two roles in their village communities. The first is that of health teacher. Only primagravidas receive formal teaching about reproductive matters. However, informal teaching and discussions about health occur frequently as women go about their daily tasks. The TBAs (a traditional birth attendant is also called *ambuya*, which means grandmother) are the community elders who pass on the traditional wisdom concerning pregnancy, birth, and childcare. They discuss such matters as nutrition, rest, sexual activities, and breastfeeding. They also advise couples about the importance of establishing moral purity, which is an essential requirement for the protection of benevolent ancestor spirits during the birth[4].

The second role of the TBAs is that of birth attendant. When asked what it meant to be a birth attendant, the midwives consistently stated that they wished to be of service to the women in their villages. Both trained and untrained midwives believe every woman should have the right to deliver in the clinic if necessary. Many said that the clinic nurses have more knowledge about birth than the TBAs. However, as one midwife stated, "for those who have pains in the night, have no money, no transport, or wish to stay in their homes, it is important that the *ambuya* know about birth."

There were some differences in roles between untrained and trained midwives. The trained midwives discussed the importance of health teaching for pregnant women and said that they stress adequate nutrition with each pregnant woman. The importance of the educational aspect of their role was not stressed as much by the untrained midwives. They gave the impression that they integrated teaching into routine care, but did not assign it the same importance as their trained colleagues.

The untrained TBAs attended all women who asked them. They prefer not to attend a birth if complications occur, but they vary in their ability to anticipate this and to refer high-risk women to the clinic. The trained midwives theoretically accepted the plan recommended by the clinic nursing staff. Under that system all pregnant women should have at least one prenatal, visit at the clinic. If they are deemed "low risk" they can choose between clinic delivery or home birth. If they are identified as "high risk" (i.e., previous cesarean section, hypertensive, previous fetal death) they are asked to go to the clinic or hospital for the birth. The trained midwives prefer to deliver women who have been examined in the clinics, and recommended in their villages that all pregnant women go to the clinic for screening. Having attended an upgrading course, advocating prenatal visits to the clinic is an important part of their role. However, if a pregnant woman called them for help when she was in advanced labor, they admitted they would not refuse to attend her. One *vanyamukuta* said: "The woman must book at clinic so if an *ambuya* delivers her and there is a problem, the *ambuya* will not be blamed."

Both untrained and trained midwives feel their role is changing. They all report they are attending fewer births each year, This is an interesting perception that is not entirely consistent with the number of births the midwives reported. In Domboshawa the untrained TBAs delivered an average of 5.5 ± 1.4 babies in 1986 and 2.3 ± 0.93 in 1987. The trained Domboshawa TBAs delivered 4.9 ± 0.90 babies in 1986 and 3.8 ± 0.88 babies in 1987. Although both Domboshawa groups reported fewer deliveries, only the untrained midwives showed a statistically significant decrease ($p \leq .05$). In Chidamoyo, the rural area with no clinic available for deliveries, the untrained TBAs reported 2.5 ± 0.33 deliveries in 1986 and 1.7 ± 0.35 deliveries in 1987, a slight decrease. The trained TBAs in this area delivered 5.8 ± 1.1 babies in 1986 and 6.1 ± 0.86 in 1987, an *increase* in births attended and a considerably higher number of births than their untrained colleagues.[‡]

The midwives' perception that they are attending fewer births each year is based on several factors. First, they feel they are better able to screen high-risk pregnant women and refer them to clinic. They also report more clinic availability (even in Chidamoyo). All of the untrained midwives feel they are losing patients to trained midwives. Given the increased status of the trained midwives and the considerable efforts to train TBAs made by nurses in the rural clinics, this certainly seems plausible. However, trained as well as untrained midwives in all areas were concerned with their decreasing patient numbers. It is likely that as the formal health-care system expands services in the rural areas, more pregnant women will be attending the clinic for birth instead of having a TBA-attended home birth. It may be this probability that is responsible for the midwives' perception that they are already attending fewer births.

As a result of less involvement in births in their villages, the TBAs say they have less credibility as health educators. The pregnant women and their husbands look to the clinic nurse for advice. As couples discard the traditional birthing system in the villages, they discard the traditional teaching as well. One midwife stated it this way: "Long ago men were told (about postpartum sex) and were afraid of the *ambuya* who delivered the baby. These days they go to clinic. No one worries about the *ambuya*. They say the *ambuyas* are full of 'I knows.' "

[‡] Data collection stopped October 1987. Data have been adjusted to give an annual rate.

PRACTICE

Antenatal

According to Shona belief, women attain spiritual purity only after they have a successful birth[4]. Therefore great effort is made to ensure a normal pregnancy and healthy baby. One such effort is to delay announcement of pregnancy. This helps to avoid jealous or malevolent witches who could jinx the pregnant woman. The result of this jinxing would be danger to the pregnant woman or her fetus. Both trained and untrained TBAs said they could diagnose pregnancy in the first trimester by noting the pregnant woman's enlarged breasts, as well as changes in her eating habits. However, because the TBAs share the belief in the power of witches, they also do not discuss the news of a new pregnancy in the village.

As a further effort to avoid danger during pregnancy, only primagravidas have formalized prenatal care from TBAs. This begins at about seven months' gestation when the pregnant woman leaves her husband's village and returns to her parent's home. There, a social ceremony called *masungiro* occurs. After *masungiro*, the primagravidas visit a family member who is a TBA for formal care during their pregnancy. They are given a special drink, *masewo*, to open and widen the pelvis for the birth. Many of the midwives stated that this drink is so powerful it works for subsequent pregnancies as well as the initial delivery! The introitus of the primagravida is also stretched manually. The TBA lubricates her hand with a soapy leaf called sepo. She introduces several fingers into the vagina and gently stretches the perineum. This process is repeated many times on subsequent days until the midwife can insert her entire hand, make a fist, and then gently withdraw it.

Many of the TBAs said that they were able to identify twins or a baby in a breech position by abdominal palpation in the ninth month, and some said that they were experienced in external version. However, the trained midwives had been told this was dangerous, and most said they had stopped attempting it as a result of the upgrading course. After the *masewo* is ingested, the perineum stretched, and the position of the fetus determined, the primagravida is thought to be physically ready to deliver. What is left for her to do is discuss any grievances or bad deeds she has done with the *ambuya*. Then, morally cleansed, she can anticipate an easy delivery.

The multigravidas receive care only in the form of discussions on general issues concerning pregnancy. For the TBAs to direct advice specifically to the pregnant women would be to acknowledge their pregnancy, and thus allow unknown dangers to prevail. As the women meet to wash clothes, process maize, or tend their gardens, it is acceptable for the village TBA to discuss general issues concerning pregnancy and birth. This would include such statements as "Most pregnant women stop having sex when their dress is too tight" or "I have a friend who has a new baby blanket to sell. Perhaps someone in this village wants to buy it."

Advice for the pregnant women revolves around nutrition, rest, exercise, and sexual intercourse. The TBAs discuss the importance of rest, although they recognize most pregnant women must continue childcare, fetching water, and/or gardening tasks to some extent. The midwives say a little exercise is good to "loosen up the baby." Sexual intercourse after the seventh month is not advised by either untrained or trained TBAs. They feel it may damage the head of the fetus.

The trained midwives stress the importance of prenatal nutrition more than the untrained. This is most likely the result of the upgrading course in which the nurses emphasized adequate nutrition. The trained midwives do not warn against eating specific foods, but suggest additions to the maize-based diet with such things as milk and a local dried fish called *matemba*. Pica, the ingestion of certain tree barks and anthill clay, is frequently practiced. This is widely accepted, although it is not assigned particular meaning. Several midwives said pregnant women ate strange things because they taste good to them.

Few Shona women drink beer or smoke, and none of the midwives interviewed knew that these practices were harmful to the baby. They also did not feel that weight gain in pregnancy was particularly important. Most stated that some women "got big" while others did not and that this did not affect the outcome of the baby. Pregnant women who were still breastfeeding an older child were advised to stop, as the TBAs believe breast milk becomes sour and will make the child sick.

Labor

The TBA is called to the pregnant woman's sleeping hut during advanced labor. Shona women are expected to demonstrate bravery during labor and prefer to labor and cope with pain in privacy. Often the TBAs are called when it is too late in the birth process to arrange transport to clinic.

The laboring women quite commonly take a special kind of *muti* to enhance labor contractions. The *muti*, called *sunungure,* is often obtained by a relative and taken before the TBA arrives. The midwife may have little idea of what or how much was taken. *Sunungure* is thought by many in the formal health-care system to be a powerful oxytocic.

The mother or mother-in-law of the pregnant woman also attends the birth, to act both as a helper and as a witness to the event. The TBAs all said they appreciated a witness so that if a problem occurred, testimony could be provided to the community that no jinxing had been done. Husbands, children, or nulliparous women are not allowed to witness labor or birth.

The untrained midwives encourage laboring women to use an upright, sitting position during the second stage of labor. They stated that flexibility was important and whatever their patent preferred was alright. However, the trained midwives stated that they asked their patients to lie "flat like in the clinic."

All the TBAs offered the laboring women warm tea or porridge and avoided using cold substances, because it is believed that they stop labor. Vaginal exams were commonly done by the untrained midwives using soap or *sepo* as a lubricant. There seemed to be little awareness of principles of hygiene in this group of midwives. The trained midwives related that they did few vaginal exams, and only for suspected complications such as breech presentation. When they did a vaginal exam, they said they washed their hands "if they had time." It was observed that when they examined a newly delivered mother or baby they did not wash their hands.

If the labor was a long and difficult one, the untrained midwives sometimes gave their patient a second dose of *sunungure* to enhance their labor. The trained midwives no longer give *sunungure*, although they complain that their patients take it before calling them for assistance. These traditional substances seem to be widely available, and one midwife told me that everyone could get *sunungure* from "one who knows."

The Shona people of Zimbabwe have deep-seated beliefs in the importance of maintaining excellent morality and as a result of this receiving protection from ancestor spirits. If labor is not progressing in a predictable, timely way, it is assumed that either the laboring women or their husbands have been immoral and thus have lost the benevolent protection of their ancestor spirits[4]. It is commonly believed by both the trained and untrained TBAs that adultery is the most frequent immoral act that has been committed by laboring women who are having difficulty. This act can be rectified if the women confess. The midwives say that many years ago they used physical coercion to force their patients to confess. Now it is said that they use verbal coercion only, including such things as scolding or threatening. Once the women have confessed, their husbands are informed. Then the midwife twirls water in her mouth to warm it and sprays it over the laboring women's abdomen. It is believed that the laboring women, then purified, will deliver shortly and have a healthy baby. If immoral women do not confess, it is assumed that either they or their babies may die.

Sometimes the TBAs suspect the husbands have committed adultery. This too can result in labor complications. If a midwife is concerned about this, the husband is called into the labor hut and a confession is demanded. When questioned about the consequences of informing either the husband or the wife of their spouse's adultery, one *ambuya* said "It is better to be divorced than dead!"

Although all the TBAs said they preferred to transfer laboring women with complications to clinic, the trained TBAs were much better able to articulate specific reasons for transfer. These reasons include an unbooked primagravida, previous cesarean section, premature labor, abnormal fetal presentation, obstructed labor, vaginal bleeding, prolapsed cord, abnormal edema or seizures, and women who are "too tired." The untrained midwives are less likely to anticipate a problem and only attempt to transfer their patients if there is an immediate birth complication such as incomplete breech delivery, shoulder dystocia, or prolapsed cord. Both trained and untrained midwives said that if a multiparous patient labored from sunup to sunset and the birth was not imminent, they would begin to think about transfer. The ability to transfer a patient to clinic depends both on what stage of labor she is in and the availability of car, bus, or cart with which to transfer her.

Interestingly, several trained midwives related tales of accompanying laboring women to clinic. Upon arrival, the nurse was busy with other patients and asked the midwife to "watch their patient." If the pregnant women delivered very quickly, the TBAs attended them in the clinic. In this way they were able to both assist the nurse and ensure professional help for their patient should a complication arise. This seems an excellent outcome of increased contact between the nurses and the midwives, and supports the idea of expanded local contact between the two kinds of providers.

Delivery

During the delivery of the baby, all of the TBAs said their most important task is to support the perineum and prevent lacerations. This is done by placing a clean cloth over the anus and perineum and pressing it with their hand. Many mentioned that "long ago" the cloth was kept in place with the midwife's foot, leaving the hands free to catch the baby. Three of the untrained midwives interviewed still preferred that method.

The complication that both trained and untrained TBAs seemed to fear the most was that of a neuchal cord. Although this cord problem had been discussed in the training course, there was no way that the trained midwives felt they could anticipate it. All said that when they saw the baby emerging with an umbilical cord wrapped around a baby's limb or neck, they lubricated their hands and tried to disentangle it. Surprisingly, neither premature rupture of membranes nor meconium-stained amniotic fluid was mentioned by the TBAs when they discussed birth complications. When questioned about these things, they were not aware that they are potential dangers. Often the membranes rupture before the midwives are called to the labor hut, so their opportunity to differentiate normal from abnormal amniotic fluid may be very limited. Shoulder dystocia was managed by stretching the perineum, and the concept of a rigid pelvic structure was not discussed by the midwives. Although the trained midwives seemed much better able to identify high-risk pregnant women, management of the actual birth seemed to be the same between groups. The only exception was that the trained midwives had a better understanding of the importance of hygiene.

If a baby appeared to be weak when born, both trained and untrained midwives said they blew warm water on the nose and mouth of the baby and, if necessary, turned it upside down. If further intervention seemed to be necessary (poor tone or inability to nurse), elders in the village decided whether consultation with a traditional healer or a clinic nurse was necessary. In some instances, both options were pursued. If an infant was born with an anomaly, management seemed to be dependent on the extent of the handicap. Minor abnormalities, such as an extra finger, were treated in the village by the midwife, who wrapped string tightly around the extra digit until it atrophied and dropped off. If the anomaly was deemed sufficient to interfere with normal function, the infant was taken to a government-run hospital for handicapped children called Jaris Juri. Many midwives told me that "long ago" a significantly handicapped baby was left to die, but that this is no longer the case since hospital placement is possible. If an infant is born dead, or dies shortly after birth, the mother is washed with a special *muti* to ensure that this tragedy does not happen again. This death may not be reported to the authorities, particularly if the mother was not booked at clinic or was delivered by an untrained midwife. Consequences of this underreporting may be failure to identify a subsequent high-risk pregnancy and inaccurate government data about perinatal mortality.

Cord care is thought to be very important by the midwives. Traditionally, the TBAs tied the cord with sisal, a readily available plant with fibrous leaves, and cut the cord with a sharp leaf. After this was done, the cord stump was dressed frequently with wood ash, fresh guinea hen droppings, or the ashes of burnt guinea hen droppings until the cord stump dropped off. TBAs who had attended the training course had been taught not to use these substances, presumably to decrease the occurrence of neonatal tetanus. They said that a new razor blade, supplied by the expectant mother, was the best cutting tool for cutting a cord. If this was not available, boiling a clean, used blade was suggested, and two trained midwives said they soaked a used blade in alcohol before using it to cut the cord. Some trained midwives said they tied the cord with string or thread, also boiled or soaked, and that the best cord dressing was alcohol. If alcohol was not available they dressed the cord with salt water. Seven of the untrained midwives also stated that they used a new razor blade to cut the cord, and they no longer dressed the cord with wood ashes.

Two trained midwives who said they used alcohol to soak the blade and dress the cord were, at a subsequent interview, presented with a small bottle of alcohol as a gift. After profuse thanks, they asked how to use it on the cord and how long to soak the blade. Discussion revealed that although they had been told to use alcohol, and believed it was a better alternative to traditional substances, they were unable to buy it in the rural shops. The local clinic where they had received their training was also short of supplies and had never been able to supply the midwives with alcohol, as had been expected. As a result of this discussion a disparity was revealed between heightened awareness of the importance of alcohol for cord care and the availability of supplies with which to actually change the midwives' practice.

Questioning of other midwives revealed that this disparity was a common problem. There was a general expectation that rural clinic staff would be able to supply both alcohol and gloves to the midwives. However, these supplies were not easily available. Thus the trained midwives were struggling with the conflict between what they had been told to do and what they were able to do. Many compromised by cutting the cord with a sharp leaf and dressing the cord with water.

Birth is not considered complete until the placenta is delivered. Until that time mothers do not ask about the sex or health of the baby and midwives speak very little. The midwives said that the womb "squeezes out" the placenta. If this did not happen "quickly," a stick, called a *chavakuru*, was used to gag the newly delivered woman, and all agreed that this facilitated the placental expulsion. Manual expulsion was not done by any midwives interviewed, although there was great fear that if the placenta was not delivered, the cord could go back into the womb and cause considerable damage. Consequently, if the *chavakuru* did not help with placental delivery, a heavy object like a stone was attached to the cord to prevent retraction into the uterus and the woman was transported to clinic.

None of the TBAs knew about fundal massage nor immediate breastfeeding to hasten placental delivery or decrease postpartum bleeding. Discussion of these interventions was met with enthusiasm and hand clapping, as everyone viewed them as practical and potentially helpful. In general, the midwives were receptive to new methods of improving their practice as long as these methods were not in conflict with traditional beliefs. The first time these interventions were suggested, it was with the trained midwives in Domboshawa. Four days later, when the untrained midwives in the same area were interviewed, several of them already knew about the suggestions, and one had tried fundal massage at a recent delivery. This finding illustrates two important points about the subjects. First, these women are very motivated to improve their practice and provide safer deliveries for their patients. Second, there is a potential "spillover" effect of efforts, as frequent communication about delivery methods occur between trained and untrained TBAs.

Postpartum

After the infant and placenta are delivered, only two of the trained midwives stated that they checked the perineum for lacerations. Most midwives pointed out that many deliveries occur at night, that there is either poor light or no light, and it would be difficult to see a tear. They also said that by the morning after the birth the new mother was embarrassed to have her vulva examined and would refuse. Lacerations were usually suspected if the women complained of pain with urination. If this occurred, they were either sent to clinic or given a poultice of traditional medicine to apply to the vulva. No examination would be done by the midwives.

The placenta is buried within 24 hours of the birth, by either the midwife or the newly delivered women. This procedure is important so that jinxing cannot be placed on the placenta, thus causing future infertility of the mother. In the rural areas the placenta is buried in the floor of the hut or in a nearby field. In the periurban areas some dwellings have cement floors. In this case, the placenta is either flushed down the toilet or taken to a rural area to be disposed of. The most important issues are to dispose of the placenta quickly and bury it deeply, so that it does not attract the attention of evil spirits or witches.

Eye contact between the mother and the newborn occurs only after the placenta is safely delivered and the new baby washed and wrapped. Then it is placed in the mother's arms. She usually does not breast-feed the day of delivery. It is widely believed that colostrum is "like water" and therefore of no benefit to the newborn. The midwives report that this belief is slowly changing. Thirty-one (77.5%) of the untrained midwives believe the colostrum is not useful and nine (22.5%) report it is "okay." Of the trained midwives, only nine (29%) stated they would advise against delivery-day breastfeeding to the new mother and 22 (71%) reported that it would not hurt the baby (although few recommend it). Frequently, warm water is given to the newborn from a spoon to "soften its throat," and only when the mother's true breastmilk comes in is the infant put to breast. This is said to occur on day 1 or 2 post delivery in Zimbabwean women.

Almost all mothers in Zimbabwe breastfeed their babies. Once breastfeeding has begun, the babies are fed on demand. Occasionally, if breast milk is slow to come in or is inadequate in amount, the mother is fed salted groundnuts several times a day until this problem is rectified. If a new mother is very ill or dies, only her mother is allowed to breastfeed the newborn. Relactation is initiated by inserting pieces of a special plant into small cuts made in the grandmother's breasts. It is believed that if any other women nurse the baby, it will die. Occasionally a newborn will be given bottled milk, although this is rare. A bottlefed baby was not seen in the rural areas by the researcher during the entire period of the investigation.

During the first few days after delivery, the new mothers are instructed by the TBAs about care of the baby and appropriate nourishment and rest for themselves. Sexual intercourse is discouraged for the first postpartum month, although the midwives say this "makes the husbands cross." As long as the postpartum women are still bleeding, sexual relations are avoided, because blood is considered unclean. After the bleeding stops however, the midwives say the husbands do not take their advice about waiting to have intercourse, and thus it is important for the mother to go to the clinic for birth control.

All midwives interviewed stated that contraceptive options available at the clinics are better than the traditional methods of birth control, such as herbs tied around the woman's waist, breastfeeding, or withdrawal practiced by the men. Although they think the contraceptive pill is good, they prefer "the injection." This refers to Depo-Provera, which is available only to grand multiparous women over the age of 35. The perceived advantages of Depo-Provera are twofold. First, its use requires only infrequent visits to the clinic, and second, the decision to use contraception can be a private one if conflict about further pregnancies exist within a couple.

One or two days after a baby is delivered in a village, the new mother is encouraged by the TBAs to go to a clinic to have her baby examined and immunized and to discuss contraception with the nurse. The trained midwives are encouraged by the nurses to accompany the new mother to clinic, and if they do, the mother is given papers that allow her to register her baby's birth. If an untrained midwife delivers the baby and accompanies the new mother to clinic, the nurses lecture the mother on the importance of using a trained midwife for delivery and sometimes refuse to supply the preregistration papers. This, of course, provides a strong incentive to use only trained midwives as birth attendants.

CONCLUSIONS

It is important to identify values and practices of the TBAs currently providing health care in Zimbabwe. In doing this, one can identify their strengths and reinforce their considerable efforts to be competent providers[5]. Studies of current TBA practices also provide data about problems or information gaps. Once identified, this information can lead to changes that will improve the midwives' skills and the health of the women they attend. Both the trained and untrained midwives that were studied are highly motivated to provide safe health care to the women of their communities. These midwives bring to their patients a deep-seated belief in the value of traditional practices. Yet, they are willing to learn and to change their practices if offered relevant options that will enhance their work as birth attendants.

Midwives who have attended the government-sponsored training courses are increasingly aware of the importance of prenatal screening visits to clinic, and they advocate this to pregnant women in their local communities. In addition, many TBAs are referring high-risk women to clinic for delivery rather than attempting to attend them in the villages. Evidence has been presented that indicates that safer care is practiced by the midwives who have attended the training course (see Table 1). Better hygiene is practiced by these women, less *muti* is used, and the very important practice of breastfeeding immediately after birth is encouraged more by the trained midwives than those who have not attended the upgrading course.

Issues were identified that may require consideration by organizers of the upgrading courses. For instance, the trained TBAs seem less flexible than the untrained TBAs when laboring women wish to use an upright position for the second stage of labor. It has been shown that, under some circumstances, an upright position enlarges the pelvic diameter and provides better uterine/placental blood flow, thus easing delivery for both mother and infant[13,14]. Perhaps this information could be incorporated into the upgrading course and result in the midwives encouraging a variety of birthing positions for their patients when in labor.

Tools for delivery (such as gloves, string, and alcohol) are frequently not available for the TBAs, despite their expectations that such items may be furnished by their local clinic. Realistic expectations may help the midwives substitute readily available supplies that are safe and approved by the upgrading course instructors. Given the world-wide concern about infection from the HIV virus, perhaps efforts could be made to obtain inexpensive, reusable gloves that could be cleaned with locally available soap or soap-like traditional herbs after each delivery.

Table 1 Differences in Practice between Trained and Untrained TBAs

Trained	Untrained
Prenatal teaching important	Prenatal teaching less important
Prenatal clinic visit advocated	Prenatal clinic visit not stressed
Do not perform external version	Perform external version
Give few traditional drugs	Frequent use of traditional drugs
Recumbent position second stage of labor	Upright position second stage of labor
Few vaginal exams	Frequent vaginal exams
Able to identify some high-risk patients	Less ability to identify high-risk patients
Accompany patient to clinic	Do not accompany patient to clinic
Attempt good hygiene	Good hygiene poorly understood
No *muti* on cord	Traditional cord care
Encourage early breastfeeding	Discourage early breastfeeding

There was little knowledge about the danger of premature rupture of membranes or of the use of fundal massage to control postpartum bleeding in several of the midwife groups interviewed. This included many midwives who had attended the classes. Incorporating these subjects into the course curriculum could be easily done, and simple interventions could be developed to enhance further the TBAs' effectiveness as safe health-care providers.

The recommendation by the government health officials that TBAs not charge for their services is very controversial and frequently resented by the midwives. One wonders if the small payment they traditionally have received for their work serves to legitimize their role as birth attendants and to enhance their status. The status of these midwives is an important issue to them. As a result of the upgrading course, TBAs are referring an increasing number of their patients to clinic for delivery. Although they understand the rationale for this, they frequently express concern about the resulting loss of status as health providers and the resulting loss of credibility as health educators as well. Consideration should be given to the positive effect of reinstating government approval of payment to the midwives (particularly the trained midwives). Patient payment for services would allow continual recognition of the midwives' efforts to be trained, as well as legitimize their importance to the health effort in the country. If legitimizing their role would enhance their credibility as health educators, their effectiveness in referring even more patients to clinic for evaluation or delivery would be enhanced.

New knowledge about attending births is quickly passed from trained to untrained TBAs. This is a measure of the enthusiasm with which both trained and untrained midwives receive and integrate new ideas into their work. This "spillover effect" is a significant benefit of the upgrading course and indicates that a wider base of birth attendants is being reached than was anticipated when the upgrading courses were being organized.

Both trained and untrained TBAs in the study welcome working relationships with personnel in the formal health-care system. There is evidence of this in their acceptance of new interventions and techniques and by their increasing referrals to the rural clinics. The trained midwives welcome the opportunities to accompany their patients to clinic and also to return to clinic for additional instruction about their work.

The motivation of Zimbabwean women to provide safe, skilled care to their family and friends during delivery is apparent. Positive changes in TBA practices have been found as a result of previously taught courses. These facts support expansion of the number of upgrading courses in Zimbabwe when resources are available, so that more TBAs can be reached. Perhaps consideration could be given to integrating some of the TBAs formally into the clinics as nursing aides and teachers for pregnant women. This would further integrate the midwives into the formal system and possibly relieve the nurses of a few of their overwhelming patient-care responsibilities. Integration of trained TBAs into the formal health-care system would also enhance their credibility as health teachers and providers. If this were done, perhaps more pregnant women would seek out their services rather than those of the untrained midwives.

The upgrading course for TBAs, developed and implemented by the Zimbabwe Ministry of Health, is an excellent example of a successful relationship between providers of traditional and modern health care. This is a concept that has been deemed essential by the World Health Organization to improving health care in developing countries[12]. As a result of this training program for TBAs, and the enormous effort of many citizens of Zimbabwe who are supporting this program, the people should come closer to "Health for All" by the year 2000.

ACKNOWLEDGEMENTS

The author would like to gratefully acknowledge the help of Dr. T.H.K. Chimbira, Dr. O.L. Mbengeranwa, Mrs. Grace Kamba, Dr. Barbara Given, and especially the dedicated traditional birth attendants who gave so freely of their time and knowledge.

This paper is dedicated to the memory of T.H.K. Chimbira, MBCHB, MRCOG, MD, who chaired the Department of Obstetrics & Gynaecology at the University of Zimbabwe during the time of this study. His untimely death is a loss for his family, his academic community, and his country.

[1] Bourdillon, M, *The Shona peoples* (3rd revised edn.) Harare. Zimbabwe, Mambo Press, 1987, pp. 149-68.

[2] *Planning for equity in health*. Harare, Zimbabwe, Ministry of Health, 1975.

[3] Gelfand, M, Mavi, S, Drummond, R, Ndemera, E, *The traditional medical practitioner in Zimbabwe*. Harare, Zimbabwe, Mambo Press, 1985, pp. 35-70.

[4] Mutambirwa J, Pregnancy, childbirth, mother and child care among the indigenous people of Zimbabwe. *Int J Gynaecol Obstet* 23:275-285, 1985.

[5] Folta, J, Deck, E, Rural Zimbabwean Shona women illness concepts and behavior. *West J Nurs Res* 9:301-316, 1987.

[6] Raisler, J, International perspective: the midwife's role in promoting safe motherhood. *J Nurs-Midwif* 33:155-158, 1988.

[7] Equllion, C, Training traditional midwives in Manicaland, Zimbabwe. *Int J Gynaecol Obstet* 23:287-90, 1985.

[8] Jordon, B, *Modes of teaching and teaming: questions raised by the training of traditional birth attendants*. Palo Alto, California, Institute for Research on Learning, Report No. IRL87-0004, 1987.

[9] Sargent, C, The cultural context of therapeutic choice obstetrical care decisions among the Bariba of Benin, In: *Culture, Illness and Healing*, Boston, D. Reidel Publishing Co., 1982, 3:157-167.

[10] Neumann, A, Nicholas, M, Ammonoo-Acquah, B, *et al.* Evaluation of a program to train traditional birth attendants in Ghana, In: Maglacas, M. (ed.), *The Potential of the Traditional Birth Attendant*, Geneva, WHO Offset Publication No. 95, 1986, pp 51-60.

[11] Chavunduka, G, *Traditional healers and the Shona patient*. Harare, Zimbabwe, Mambo Press, 1978, 3:1-19.

[12] Maglacas, A, Simons, J, *The potential of the traditional birth attendant*. Geneva, WHO Offset Publication No. 95, 1986, p 6.

[13] Liu, Y, The effects of the upright position during childbirth. *IMAGE: J Nurs Scholarship* 21:14-8, 1989.

[14] Rossi, M, Lindell, S, Maternal positions and pushing techniques in a non-prescriptive environment. *JOGNN* 15: 203-8. 1986.

JIDDA: THE TRADITIONAL MIDWIFE OF YEMEN?

Lidwien M. Scheepers [†]

ABSTRACT

Contrary to what is assumed, traditional birth attendants (TBAs) do not appear to be a clearly defined category of women with specialized knowledge and experience of assistance at deliveries in the local cultural situation at village level in the Anis region of the central highlands in Yemen. In the actual design of training for TBAs in Yemen, this results in problematic provision of basic mother and child health care, in particular safe and clean deliveries to all women at village level.

The policy of Primary Health Care (PHC) of the World Health Organization (WHO), launched in 1978, emphasizes the training of traditional birth attendants (TBAs). The objective of this training is to provide basic mother and child health care, in particular, safe and clean deliveries for women in the rural areas surrounding the health centre or unit. In this way, the WHO is trying to reduce the high rates of maternal and perinatal mortality. A TBA is defined by the WHO as "a person (usually a woman) who assists the mother at childbirth and who initially acquired her skills delivering babies by herself or by working with other traditional birth attendants" [1]. This global definition embraces a broad variety of different categories of TBAs classified from professional midwives to a less clearly defined category of women with no specialized knowledge and experience of assistance at deliveries. Although the original global definition indicates, in theory, divergent categories of TBAs, in reality it is very often put on a level with only one category of TBAs; i.e. the indigenous midwife, empirical midwife and traditional midwife. Also in WHO-documents this occurs explicitly [1, p.7; 2], while at the same time, these texts implicitly state that not in all cases are TBAs a clearly defined category of women specialized in deliveries.

Therefore, it is of utmost importance that the category of TBAs should be redefined in more detail by additional research in relation to the local situation of a particular country or region, since only when the training is geared to the correct target group will the above-mentioned objective be achieved.

Originating from experiences in other countries in the Middle East, it is also generally assumed in Yemen that there exists in the traditional context a category of women who have specialized knowledge and experience in assisting at deliveries and that there also exists a term to refer to them. In the Sudan [3] the term '*dayat el habil* (midwives of the rope)' [4] and in Egypt [5] the term '*daya* (midwife)' refer to such a category of women. The term *jidda* is used in Yemen at project level [6], since in searching for a term to indicate this assumed category of women the term *jidda* seemed to be the obvious choice.

Jidda literally means grandmother. It is, in fact, quite often the grandmother who assists at deliveries. This might be the mother-in-law of the pregnant woman who is always present due to the patrilocality of the couple, or it might be the mother of the pregnant woman because of her preference for someone familiar. But even if an older woman, unrelated to the pregnant woman, assists at the delivery, she is also referred to with the term *Jidda*. This manner of address, however, does not relate to the fact that she is assisting at deliveries but is used generally to address older, even unrelated women, as a way of expressing respect for them [7].

[†] *Social Science & Medicine* 33(9), 1991: 959-62. Copyright by Elsevier Science.
Contact address: L Scheepers, Groesbeeksedwarsweg 302, 6521 DW Nijmegen, The Netherlands

Since the early 1980s, the term *jidda* has been used as the appropriate Yemeni Arabic referent for a TBA. This term is generally accepted within the PHC terminology in Yemen (Swagman, personal communication). In general it is supposed that the term *jidda* in the traditional context refers to the category of women assumed to be specialized in deliveries and therefore the training is geared to them. Within the scope of the above-mentioned policy of the WHO, it is assumed that the training of one or two TBAs/*jiddat* in each village will provide all women with basic mother and child health care.

In the Dhamar Governorate in the former YAR, a health project has a training department which organizes the training of TBAs. After conducting a few years of training and letting the trained TBAs work in their communities for a while, doubts began to emerge with regard to the results of the training and so I was employed to look into the issue.

From July up to and including November 1989, I collected data relating to TBAs, mainly in villages in the Anis region of the central highlands: at Taalibi, Hamaam Ali and Dhi Hud and surrounding villages. Through participation in a selection procedure in the area of Al Mashahidhah and the surroundings of Al Masna'ah I gained insight into the selection of women for the training. At Taalibi and Hamaam Ali were chosen because they were two of the villages where the first training courses of the project were carried out. Dhi Hud was chosen because a training course had recently come to an end. In these villages 16 trained TBAs (out of the 26 that had been trained), ±28 non-trained TBAs and village women were selected at random and semi-structured interviews were carried out with them. Then structured interviews with 14 trained TBAs were executed and quantitative data on the number of deliveries conducted before and after the training by seven of the trained TBAs was made available to use as statistical comparison with the aid of a chi-square test [8].

When I first went to the villages in the Anis region of the central highlands to visit the *jiddat*, I encountered a confusing mixture of terms to indicate women who assist at deliveries. Next to the term *jidda*, which was known to me from the project level, I discovered that a woman who assists at deliveries is referred to at village level as *il-mara illi tquss is-surr* (the woman who cuts the cord), *il-mara illi ta'amal is-surr* (the woman who does the cord) or they use the verb *sarra* (to cut the umbilical cord). At village level I did not find an equivalent in Yemeni Arabic to the word midwife, which might be an indication that such a category of TBAs does not exist in this rural region of Yemen. The term *jidda* and the other terms at village level for women who assist at deliveries were used, in what seemed to me initially, a confusing way. Finally, however, it became clear that, in this region, the term *jidda* is being used at village level to indicate the project-trained women. Non-trained women are referred to amongst other things as "they who cut the cord". I concluded that the term *jidda,* as used to indicate the assumed category of women in the traditional context who have special knowledge and experience with deliveries, finds its origin outside the village context. As a result of the training of TBAs/*jiddat*, the term *jidda* has been introduced at village level and is only used by the women to indicate project-trained women. The term is in no-way connected to the traditional terms for women who, of old at village level, assisted at deliveries. These women are still referred to, among other things, as "they who cut the cord".

In summary, it can be concluded that in the Anis region the term *jidda* at village level means grandmother and is also used to address older, even unrelated women, as a way of expressing respect. Through the training of TBA/*jiddat*, a new significance of the term *jidda* has been introduced at village level, i.e. a project-trained woman who assists at deliveries. In addition to other references, the traditional term "they who cut the cord" is the most common way to refer to non-trained women who assist at deliveries.

Table 1. (a) Ways used at village levels to indicate women who assist at deliveries

Before the training	After the training
The woman who cuts the cord	*idem*
The woman who does the cord	*idem*
Use of the verb *sarra*	*idem*
	jidda

(b) Significance of the term *jidda* at village level

Before the training	After the training
Grandmother	*idem*
The term *jidda* is used to address older, even unrelated women as a way of expressing respect for them	*idem*
Project-trained woman who assists at deliveries	

In the Anis region the term *jidda* appears not to be an appropriate term for a woman who traditionally assists at deliveries at the local level. This leads me to question, therefore, as to whether the assumption that women who assist at village deliveries are a clearly defined category of women specialized in deliveries. Everywhere in the world women assist each other at deliveries, but when can a woman be said to have special knowledge and experience with regard to this? To acquire some insight into the issue for the Anis region, this article gives a description of "women who cut the cord". The description aims to answer the following questions: Who assists who at the delivery? Is assistance at deliveries a full-time occupation by means of which one can earn a living? In what way is a delivery assisted?

To determine who assists at the delivery of whom, I asked "women who cut the cord" for more specific information about each pregnant woman they assisted. In the first instance, I asked her to classify the pregnant woman as being her neighbor or not [9]. Then I asked her to classify the same pregnant woman again, this time according to whether she was related to her or not [9, Annex 2]. It soon became evident that "women who cut the cord" differ considerably with regard to the number of pregnant women they assist at the delivery. There are women who merely incidentally assist at a delivery, women who only assist at the deliveries of their own daughters or daughters-in-law and women who mainly give assistance both at the deliveries of neighboring women unrelated to them, and to related women living further away (Appendix A).

Thus it looks as if assistance at deliveries is provided from within the network of neighbors and related women. This is not surprising, since the unpredictability of the time of delivery and the restrained mobility of women, especially at night, makes the proximity of a woman with whom the pregnant woman is familiar, a necessity.

The confining of the working area of "women who cut the cord" to the neighborhood and their kinship networks is also connected to the fact that assistance at deliveries is not a full-time occupation but only one amongst many of their duties. "Women who cut the cord" are not paid in money or in kind for their services. They work for *ajr*: the promise of rewards given in the afterlife for good deeds done on earth. Thus, contrary to the Sudan for example, where women earn their living from this occupation [10], rendering assistance at deliveries in this rural region of Yemen is not an occupation from which women can earn a livelihood. Even if "women who cut the cord" were paid for their assistance they would not earn a living because the number of deliveries they conduct each year is too small. I estimated 25 deliveries to be the maximum that might be conducted, in theory, by "women who cut the cord", in any one year. In reality, however, this is supposed to be less. This number is very small, in comparison with Egypt for example, where *dayat* conduct 100 deliveries a year [11].

Thus assistance at deliveries is not a full-time occupation by which women earn their livelihood. The following can be remarked with regard to the way a delivery is assisted. Since the woman in labour is covered with a blanket, the crying of the baby is the sign that it is born. The cord is cut with anything that is close at hand at a distance ranging from two to four fingers from the baby's abdomen. In general, the cord is first cut and then left to bleed for a moment before being tied on the baby's side. Sometimes hot *samn* (clarified butter) is applied to the end of it. It is possible that the whole body of the baby is rubbed with *samn*. For the first 3 days the baby is fed *samn* because, according to the women, there is no breastmilk. The cord is not tied on the mother's side. The mother will stand up in order to expel the afterbirth. "Women who cut the cord" do not know what to do if the placenta is not expelled normally.

The way in which women assist at deliveries indicates that the traditional reference to them as "they who cut the cord" is significant. This reference indicates her most important task during the delivery, next to the emotional support she renders. Any woman who is not afraid to cut the cord can and does assist at a delivery.

The above-mentioned description of "women who cut the cord" indicates that there exists no category of women with specialized knowledge and experience of assistance at deliveries [12]. It is obvious on the ground of their knowledge and experience that they are not clearly distinguishable from women who do not assist at deliveries. There is every indication that assistance at deliveries is rendered by women out of a religious duty within their own neighborhood and kinship networks. It is also apparent, from the problematic acceptance, after training, of "women who cut the cord" that assistance at deliveries is not seen as the speciality of one or two women in a village. The training gives the project-trained women an image of professionality and specialization, especially by providing them with a bag of instruments at the end of the training. That this image does not conform to the local cultural situation at village level is confirmed by the difference, inequality and confusion that the training creates between the project-trained women and the non-trained women. The non-trained women feel overlooked because they also give assistance at deliveries. Moreover, the fact that the initial working area of the seven trained TBAs (Appendix A) after the training (Appendix B) does not expand significantly (Chi-squared = 0.08, N = 281) to a greater number of women outside the neighbourhood, indicates that project-trained women are not automatically accepted by women in a village for assistance at their deliveries. Women still call upon women in their neighbourhood and kinship networks for assistance at such times. The absence of expansion in the initial working area of the project-trained women also indicates, that the training of one or two TBAs/*jiddat* will not provide basic mother and child health care and, in particular, safe and clean deliveries to all women in a village. The objective of the training is not achieved as a consequence of the discrepancy between the assumption on which the training is based and the local cultural situation at village level.

At first I stated that although the original global WHO definition of a TBA indicates in theory divergent categories of TBAs, in reality it is often reduced to only one category of TBAs: the midwife. As a consequence the training will then automatically be geared to this category of women and does not always lead to the most appropriate training. It is of the utmost importance that by research in the local situation of a particular country or region the concerned category of TBAs should be redefined in more detail.

From the description of the local cultural situation at village level in the Anis region of the central highlands in Yemen it appears that the training is not geared to the correct category of TBAs, resulting in the objective of the training not being achieved. For the successful training of TBAs, the importance of adapting training to the traditional knowledge and skills of birth-practices in an area is frequently pointed to. To this must be added, learned from Yemen, that it is also of the utmost importance for achieving the objective of the training, that training is geared to the correct target group.

For the training of TBAs in the Anis region of the central highlands, it is important to recognize that no specialized category of women who conduct deliveries exists. In principle any woman who is not afraid to cut the cord can and does assist at a delivery, although some women will conduct more deliveries than others. This implies that training should not focus on one or two TBAs/*jiddat* in a village, but perhaps a less sophisticated training should be directed to all women who have at least some experience in conducting deliveries.

Provided that the training is adjusted in every respect to the local cultural situation, the training of TBAs will supply safe and clean deliveries to women in rural areas and thus contribute to the realization of basic health care for all in the year 2000.

ACKNOWLEDGEMENTS

As this study has been carried out for and has been funded by the Dhamir Rural Health Project (DRHP), I wish to thank the team of DRHP and their respective staff who supported the research. My gratitude goes also to the women of At Taalibi, Hamaan Ali and Dhi Hud and surrounding villages, who, in between their many household duties, were willing to spend time with me to discuss, and whose hospitality made my fieldwork very enjoyable.

APPENDIX A

Tables A1 and A2 could be composed as a result of information obtained about 194 deliveries conducted by seven trained TBAs *before the training*.

Table A1

N deliveries: related women (=r)		N deliveries: related women (=r)		Total
56		138		194
a1	a2			
49	7			

Table A2

N deliveries: neighbouring women			N deliveries: non-neighbouring women		
141			53		194
a1	a2	nr	a1	a2	nr
14	7	120	35	0	18

a1 = N deliveries: TBAs own group

a2 = N deliveries: TBAs husband' group

APPENDIX B

Tables A3 and A4 could be composed as a result of information obtained about 87 deliveries conducted by the same seven trained TBAs (Tables A1 & A2), but this time *after the training*.

Table A3

N deliveries: related women (=r)		N deliveries: related women (=r)		Total
18		69		87
a1	a2			
15	3			

Table A4

N deliveries: neighbouring women			N deliveries: non-neighbouring women			
64			23			87
a1	a2	nr	a1	a2	nr	
2	2	60	13	1	9	

a1 = N deliveries: TBAs own group

a2 = N deliveries: TBAs husband' group

[1] World Health Organization. Traditional Birth Attendants. A Field Guide to Their Training, Education, and Articulation with Health Services, p. 7. WHO Offset Publication No. 44, Geneva, 1979.

[2] de Lourdes V. M. & Turnbull L. M. The Traditional Birth Attendant in Maternal & Child Health & Family Planning. A Guide to her Training and Utilization, p. 2. WHO Offset Publication No. 18, Geneva, 1975.

[3] El Hakim S. Sudan: Replacing TBAs by village midwives. In The Traditional Birth Attendant in Seven Countries: Case Studies in Utilization and Training (Edited by Mangay-maglacas A. & Pizurki H.), p.133. World Health Organization, Geneva, 1981.

[4] This is "a literal, descriptive name derived from the traditional method of delivery in which the woman in labour takes a squatting position, supporting herself by a rope (habil) suspended from the ceiling" [3, p. 133].

[5] Van der Most-van Spijk M. Who Cares for Her Health? An Anthropological Study of Women's Health Care in a Village in Upper-Egypt, p. 41. Women and Development Series, Egypt, 1982.

[6] In the following the project level is in most cases contrasted against the village level as this is the obvious contrast when conducting research in villages covered by a project. It has to be kept in mind however that the assumptions are not necessarily those of the project level.

[7] This is one example of the frequent use of kinship terms in Muslim/Arab society to address non-related persons as a way of expressing respect.

[8] Furthermore, information has been collected by direct observation and review of secondary data. As only in the Anis region of the central highlands data has been collected, conclusions drawn can only be applied to this area and cannot be generalized to all of Yemen.

[9] Scheepers L. M. Functioning of traditional birth attendants, Annex 2. Unpublished Manuscript, Dhamar Rural Health Project, Nijmegen, 1990.

[10] Swagman C. F. Health, culture and change: health care development in highland Yemen, p. 153. Unpublished Manuscript.

[11] Lewis, J.H., Janowitz, B. & Potts, M., Methodological issues in collecting data from traditional birth attendants. Int. J. Gynaecol. Obstet. 23, 295, 1985.

[12] Swagman [10, p152, 173] also indicates that the TBA "is a much less formal social role" and that "the culturally-defined profession of midwife is not nearly as developed or elaborate in rural Yemen as it is in other Middle Eastern countries".

Traditional Birth Attendants in Rural North India: The Social Organization of Childbearing

Roger Jeffery & Patricia M. Jeffery [†]

Anthropological knowledge produced in connection with midwifery and childbirth has often been used for political purposes in both Western Europe and North America. On the one hand, negative assessments of indigenous childbearing practices are taken as one indicator of women's low status and used as a stick to beat colonial regimes or colonized peoples. On the other hand, non-Western methods of childbirth are examined in order to compare them with what are taken to be the ill effects of technologically controlled childbirth in formal medical settings. The first approach (called a biomedical perspective by Carol McClain 1982:26) focuses on the disasters—on rates of maternal and neonatal mortality and on the experiences of doctors in Third World hospitals often faced with the effects of undiagnosed obstructed labors and long delays before hospitalization. The second (which McClain calls a sociocultural perspective) looks for social and psychological evidence of supportive environments, or for beneficial techniques (massage, positions during delivery) which are absent from standard Western practice[1].

Both approaches tend to allow Western medical concerns to propose the agenda. The first sets out to modernize the traditional, but has often been accused of ethnocentrism (see, for example, Jordan 1987). The second calls for the insertion of traditional techniques into technocratic obstetrics, but often relies on a romanticized borrowing from the past of "exotic" cultures (Macintyre 1977). The recent advocacy by the World Health Organization of training programs for traditional birth attendants as a means of improving the conditions of maternal and child health around the world belongs to this second category (Maglacas & Simons 1986).

We are concerned with two features common to these otherwise contrasting perspectives: first, a tendency to homogenize midwifery by underplaying or ignoring cultural variation; and second, a propensity to detach pregnancy, the birth event, and the postpartum period from their social moorings. In this chapter we wish to argue for strengthening what has been a minority position, one that examines childbirth and midwifery as practices within specific social and economic contexts, especially by locating women in production and reproduction. In other words, we advocate a position that looks for the bases of variation.

One reason for the relatively stereotypical view of midwifery in anthropology is its narrow selection from the many studies undertaken, and particularly its focus on the more detailed, anthropologically oriented accounts that tend to celebrate indigenous midwives or birthing systems. The burgeoning of such studies followed the growth of feminist perspectives in social science, in which the proper task of feminist anthropology was considered to be the recovery of women's knowledge and sources of power and influence. Sheila Cosminsky (1982), Brigitte Jordan (1983), Carol Laderman (1983), Carol MacCormack (1982), and Lois Paul and Benjamin Paul (1975), for example, describe childbirth among Mayan Indians or neighboring tribes in Guatemala, Sierra Leone, and Malaysia. We do not question the value or conclusions of these excellent reports. We do, however, point to the disadvantages of generalizing from such a

[†] Chapter 1 In: Shirley Lindenbaum & Margaret Lock (eds.) *Knowledge, Power & Practice: The Anthropology of Medicine & Everyday Life*, Berkeley: University of California Press, 1993

relatively narrow set of social contexts. McClain's literature review of 1982, for instance, summarizes the earlier reviews by Ford (1945), Montagu (1949), Spencer (1950), Mead and Newton (1967), and Oakley (1977), which draw their material from a wide geographic range, but which deal predominantly with small-scale, relatively isolated communities or tribes, often slash-and-burn agriculture or hunter-gatherer societies.

Although this research potentially grants every separate cultural form its own significance, it has tended to downplay the densely populated, settled agricultural regions where most of the world's women live. Accounts of Han Chinese childbearing or childbearing in Indo-Gangetic plains India, Pakistan, and Bangladesh are relatively rare. Such regions have been characterized in terms of their dominant agricultural practices as male farming systems (Boserup 1970) illustrating the Eurasian model of plough agriculture (Goody 1976), and have been associated with hierarchical social systems and relatively restricted roles for women. Both of these authors have been criticized for their inability to deal with cultural variation within these broad regions. Nevertheless, they offer a useful vantage point from which to develop an understanding of how childbearing experiences vary, and along which dimensions, in different social settings.

In what follows we will argue that the nature of midwifery in any society must be understood in the context of a wide set of relationships that include the society's range of medical resources (even if childbirth is not usually perceived as a medical event) and people's understandings of anatomy and physiology, as well as the ability of women to enter healing roles, their access to different kinds of healers, and the access of healers to them. Midwifery is also affected by the particular constraints on the organization of delivery and by the roles adopted by those who are permitted to attend a birth. These childbirth events are set in a wider context of the dominant symbolic understandings of the childbirth process and of women's other work roles, their kin relationships, and their access to property. As a result, childbearing women have differing abilities to organize resources on their own behalf, whether these are in the form of social support, cash, or access to scarce knowledge. In this dense context we find differences in the roles of specialized birth attendants, the evaluation of what they do, and their opportunities to develop specialized knowledge. That is, the practice of midwifery in any one place is conditioned by a wide set of social, economic, and symbolic considerations that give it particular shape and meaning.

If societies are placed on a continuum according to the degree of women's subordination, north Indian society would be located toward the "most subordinated" end. As we argue below, this is closely tied to women's childbearing experiences and the status of traditional birth attendants[2]. Many aspects of childbearing in north India confound the generalizations in the anthropological literature on childbirth and midwifery in non-Western societies. For example, traditional birth attendants are usually described as supportive and sisterly, in contrast to the presumed Western model of professional medical domination. What we describe below, however, is a third model—midwifery as a perfunctory service (Goffman 1968: 285). The north Indian traditional birth attendant and the hierarchical biomedical expert are thus located at polar extremes, with the sisterly relationships of Yucatan midwives (Jordan 1983) occupying a middle position. Further, we would predict that conditions similar to those we outline below will obtain in many other areas, and may even be the predominant non-Western pattern in terms of the numbers of women involved.

Our data come from recent research in Bijnor District in the state of Uttar Pradesh in north India. The research was based in two adjacent villages (one Muslim, one Caste Hindu and Harijan) less than five kilometers from the bed of the River Ganges. We also conducted a survey in eleven other villages in the District, interviewing 301 recently-delivered women[3]. In the base villages, maternity histories were collected from all 236 ever-married women. Of those currently pregnant or recently delivered, forty-one key informant women and their husbands were chosen to provide a wider range of detailed information on their work, aspects of kinship and gift-exchanges, and reproductive behavior. Patricia also attended births in the two villages and accompanied one woman who finally delivered in the local women's hospital. This material is complemented by interviews with twenty-four women identified as birth attendants in the two base villages and the eleven survey villages.

In her critique of Western obstetric techniques, Oakley contrasts "preliterate societies" and "modern industrial societies," distinguishing five aspects of childbearing: cultural definitions of pregnancy and childbearing; who controls the management of childbirth; the location of labor and delivery; labor and delivery positions; and the degree and kind of intervention in birth and the emotional and social supports for the laboring woman (Oakley 1978: 18). Her portrait of childbearing in "preliterate societies" contrasts sharply with the picture of the passive laboring woman in the West, who gives birth in unfamiliar hospital surroundings away from supportive kin and friends, and who is subject to expert medical management of her birthing experience and the intervention of alien medical techniques. Oakley's framework provides the basis for our discussion below. We begin briefly by describing the role of traditional medical systems in childbearing, and the social and economic location of the typical childbearing women in this part of north India.

WOMEN AND MEDICINE IN INDIA

India, like China, has one of the most sophisticated medical systems to have survived to the present day. Long traditions of literacy—in Sanskrit and Arabic—and a large, wealthy clientele have supported elite practitioners' schools in *Ayurveda* ("the science of life") and *Unan-i Tibb* ("Greek medicine"). The classical texts offer only partial insight, however, into the nature of everyday medical practice. Understanding the relationship of these systems of medicine to the medical care given to and by women remains a major problem.

The classical texts and recorded practice mention only male practitioners. Some hints support the idea that *vaids* and *hakims* (Ayurvedic and Unani healers) were unlikely to play a substantial part in childbirth. Indeed, they might have given a prior claim to Brahman priests to provide amulets or to pray for recovery. But some classical texts discuss gynecological and obstetric issues, and some hakims in Bijnor prescribe remedies for infertility or for the inability to bear a son, or to accelerate labor. Direct consultations on matters of pregnancy or delivery, however, seem to have been very uncommon, both in the distant and recent past. Respectable women were constrained by issues of shame, for poorer women, their poverty was an additional hurdle, and all women had limited time for medical consultations. In the nineteenth century, at least, it seems that in north India women in need might have their symptoms described by another woman or by a related man, but male healers could not touch or examine a pregnant or delivering woman[4]. The only female folk healers described in the census or in the reports of British medical administrators are *dais,* a term that usually translates as "midwife," or more recently, traditional birth attendant[5]. Dais are well represented in contemporary north India: in Uttar Pradesh they are reported to attend over 90 percent of all deliveries, whereas in south India they attend fewer than half[6].

WOMEN, PROPERTY AND KINSHIP

An appreciation of the position of young married women contributes to setting the context of midwifery in Bijnor. This can be done in terms of three key roles: as wealth-bringers, workers, and bearers of children[7]. Even in landowning families, a woman rarely owns productive property in her own right. Access to any parental land (the main rural resource) is effectively foreclosed when women leave home at marriage. Marriage establishes patterns of gift giving in which a woman acts as a conduit for wealth (usually in nonproductive forms: jewelry, clothing, foodstuffs, and sometimes cash) from her parents or brothers to her husband and his parents. A young married woman rarely controls the distribution of these resources and she cannot reclaim them if the marriage ends. Such gifts, and a woman's dependence on her brothers to continue to send them if her position with her in-laws is to remain secure, effectively prevent a woman from insisting on her legal right to a share in any productive property when her parents die. Further, marriage migration severs women from supportive relationships with their natal kin and the friends of their youth. Young married women control very few material and social resources.

Regardless of their class position, young married women work long hours at hard labor, but their work is devalued. Wherever possible, a young married woman is excluded from work in the field, except to labor on the land owned by her marital kin or as part of a kin-based work group. Her contribution to agricultural production (winnowing, threshing, grinding) is done inside the domestic compound, and is usually ignored or described by men as light and unimportant. Most women have specific responsibilities for many other tasks such as cooking, cleaning, and rearing young children, as well as the maintenance of courtyards, huts, and grain stores, the collection of fuel, and the conversion of cow-dung into fuel or fertilizer. Men regard this work as demeaning. Women's work is thus trivialized and brings them little credit, yet a woman who wishes to visit her parents may have trouble negotiating leave unless another woman is available to take her place. Women's employment outside the domestic enterprise is rare: young women should not do such work, and men will often deny that it happens. Even when women work outside the home, they rarely gain access to the pay they earn.

As a potential bearer of children, a young woman is carefully chaperoned in her natal village. She has little say in whom she marries. She must observe norms of respect and seclusion during adolescence to achieve a respectable marriage at a proper age—norms designed to ensure a sexual purity not demanded of a young man. Her standing with her in-laws begins at a very low level; she provides sexual services for her husband and offers work and respect to her mother-in-law. Inadequacies or resistance may be met with beatings. Her capacity to bear children is vital for the future well-being of her husband's household since sons, in particular, support their aged parents. The birth of a child begins to raise her status and secure her position, a process that culminates (if she is lucky) in her becoming a mother-in-law herself. The failure to bear a child has serious implications for a young married woman, but the process of childbearing is itself fraught with many problems.

CULTURAL DEFINITIONS OF PREGNANCY AND CHILDBEARING

Three concerns shape women's views of pregnancy and childbearing: shame, pollution, and issues of vulnerability and danger.

Shame

It is important for a married woman to bear children, but matters connected with sexual and gynecological functions are considered *sharm-ki-bat,* matters of shame and embarrassment. As a sexual being, a young married woman must not publicize her sexual relationship with her husband. She should be demure in his presence, and neither of them should hint at their sexual activities, either verbally or through body language. Pregnancy and childbirth, however, provide dramatic and conspicuous evidence of sexual intercourse. During pregnancy, a woman should cover her body even more assiduously. Other people's allusions to her condition should be met with a discreetly bowed head. The act of giving birth is also profoundly shameful, entailing as it does the exposure and even touching by others of body parts that should always be concealed.

Childbirth Pollution

During pregnancy, the mother nurtures the fetus with her own blood. At the moment of transition to motherhood, she loses some of this blood, which is considered much more polluting than menstrual blood. *Sutak* (the blood of childbirth) or more prosaically *maila* or *gandagi* (dirt, foulness, filth) is the most severe pollution of all, far greater than menstruation, sexual intercourse, or that of death. Only a profuse flow removes the defilement and causes a complete cleansing. Following the birth, the newly delivered woman *(jacha)* remains impure *(a-sudh* among Hindus and *na-pak* among Muslims) or simply dirty and defiled *(gandi)* and can herself be poisoned by this blood. Some defilement *(gandagi, maila)* also adheres to the baby: Hindus and Muslims alike consider the baby's first hair to be contaminated by contact with the mother's blood, and the hair is shaved off during the first year. Touching the amniotic sac, placenta, and cord (known collectively as the "lump"), delivering the baby, cutting the umbilical cord, and cleaning up the blood are all the most disgusting of tasks. Considered defiling work *(ganda kam),* these practices are the concerns of the dai.

After the birth, the dai presses the jacha's belly and tells her to bear down to make the placenta deliver quickly. If it is slow to arrive, she may massage the belly. Half the dais said that they simultaneously insert their other hand into the vagina and tug the cord robustly, but the others said that this causes sepsis. The dai cuts the cord only after the placenta has been delivered, since the cut cord could vanish inside the jacha's tubes and spread the poison in the placenta throughout her body.

In some aspects of childbearing, Hindu and Muslim practices differ. For example, Hindus invariably wait for the dai to arrive to cut the cord. One socially isolated woman, totally alone when her baby was born, was found by a neighbor who massaged her until the placenta delivered, and then helped her onto her bed. Neither woman cut the cord, but waited for the dai, who arrived over an hour later. Muslims, on the other hand, do not necessarily leave the cord uncut if the baby is born before the dai arrives. An old Faqir woman in the Muslim village will cut cords for a certain payment. Three other women will also cut cords, but only if no dai is present, and they are not paid or considered to be dais. Nonetheless, many Muslim women say cutting the cord is the dai's right, and this is one of the tasks for which she is paid.

Touching the jacha and baby is also defiling-work. Following the birth, the dai gives the jacha some old cloth or a lump of dried mud to clean herself. Women feel disgust at touching a newborn baby and the infant's preliminary cleaning is the dai's responsibility. The dai bathes the jacha to remove pollution, handles the placenta, and cleans the dried mud floor. During labor she will mop up any feces, vomit, and waters (*pani*), tasks too defiling for the laboring woman's marital kin. After the birth the dai also chips away the stained portions of the floor and puts the pieces into an old basket, along with the placenta and any rags used during the delivery. She then repairs the broken floor with fresh mud and diluted cattle dung.

Dealing with the jacha's soiled cloths and the jacha's and baby's excreta is also defiling, although not as polluting as delivering the placenta or cutting the cord. Since there are no domestic latrines and people usually defecate in scrubland or in the fields, a pit is dug in the Hindu jacha's house for her excreta and soiled cloths, and someone also cleans up the baby's excreta and washes its cloths. Dais prefer to avoid this work, but have little choice if they wish to be paid for cord cutting. If the dai does not perform this defiling work, it may be done by the jacha's mother-in-law. Only two Hindu women, both Harijans (so-called untouchables) did the work themselves. By contrast, the Muslim jacha takes responsibility for this task. Some said there was no need to employ another person, since the baby did not defecate for several days, or that they were not "dirty" enough to warrant paying for a dai. In the Muslim village, domestic compounds have dry latrines and jachas use them (at least after the first day), leaving their soiled cloths there to be collected by the Sweeper. They also clear up the baby's excreta and wash its soiled cloths.

Because she endangers them, the jacha has restricted contact with others. People avoid touching her, and those wearing amulets believe that entering the jacha's house would destroy their efficacy. Fear of childbirth pollution makes the jacha temporarily untouchable, even to the Harijans. Food cooked by a jacha is also considered dangerous, more so for a man than for his children, and a jacha is absolved from cooking. Sexual intercourse with a jacha would also affect a man's health, though informants were unspecific about the symptoms that would ensue. Another woman usually sleeps with the jacha to prevent the husband approaching, though rarely for the specified number of weeks.

Vulnerability and Danger

Many features of menstruation, pregnancy, and delivery are understood in terms of humoral contrasts, especially *garm-thand* ("hot-cold"). A profuse flow of blood after birth is necessary for cleansing, but blood is *garm* and the blood loss that upsets proper balance makes the woman vulnerable. *Thand* could lodge in her tubes, expressed as shivering fever with diarrhea.

Since mustard oil is garm, women consider an oil massage beneficial, but this rarely occurs and few dais report massaging the baby before bathing it. Dais complain that their clients are too miserly to pay the extra for such services. The jacha and baby are bathed in warm water, however, often with mustard oil added. Water is poured over the woman, she is rubbed vigorously, and hot compresses are applied to her shoulder and knee joints (the particular sites where thand penetrates). Nowadays, few Muslim jachas are bathed daily, as there is no resident dai, and women do not bathe for several days unless they are helped to do so by their mother-in-law. The jacha's diet is also carefully regulated to ensure that she does not succumb to thand.

Other people can pose a threat to the jacha and baby, who are both vulnerable to *asar* (spirits) and *nazar* (evil eye). The safety of mother and child is ensured by keeping them inside the house for several days, and within the domestic compound for perhaps several weeks. Evil influences are reduced by the careful regulation of visitors, especially menstruating women whose shadows endanger the newborn. Some Hindu households place an earthenware tub containing a small fire outside the door and tie a sprig of *neem* (margosa) leaves above the lintel. Those entering pause to let the fire drive evil influences away. Muslims are no more welcoming to guests. At most, people make very circumspect comments about the jacha and baby to avoid activating the envy of the evil eye. Evil spirits are frightened by an iron sickle on the floor at the bedhead, or by a lamp burning through the night.

The placenta is also a potent source of danger to the newborn baby. In the Muslim village, all placentas are interred in the household hidden pit on the village outskirts, for a placenta is "not a thing to be buried inside." It must be hidden so it cannot be unearthed by a barren woman who, wishing to conceive, uses it for her own magic, but harms the baby in the process. Among Hindus, practice is more varied. Caste Hindus generally ask the dai to bury placentas inside the house. A small pit is dug in the floor, the placenta is buried, and a fire is lit on top to ward off evil. In some cases a boy's placenta is said to be buried by the mother's bedhead, while a girl's is buried by the foot (as befits the children's relative status). Others say that boys' placentas are buried inside and girls' outside, since magic is unlikely to be practiced on them. Following the Caste Hindu key informants' last deliveries, only two placentas were buried in the midden, both those of girls with elder siblings. The dai follows her clients' practice when dealing with placentas.

Thus, although a new baby's arrival may be a matter for celebration, local understandings are reflected in the pejorative terms used for the birth process. The belief that the jacha is a danger to herself and to others, the belief that she is in a state of vulnerability, and the view of childbirth as shameful all affect other aspects of the birth experience.

Attending Birth and Managing Labor

The social construction of birthing practices is further accentuated by considerations of shame and pollution that influence the selection of the laboring woman's attendants and determine those who must not attend her during delivery.

Childbirth is unsuitable for male involvement. Male healers are rarely consulted during pregnancy and are very unlikely to play any part in the delivery unless some crisis occurs. Male involvement demeans the man and shames the woman. When a Hindu woman recently allowed the male health center pharmacist to deliver her child by forceps, Muslim husbands said that their wives would not be allowed such treatment even if they were near death: "*Purdah* must not be broken." Further, the normal distancing between a woman and her male marital kin is exaggerated when she is in labor. If the husband needs to fetch something in the room he does it quickly, averting his gaze and remaining aloof. The laboring woman's other male marital kin remain outside. Indeed, if the woman is in labor during the day, the menfolk working in the fields may be unaware of her situation.

Moreover, a woman's male and female natal kin should not have direct involvement in her pregnancy and delivery. Childbearing is "a matter for the in-laws." A woman should not visit her parents or brothers while obviously pregnant, since this would present them with evidence of her sexual activity. It is even more shameful for them to attend the birth, and it would be unthinkable for the woman to call her father or brothers to her side. Considerations of shame also exclude female natal kin, especially her mother and sister. Unlikely to be called from another village, they too may not know that their daughter or sister is in labor.

Unmarried girls who should not learn about shameful matters before marriage are also excluded, and barren women may be kept away for fear of mishap, although there is no consensus on this. The delivery is thus attended by married women from among the laboring woman's close marital kin and from neighboring households. While the mother-in-law is alive she is central; otherwise her position may be taken by the laboring woman's sister-in-law (husband's brother's wife) or her husband's aunt (husband's father's brother's wife). An older woman may sometimes be assisted by her daughter-in-law or married daughter. More distantly related women come and go, the largest crowd being present for the birth itself. Several others stay throughout the birth process, taking turns to support or simply to watch. A laboring woman is rarely alone.

The social management of childbirth in Bijnor becomes readily apparent during a slow labor. The senior attendant may examine the laboring woman's belly to assess the baby's presentation and ascertain that it is still moving and to check the strength of the pains. She may also try to hasten delivery by using domestic remedies drawn from a repertoire known to most adult women. The attending women may suggest various measures, citing past cases where they seemed beneficial. The laboring woman, however, plays little part in this discussion. She may refuse a chosen treatment, but management of the labor is not in her hands.

The woman's mother-in-law (or other senior attendant) usually calls the dai when she considers the labor well established. In Bijnor there is often only one accessible dai, but if there is a choice, the decision rests with the senior attendant rather than with the laboring woman. In villages without a resident dai, women must rely on men to fetch a dai from beyond the village. Within the village, a woman will fetch her. In the Hindu village most women rely on a Muslim *Julaha* (weaver) widow from a neighboring village, who recently replaced a Hindu *Chamar* (leatherworker) dai when she died. A Chamar widow in the Hindu village also attends a few births under duress, although she resists being defined as a dai. In the Muslim village, women call on two Muslim *Qasai* (butcher) dais from another village, both with government training. They serve a cluster of villages and complain that they are being undercut by untrained dais.

After the dai's arrival, the senior attendant remains central in the conduct of the delivery and in decisions about whether labor should be accelerated, what the laboring woman's position should be, and so on. Certainly the dai voices her opinion, but her suggestions are not always heeded and she does her work under the watchful (and sometimes critical) eye of the other women. Even after the birth, the senior attendant reserves the bulk of decision making for herself and expects the dai to carry out tasks under her direction. She provides the thread for tying the cord, but the dai ties it. She decides what the cord should be cut with, even rejecting the dai's suggestions on occasion, but leaves the dai to do the job; she then instructs the dai about burying the placenta.

It is thus inappropriate to regard the dai as a "midwife" in the contemporary Western sense. Even in the absence of medically trained personnel, the dai does not have overriding control of the management of deliveries. Furthermore, the laboring woman herself rarely plays an active part, but merely responds to the instructions of her senior attendant and the dai.

Location of Labor and Delivery

Hospital deliveries are very rare and generally occur only when the life of the laboring woman and her baby seem to be threatened. The majority of deliveries are home births. This needs to be specified more clearly, however.

Young married women in effect lead double lives: as controlled daughters-in-law subject to surveillance in their marital villages, and as carefree daughters cherished in their natal villages. It can be said that the mother-in-law *(sas)* is a legendary ogre and the word *susri* (a debased form of sas) is a term of abuse. Nevertheless, young married women were appalled at our suggestion that they might find it congenial to give birth with their mother in attendance; shame outweighs any benefits. At the time of delivery, a woman should be in her "own" (i.e. her husband's) house, her natal kin excluded from the birth and from subsequent celebrations. Their role is to provide food and gifts for the jacha and her marital kin.

This restriction of women to their husband's house during childbirth is unusually rigid. In Punjab to the west, Madyha Pradesh to the south, and in eastern parts of Uttar Pradesh, it is common for at least the first birth to take place in the woman's natal village, although negotiating a later delivery away from the husband's house may also be difficult (Brown *et al.* 1981, Gideon 1962, Jacobson 1980:80, Karve 1968: 403, Luschinsky 1962: 94, Thompson 1984: 268-9). But in Bijnor, even those few married women living in their natal village (with the wife's kin or as within-village marriages) give birth in their marital home. Muslim women in within-village marriages are attended by their female marital kin, not mothers or sisters, except in cases of obstructed delivery or where the woman is isolated from her marital kin.

Labor and Delivery Positions

Women's labors are not merely monitored but managed. One means of doing this is to alter the laboring woman's position. Some dais said the woman herself decides what is the most comfortable position, but others often intervene and suggest that the woman adopt a prone or upright position. One dai said:

Some women crouch on bricks as that makes them stronger and the baby can be born faster. Other women stay on the bed and I hold their legs and push their heels against their buttocks. That way the woman gets strength and the mouth of the uterus opens quickly. (Dai #4)

Other dais said the force of contractions could be increased by pressing down on the woman's belly, or by raising the woman's head so that the baby's head presses more firmly against the cervix. The woman's legs may be lifted onto a pair of bricks, or she may walk around for a while inside her house[8]. Several dais believe delivery is hastened if they help the woman squat beside the bed, her feet placed slightly apart on a pair of bricks; in this position the woman gains the strength to push and the baby shifts forward from the lower gut where it is believed to be in danger of becoming wedged. Despite these descriptions of the many possible positions to be adopted, two-thirds of the key informants lay down under a quilt during their last deliveries. Most had been in that position throughout labor, though a few had squatted on bricks for a brief time.

After reading the literature on childbirth, we did not expect to find that most women deliver lying on their backs. For example, Jordan (1987: 314) writes that "traditionally, women in developing countries go through labour and give birth in upright or semi-upright positions, such as sitting, squatting, half-reclining, kneeling or standing, and often adopt several of them in sequence." Similar generalizations are provided by others (Newton & Newton 1972: 165-7, Ford 1945: 58, MacCormack 1982: 14, Blanchet 1984: 87), although in Punjab "care was taken that the patient was flat on her back, knees drawn up, and the belief prevailed that shifting of position led to trouble" (Gordon, Gideon & Wyon 1965:737). Several of our informants said that squatting during delivery exposes the woman and encourages defecation. Nevertheless, a third of the key informants did squat on bricks and felt the delivery had been speeded by this method.

Other Interventions in Labor and Delivery

In local understanding, menstrual blood accumulated during pregnancy causes a build-up of such "heat" (garmi) that uterine contractions are triggered and the mouth of the uterus opens. Anxious that the process should not be too protracted, the attending women use various means to assess progress. They discuss the intensity of pains and compare the duration of labor with the woman's earlier deliveries. Women describe very varied experiences, from sporadic light pains or severe pains for several days to precipitate deliveries after only a few hours. When severe pains begin, the woman lies on the bed designated for delivery, her head slightly raised on a pillow, her knees bent and her heels pressed against the sides of the bed. During pains, an attending woman squats behind her on the bedhead supporting her shoulders, while another may squat at the foot, keeping her bent legs upright.

The dai squats on the foot of the bed. She has no instruments, nor does she shave the woman's pubic hair, perform an enema, or wash herself or the laboring woman, for cleansing (safai) occurs after birth, not before[9]. The dai touches the woman's genitals and inserts a hand inside her body—shameful and defiling work—which other women would be appalled to do. (Women often use the words chut and ghosri (vulva) as terms of verbal abuse). The dai keeps the laboring woman concealed under the quilt and uses her left, inauspicious hand[10] for an internal examination to assess cervical dilation, to check that the baby's head is engaging properly, and to see if a dry vagina might impede the baby's transit. The dai's information contributes to the general discussion about the progress of labor. If there are severe pains without cervical dilation, or dilation with the easing of pains, a range of domestic or "country" remedies (ghar-ka-ilaj, desi ilaj) may accelerate labor, or in local terms "amplify the pains" (dard barhana).

Some Hindu families call a pandit to say prayers, and some Muslims send money to the mosque or ask that the Qu'ran Sharif be recited over lumps of gur (unrefined sugar), which the laboring woman then eats. None of our key informants has done this, but several had had amulets retied during labor. Others reported that a metal sieve containing grain and a small amount of money (1.25 rupees = $.09 U.S.) was circled around their head, and then placed under the bedhead to absorb the inauspiciousness thought to be slowing labor[11]. Balls of gur may also be circled around the woman's head and placed under the bedhead. A small sickle under the bedhead is considered beneficial as well. To encourage her cervix to release the baby, a woman's plaited hair may be undone, for loose hair is a potent symbol of sexual "heat" associated with the opening of the cervix during intercourse. Lids may be lifted from earthen cooking tubs, and the grain store or trunks may be unpadlocked, especially if the woman had placed something inside them while pregnant[12].

If pains become less rapid and intense, women say they have become "cold" (thanda). To avert this, the woman is warmly wrapped in an old quilt (which also provides concealment). No heavily pregnant woman should be present in case she "cools" the pains by drawing them to herself. If such precautions fail, steps are taken to "heat" the pains again. Occasionally, the dai is asked to insert a vaginal pessary to stimulate pains, dilate the cervix, and make the birth easier by moistening the vagina. More commonly the woman is given "hot" foods. In wealthy households, the attending women prepare warm milk with almonds, hot milky tea, or (less often) hot milk with clarified butter, eggs broken into hot milk, dried grapes, or gruel made from a "hot" ingredient. Generally, however, sweetened hot water or hot water with ginger and ajwain (medicinal seeds) are used to reactivate pains.

During one-third of the key informants' last deliveries, no domestic remedies were used because labor was satisfactory, because the baby was born before any remedy was given, or because no suitable ingredients were available. One-fifth had nothing to eat, but squatted to encourage delivery, and the remainder used a combination of techniques, including an injection of oxytocin. Male medical personnel called in for this task usually performed no examination beforehand[13].

There are no remedies for reducing the discomfort of labor. Intense pains are thought necessary to ensure a speedy delivery, and women are considered shameless if they make noises audible to people outside. Since pain is inevitable, they should merely "call on God's name." The laboring woman's silence is considered very important in other parts of South Asia as well; crying out draws attention to her shame (Gideon 1962: 224, Luschinsky 1962: 94, McGilvray 1982: 57-8, Thompson 1984: 273-4).

This account suggests that women obtain little emotional or social support during labor and delivery. As they are in a polluting state, few other women will touch them. The company of mothers and sisters is expressly excluded. Childbearing thus generates little solidarity among women. As C. S. Thompson (1984: 308) argues for central India:

The rituals surrounding birth make female physical sexuality seem low status and degrading. Birth isolates women from one another, from their own caste mates and it is not seen as a source of prestige or power.

We do not wish to exaggerate this picture, but we would suggest that laboring women in Bijnor appear to have less social and emotional support than indicated in most of the other anthropological accounts we have read.

Midwives or Menials?

Childbearing is a necessary part of a woman's marital career, but it is profoundly polluting, and women regard their bodily functions with distaste. Women are capable of doing the dai's work, but are inhibited by its demeaning nature. Nevertheless, someone must cut the cord and remove the placenta. While all women who give birth are subject to defilement, only a few are obliged to earn their keep by doing defiling work for other people. This is reflected in the dais' accounts of their own work.

Financial independence is a problematic condition for a woman in north India: women should be dependent on their menfolk. In Bijnor only a very poor woman with no male support, or one who depends on a man whose earnings cannot fully keep his family, seeks employment. The few job opportunities for rural women, such as agricultural labor, domestic work for rich peasants, or craft-work, are low in status and poorly paid. Some women, therefore, become self-employed dais, unattached to the government health services. Almost all village dais in Bijnor say they began work out of economic necessity.

How can I think this work is good or bad? I work hard and I do no wrong.

But if it was bad, what could I do? I do it because I have to. (Dai #8)

Most village dais are landless Harijans or Muslims. Some are childless, but most have grown sons who could not or would not support them. Generally, widowhood or the husband's incapacity has led them to work to "fill the stomach."

I used to go out very little and I never liked to take food and water in other people's houses. I used to be very careful about cleanliness. But then my husband died—so, I became a dai. (Dai #3)

I must think well of work which gives me bread to eat. But I work as a dai out of necessity. Would I do this work or would my sons be laborers if we owned land? (Dai #17)

The dais thus present their work as undesirable. They see themselves as unwilling recruits, dragged to their first delivery when another dai was unavailable, not seeking out clients, but going "just where I am called." The work is more despised than most other occupations available to them:

When I became a dai my sons thought very badly of it. But I replied that without work, how could I eat—unless they provided my food and clothes? At that they became silent. But one son-in-law is still angry that I do this work. Since I started it he has never visited me. (Dai #14)

Most dais, indeed, report objections from their kin: two said that their own relatives had refused to eat food they cooked since they became dais.

Dais who were widowed young may practice for many years, but many become dais relatively late in life. This reflects in part the age at which women are likely to lose male support. Further, the mobility of women in childbearing years is restricted by considerations of propriety and because domestic obligations in their marital home bind them in ways that are compatible with providing obstetric services. Moreover, pregnant women should not attend deliveries, and menstruating women endanger the newborn. Thus, postmenopausal women are the most likely candidates. Consequently, village women do not expect or achieve long-standing relationships with individual dais, but call on a succession during their childbearing years as dais become senile or die. The dai's weak financial condition compels her to seek the work that erases the respect otherwise due to her age.

Few dais are literate or have any formal midwifery training. Some Bijnor dais do come from families in which being a dai is part of a family tradition. Just under half reported learning to deliver babies by accompanying a relative (usually the mother or mother-in-law). The others, however, had simply watched a few deliveries. Village dais are thus not viewed as having esoteric knowledge or specialized techniques. Their distinctiveness rests on willingness to accept payment for the unpalatable work of cutting cords.

The dais main tasks occur during delivery. She has little involvement in prenatal or postnatal care. Nor is she likely to administer remedies for abortions or infertility. Most reported attending births only in their own village, though a few had worked in neighboring villages. Muslim and Caste Hindu dais often claimed not to attend Harijan deliveries because the defilement was too great. Some non-Muslim dais denied attending Muslim births. Caseloads were generally between twenty and forty births a year, though some dais reported as few as ten, and a few over sixty. Such restricted clientele limits their experience and keeps income low—15-30 rupees ($1.13-2.25 U.S.), plus some grain and sometimes cloth at each delivery. Several dais had additional sources of income, such as weaving cloth, basket making, laboring on cane crushers, or working as Sweepers removing night soil, taking on tasks too defiling for their caste superiors.

Historical sources rarely describe dais or give details about women's experiences of childbearing[14]. Thus, we can only speculate about how dais' skills and status might have changed in the wake of the major changes in agricultural life since the mid-1960s. It is possible that restricted employment opportunities have persuaded more women from families without traditions of dai practice to take up this work. Further, as urban facilities have expanded, the prenatal, abortion, and infertility work of dais may have declined. Yet elderly women (including dais) generally deny any reduction or enhancement in the skills of village dais. Some urban dais have reputations as wisewomen healers, but whatever they may have done in the past, women healers are not now birth attendants. The average woman in rural Bijnor is attended in childbirth by a dai such as we have described.

Most dais, then, are regarded as low status menials, necessary for removing defilement, with no special delivery techniques. Their lowly status is reflected in several ways. Most Hindu dais are Harijans who perform other defiling-work, and their presence is generally anathema to Caste Hindus (and many Muslims too). Muslim and Hindu women rarely mix socially and, because of their dietary practices, many Caste Hindus regard Muslims as little better than outcastes. Thus, in relation to most of her clients, a Harijan or Muslim dai starts with grave social disadvantages. Moreover, by virtue of performing her work, a Harijan dai may become polluted even in the eyes of her own relatives, a double stigma that is reflected in her clients' behavior. Many people admit a dai to their home only for the delivery and for subsequent cleansing work.

Once the jacha has a purifying bath, physical contact between her and the dai ceases (unless they are related). However, some Muslim dais are less despised in the eyes of their Muslim clients. The dai formerly in the Muslim village, for instance, was said to remain with a newly delivered woman performing everyday work for up to a week—even cooking for the household. Similarly, dais who now serve the Muslim village visit freely, although their attempts to find out if women are pregnant are often resented.

After the birth, the payment to the dai further underlines her inferiority. She is expected to accept the cash given to remove inauspiciousness, but risks acquiring the bad luck herself. During the following days, she is paid in installments for cutting the cord, burying the placenta, and bathing the jacha, payments specifically for the removal of defilement. She is not paid for advice, and she receives nothing if the baby is stillborn. Among Hindus a stillborn baby's cord is not cut; Muslims expect the dai to cut the cord of a stillborn baby, but they do not pay her. If the dai withdraws from the case before the birth, she is not paid. Few dais receive customary payments from their clients—after harvests or at marriage, for example—and their low level of income further weakens their bargaining position. Dais report acrimonious negotiations over pay, and after each delivery Patricia attended, the dai was abused and sworn at for claiming "unreasonable" fees. Several dais reported the promise of payments which were never fulfilled. The dai, then, is not a respected professional who can propose a standard fee for service or enforce claims[15].

Safety and Risks

Since childbirth is socially defined as undesirable, it is not surprising that women who become dais do not claim competence to deal with complicated cases. Dais have no obstetric equipment (apart from the scissors to cut the cord), though they do examine the woman manually, both internally and externally. They fully understand the importance of recognizing complications and try to assess if the baby is correctly positioned—inverted or obstructed. Several dais said they could turn a baby even during labor. Others said this was impossible, although they might try to deliver a footling but not a breech presentation. Dais also recognize the danger of waning contractions and cessation of movement by the baby (in their terms, the woman's belly becoming thanda). But they have no stethoscopes and no means of detecting fetal distress other than by feeling the woman's belly. Equally, dais themselves said they could not remedy such problems as hemorrhage or failure of cervical dilation, nor could they arrest premature labors, induce labor in an over-long pregnancy, or cope with prolapsed cords and placenta previa.

Altogether, dais have very modest perceptions of their capabilities, as do their clients. Dais said that they only like to deal with normal presentations; their clients describe them as cord-cutters (nal-katne-wali). If dais perceive a problem, they are likely to withdraw from the case; for this reason, they claim to have few mishaps.

Of course, this is not to criticize individual dais for being unsupportive. They appreciate that their reputation (and livelihood) is imperiled by maternal or fetal deaths. For the vast majority of normal deliveries, the village dais suffice. However, the forceful way problem deliveries are handled exposes the limitations of obstetric care available to rural woman.

There used to be no treatment for a woman having trouble during delivery. She might be in labor for eight or ten days without being given anything. Often the woman's lips would go blue with clutching the bed so tightly. There are country medicines, but there is no hakim in this village. Everyone just lived by God's grace. (Dai #20)

In the old days, people said, the outcome depended on God's will. Since about 1960, however, Western medicine has become increasingly accessible through government health services and independent (often untrained) private practitioners. Nowadays, the dai may call in a medical practitioner or recommend that the laboring woman go to the hospital. But this does not necessarily improve the conditions of childbirth. The practitioners' main technique, an injection of oxytocin given in standard units without a preliminary examination, causes rapid, painful contractions and a high risk of afterpains, and, when the woman is not ready to deliver, is a threat to the life of mother and child.

CONCLUSION

Several aspects of our account of the dai in north India depart significantly from the generalizations that have become commonplace in the literature on midwifery and childbearing in non-Western contexts. These stereotypes, which have been part of a critique of alienating, medicalized birthing practices in the West, tend to divert attention away from variations that exist in non-Western birthing practices. We began this chapter by arguing that the social meanings of childbirth and its management must be understood in terms of women's position in relation to property ownership and their position as workers and childbearers in specific social and economic contexts. In the space available, we chose to focus on the childbirth event itself and on the role of traditional birth attendants as exemplars of how wider social and economic considerations relate to the social organization of childbearing.

Our account is relevant for those planning to use trained traditional birth attendants in the provision of primary health care. Portraits of the dai in north India similar to our account can be gleaned from several contemporary sources, especially from evaluations of the dai training programs initiated recently by the government of India (Gandhi and Sapru 1980, Ghosal, Hiramani, Gupta, et al. n.d., Ghosal, Hiramani, Srivastava, et al. n.d.). The conditions of childbearing that we have sketched prevail throughout much of north India and the neighboring regions and affect millions of women. Moreover, the problems of maternal and child health appear to be more widespread. India, with one-fifth of the world's population, accounts for almost half of the world's maternal deaths each year, with a disproportionate number occurring in the northern plains. In Uttar Pradesh alone, between fifty and one hundred women die in childbirth or from related causes each day, and about eight hundred of the ten thousand or so children born each day will not survive to the end of their first week[16]. It is in this context that the vogue for training traditional birth attendants has taken hold.

Our research, however, leads us to question the efficacy of dai training programs in north India. Most dais are elderly and any benefits from training them will be short-lived. Moreover, their social standing is such that they are not plausible channels for the dissemination of general health information; several of the trained dais we knew found they could not incorporate their training into their obstetric practice. Indeed, this has been a recurrent feature of dai training programs in India since the nineteenth century (Jeffery *et al.* 1985). More fundamentally, however, we would argue that the focus on the dai represents a maldiagnosis of the problems to be remedied. Certainly, there are obstetric crises that the village dai cannot handle, but the main sources of maternal and child health problems are not located there but in the lack of economic and social leverage that childbearing women have over their lives. The lowly dai is just another symptom of these wider realities so poignantly reflected in mortality statistics. Consequently, we consider that dai training programs are not the envisioned panacea for providing maternal and child health services in non-Western settings.

We can well understand why the more positive views of midwifery in non-Western societies have become so widely accepted. They are a refreshing departure from earlier ethnocentric accounts that devalued women's knowledge and expertise. They also provide an attractive (if flawed) foil for debates about Western obstetric practice. Nevertheless, a challenge to this new orthodoxy is timely. By linking variations in childbirth practices, social status, and the differential contributions of women to production and reproduction, we hope to contribute to a better understanding of the bases of these variations.

ACKNOWLEDGMENTS

We are grateful to the Economic and Social Research Council (U.K.) and the University of Edinburgh for funding the research on which this chapter is based. Our thanks also go to numerous colleagues who have commented on drafts of this chapter.

REFERENCES

Agarwal, Bina, 1988, Who Sows? Who Reaps? Women & Land Rights in India. *Journal of Peasant Studies* 15(4):531-81.

Blanchet, Therese, 1984, *Women, Pollution and Marginality: Meanings and Rituals of Birth in Rural Bangladesh.* Dhaka, Bangladesh: Dhaka University Press.

Boserup, Ester, 1970, *Woman's Role in Economic Development.* New York: St. Martin's Press.

Brown, Penelope, Martha Macintyre, Ros Morpeth & Shirley Prendergast, 1981, 'A Daughter: A Thing to be Given Away', In: *Women in Society,* Cambridge Women's Study Group, pp. 127-145. London: Virago.

Browner, Carole H., & Sondra T. Perdue, 1988, Women's Secrets: Bases for Reproductive and Social Autonomy in a Mexican Community. *American Ethnologist* 15(1):84-97.

Cosminsky, Sheila, 1982, Childbirth and Change: A Guatemalan Study. In *Ethnography of Fertility and Birth,* Carol P. MacCormack, ed., pp. 205-229. London: Academic Press.

Dyson, Tim & Mick Moore, 1983 On Kinship Structure, Female Autonomy and Demographic Behaviour in India. *Population & Development Review* 9(1): 35-70.

Ford, Clellan S., 1945, *A Comparative Study of Human Reproduction.* New Haven: Human Relations Area Files Press.

Gandhi, H. S. & R. Sapru, 1980, *Dais as Partners in Maternal Health.* New Delhi: National Institute for Health and Family Welfare. Mimeographed.

Ghosal B. C., A. B. Hiramani, Y. P. Gupta, U. Srivastava & S. P. Verma, no date, *Dais Training Scheme in Himachal Pradesh-An Evaluation.* New Delhi: Central Health Education Bureau.

Ghosal B. C., A. B. Hiramani, V. P. Srivastava, U. Srivastava, S. P. Verma & A. Sarkar, no date, *Dais Training Scheme in Haryana-An Evaluation.* New Delhi: Central Health Education Bureau.

Gideon, Helen, 1962, A Baby is Born in Punjab. *American Anthropologist* 64:220-234.

Goffman, Erving, 1968, *Asylums.* Harmondsworth, England: Penguin.

Goody, Jack, 1976, *Production and Reproduction.* Cambridge: Cambridge University Press.

Gordon, John E., Helen Gideon & John B. Wyon, 1965, Midwifery Practices in Rural Punjab, India. *American Journal of Obstetrics & Gynecology* 93:728-737.

Gupta, R., 1982, *Census of India 1981. Series 22 Uttar Pradesh, Paper 1 of 1982: Final Population Totals.* Lucknow: Director of Census Operations, Uttar Pradesh.

Hershman, Paul, 1974, Hair, Sex and Dirt. *Man* 9: 274-98.

Jacobson, Doranne, 1980, Golden Handprints. In *Unspoken Worlds: Women's Religious Lives in Non-Western Cultures.* Nancy A. Falk & Rita M. Gross, eds., pp. 73-93. New York: Harper and Row.

Jeffery, Patricia M., Roger Jeffery, & Andrew Lyon, 1985, *Contaminating States and Women's Status.* New Delhi: Indian Social Institute.

Jeffery, Patricia M., Roger Jeffery & Andrew Lyon, 1989 *Labour Pains and Labour Power: Women and Childbearing in India.* London: Zed Books.

Jordan, Brigitte, 1983, *Birth in Four Cultures.* 3rd ed. Montreal: Eden Press.

Jordan, Brigitte, 1987, High Technology: The Case of Obstetrics. *World Health Forum* 8: 314-20.

Karve, Irawati, 1968, *Kinship Organisation in India.* 3rd ed. Bombay: Asia Publishing House.

Laderman, Carol, 1983, *Wives and Midwives: Childbirth and Nutrition in Rural Malaysia.,* Berkeley, Los Angeles, London: University of California Press.

Luschinsky Mildred S., 1962, The Life of Women in a Village of North India. Ph.D. Cornell, University.

MacCormack, Carol P., 1982, Biological, Cultural & Social Adaptation in Human Fertility and Birth: A Synthesis. In *Ethnography of Fertility & Birth,* C. P. MacCormack, ed., pp. 1-23. London: Academic Press

Macintyre, Sally, 1977, Childbirth: The Myth of the Golden Age. *World Medicine* 15 (June): 17-22.

Maglacas, A. Mangay & John Simons, eds., 1986, *The Potential of the Traditional Birth Attendant.* Geneva: World Health Organization.

Mandelbaum, David G., 1988, *Women's Seclusion and Men's Honor: Sex Roles in North India, Bangladesh and Pakistan.* Tucson: University of Arizona Press.

McClain, Carol, 1982, Toward a Comparative Framework for the Study of Childbirth: A Review of the Literature. In *Anthropology of Human Birth,* Margarita A. Kay, ed., pp. 25-59. Philadelphia: E A. Davis.

McGilvray, Dennis B., 1982, Sexual Power and Fertility in Sri Lanka. In *Ethnography of Fertility and Birth,* Carol P. MacCormack, ed., pp. 25-73. London: Academic Press.

Mead, Margaret & Niles Newton, 1967, Cultural Patterning in Perinatal Behaviour. In *Childbearing: Its Social and Psychological Aspects.* Stephen A. Richardson & Alan F. Guttmacher (eds.) pp. 142-244. Baltimore: Williams and Wilkins.

Mistry, Jerbanoo E., 1936, My Experience of the Harm Wrought by Indian Dais. Extracted in Vera Anstey, *The Economic Development of India,* pp. 489-91. 3d ed. London: Longmans Green.

Montagu, Ashley, 1949 Early History of Embryology. *Ciba Symposia* 11:4.

National Archives of India, 1872, Home, Public 266-67-A.

National Archives of India, 1887 Home, Medical, August 32-A

Newton, Niles & Michael Newton, 1972, Child-birth in Cross-cultural Perspective. In *Modern Perspectives in Psycho-Obstetrics,* John G. Howells, ed., pp. 150-72. Edinburgh: Oliver & Boyd

Oakley, Ann, 1977, Cross-cultural Practices. In *Benefits and Hazards of the New Obstetrics,* Tim Chard & Martin Richards, eds., pp. 18-33. London: Heinemann.

Paul, Lois & Benjamin Paul, 1975, The Maya Midwife as Sacred Specialist. *American Ethnologist.* 2:707-26.

Raheja, Gloria G 1988 *The Poison in the Gift.* Chicago: University of Chicago Press.

Registrar-General of India, 1983, *Survey on Infant and Child Mortality 1979.* New Delhi: Office of the Registrar-General of India

Registrar-General of India, 1985, *Sample Registration System 1982.* New Delhi: Ministry of Home Affairs, Office of Registrar-General of India.

Roberton, John, 1846, On Hindu Midwifery. *Edinburgh Medical & Surgical Journal* 65(167):308-19.

Sharma, Ursula, 1980, *Women Work and Property in North-West India.* London: Tavistock.

Spencer, Robert F.1950 Primitive Obstetrics. *Ciba Symposium* 11(3):1158-88.

Thompson, Catherine S., 1984, Ritual States in the Life-cycles of Hindu Women in a Village of Central India. Ph.D. diss., University of London.

World Health Organization 1986, *Maternal Mortality Rates: A Tabulation of Available Information.* 2nd ed. Geneva: World Health Organization.

[1] McClain also distinguishes those anthropologists who treat midwifery and childbirth as part of a cultural, holistic analysis, and who explore issues of symbolic relationships (particularly in interpreting ritual observances) from those who either stress the sociocultural definitions of childbearing in order to make health workers more sensitive to the values of their clients, or who stress the biomedical risks attached to various "traditional" childbearing practices (McClain 1982: 46-50).

[2] We can do little but speculate about conditions at the other end of the spectrum. Browner and Perdue (1988) provide a cautionary note: in a relatively egalitarian society they found no separate sphere of women's knowledge with respect to pregnancy and childbirth.

[3] More details of this research can be found in Jeffery *et al.* 1989.

[4] For some British accounts see J. E. Mistry 1936; National Archives of India 1872, 1887; J. Robertson 1846. See also Jeffrey *et al.* 1985.

[5] The word dai can also mean a wet nurse, and some Muslim dais claim that they are due the same respect the Prophet Muhammad showed his wet nurse.

[6] A summary statement of patterns of attendance at childbirth for the different Indian states can be found in Registrar-General of India 1983.

[7] General overviews of the position of women in north India can be found in Agarwal 1988; Dyson and Moore 1983; Karve 1968; Mandelbaum 1988; see also Sharma 1980.

[8] The foot of the bed is sometimes raised to prevent a miscarriage.

[9] We are not endorsing these practices, but mention them merely to show that the dais internal examinations are the only interventions different from those of the other women present.

[10] The left hand is used for all tasks considered "dirty," such as washing the genital area after defecating or touching the genitals in sexual intercourse; the right hand is kept "clean" for eating, gift-giving, etc.

[11] Raheja (1988:72, 82-83) notes how one-and-a-quarter is a quantity frequently used as a means of removing inauspiciousness ("bad luck") and passing it on to others—in this case, the dai.

[12] Hershman 1974 provides an extended discussion of these relationships.

[13] More information on the use of oxytocin injections can be found in Jeffrey *et al.* 1989, chap.5

[14] See, for example, the references in note 4 above.

[15] For instance, the relative value of sons and daughters is reflected in the lower payments made to the dai when a girl is born—but that is another story.

[16] In Uttar Pradesh, the rural population was about 91 million in 1981 and about 93 million in 1982 (Gupta 1982). The crude birth rate in Uttar Pradesh was 40 per 1,000 population in 1982 and the perinatal mortality rate (stillbirths and deaths of children under one week per 1,000 live births and stillbirths) was 80 (Registrar-General of India 1985). On the basis of these figures, we have estimated that there are about 10,200 births each day, 820 of whom will die by the end of their first week. Estimates of maternal mortality in India range from 500 to 1,200 per 100,000 live births (World Health Organization 1986). In Uttar Pradesh, the higher estimates are almost certainly nearer the mark than the lower ones.

An Alternative to Unattended Delivery-
A Training Programme for
Village Midwives in Papua New Guinea

William A. Alto, * *Ruth E. Albu*† *& Garabinu Irabo*†

Abstract

Certain linguistic groups in the Southern Highlands of Papua New Guinea are unique in that there is no cultural role for a traditional birth attendant and, therefore, women deliver alone unattended. A programme to train village women as midwives was begun at Nipa Health Centre in 1981 and later expanded to a province-wide scope in 1986. Thirty-two Angal Heneng village midwives were trained during the period 1981-1989. Women of this language group have traditionally given birth alone. By 1989 the Angal Heneng village midwives had supervised 623 deliveries while 24 of them were still practicing. Well accepted in the community, they attended 11% of all births in 1989. Their efforts contributed to infant and perinatal mortality rates that were lower among the Angal Heneng than those of the neighbouring language group.

Introduction

Childbirth is a life crisis that is rarely approached alone. Most societies have included the role of a traditional birth attendant as an assistant to support and care for the labouring mother and newborn infant. However, several language groups in Papua New Guinea are without indigenous birth attendants. The Angal Heneng are one of these groups who still maintain the custom of unattended delivery. Local Angal Heneng women have recently been trained as village midwives and their role has been integrated into their culture, contributing to an improved maternal and perinatal survival.

The Southern Highlands Province is located in the centre of the island of New Guinea. Within the Nipa District of the Southern Highlands reside the 30,000 people of the Angal Heneng language group. They live in scattered hamlets in the intermountain valleys of 1500-1800 m elevation. Their houses are constructed of local wood, bark and grasses with an earthen floor and a central firepit. The staple diet consists of sweet potato and greens with occasional pig meat and, for those with a cash income, tinned fish or meat and rice. First contact with Westerners was in 1935, although modern health services did not become available in Nipa until the 1960s.

* St Mary's Family Practice Residency Program, 2333 North Sixth St, Grand Junction, CO 81501, US
† Nipa Health Centre, Nipa, Southern Highlands Province, Papua New Guinea
Social Science & Medicine 32(5); 1991: 613-8

LOCAL CUSTOMS

Due to cultural prohibitions the Angal Heneng-speaking woman is expected to deliver alone[1]. Woman's blood is considered dangerous and contact with blood is believed to result in illness or death. Other village women are not willing to assist one another in labour or delivery for fear of becoming contaminated. Conception and pregnancy are forbidden topics of discussion between men and women and a source of embarrassment even between women themselves. Congenital defects are believed due to a cultural infraction by the mother, and twins are often attributed to maternal adultery. Infanticide has been practiced rather than returning in shame to the village with such infants.

When confinement draws near, the husband builds a small delivery hut in a nearby garden. As labour commences, the parturient retires alone to this hut to await delivery. Custom allows another woman to call out to her but not to actually enter the delivery hut. Only after one or two days of unsuccessful labour might a decision be reached by the village women to seek assistance at a health centre. The husband may assist in arranging transportation but rarely accompanies his wife to the health facility.

MATERNAL HEALTH SERVICES

Through the efforts of the local churches and the Division of Health, the percentage of Angal Heneng women who attended antenatal clinic at least once during their pregnancy has increased from 73% in 1979[2] to 98% in 1987[3], although many women visit only a single time in the second trimester to have the pregnancy medically confirmed. The percentage of deliveries that are supervised in the health centre has increased from 35 to 45% over this same time period[2,3]. A number of measures have been instituted to increase the rate of supervised deliveries. A traditional bush material house and garden have been provided at Nipa Health Centre for high-risk women to live in while they await delivery. Around-the-clock transport to the health centre is offered to any woman in labour. Women who deliver their infants at the health centre or who are supervised by a village midwife receive a free 'road to health' book and birth certificate. Those who deliver their infants in the village in the traditional manner are required to purchase the book and certificate.

This improvement in antenatal coverage has approached the maximum contact the health service can establish with the pregnant population because of the remoteness of the region and the scarcity of roads. Prior to 1985, 25% of all Angal Heneng women lived within a one hour walk from the health centre[3] at Nipa; this figure improved to 31% in that year with the opening of a new health facility at Karinja. A one hour walk is believed the longest a labouring woman might undertake, although it is unlikely that even this distance would be attempted after dark. Expectant women are reluctant to be admitted to the health centre prior to the onset of labour because of their responsibilities at their homes and gardens. The 17 aidposts in the area serve out-patients exclusively and are staffed by male orderlies which renders them culturally inaccessible for obstetrical care even in an emergency. Thus for many, culture and distance combine to limit access to a supervised delivery. It is because of these constraints to supervised delivery and the subsequently high maternal and perinatal morbidity and mortality that a village midwife programme was started in 1981 at Nipa Health Centre.

The maternal mortality rate for the Angal Heneng is unknown, but the Huli language group with whom they share a common border had a maternal mortality of 4.6/1000 during the period from 1977 to 1983[4]. The Huli culture encourages delivery in a health facility and a majority of their births are supervised so that it is unlikely that the maternal mortality of the Angal Heneng is considerably lower. There were no Huli village midwives in the study area over this time period. In the Southern Highlands Province, maternal mortality was reported as 9.0/1000 in 1984[5] and 15.6/1000 in 1986[6]. However, communication of maternal deaths to health officials is sporadic and incomplete, and the actual figures are probably much higher. About 50% of all maternal deaths in Papua New Guinea have been reported to be due to haemorrhage or sepsis[7].

Infant mortality was reported as 116/1000 in the Southern Highlands Province in 1980[8] which was the highest in all of Papua New Guinea, and it was estimated to be 68/1000 in 1986[9]. The infant mortality rate among the Angal Heneng language group's area is unavailable for 1980 and was estimated as 62.3/1000 in 1986[9] using the method of determining the survival of previous infant at the time of birth registration and life tables[10]. No accurate data are available concerning perinatal or maternal morbidity of the Angal Heneng.

Because of the inability of the government and church health services to further extend maternal child health services to this remote population, a village midwife training programme was restarted in 1986 after a lapse of 5 years. The programme was based on a pilot project conducted in 1981 that trained the initial four Angal Heneng village midwives. Funding was provided in part by the Asian Development Bank Rural Health Improvement Loan II which purchased a vehicle and paid the salaries of its driver and a village midwife tutor. The total grant for the 5 year programme was 70,000 U.S. dollars.

METHODS

Beginning in 1981 and continuing through 1989, 32 Angal Heneng women have received instruction as village midwives (VMW) at Nipa Health Centre (Table 1). The 1981 class were midwives number 1-4 while the others were trained during the years 1986-1989. As is the traditional custom, they were chosen as VMW candidates by the men of their community after discussion with the midwife trainer. The would-be students were enrolled into the course only after the local men had built a delivery house with a pit latrine and rubbish hole. None of the women had more than a grade 6 education and most were illiterate. Only older women with several children were accepted for training. For the most part, the VMWs were the wives of indigenous pastors, headmen or health workers. They undertook their studies and conducted their work as a Christian duty to serve the women of their village and relied on their faith to overcome the traditional taboo against becoming soiled by women's blood. All of the VMWs were unpaid by the Health Department.

The curriculum of the course has been described previously[11] and is briefly presented here. During a 4-week course, VMW students were instructed in basic anatomy, the normal progression of pregnancy and how to determine foetal lie. Each student conducted five normal deliveries and had the opportunity to observe several complicated deliveries. They were taught what is an appropriate obstetrical referral. All women that are nulliparous, grand multiparous, noncephalic lies, in premature labour, have multiple pregnancies and those with previous obstetrical complications were to be sent to the health centre for delivery. Umbilical cord care and general hygiene and sanitation were also included in the course syllabus. The teaching was non-formal in style and much of the curriculum was taught through plays and skits rather than classroom lectures. The utilization of these teaching techniques avoided the student embarrassment that would have resulted from a more direct discussion of reproductive function. The students lived in a traditional house on the health centre grounds and were on call and available for all deliveries.

A delivery kit consisting of a sharp knife, cotton cord ties, gentian violet for umbilical cord care and ergometrine tablets were supplied. New banana leaves provided a clean delivery area and moss was used as surgical sponges. A fire or a kerosene lamp furnished light.

Supervision of the VMWs is carried out at monthly MCH clinic sites by the neighbouring health centre clinic sisters. They reviewed the past obstetrical history of potential VMW clients and together they examine the antenatal women. The nurses also conduct a verbal history of the VMW's recent deliveries and record them in a permanent record book that is kept by the VMW as well as on the routine Department of Health reporting forms. The VMW tutor visits the VMW at her delivery house at 1, 2, 6 and 12 months after completion of the training course and then again at 6-12 month intervals thereafter or whenever the need arises. In addition a yearly one week in-service training course is held for all the VMWs. The tutor also maintains contact with the male leaders of the village, encourages their continued support and intervenes on behalf of the VMW if necessary.

Remuneration to the VMW is primarily through an increase in status within the community, although food or firewood are often offered by the patient. The VMWs also receive a tin of fish and a bar of soap, or similar pay, for their assistance at the MCH clinics.

Table 1. Deliveries supervised by Angal Heneng village midwives

| Midwife number | Village | Date trained | Deliveries through | | | | | |
			1986	1987	1988	1989	total	Stillbirths
1	Sogura	1981	112	14	15	6§	147	0
2	Kanj	1981	91*	3	3	0§	97	2
3	Obal	1981	49	3	4	4§	60	0
4	Hebinja	1981	0‡	0	0	0	0	0
5	Semin	1986	0	5	3	6	14	0
6	Semin	1986	0	11	15	6	32	0
7	Semin	1986	0	11	4	6	21	1
8	Tepigo	1986	0	8	1	0•	9	0
9	Montanda	1987	—	2	4	0•	6	1
10	Ungubi	1986	0	5	5	4	14	0
11	Ungubi	1986	0	6	9	4	19	1
12	Ungubi	1986	0	6	5	3	14	0
13	Haralenja	1987	—	2	6	4	12	0
14	Haralenja	1987	—	2	4	4	10	0
15	Ingin	1986	0	3	4	2	9	0
16	Ingin	1986	0	1	5	2	8	0
17	Suma	1987	—	0	11	3	14	0
18	Sekib Te	1987	—	14	13	5	32	1
19	Suma	1987	—	0	6	2	8	0
20	Lloab	1986	0	2	1	4	7	0
21	Solbaem	1986	2	6	8	1	17	0
22	Kabendaka	1986	0	9	6	4	19	0
23	Imilhoma	1987	—	3	6	9	18	0
24	Tiwao	1987	—	3	10	5	18	0
25	Sumbi	1987	—	1†	2†	0†	3	0
26	Sumbi	1987	—	1†	1†	0†	2	0
27	Salenda	1987	—	0	2	1	3	0
28	Salenda	1987	—	0	1	2	3	1
29	Songura	1989	—	—	—	3	3	0
30	Obal	1989	—	—	—	3	3	0
31	Wara Wagi	1989	—	—	—	1	1	0
32	Wara Wagi	1989	—	—	—	0	0	0
Total VMV-supervised deliveries			254	121	154	94	623	7
Estimated Angal Heneng births				838	856	975		
Percentage of births supervised by VMWs				14%	18%	11%		

• Resigned, no village support, still evaluating and referring women.
* Employed at Karinja Health Subcentre.
‡ Resigned, no support by husband.
† Tribal warfare in area.
§ Retired and replaced by younger VMW.

RESULTS

Deliveries and Referrals

During the period 1981 through 1987 there were 254 deliveries supervised by 3 VMWs with no maternal deaths (Table 1). At least 10 of these deliveries were of primigravida, and an unknown number were grand multiparous women who went to the village midwife rather than risk a long walk to a health centre and a possible delivery enroute. Thus, although an effort was made by the MCH-VMW team to deliver all 'high-risk' parturients at the health centre, this proved impossible due to distance and the woman's preference.

In 1987, the first year complete data was collected, 23 VMWs supervised the deliveries of 121 infants. Eighteen antenatal referrals (12.9%) of high-risk women were sent to the health centre from a total of 139

VMW clients. Details of the reasons for referral are shown in Table 2. There were no deaths among these antenatal women or of an additional 4 postpartum women who were also referred. VMWs attended 121/429 (28%) of all supervised deliveries in 1987, or 121/838 (14%) of all deliveries.

In 1988 there were 27 VMWs in independent practice, another was employed at Karinja health subcentre, and one was inactive. Detail of the numbers of supervised deliveries in that year are presented in Table 1. Midwife number 4 never practiced in her village. She had been chosen by her village headmen while her husband was away and when he later returned he forbid her working. Midwives 25 and 26 lived in an area that was engulfed by tribal fighting late in 1987, and their houses and gardens were destroyed as was the local school and health aidpost. The people affected moved off to the bush, and all government services have ceased since then. In 1988 the reporting of referrals and delivery complications was available only for the Nipa Health Centre administered VMWs (numbers 5-19). These 16 VMWs referred 41 antenatal or postpartum women. Thirty two of these were antenatal complications or high risk patients; 7 were complications of labour or delivery; and 2 were threatened abortions. The reasons for referral to the health centre are listed in Table 2. There was one maternal death of a woman from the Nipa area as a result of a postpartum haemorrhage. The VMW who was helping the haemorrhaging woman was unable to find transport to carry her to the health centre. This was the only maternal death of a VMW-supervised delivery since the programme's inception. Seven other women, out of a total of 155 (4.5%) women in labour, required referral to a health centre for peripartum complications. Village midwives attended 26% of all supervised deliveries and 18% of an estimated 856 total deliveries in 1988.

Table 2. Reasons for referral by all Angal Heneng village midwives in 1987 and 1989 and by village midwives from the Nipa Health Centre Area in 1988

	1987	1988	1989
Antenatals:			
Nulliparity	4	7	13
Grand multiparity	11	9	17
Medical illness with pregnancy:			
Anaemia	1	1	1
Malaria	0	1	0
Pneumonia	1	1	0
Complications of pregnancy:			
Twins	0	1	0
Oedema	1	1	0
Previous delivery with retained placenta	0	1	0
Complications of labour and delivery:			
Retained placenta	1	1	0
Premature labour	0	1	0
Postpartum haemorrhage	0	2	0
Perineal tears	0	2	0
Prolonged labour	1	1	1
Postpartum fever	4	0	0
Other	0	0	2
Gynaecological:			
Threatened abortion	0	2	2
Incomplete abortion	0	0	1
TOTAL	24	41	37

In 1989 the number of supervised deliveries declined to 94 or an estimated 10.7% of all Angal Heneng deliveries. There were 37 maternal referrals and no maternal deaths. Twenty-five VMWs were supervising village deliveries, 2 VMWs were only evaluating and referring pregnant women, and the 3 older VMWs trained in 1981 retired after 10 years of service. Two of the three retirees were replaced by recently-trained VMWs from the same area.

The maternal mortality of the first 623 VMW-supervised deliveries over the period 1981-89 was 1.6/1000 compared to 4.6/1000 in Tari in 1984[4]. Each midwife who ever practiced has averaged 5.7 deliveries per year of service.

PERINATAL COMPLICATIONS

Two stillbirths and no neonatal deaths of VMW-supervised deliveries were recorded prior to 1987. In that year there were 1 macerated stillbirth and 2 obstructed breech presentations that sought assistance too late with dead foetuses.

Neonatal Complications occurred in 5 of 166 (3.0%) VMW-supervised deliveries from the Nipa Health Centre area in 1988 (midwives 5-19, Table 1). There was 1 premature infant that died shortly after birth and 1 stillbirth. A second premature infant died at 2 weeks of age of an unknown cause. Two neonates received respiratory resuscitation by a VMW and survived. Karinja Health Subcentre and the other VMWs reported perinatal and neonatal mortalities of zero in 1988.

In 1989 there were 1 neonatal death of a premature infant and 1 stillbirth of all VMW-supervised deliveries. Table 3 presents the comparison between the mortality rates from the 1981-1989 VMW-supervised deliveries with that reported in 1984 for all health centre and unsupervised village deliveries occurring in the neighbouring Tari Basin[4]. The two groups are not identical, as the majority of the VMW-supervised deliveries were from a low risk maternal group. Therefore the results cannot be compared statistically. The difference between the neonatal mortality rate in the Tari Basin and the lower rate of the VMW infants is considerable. The perinatal mortality rate is also lower for the VMW-supervised deliveries in comparison with the Huli. Table 4 shows the comparison between infant mortality rates between the Tari Valley (Huli language) with that of the Angal Heneng group. The Angal Heneng have a lower infant mortality rate.

Table 3. Mortality rates of the Huli People (Tari) compared with the Angal Heneng village midwife-supervised deliveries

	Tari 1984*	Angal Heneng-VMW 1981-1989
Stillbirth rate	16.3/1000	11.2/1000
Neonatal mortality	19.4/1000	4.8/1000
Perinatal mortality	31.0/1000	12.8/1000
Maternal mortality	4.6/1000	1.6/1000

* 59.5% of all deliveries attended by a health worker.

Table 4. Estimated infant mortality Tari District & the Angal Heneng linguistic group in 1986*

Tari	Angal Heneng
83.7 / 1000	62.3 / 1000†
n = 942	n = 757

* Using method of Hill and Macrae[10] and Coale and Demeny life tables of the West model.
† Chi squares = 5.99; $P = 0.01437$.

DISCUSSION

Despite customary prohibitions, it has been possible to train village midwives to provide obstetrical services in a remote part of Papua New Guinea where there was previously no cultural role of traditional birth attendant. Extensive preliminary health education of village headmen and careful selection of VMW trainees has allowed the development of an accepted and accessible maternity service to women who would otherwise have delivered their infants unattended. Of greater significance has been the relative safety of VMW-supervised deliveries both to the mother and her newborn. The single maternal death that occurred in 1988 might have been prevented had the delivery occurred at a health centre that had transport available. Nipa Health Centre is one and one-half hours by road from the Provincial Hospital at Mendi where transfusion services are regularly available. However, as the woman who died was at low risk for perinatal complications and she lived a considerable distance from a health centre, it is likely that she would have delivered in the traditional manner and died alone.

The neonatal mortality rate of infants delivered of mothers under the care of VMWs is less than that in Tari, a well studied and adjacent area; and there was a lower perinatal mortality rate among the infants of VMW-supervised deliveries. Although the VMWs cannot be solely credited with the lower infant mortality rate among the Angal Heneng people compared with that of their neighbours, these better MCH health indicators are of considerable interest. Perhaps the community support of the VMWs is a reflection of greater health consciousness of the Angal Heneng as compared to the Huli. In other health and social-economic indicators the two groups are similar.

Access to health services is better among the Huli than in the Nipa area. Nutritional status of Huli children is superior to those in the Nipa District[3], which has one of the most serious malnutrition problems in the nation. Maternal education levels, birth spacing and per capita income are approximately equal in both areas where subsistence agriculture is universal and small coffee gardens provide a small cash income. A majority (86.7% in 1987) of Huli women deliver in a health centre or hospital compared with the Angal Heneng (64.0% in 1987). The percentage of women of childbearing age that use artificial methods of contraception is similar in each area and less than 7%[3]. Antenatal clinic registration is nearly 100% in both groups but attendance after the first visit is equally poor averaging 2.3 additional attendances per woman in Tari and 1.2 in the Nipa area in 1987[3].

The maternal and infant health of the Angal Heneng appears to be superior to that of its neighbours, the Huli, although there are differences between the two populations studied. The reasons for this difference are uncertain, but the village midwives have probably contributed to the reduced mortality by encouraging antenatal care, referring high risk pregnancies to deliver in health facilities, and providing delivery services for women who are too distant from health centres. The VMWs are believed to have contributed to the improved neonatal survival and have enhanced attendance of infants and children at MCH clinics.

Although the number of VMW-attended deliveries is small and the women they serve are in a relatively low risk group, there would have been at least 2 maternal and 19 neonatal deaths expected (using Tari Research Unit's maternal and neonatal mortality rates) rather than the 1 or 3 observed. Frequent supervisory visits and in-service training along with VMW-MCH clinic staff co-operation have allowed identification of women with potentially high risk deliveries and facilitated timely referral to a health centre. This teamwork has contributed to the relative safety of a VMW-supervised birth.

The programme has been enthusiastically supported by most of the communities and a waiting list of villages and their trainees has developed. Only two women have stopped providing midwifery services because of the loss of village support although this continues to be a hindrance to another VMW (No. 15). Two other VMWs have curtailed their services because of a prolonged tribal war in their area. The Kanj VMW (No. 2) was offered employment at Karinja Health Subcentre after it opened near her village in 1985. The deliveries she conducted at the health centre were not counted as VMW-supervised although she also continued to attend a few deliveries outside the health centre. Three VMWs have retired after 9 years of service having supervised 304 deliveries in all.

Four community councils have offered cash financial support to their midwives. Other VMWs are rewarded directly by their clients. It is surprising that the VMWs who have been paid have supervised 4.7 deliveries per year as compared with the 7.3 deliveries per year conducted by the midwives who did not receive any form of payment. The increase in social status and doing one's Christian duty appear to be the motivating force behind these women. No midwife has been approached to pay compensation for a delivery-related complication. The attrition rate of the VMWs for all causes has been 8 of 32 (25%).

Over 80 VMWs are now working among 8 different language groups in the Southern Highlands [11]. They have been trained in Nipa and Tari by two VMW tutors and two assistants and at a third *ad hoc* programme in the Koroba District. Several other VMW training courses are currently in operation in Papua New Guinea including one in Morobe Province[12] while other programmes are in the planning stages.

CONCLUSION

In rural areas of the less developed countries of the world, health services are often inadequate because of financial constraints and inaccessibility of the people to health facilities. In many societies, the traditional birth attendant fills this gap in the provision of maternal-child health care. There was no cultural role for the TBA in the Angal Heneng community, and the village midwife has now filled this void. The VMWs' geographic accessibility in the village and their sharing of the same cultural orientation as their clients have permitted their easy integration into the birth practices of the women. Their presence has contributed to the increased number of supervised births and is believed to have contributed to the decreased neonatal and infant mortality of the Angal Heneng.

ACKNOWLEDGEMENT

The authors wish to thank Sister Elsie Schlatter at Karinja Health Subcentre for her assistance in providing follow-up information on the village midwives.

[1] Townsend P. K. Traditional birth attendants in Papua New Guinea. IASER Discussion Paper No. 52, p. 21. Papua New Guinea Institute of Applied Social & Economic Research, Boroko, Papua New Guinea, 1985.

[2] Clark L. Extracts from the Southern Highlands Province official briefing paper 1979. For SHP Rural Development Project. Mimeograph, Div. of Health, Mendi, Southern Highlands, Papua New Guinea.

[3] Division of Health Annual Report 1987. Provincial Printer, Mendi, Southern Highlands, Papua New Guinea

[4] Lehman D. Summary of Financial Report, Tari Research Unit. Provincial Printer, Mendi Southern Highlands, Papua New Guinea, Nov.1984.

[5] Division of Health Annual Report 1984. Provincial Printer, Mendi, Southern Highlands, Paupa New Guinea.

[6] Division of Health Annual Report 1986. Provincial Printer, Mendi, Southern Highlands, Papua New Guinea.

[7] Mola G. & Aitken I. Maternal morbidity in Papua New Guinea. *Papua New Guinea med. J.* 27, 65 1984

[8] National Statistical Office. 1980 Census, Govt. Printing Office, Port Moresby, Papua New Guinea.

[9] Prybylski D. Division of Health, Mendi, SHP. Personal communication.

[10] Hill A. G. & Macrae S . Measuring childhood mortality levels: a new approach. UNICEF *Soc. Statist. Bull.* 8, 1, 1985.

[11] Albu R. & Alto W. Training of village midwives in the Southern Highlands Province. *Papua New Guinea med. J.* 32, 89-95, 1989.

[12] Schumacher E. Village midwife training on the Huon Peninsula. *Papua New Guinea med. J.* 30, 213, 1987.

THE POLITICS OF MIDWIFERY: INTRODUCTION

Peter McCaffery

This introduction to the readings on the politics of midwifery is intended chiefly to outline some of the issues which arise in any discussion of the topic: notably, those of medicalization, ideology and competitive strategies. In the process, it will become evident why these eight readings have been chosen for inclusion in this book. An additional aim is to introduce the reader to some of the wealth of writing on this topic which it has unfortunately not been possible to include here.

CONFLICT OR CO-OPERATION?

To begin with, in order to make sense of the widely varying position occupied by the midwifery profession in the healthcare systems of different countries, we need some basis for comparing the variety of ways in which the politics of interprofessional relations in the sphere of health have evolved in specific national contexts. How does it come about that midwives relate to doctors so differently in the Netherlands, for instance, than they do in the United States? One of the outstanding contributions made in recent years toward the task of constructing a suitable framework within which we can address this type of question was put forward by Andrew Abbott in 1988. Professions, in Abbott's view, have to do with the exercise of power. An older tradition in sociology had seen professions as being primarily concerned with the application of a shared fund of specialized knowledge to the furthering of their clients' best interests. Like most of those who have addressed these questions since the 1970s, Abbott takes it for granted that this is an inadequate view, because it risks taking professional ideology at face value, instead of acknowledging that it often serves as a cloak for the competitive strategies which one profession adopts in seeking to enhance and deploy its members' collective power vis-à-vis their clients and other occupational groups. Abbott explains the differences between the medical profession in, say, Britain and France in the choice of competitive strategies as being due to a considerable extent to the historical role of the State in regulating health care. (See also Johnson *et al.*1995.) Because his focus is not on midwifery, this reader contains no extract from Abbott's work. Nor does it include the feminist analysis of the concept of professionalism put forward in 1995 by Celia Davies, who in the context of a consideration of nursing argues that this has hitherto been a strongly masculine concept. But the contributions which have been made by Abbott, Davies and like-minded authors are crucially important for anyone wishing to appreciate recent sociological writing about the politics of midwifery, by reason of their concern with the competitive aspects of relations between doctors and midwives, rather than with their potentially complementary character.

The history of relationships between the medical profession and the midwifery profession in any given national context can, then, be analyzed in terms of competition between them, at times amounting to a power struggle. However, analysing developments within this type of framework is not the only possible option, and it is one which can have disadvantages at the theoretical level (Baldwin 1992). For instance, it may lead one to underemphasize both the scope for harmonious cooperation between the two professions and the internal conflicts within each of them. However, the conflict perspective has been consciously espoused as a basis for collective action in the political sphere by doctors' leaders at various times, notably in the United States since the late nineteenth century (Kobrin 1966; Litoff 1978, 1986; Arney 1982). Where this has been so, it is of course tempting for the sociologist to follow suit and to depict the process as a zero-sum game, in which every factor that holds advantages for one side automatically becomes a disadvantage for the other side. In what follows, I shall enumerate the issues involved in conflicts between medicine and midwifery in more or less these terms. Nevertheless, an initial word of caution is appropriate.

Physician-midwife relationships can also be viewed as a positive-sum game. The potential winners, on such an interpretation, are childbearing women and their families (Keirse 1989). After all, the underlying situation is one in which they are anticipating an event which can issue either in euphoria or in tragedy, and is seldom a totally unemotional affair even if it does not involve either of these extremes (Lane 1996; Graham & Oakley 1981). A profession whose members are accustomed to attending relatively unproblematic deliveries has much to offer its clients by way of advice and moral support. Ann Oakley (below) does not hesitate to equate this with love—a term rarely used in sociological writing about professions. (See also Oakley & Houd 1990.) Moreover, this moral support can in itself directly contribute to a happy outcome, since the psychological wellbeing or otherwise of the parturient woman is capable of exerting a powerful influence on the physiological processes of birth—and on the establishment of breast-feeding thereafter, with all its benefits to health (Naaktgeboren 1989, Rajan 1994).

However, the multifarious dangers of harm to mother and/or baby cannot be reduced to a minimum unless a very different set of professional skills can, when required, be brought to bear. It has to be acknowledged on the one hand that these skills rest on a knowledge base demanding many years of study, and also that on the other hand they tend to foster an attitude of mind that is alert to signs of risk (just as someone who has been trained for police work is generally more prone than most people are to interpret a given piece of behavior as suspicious).

In principle, it is possible to envisage a co-operative pattern of relationships between the two professions. However, the problem in practice lies in the difficulty of establishing a suitable institutionalized basis for a division of labor between them, wherein the special abilities of each receive due recognition. Where this is lacking, a zero-sum approach can hardly be avoided. In its wake, as we shall see, comes a strong tendency for stereotyped assumptions about the characteristics of the two professions to prevail over the quest for solid evidence about what each of them does in practice (Graham 1991).

What, then, are the aims pursued in the competition, and even bitter conflict, which can arise between medicine and midwifery? And what resources are capable of being deployed?

MEDICALIZATION

For Charles Ziegler in 1913, the American medical profession's ultimate objective was to be "the elimination of the midwife" (below). Ziegler was not alone in identifying this as the goal. The climate of opinion existing in medical circles in the United States in the wake of the Flexner Report was highly optimistic about the prospect of creating a scientifically trained body of practitioners who would possess unparalleled expertise in the treatment of illness and could thus claim a monopoly over the treatment and prevention of illness (DeLee 1934; Starr 1982; Osherson & Amara Singham 1981). Reagan (1995) has pointed out that several medically-trained women, too, were among those who wished to see midwives replaced by doctors as the providers of maternity care. The same radical programme of eliminating midwifery altogether was pursued in Canada (Arnup et al. 1990). Elsewhere, however—as, for instance, in Britain—doctors were content to pursue the more limited aim of preventing midwives from taking on cases which they themselves wished to attend, and more generally of ensuring that midwives would have to defer to doctors (Fox 1991; Oakley 1984; Robinson 1990; Witz 1991).

The arguments used by campaigners for either a medical monopoly or medical control centred on the allegedly greater competence of doctors in safeguarding the lives and health of mothers and babies. This was assumed to result from the superior training they received in medical school. It was a type of argument which enjoyed much resonance in the climate of thinking that prevailed for most of the first half of the twentieth century, characterized by enthusiasm for science and (in North America, especially) eagerness to shake off the legacy of backward-looking traditions (Davis-Floyd 1994; Vallgårda 1996). It has to be said at once that the evidence in favour of these highly generalized arguments was far from strong: the rhetoric owed more to hope for the future than to solid statistics. But it will be time to consider the statistical issues in more detail when we move to listing the strategies deployed in the conflict. At present we are concerned with the aims being pursued. The chief goal was the medicalization of birth, and this has been achieved with a greater or lesser degree of success throughout the Western world, as witness the very high percentage of deliveries taking place in hospital in every industrialized country, apart from the Netherlands (Arms 1975; Torres & Reich 1989; Wagner 1986a; Van Teijlingen in this volume).

IDEOLOGY

Besides wishing to monopolize, or at least control, the provision of maternity care, leaders of the medical profession had in their relationship with midwifery a general objective which corresponded at the level of ideas to their practical aims. This was to secure public acceptance of an emphasis on the risks inherent in childbirth rather than on the fact that not every birth did in reality involve a crisis. This emphasis is enshrined in the maxim, "Only with hindsight can we say that a given birth was normal."

Just as the aspirations of the medical profession to see the introduction of medicalized childbirth chimed in with a public mood of reverence for science in the first half of the twentieth century, so too it was an already-widespread public concern over persistently high levels of maternal mortality that did much to facilitate people's acceptance of the ideological message which accompanied and complemented the practical steps taken toward the medicalization of birth. This is rather a paradox. The anticipated achievements of medicine in a future golden age of safety in childbirth constituted the chief argument for changing hitherto accepted practices; but it was the shortfall between future aspirations and present realities which lent force to the efforts to persuade people to concentrate on that aspect of birth which doctors sought to emphasise, namely its dangerous aspect. In other words, the leaders of the medical profession pursued a two-pronged strategy at the ideological level: they held out the prospect of a coming golden age of safe births, which was to be dependent on doctors being in charge of maternity care, and they used the grim pattern of contemporary maternal death rates to argue that more medical control was needed (largely disregarding any responsibility that the medical profession might bear for the current situation). Not until the mid-1930s did the proportion of mothers dying in childbirth begin its sustained fall to present low levels. And as maternal mortality fell, attention was shifted to the risk to babies' lives, with the same ideological themes being developed here too.[1]

However, it needs to be pointed out that in the course of the second half of the twentieth century not only did the prestige of science begin to wane, but falling rates of maternal mortality played some part in the rise of an ideology directly opposed to the emphasis on the risks to the lives of mother and baby. This newer ideology, associated with sections of the women's movement especially in the 1970s, directed attention away from dangers to life and physical health, and towards the opportunities for psychological bonding between mother and newborn infant. The dangers here emphasized were those of alienation leading to postpartum depression, and the physical dangers were liable to disappear from view.[2]

So far, then, we have identified the twin objectives informing the strategies of the medical profession's leaders in their activities vis-à-vis midwifery: the project of medicalization, and the ideological aim of stressing the dangerous nature of childbirth. We have not considered the objectives pursued on behalf of midwifery, because no such clear-cut priorities can be discerned, and because midwives have in most countries suffered from a lack of leadership until recent years, so that they have largely found themselves dancing to the tunes dictated by the interests of the medical profession.[3]

COMPETITIVE STRATEGIES

Three strands can be distinguished in the strategies adopted by doctors' leaders. These correspond to three broad areas. These are: public opinion; legislation and litigation; and regulation and training. As we consider the issues raised under each of these headings, it will become evident that all generalizations have to be treated with suspicion, and that the greater appropriateness of conflict models over complementarity models of the relationship between medicine and midwifery should not be taken for granted.

PUBLIC OPINION

As with all public relations campaigns, the effort to secure widespread acceptance for the medicalization of childbirth required the projection of appropriate images: in this case, the image of 'the doctor' as more competent, and thus more likely to ensure the survival of mother and baby; and the image of 'the midwife' as ignorant, unhygienic and in thrall to tradition. In reality, there were individual doctors who were incompetent, and there were well-trained, conscientious midwives, even in the United States, where their image suffered most from the consciously-orchestrated publicity campaign against them.

Ideally, the question would have been resolved by the gathering of statistical information regarding the outcomes of medically-supervised labors and those attended by midwives. And of course, the practical conclusion to be drawn from any evidence of incompetent practice might have been simply to improve training where it was proving inadequate, rather than to implement a winner-takes-all policy reflecting success in public debate. To a greater or lesser extent, these were the conclusions drawn in many countries. But in the one country where statistics were already by 1900 most firmly entrenched as part of the policy advocate's rhetoric, namely the United States, the social situation was least favourable to midwifery's image.

There were two main reasons for this. One was that the country had inherited the British tendency for midwifery training to be a neglected element in public health planning. The other was that, partly in consequence of this, the more prosperous section of society was more wedded to the ideal of having a doctor to attend childbirth, whereas recourse to midwife care was associated with poverty. This pattern was observable in other countries as well. But the situation in the Northern United States was complicated by the phenomenon of massive immigration during the late nineteenth century and the early twentieth century; and in the Southern states by the legacy of slavery (Schaffer 1991). Communities of immigrants often included midwives. Some of these (principally those from North Western Europe) had received systematic state-regulated training (Borst 1988). Trained or not, these midwives were able to provide a cheaper service than doctors—which in the long run proved their undoing (Declercq 1985; Declercq & Lacroix 1985). Advocates of medical monopoly in maternity care were able to play upon prejudice attributing the stigma of backwardness to immigrant status. The image of 'the immigrant midwife' began to suffer opprobrium almost as great as that of the granny midwives found among the Southern black population. True, statistics were gathered. But the spin-doctors who spoke for the American medical profession chose to interpret the findings as evidence in support of greater medicalization – whereas recent researchers have argued that the figures pointed to a different set of conclusions: namely, that incompetent doctors abounded, and that midwife care held the key to reducing mortality.[4] Loudon's comment, in particular, is striking (see below): as a doctor himself, he had not anticipated before he undertook the thorough research which is presented in his cross-national analysis of maternal mortality data how clearly it would emerge that midwifery training was the crucial explanatory factor.

The acceptance by public opinion of the logic of medicalization underpinned the shift towards regarding hospitals as the most suitable places for babies to be born in, provided that the parents could afford it. This was a trend wherein the United States led the way, but the notion that hospital delivery was more modern and therefore safer became more and more widespread in other countries, too (Peretz 1990; Vallgårda 1996). The urbanisation of industrialised populations meant that the problems posed by this philosophy for rural families did not have enough salience, during the middle decades of the century, to prompt widespread doubts about reliance on obstetricians in hospitals rather than on local healthcare professionals.

Admittedly, steps were taken here and there during the 1930s towards training women who could provide both nursing and maternity care in districts inadequately served by doctors, including both the countryside and the poorer urban areas. These efforts foreshadowed the overlap between community nursing and midwifery which led to a blurring of the distinction between these two professions.[5] But it was only with the rise of the women's movement and the growth of interest in alternative and complementary medicine that a reaction began to manifest itself on any significant scale against this enthusiasm for a policy that reflected, so it was argued, a masculine notion of rationality (Martin 1987). The 1970s and 1980s saw increasing concern with the ideal of maternity care that would respond to women's own preferences, and by the 1990s this was beginning to make an impact on politicians and policy-makers (Winterton 1992). Even in the United States, the percentage of all births which were attended by midwives rose from 1.7 in 1980 to 5.5 in 1994 (Rooks 1997: 149, see also Declercq 1992).

The reaction against medical dominance in the sphere of childbirth, and indeed against professional dominance in many spheres, reflected the widening access to higher education in the period following the Second World War. But even this trend had only a limited impact on the conventional wisdom which had meanwhile become firmly established in most countries, that midwife care carried greater risks than did maternity care provided either directly by a doctor, or at any rate under medical supervision.

LEGISLATION AND LITIGATION

Without a widespread and genuine acceptance of this view by the lay public—fathers, as well as mothers—it would scarcely have been possible for legislative and administrative changes to have occurred, as they did during the greater part of the twentieth century, favouring the presumption that childbirth was properly a matter for doctors. The starkest form taken by this presupposition was the classification of midwifery as a form of medical practice, so that any woman offering her services of a midwife became liable to a criminal charge of "practicing medicine without a license". Declercq's poignant retelling of the story of the Massachusetts immigrant midwife Hannah Porn, who was sent to prison on this count during the early years of the century, brings home forcefully how implacably the campaign was waged at this period. (Declercq 1994a; see also Kraut 1994.) But the heat has certainly not gone out of the issue yet, as witness some of the cases cited by Sullivan & Weitz (1988), wherein lawsuits were brought against women practicing as midwives without explicit legal authorization.

Use of the emotive accusation of "child abuse", admittedly not in a formal legal context but as a form of hyperbole, underlines how eager the defenders of medical monopoly over the control of maternity care have been to brand all other practices irresponsible. This vulnerability of midwives to hostile propaganda ultimately underlies Declercq's analysis of the tactical options available for those concerned to enlarge midwifery's scope, whether in the United States or elsewhere (see this section of the reader). Sandall's discussion of the social constraints and possibilities (below) has also to be read against this background.

A number of authors have tried to clarify the legislative situation in the United States regarding the practice of midwifery.[6] To summarise very briefly, there are states where the matter is left obscure; there are others where it is explicitly laid down by statute that in specified circumstances midwives may provide maternity care; and there are some where the practice of midwifery is against the law. Study of the fine print in some of the laws in states belonging to the second category reveals how heavily legislators have often been influenced by medical advice as to what is appropriate. Thus, California law permits nurse-midwives to practice, but stipulates that they may do so only under the supervision (though not necessarily in the presence) of "a licensed physician and surgeon who has current practice or training in obstetrics". No more than four nurse-midwives may practice under the supervision of any one doctor (Barickman et al. 1992: 196). Though the terms in which laws are couched vary from state to state, the theme of supervision in one form or another constantly recurs. This is the basis for the case which DeVries presents (below) for the somewhat pessimistic conclusion that campaigns to secure legislation to authorise licensure of midwifery, even where apparently successful, can be expected to yield little by way of genuine enhancement of the scope for midwives to practice their profession autonomously.

Even where the laws do not spell out what is required, the fear of litigation may make a midwife wish to hand over responsibility to a doctor in difficult cases. If this is to be a practical possibility, she will wish to have established a working relationship with the doctor whose help may be needed in such an emergency. This may not be easy. Moreover, even when assistance is forthcoming, the doctor's willingness to be helpful in a crisis is liable to have strings attached to it. Thus, there are restrictions formally imposed by law; and there are also restrictions which in practice may arise from the need to cultivate cooperative relationships with local doctors. Furthermore, a midwife will desire to be eligible for payment from health insurance funds or federally-subsidised reimbursement schemes. Restrictions may well arise here, too, as also from the insurance company upon which the midwife as a healthcare practitioner depends to underwrite the risk of litigation by clients.

But over and above the restrictions on those individuals who have gained the legal right to style themselves "midwives", there are limitations on who may enjoy this right in the first place. Here, too, one state differs from another. But a recurrent feature of the legal and administrative provisions for spelling out which practitioners are allowed to make public claim to be midwives, naturally, is the requirement that they must have followed an approved course of study. After all, who would wish to be attended in labour by someone with inadequate training? No one, surely.

REGULATION AND TRAINING

The question that immediately arises from this way of posing the issue is: who decides what this adequate level of training must involve? Whose opinion should prevail when a judgement must be made as to what counts as a properly-trained midwife? In addressing this question, we find ourselves considering the third strand in the medical profession's strategies in relation to maternity care, namely, regulation and training. For it has frequently been taken for granted that a medical education is both broader and deeper than that of a midwife, and that therefore those who teach medicine are the most suitable people to advise on the content of midwifery courses.

In many ways, of course, an obstetrician will know far more, and in greater depth, about the range of possible complications which may occur in childbirth. On the other hand, this knowledge is a preparation for managing pathological situations. Whether that necessarily makes obstetricians the best judges of the knowledge and skills required by a midwife may be questioned. The question becomes a practical one when state legislators are seeking to establish criteria for assessing the adequacy of a proposed course of midwifery training. Weitz & Sullivan (1986) cite instances where women wishing to become midwives found fault with the syllabus they were expected to cover, on the grounds that it included subject-matter more appropriate to an obstetrician's training. Clearly, legitimate differences of opinion can arise here. But from a sociological perspective, the significant point is that where the relationship between the two occupations has been as fraught with tension as it has in the United States, one can expect that the more powerful profession will tend to impose its definition of what counts as the most valuable type of knowledge on would-be practitioners of the less powerful profession. This definition will tend to be one which emphasises theoretical understanding relevant to coping with abnormalities, while attaching less weight to practical manual skills and to the handling of personal relationships (Böhme 1984). Conversely, where medicine and midwifery are on less unfriendly terms with each other, one can expect some willingness on the part of the medical profession's leaders to acknowledge that different criteria should apply to midwifery training than to medical training.[7]

It is worth mentioning, in connection with the topic of training, that in the early years of the twentieth century one focus of rivalry between doctors and midwives was access to the birth-room as an opportunity for gaining practical experience. Advocates of a medical monopoly in maternity care argued, as Ziegler did (below), that only if midwives were driven out of business would medical students be able to gain the requisite wealth of experience. The women in labor over whom this competition was being waged were in this context referred to as "obstetric material".

The Dutch obstetrician and advocate of midwifery care for normal deliveries, Kloosterman, used an argument which was in some ways analogous to Ziegler's, but which points in the opposite direction. He warned that the transition to almost universal hospital birth which had taken place everywhere else in the Western world entailed the disappearance of a body of practitioners accustomed to treating home birth as a normal event. The skills demanded of midwives by the Dutch pattern of maternity care would, he pointed out, be hard to recreate in future generations if once they were allowed to fall into disuse, as seemed likely in 1978 when he put this argument forward. In effect, the advocates of medically supervised birth for all would have made a self-fulfilling prophecy if, thanks to their doubts as to whether midwives could achieve the highest levels of safety and efficiency, the day-to-day experience of independent practice were denied to Dutch midwives–for it was on this experience alone that such competence could rest. His views are presented through the medium of an interview with Van Daalen & Van Goor (below: see also Kloosterman 1978).

While the Dutch pattern is unique, the problem of how midwives are to maintain confidence in their own ability to manage normal births and reliably identify the abnormal cases that have to be left to their medical colleagues arises wherever there is a wish to counteract the effects of the twentieth-century medicalization of childbirth. One form in which the same issue presents itself is that of standardized protocols to be followed in particular hospitals. Staff are expected to manage recurrent situations in the specific ways that have been laid down by the medical directors of the unit. In practice, since not every experienced obstetrician has the same preferences, the policies embodied in the prescribed protocols will vary from one hospital to another depending on who happens to be the senior and the policy-maker, or on whether protocols are formulated through a process of joint consultation between care-providers at different levels in the hierarchy. The resulting lack of autonomy can be irksome to midwives, especially those whose earlier experience may have been gained under a regime different from that prevailing where they happen to be working at a later point in their career.[8] However, this issue of autonomy arises not only where the senior and policy-maker is an obstetrician. It is also potentially relevant in any situation where the limits of an individual's professional autonomy are liable to be experienced as excessively restrictive, and is thus capable of generating tensions between seniors and juniors within the ranks of midwives themselves.[9]

A final point which can appropriately be made here is that research bearing upon questions of what might be best practice in specific situations has in the past been carried out almost exclusively by obstetricians. Midwives have thus become accustomed to being the consumers but not the producers of research-findings (Rothman 1984). Yet it is on such findings that claims to lay down what constitutes best practice ultimately rest, in principle at least, for their legitimacy. In practice, of course, there has historically been an element of fiction in the appeal to well-founded scientific research as the basis for day-to-day hospital practice. To put this in sociological terminology, scientific justifications for current orthodoxy in the management of childbirth are socially constructed and may have been shaped partly by power-relationships as well as by the disinterested analysis of dispassionate clinical observation (Berg 1992). On the other hand, two developments have taken place in recent years which lessen the force of this type of comment. One is that there has been a sustained effort to assemble and re-assess in a sceptical spirit the available scientific evidence relating to obstetrical practice.[10] This in itself does nothing to lessen the dependence of midwives on research carried out by doctors, but it is a potential source of encouragement to midwives and to child-bearing women to question received medical wisdom. Secondly, midwives themselves have increasingly been carrying out and publishing their own research, thereby reducing the danger that their distinctive professional perspectives will be neglected in the quest for 'evidence-based' maternity care.[11]

MIDWIFERY AND NURSING

Having reviewed the three main strands in the competitive strategies adopted by medical practitioners in relation to midwives, this introduction concludes by drawing attention to some of the strategic dilemmas faced by midwives themselves, notably in the United States.

The reader is referred in particular to the piece by Judith Rooks reproduced below (below), concerning the relationships between midwives and a number of other professional groups whose professional concerns overlap with theirs. This text was originally delivered as the President's annual address to the American College of Nurse-Midwives. Rooks is also the author of a magisterial survey of midwifery and maternity care in the United States between 1980 and 1995 (Rooks 1997).

The profession with whom there is potentially the greatest overlap is nursing. As the ACNM's name indicates, it represents the interests of the substantial number of midwives in the United States who are qualified to practice either profession. For each of these practitioners considered individually, the ability to do either type of job constitutes a valuable advantage from the point of view of prospects in the labor-market. Whether the midwifery profession collectively is thereby strengthened is open to question. One reason for doubting it is that somebody with a dual professional identity may be psychologically less ready to invest a great deal of effort in the struggle to achieve public recognition for midwifery – for instance, by campaigning to reduce the legislative restrictions which we have already referred to above (Langton 1991). In addition, it is argued by the proponents of 'pure' midwifery practice that nursing has a fundamentally different professional ethos, having arisen historically in the role of a profession subordinate to medicine. Nurses, so this argument runs, are trained to handle sickness, which makes it necessary for them to think of themselves as assistants to the medical practitioners who give them guidance; however, pregnancy and labour are not inherently pathological episodes in a woman's health-career; and unless they start to go wrong they are better dealt with by someone trained to regard them as fully compatible with excellent health. In this view, direct entry into midwifery training has positive advantages over becoming a midwife after first having trained as a nurse (Radford & Thomson 1994).

Partly on these grounds, a significant number of women in the United States have chosen to practice midwifery without initially acquiring qualifications in nursing (Reid 1989; Gaskin 1991). The legislative changes which have taken place in many states during recent years have to a greater or lesser extent reflected the presence of both types of midwife. In the forty or so years since its formation, the ACNM has set about ensuring that its members at any rate shall be entitled to practice in as many states as possible. For their part, midwives who were not nurses have campaigned for laws framed broadly enough to allow them, too, to practice with or without specified midwifery qualifications. In this they have had rather less success than their counterparts in the ACNM. Initially, these women were content to be called "lay midwives". More recently, this label has come to be seen as a political disadvantage, and nowadays their preferred designation is "traditional midwives". From time to time, some hostility has existed between the two sections of American midwifery, especially where nurse-midwives have played an active part in resisting the passage of legislation permitting the practice of traditional midwifery (Tjaden 1987). On the other hand, there have been attempts to coordinate the campaigning activities on both sides of the divide, under the aegis of the Midwives Alliance of North America (Rooks 1997: 241-246).

Although this sharp division within the ranks of midwives seems to be a phenomenon peculiar to North America, the question of midwifery's relationship with nursing arises in other countries, too (Cochrane 1995). The more securely the medical profession is able to exercise control over the shaping of maternity services, the greater become the attractions of a conception of midwifery as a branch of nursing. Conversely, the difficulties faced by any midwife wishing to practice independently become more daunting. Perhaps, however, instead of accepting as a given fact of life the entirely subordinate status of nurses vis-à-vis the medical profession, sociologists interested in the prospects for midwifery should give due weight to the strenuous efforts being made to reduce the degree to which nurses are defined as assistants to doctors and to enhance the notion that their work is complementary to that which doctors do. After all, one of the problems touched upon by Rooks in her presidential address to the ACNM was the fact that by the 1980s it was not uncommon for nurses to possess higher academic qualifications, whereas nurse-midwives were not so likely to be in this position, because they already needed extra years of study to acquire their dual qualification. The increasing confidence of nurses that their own role merits a certain autonomy rather than making them a mere adjunct to the work of doctors could be seen as a basis upon which independently-minded midwives might in the long term make common cause with them.

Having addressed the major strategic dilemma which confronts the midwifery profession, this introduction may appropriately end with a mention of one of its greatest strengths: namely, the fact that on average it tends to be less expensive than medical care. Among the professional groups listed in the title of Rooks's presidential ACNM address in 1983, it was surely the health economists who were destined to be midwifery's most valuable allies (Butter & Lapré 1986). It is true that efforts to reduce the extent of medical control over maternity services have relied heavily on achieving a reversal in the tide of public opinion; but the consideration that will appeal most of all to policy-makers is a reduction in the cost of healthcare.

BIBLIOGRAPHY

Abbott, Andrew (1988), *The System of Professions*, Chicago: Chicago University Press.

Abraham-van der Mark, Eva, ed. (1993), *Successful Home Birth and Midwifery: the Dutch model*, Westport CT: Bergin & Garvey.

Allison, Julia, & Gillian Pascall (1994), "Midwifery: a career for women?", In Julia Evetts, ed., *Women and Career: themes and issues in advanced industrial societies*, London: Longman, pp.203-217.

Allison, Julia (1996), *Delivered at Home*, London: Chapman & Hall.

Alten, D. van (1989), "Midwifery in The Netherlands. The Wormerveer study" *British Journal of Obstetrics & Gynaecology* 96: 656-662.

Arms, Suzanne (1975), *Immaculate Deception: a new look at women and childbirth in America*, Boston MA: Houghton Mifflin. Second edition, Berkeley CA: Celestial Arts, 1994.

Arney, William (1982), *Power and the Profession of Obstetrics*, Chicago: Chicago University Press.

Arnup, Katherine, *et al.*, eds. (1990), *Delivering Motherhood*, London/New York: Routledge.

Baldwin, L.M., *et al.* (1992), "Professional relationships between midwives and physicians: collaboration or conflict?" *American Journal of Public Health* 82.2: 262-264.

Barickman, C. *et al.* (1992), "Nurse-midwifery today: a legislative update, 2" *Journal of Nurse-Midwifery* 37.3: 175-210 (May-June).

Benoit, Cecilia (1989), "The professional socialisation of midwives: balancing art and science", *Sociology of Health & Illness* 11.2: 160-180.

Benoit, Cecilia (1991), *Midwives in Passage*, St John's, Newfoundland: Institute of Social and Economic Research, Memorial University.

Berg, Marc (1992), "The construction of medical disposals", *Sociology of Health & Illness* 14: 151-180.

Bidgood-Wilson, M., *et al.* (1992), "Nurse-midwifery today: a legislative update, 1" *Journal of Nurse-Midwifery* 37.2: 96-150.

Bidgood-Wilson, M. (1992), "The legislative status of midwifery: trends and future implications" *Journal of Nurse-Midwifery* 37.3: 159-161.

Böhme, G. (1984), "Midwifery as science: an essay on the relationship between scientific and everyday knowledge", In Stehr, Nico, & Volker Meja, eds., *Society and Knowledge: contemporary perspectives on the sociology of knowledge*, New Brunswick NJ: Transaction Books.

Borst, Charlotte (1988), "The training and practice of midwives: a Wisconsin study", *Bulletin of the History of Medicine* 62: 606-627.

Borst, Charlotte (1995), *Catching Babies: the professionalization of childbirth, 1870-1920*. Cambridge, Mass.: Harvard University Press.

Butter, Irene H., & Ruud Lapré (1986), "Obstetric care in the Netherlands: manpower substitution and differential costs" *International Journal of Health Planning and Management* 1: 89-110.

Butter, Irene H., & Bonnie J.Kay (1988), "State laws and the practice of lay midwifery", *American Journal of Public Health* 78: 1161-1169.

Butter, Irene H., & Bonnie J.Kay (1990), "Self-certification in lay midwives' organizations: a vehicle for professional autonomy", *Social Science and Medicine* 30.12: 1329-1339.

Chalmers, Iain, Murray Enkin & Marc Keirse, eds. (1989), *Effective Care in Pregnancy and Childbirth* (2 vols), Oxford: Oxford University Press.

Cochrane, A.R. (1972), *Effectiveness and Efficiency*, Nuffield Provincial Hospitals Trust.

Cochrane, Sharon (1995), "Midwives, nurses and doctors: interprofessional relationships", in Murphy-Black, Tricia, ed., *Issues in Midwifery*, Edinburgh: Churchill-Livingstone, pp.253-273.

Daalen, Rineke van, & Reinie van Goor (1993), "Interview with Prof. Gerrit-Jan Kloosterman", in Eva Abraham-van der Mark, ed., *Successful Home Birth and Midwifery: the Dutch model*, Westport CT: Bergin & Garvey, pp.191-200.

Davies, Celia (1995), *Gender & the Professional Predicament in Nursing*, Buckingham (UK): Open University Press.

Davis-Floyd, Robbie E. (1992), *Birth as an American Rite of Passage*, Berkeley: University of California Press.

Davis-Floyd, Robbie E., & Carolyn F.Sargent, eds. (1997), *Childbirth and Authoritative Knowledge: cross-cultural perspectives*, Berkeley CA: University of California Press.

Davis-Floyd, Robbie E., & Elizabeth Davis (1997), "Intuition as authoritative knowledge in midwifery and home birth", In Davis-Floyd, Robbie E., & Carolyn F.Sargent, eds., *Childbirth & Authoritative Knowledge: cross-cultural perspectives*, Berkeley CA: University of California Press, pp.315-49.

Davis-Floyd, Robbie E., (1996), "The technocratic body and the organic body: hegemony and heresy in women's birth choices", In Sargent, Carolyn F., & Caroline B.Brettell, eds., *Gender & Health: an international perspective*, Upper Saddle River: Prentice Hall, pp.123-166.

Declercq, Eugene R. (1985), "The nature and style of practice of immigrant midwives in early twentieth century Massachussetts", *Journal of Social History* 9: 113-129.

Declercq, Eugene R. (1992), "The transformation of American midwifery: 1975-1988", *American Journal of Public Health* 82: 680-684.

Declercq, Eugene R. (1994a), "The trials of Hanna Porn: the campaign to abolish midwifery in Massachussetts", *American Journal of Public Health* 84.6: 1022-8.

Declercq, Eugene R., (1994b), "A cross-national analysis of midwifery politics: six lessons for midwives" *Midwifery* 10: 232-237 (1994).

Declercq, Eugene R., & R.Lacroix (1985), "The immigrant midwives of Lawrence", *Bulletin of the History of Medicine* 59: 232-246.

DeLee, Joseph B. (1934), "Obstetrics versus midwifery" *Journal of the American Medical Association* 103: 307-311.

DeVries, Raymond (1996), *Making Midwives Legal*, Ohio State University Press.

Devitt, Neal (1979), "The statistical case for the elimination of the midwife: fact versus prejudice, 1890-1935", *Women and Health* 4: 81-96 and 169-186.

Dye, Nancy S. (1983), "Mary Breckinridge, the Frontier Nursing Service and the introduction of nurse-midwifery in the United States", *Bulletin of the History of Medicine* 57: 485-507.

Flint, Caroline (1991), "On the brink: midwifery in Britain", In Kitzinger, Sheila, ed., *The Midwife Challenge*, London: Pandora Press, 2nd edition, pp.22-41.

Fox, Enid (1991), "Powers of life and death: aspects of maternal welfare in England and Wales between the wars", *History of Medicine* 35: 328-352.

Fox, Enid (1993), "An honourable calling or a despised occupation: licensed midwifery and its relationship to district nursing in England & Wales before 1948", *Social History of Medicine* 6: 237-59.

Garcia, Jo, *et al.*, eds. (1990), *The Politics of Maternity Care*, Oxford: Oxford University Press.

Garcia, Jo, & Sally Garforth (1991), "Midwifery policies and policy-making", in Robinson, Sarah, & Ann Thomson, eds., *Midwives, Research and Childbirth*, Vol **2**, London: Chapman & Hall, pp.16-47.

Gaskin, Ina May (1991), "Midwifery reinvented", in Sheila Kitzinger, ed., *The Midwife Challenge*, London: Pandora Press, 2nd edition, pp.42-60.

Goer, Henci (1995), *Obstetrical Myths versus Research Realities*, South Hadley, MA: Bergin & Garvey.

Graham, Hilary, & Ann Oakley (1981) "Competing ideologies of reproduction: medical & maternal perspectives on pregnancy", In Roberts, Helen, ed., *Women, Health & Reproduction*, London/New York: Routledge, pp.50-74.

Graham, S.B. (1991), "A structural analysis of physician-midwife interaction in an obstetrical training program", *Social Science and Medicine* **32**: 931-942.

Hicks, Carolyn (1992), "Research in midwifery: are midwives their own worst enemies?", *Midwifery* **8**: 12-18.

Hunt, Sheila C., & Anthea Symonds, eds. (1995), *The Social Meaning of Midwifery*, Basingstoke (UK): Macmillan.

Johnson, Kenneth C. (1997), "Randomized controlled trials as authoritative knowledge: keeping an ally from becoming a threat to North American midwifery practice", In Davis-Floyd, Robbie E., & Carolyn F.Sargent, eds., *Childbirth & Authoritative Knowledge: cross-cultural perspectives*, Berkeley CA: University of California Press, pp.350-361.

Johnson, Terry, Mike Saks & Gerald Larkin, eds. (1995), *Health Professions and the State in Europe*, London/New York: Routledge.

Keirse, Marc J.N.C. (1989), "Interaction between primary and secondary care during pregnancy and childbirth", in Chalmers, Iain, Murray Enkin & Marc Keirse, eds., *Effective Care in Pregnancy and Childbirth*, Oxford University Press, Vol.1, pp.197-204.

King, Charles R. (1991), "The New York Maternal Mortality Study: a conflict of professionalization", *Bulletin of the History of Medicine* **65**: 476-502 (1991).

Kitzinger, Jenny, *et al.* (1990), "Labour relations: midwives and doctors on the labour ward", in Garcia, Jo, *et al.*, eds., *The Politics of Maternity Care*, Oxford: Oxford University Press, pp.149-162.

Kitzinger, Sheila, ed., (1991), *The Midwife Challenge*, London: Pandora Press (2nd edition).

Kloosterman, G.J. (1978), "Organization of obstetric care in the Netherlands", unpublished translation of "De Nederlandse verloskunde op de tweesprong", *Nederlands Tijdschrift voor Geneeskunde* **27**: 1161-1171.

Kobrin, Frances (1966), "The American midwife controversy: a crisis of professionalization", *Bulletin of the History of Medicine* **40**: 350-361.

Kraut, Alan M. (1994), *Silent Travelers: germs, genes, and the "immigrant menace"*, New York: Basic Books.

Lane, Karen (1996), "Birth as euphoria: the social meaning of birth", in Colquhoun, Derek, & Allan Kellehear, eds., *Health Research Practice—Vol.2: personal experiences, public issues*, New York: Chapman & Hall, pp.153-173.

Langton, Phyllis A. (1991), "Competing occupational ideologies, identities and the practice of nurse-midwifery", in Levy, J., ed., *Current Research on Occupations and Professions*, Greenwich CT: JAI Press, pp.149-177.

Lichtman, R. (1988), "Medical models and midwifery: the cultural experience of birth", in Michaelson, K., *et al.*, *Childbirth in America: anthropological perspectives*, South Hadley, MA: Bergin & Garvey, pp.130-141.

Litoff, Judy B. (1978), *American Midwives—1860 to the present*, Westport, CT: Greenwood.

Litoff, Judy B., ed. (1986), *The American Midwife Debate: a sourcebook on its modern origins*, Westport, CT: Greenwood.

Loudon, Irvine (1992), *Death in Childbirth: an international study of maternal care and maternal mortality 1800-1950*, Oxford: Clarendon Press.

McCormack, Carol P. (1989), "Status and the training of midwives" (and "Comment" by L A Rhodes), *Social Science and Medicine* **28**.9: 941-944.

Macintyre, S. (1977), "Childbirth: the myth of the Golden Age", *World Medicine* **12**.18: 17-22 (15 June).

Marland, Hilary (1995), "Questions of competence: the midwife debate in the Netherlands in the early twentieth century", *Medical History* **39**.3: 317-337.

Marland, Hilary, & Anne-Marie Rafferty, eds. (1997), *Midwives, Society and Childbirth: Debates and controversies in the modern period*, London/New York: Routledge.

Martin, Emily (1987), *The Woman in the Body*, Buckingham (UK): Open University Press.

Mitford, Jessica (1992), *The American Way of Birth*, London: Victor Gollancz.

Murphy-Black, Patricia (1995), "Comfortable men, uncomfortable women", In Murphy-Black, Tricia, ed., *Issues in Midwifery*, Edinburgh: Churchill-Livingstone, pp.275-297.

Naaktgeboren, Cornelius (1989), "The biology of childbirth", in Chalmers, Iain, Murray Enkin & Marc Keirse, eds., *Effective Care in Pregnancy & Childbirth*, Oxford University Press, vol.2, pp.795-804.

Nelson, Margaret (1983), "Working class women, middle class women and models of childbirth", *Social Problems* 30: 284-297.

Oakley, Ann (1984), *The Captured Womb: a history of the medical care of pregnant women*, Oxford: Blackwell.

Oakley, Ann (1989), "Who cares for women? Science and 'love' in midwifery today", *Midwives Chronicle and Nursing Notes* (July), pp.214-221.

Oakley, Ann, & Susanne Houd (1990), *Helpers in Childbirth: midwifery today*, New York: Hemisphere.

Osherson S., & L. Amara Singham (1981), "The machine metaphor in medicine", in Mishler, Elliot G., ed., *Social Contexts of Health, Illness and Patient Care*, Cambridge University Press, pp.218-249.

Pantin, C.G. (1996), "A study of maternal mortality and midwifery on the Isle of Man 1882 to 1961", *Medical History* 40.2: 141-172.

Peretz, Elizabeth (1990), "A maternity service for England and Wales: local authority maternity care in the inter-war period in Oxfordshire and Tottenham", in Garcia, Jo, *et al.*, eds., *The Politics of Maternity Care*, Oxford: Oxford University Press, pp.30-46.

Radford, N., & Ann Thomson (1994), "A study of issues concerning the implementation of direct-entry midwifery training", in Robinson, Sarah, & Ann Thomson, eds., *Midwives, Research and Childbirth*, Vol.3, London: Chapman & Hall, pp.260-292.

Radosh, Polly F. (1986), "Midwives in the United States: past and present", *Population Research and Policy Review* 5.2: 129-146.

Rajan, Lynda (1994), "The impact of obstetric procedures and analgesia/anaesthesia during labour and delivery on breastfeeding", *Midwifery* 10: 87-103.

Reagan, Leslie J. (1995), "Linking midwives and abortion in the Progressive Era", *Bulletin of the History of Medicine* 69.4: 569-598.

Reid, Margaret (1989), "Sisterhood and professionalization: a case study of the American lay midwife", in McClain, Carol, ed., *Women as Healers*, pp.219-238, New Brunswick NJ: Rutgers University Press.

Robinson, Sarah (1990), "Maintaining the independence of the midwifery profession: a continuing struggle", in Garcia, Jo, *et al.*, eds., *The Politics of Maternity Care*, Oxford: Oxford University Press, pp.61-91.

Robinson, Sarah, & Ann Thomson, eds., (1989), *Midwives, Research & Childbirth*, Vol.1, London: Chapman & Hall.

Robinson, Sarah, & Ann Thomson, eds. (1991), *Midwives, Research & Childbirth*, Vol.2, London: Chapman & Hall.

Robinson, Sarah, & Ann Thomson, eds. (1994), *Midwives, Research & Childbirth*, Vol.3, London: Chapman & Hall.

Robinson, Sarah, & Ann Thomson, eds. (1996), *Midwives, Research & Childbirth*, Vol.4, London: Chapman & Hall.

Rooks, Judith P. (1983), "The context of nurse-midwifery in the 1980s: our relationships with medicine, nursing, lay-midwives, consumers & health-care economists", *Journal of Nurse-Midwifery* 28.5: 3-8.

Rooks, Judith P. (1989), "Outcomes of care in birth centers: the National Birth Center Study", *New England Journal of Medicine* 321: 1804-1811.

Rooks, Judith P. (1997), *Midwifery and Childbirth in America*, Philadelphia: Temple University Press.

Rothman, Barbara K. (1983), "Midwives in transition: the structure of a clinical revolution", *Social Problems* 30: 262-271.

Rothman, Barbara K. (1984), "Childbirth management and medical monopoly", *Journal of Nurse-Midwifery* 29: 300-306. Reprinted in Sapiro, Virginia, ed., *Women, Biology & Public Policy*, Beverly Hills: Sage, 1985, pp.117-135.

Sandall, Jane (1995), "Choice, continuity and control: changing midwifery, towards a sociological perspective", *Midwifery* 11: 201-209.

Sargent, Carolyn F., & Caroline B.Brettell, eds. (1996), *Gender and Health: an international perspective*, Upper Saddle River: Prentice Hall

Schaffer, Ruth C., (1991), "The health and social functions of black midwives on the Texas Brazos Bottom 1920-1985", *Rural Sociology* **56**.1: 89-105.

Starr, Paul (1982), *The Social Transformation of American Medicine*, New York: Basic Books.

Sullivan, Deborah, and Rose Weitz (1988), *Labor Pains: modern midwives and home birth*, New Haven: Yale UP.

Tew, Marjorie (1998), *Safer Childbirth? A critical history of maternity care*, 3rd edn. London: Free Associations Books.

Thompson, Anne, & Joan Walker (1993), "The International Confederation of Midwives—promoting midwifery worldwide", *British Journal of Midwifery* 1: 42-7. (Also Walker & Thompson 1996, below.)

Tjaden, Patricia G. (1987), "Midwifery in Colorado: a case study in the politics of professionalization", *Qualitative Sociology* **10**.1: 29-45.

Tom, Sally A. (1980), "The evolution of nurse-midwifery: 1900-1960", *Journal of Nurse-Midwifery* **27**.4: 4-13.

Torres, A., & M.R.Reich (1989), "The shift from home to institutional childbirth: a comparative study of the United Kingdom and the Netherlands", *International Journal of Health Services* **19**: 405-414.

Vallgårda, Signild (1996), "Hospitalization of deliveries: the change of place of birth in Denmark and Sweden from the late nineteenth century", *Medical History* **40**.2: 173-196.

van Alten, D. (1989), "Midwifery in the Netherlands. The Wormerveer study", *British Journal of Obstetrics & Gynaecology* **96**: 656-662.

Wagner, Marsden (1986a), "The medicalization of birth", in Claxton, Ros, ed., *Birth Matters: issues and alternatives in childbirth*, London: Unwin Paperbacks, pp.11-22.

Wagner, Marsden (1986b), "Birth and power", in Phaff, J.M.L., ed., *Perinatal Health Services in Europe*, London: Croom-Helm.

Walker, Joan & Anne Thompson (1996), "Organizing midwives internationally: the story of the International Confederation of Midwives", in Murray, Susan F., ed., *Midwives and Safer Motherhood*, St Louis: Mosby, pp.143-158.

Weitz, Rose, & Deborah Sullivan (1986), "The politics of childbirth: the re-emergence of midwifery in Arizona", *Social Problems* **33**:163-175.

Weitz, Rose (1987), "English midwives and the Association of Radical Midwives", *Women & Health* **12**.1: 79-89.

Winterton, Nicholas (1992), (for House of Commons Select Committee on Health), *Report on Maternity Services* (House of Commons Papers 29-I). London: Her Majesty's Stationery Office.

Witz, Ann (1991), "Medical men and midwives", in *Professions and Patriarchy*, New York/London: Routledge, pp.104-127.

Ziegler, Charles (1913), "The elimination of the midwife", *Journal of the American Medical Association* **60**: 32-38.

---

[1] Loudon 1992 discusses extensively the maternal mortality rates in a variety of Western countries since such figures began to be recorded, and the causes of their persistence and eventual decline.

[2] See Macintyre 1977. Nelson 1983 presents evidence that working class women are relative immune to this ideology insofar as it relates to maternity care. Perhaps there are links between its spread and the rise of the middle class.

[3] Here again, the Netherlands appears to be something of an exception: see Marland 1995, where attention is paid to the role of some Dutch obstetricians who advocated giving more responsibilities to midwives rather than less.

[4] Devitt 1979, King 1991, Loudon 1992. In addition to mortality figures, evidence about abortion (illegal, of course, at this period) was deployed in a similarly misleading way: see Reagan 1995. For an unorthodox reinterpretation of the significance of available statistical data regarding the relative safety of hospital birth as against home birth, see Tew 1998. For less contentious data concerning the competence of English midwives in the 1950s and 1960s, see Allison 1996 and Allison & Pascall 1994; on Manx data see Pantin 1996. For data on the safety of birth in 'free-standing birth centers' in the USA (that is, birth centers not forming part of a hospital complex), see Rooks 1989. Statistics on the safety of home birth in the Netherlands are given in Van Alten 1989.

[5] See Dye 1983, Loudon 1992 and Rooks 1997 on the Kentucky origins of the Frontier Nursing Service, which was one element contributing to the establishment in the United States of the mixed profession of nurse-midwifery. Fox 1993 and Marland 1995 point out the economic pressures leading to this overlap between nursing work and midwifery work in rural areas at this period, in articles dealing respectively with England and Wales and with the Netherlands.

[6] See Butter & Kay 1988; Bidgood-Wilson et al. 1992 and Barickman et al.1992; and DeVries 1996 (second edition of his 1985 work on the same topic). Sullivan & Weitz 1988 discuss the restrictions which are imposed by the laws of certain states. See also Butter & Kay 1990.

[7] The syllabus of the Dutch midwifery schools reflects the concern of obstetricians like Kloosterman to ensure that midwife training is not distorted by alien professional preoccupations, more appropriate for those whose career will consist of dealing with abnormalities.

[8] Garcia & Garforth 1991. See also Rothman 1983: the midwives whom Rothman interviewed had been trained in a hospital setting to apply fairly inflexible rules about the length of time appropriate for each stage of labor. When the same midwives began attending home births, they became more skeptical about the validity of these rules.

[9] Benoit has explored the complexities of intraprofessional relationships in her studies of Newfoundland midwives (1989, 1991). Flint 1991 comments forcefully on the tensions within the midwifery profession in Britain. Both authors remark that whereas even the most senior obstetricians normally continue to practice their professional skills in the delivery ward, it is not customary for midwives to continue delivering babies after promotion to managerial positions.

[10] The most obvious manifestation of this endeavor is Chalmers et al. 1989. A more polemical account of what has emerged can be found in Goer 1995. The project of questioning received medical wisdom owes much to the lead given in Cochrane 1972.

[11] See four volumes edited by Robinson & Thomson under the title *Midwives, Research & Childbirth* for plentiful examples of research by midwives. Whether this research is widely read by members of the medical profession may be doubted. Hicks 1992 suggests that even fellow-midwives tend to accord it less respect than research published by authors with medical qualifications, having long been accustomed to attaching privileged status to this latter type of research.

THE CONTEXT OF NURSE - MIDWIFERY IN THE 1980S: OUR RELATIONSHIPS WITH MEDICINE, NURSING, LAY-MIDWIVES, CONSUMERS AND HEALTH CARE ECONOMISTS[*][†]

Judith P. Rooks[‡]

ABSTRACT

Nurse-midwifery's interrelationships with several significant groups are analyzed and several conclusions are reached. Collegiality, cooperation, communication, and complementarity—not competition—should be the characteristics of nurse-midwives' relationships with physicians. Nurse-midwifery's association with nursing brings the profession both benefits and risks that merit close scrutiny. The ACNM should establish good interorganizational relationships with other groups of midwives, but should not merge with them. While sensitivity and responsiveness to consumers' needs, demands, and preferences have become hallmarks of nurse-midwifery care, nurse-midwives need to examine the continuum between authoritarian and permissive care, especially its implications for out-of-hospital birth situations. Finally, nurse-midwives must collect the information needed to convince the country's health-care financial planners that CNMs can do a better job for less expense.

Despite the temptation, this paper will not focus on the challenges that lie ahead for nurse-midwifery. We live with and are part of so much change, that who knows what lies ahead? Often, just as one anticipates and plans for a continuation of the present trend, unforeseen forces significantly alter the context, and thus change the situation.

Thus, rather than attempt to predict the future, it would seem more advantageous to try to analyze the present in light of insights from the past. The emphasis will, therefore, be on nurse-midwifery's relationships with several significant groups. In particular, our relationships with medicine, nursing, lay-midwives and consumers will be examined. In addition, the need for nurse-midwives to begin to relate to those people who have a particular responsibility for health-care economics will be addressed.

MEDICINE

Because it is so important, this discussion will begin by considering nurse-midwifery's relationship with medicine. The practice of nurse-midwifery is predicated upon collaboration with physicians. To be

---

[*] This paper was adapted from the President's Address: 28th Annual Meeting of ACNM. May 1983. Los Angeles. Address correspondence to: Judith Rooks, American College of Nurse-Midwives, 1522 K Street, N.W., Suite 1120, Washington DC. 20005

[†] Reprinted by permission of Elsevier Science from The context of nurse-midwifery in the 1980s: our relationships with medicine, nursing, lay-midwives, consumers and health-care economists, by J. Rooks Journal of Nurse-Midwifery, Vol. 28: 3-8, Copyright 1983 by the American College of Nurse-Midwives.

[‡] *Journal of Nurse-Midwifery*, **28** (5), Sept./Oct., 1983: 3-8

sure, nurse-midwifery would not have survived in this country without the essential support of numerous outstanding physicians. In fact, every nurse-midwife practicing today is doing so in collaboration with one or more physicians.

The history of our relationship with medicine has been generally good, although not without conflict. But it is changing—not necessarily becoming bad, but changing—due to changes physicians are experiencing as well as changes in nurse-midwifery.

To understand changes in relationships, it is always important to try to understand the other person's point of view. We can get some inkling of what physicians are experiencing from the report of a Harris poll conducted in 1981 at the request of the Henry J. Kaiser Family Foundation. The poll was based on interviews with a representative sample of more than 1800 physicians. Its purpose was to learn how they view changes in their own profession. The results of that poll show that, like us, physicians are embroiled in change.[1]

- Most physicians believe that we are moving into a period of a surplus of physicians, and this colors their attitudes and perceptions on many issues.
- Half the physicians interviewed felt sufficient doubts about the future of medical practice that they would not recommend it as highly today as they would have ten years ago.
- Their major concerns about the future relate to loss of autonomy, mainly as a result of regulatory interference and external intervention.
- Young practitioners and residents are concerned about a lack of opportunities.

The study also found that, overall, physicians accept the idea of physician's assistants and nurse-practitioners providing care to the poor and other medically underserved groups. However, they are much less supportive and, indeed, are quite divided in their opinion of the value of such care for non-poor mothers and children.

Overall, the results of the poll show that physicians are having to adapt to many changes, most of which they feel will not be favorable to them. We are involved in changes too, but overall, most of ours are favorable. They anticipate an oversupply of doctors, while we are trying to figure out how we can possibly train enough nurse-midwives to meet the demand.

Physicians fear a loss of autonomy due to regulations and external interventions. A glaring example in this arena was the recent unsuccessful fight by the American Medical Association (AMA) to remove medicine from the jurisdiction of the Federal Trade Commission (FTC). We, in contrast, support strong antitrust and consumer protection laws, and an active FTC, because we know they are necessary to protect us from unfair and arbitrary withholding of hospital privileges, eligibility for third-party reimbursement, and access to the other prerequisites for a viable nurse-midwifery practice. Although the AMA is said to have spent four million dollars in their effort to rid themselves of the FTC's interference, it was our position, supported, of course by many others, which prevailed.

At the same time that physicians fear loss of autonomy, nurse-midwives are gaining more control over our practice, even to the extent of successfully establishing new service environments outside of the institutions controlled by physicians. In addition, obstetrician-gynecologists have had to deal with changes that consumers have demanded, and for which we have provided models. These changes have forced them to alter some of their own ways of giving care.

With these things in mind, it seems safe to say that our relationships with medicine are changing. And, as always, when relationships change both parties are uncomfortable. This may be especially true in the case of nurse-midwives and obstetricians, and of the American College of Nurse-Midwives (ACNM) and the American College of Obstetricians-Gynecologists (ACOG), because in the past we have benefited from an almost protective "younger sister" relationship with them. It may be especially traumatic as we begin to deal with them on more nearly equal terms.

Nevertheless, most CNMs have strong collegial relationships with the physicians with whom they work. In fact, the ACNM and ACOG—with great skill on the parts of former ACNM Presidents, Sister Angela Murdaugh, Eunice Ernst. and Helen Burst—have successfully negotiated an excellent Joint Statement on Practice Relationships between our two professions.

Our relationships with our physician colleagues, with ACOG. and with all of the physicians and groups of physicians whose care, in addition to our own, is needed by mothers and babies, must have high priority on our agenda.

The FTC views nurse-midwives as competition for physicians; but we are not competitors. Physicians provide services which we cannot provide, for which we are not trained, and to which our clients must have access in case they become ill or experience serious complications. We, on the other hand, provide care which physicians cannot provide, for which they are not trained, and which our clients want and need. We are not interchangeable and thus we cannot really be competitive. Rather we are complementary professions. Collegiality, cooperation, communication, and complementarity—not competition—are the characteristics we should strive for in our collaboration with physicians.

NURSING

We also have a longstanding and essential relationship with nursing, but one that is quite different from our association with the separate profession of medicine. Our relationship with nursing is much more intimate; nurse-midwifery developed from a nursing base.

The necessity of our nursing base is being challenged both from within and outside nurse-midwifery. We are being asked to document why we consider nursing essential and, in particular, if and why nursing education and licensure should continue to be prerequisites for nurse-midwifery. It is a basic, complicated, and challenging question.

I believe we should retain our nursing base. I also believe it is possible to prepare adequate professional midwives who are not nurses. They are apparently doing so now at the Midwifery School in Seattle. Their graduates may well be as good midwives as we. I am not against having another type of more narrowly trained professional midwives in addition to ourselves. But I also believe there is critical value to the nursing component of nurse-midwifery—a proven value that we should retain.

Our clients do not just have normal pregnancies: they also experience complications, and we are prepared—as nurses—to provide essential services during a medical emergency. In addition, many of our clients and their family members also have other physical health problems, mental health problems, and environmental health problems; our broader backgrounds of knowledge, skill, and experience in both clinical and public health nursing must sometimes come into play. In addition, our experience as nurses has taught us the value of the many other health-care disciplines, how to collaborate with other health-care providers when our clients have multiple problems and needs, and how to negotiate on our clients' behalf within what very often is a complicated health-care system.

I believe that the breadth we have gained from our base in nursing enhances the quality of our care. That might not be necessary if managing childbirth were all we needed to do, but often it is not. Our record is studded with jewels—our accomplishments in reducing infant and maternal morbidity and mortality among some of this nation's sickest, poorest, and hardest to serve populations, isolated families in Appalachia, poor black families in the rural southeast, native Americans on their reservations, and pregnant inner-city teenagers. We did not achieve these results just by delivering their babies, or even with excellent prenatal and childbirth care alone. To wrest success from these situations required midwives who were also public health nurses: schooled and skilled in family planning; nutrition; mental health; disease screening, case finding and referral: health education; immunization; and the whole array of public health concerns, from substance abuse to rat control and basic sanitation.

Nurse-midwifery has earned and enjoyed high respect for our past and current contributions to producing better health outcomes among some of the country's highest risk mothers and babies. We are now garnering new respect, from other quarters, for engaging the problem of the inappropriate use of childbirth technology and for providing a safe and sane alternative to technology-oriented childbirth care.

Because this is our major challenge at the moment—to lead the country towards a better, more satisfying mode of giving birth—we are now very focused on the midwifery part of our repertoire of skills, and so it seems to some of us that midwifery by itself may be enough. Indeed, there may be a permanent place in America for women prepared as midwives only. But our role, as nurse-midwives, is broader and more flexible, and thus better able to meet evolving needs. Even today, in addition to the problem of high-technology childbirth, the other two most important health problems in our field are low birth weight (which continues to affect almost 7% of U.S. infants, at least one-half of which is preventable) and the continuing high incidence and recurring cycle of unplanned, unwed, suboptimal-outcome teenaged pregnancies and parenthood. Our broader base gives us more to contribute to the solution of these national problems.

In addition, although I do not know about midwifery in every country, I have visited India, Nepal, Brazil, Nigeria, Ghana, Kenya, and Tanzania. In each of those countries there are at least two levels of midwives—traditional birth attendants or village midwives with relatively brief training limited essentially to pregnancy and childbirth, and, at a higher level, fully prepared nurses with additional midwifery education and training, i.e., nurse-midwives. In each of these countries it is the more broadly educated nurse-midwife who exerts the leadership for midwifery within that country,

However, as strongly as I believe that we should retain our nursing base, I also recognize that problems within the nursing profession make the cost we pay to be nurses very high—so high that I cannot guarantee that we will always be able, or willing, to pay the price.

The basic problem I think, is that many nursing leaders do not understand that clinical competence—the ability to provide an essential service very well—is the only real basis for security and respect in the healthcare field. Instead, they have thought. that higher educational degrees would ensure nursing of better professional status.

As a result of nursing's preoccupation with higher and higher educational degrees, we are suffering a variety of problems:

- We need nurses who are well prepared clinically to enter our programs as students, but graduates of today's baccalaureate nursing schools are not necessarily competent clinically.
- In 1977, when we last studied this matter, more than half of all nurse-midwives in clinical practice had received their basic nursing education in a diploma program. Almost half had received their nurse-midwifery education in a program providing a certificate rather than a degree.[2] Almost half of the nurse-midwives certified last year were graduates of non degree programs.[3] Many of our most experienced and expert nurse-midwives are among them. We need to be able to utilize these master nurse-midwife clinicians to teach our students and to be role models for them. Yet until and unless they get degrees in nursing—no other degree will do—many of our most experienced clinicians are not eligible to serve as faculty in some of our educational programs because of the placement of those programs in graduate nursing schools.
- In my own state of Oregon, the nursing lobby has put into effect a law that requires all nurse-practitioners (and thus, all nurse-midwives) to have bachelor of nursing degrees and. by 1986, we will all have to have *master's* degrees in nursing. It is bizarre to exclude from practice, in Oregon, nurse-midwives prepared at the Frontier Nursing Service, the University of Mississippi, Downstate, or any of our other excellent nurse-midwifery programs that do not grant degrees.
- In addition, many schools of nursing refuse to give any kind of security or status to faculty without doctoral degrees. There must be a terrible pressure on nurse-midwives to obtain doctoral degrees because so many of the super-qualified CNMs who should have run for President this year were already overcommitted to working towards PhDs. Of course, that is wonderful in many ways. We need master educators and theoreticians, and we badly need researchers, and we need PhDs to exert leadership in many vital roles.

But most of all, we need confident, thoroughly competent clinicians. Therefore, we have to resist as much as possible nursing's tendency to confuse credentials with ability.

Our association with nursing brings both benefits and risks. These two elements should be kept clearly in mind as we continue to deal with the issue of nursing.

LAY AND OTHER MIDWIVES

This brings us to lay-midwives which, in some ways, is simply the other side of the question on nursing. It is also an issue that we, as a College, have discussed considerably. The members of the College were asked to address this issue through polls conducted during the winter of 1983 by their Regional Representatives. Asked whether ACNM should open its membership to other midwives, a large majority of those who responded said that the College should remain an organization only for CNMs.

Nevertheless, we are far from a consensus on this issue; in two regions, the majority of respondents would prefer that we open the ACNM to other kinds of midwives. It is quite clear that the question of how we should relate to other midwives will remain on our agenda. Lay midwives and midwives prepared through means other than our educational programs are growing in numbers and influence. They are increasingly challenging us to demonstrate the validity of the differentiation between themselves and CNMs. Some of them are excellent clinicians, and our tradition of openness. fairness, and nonelitism make many of us want to extend ourselves to them.

Although our resources are limited and our own needs are great, I agree that we should help them to an extent. In particular, I believe that nurse-midwives who work in communities in which lay-midwives also work should endeavor to share access to local continuing education opportunities with those lay-midwives. We should do this first because we care about the safety and well-being of all childbearing families. If other midwives are serving families, then I hope for them to provide maximally safe and competent care. In addition, we have a long and admirable history and tradition of training lay-midwives. In her Keynote Speech at the 20th Annual Meeting of the College in 1975, Aileen Hogan, who was our leading archivist, described supervision and training of granny midwives as the major responsibility for which the first American-trained nurse-midwives were prepared.[4] She also paid tribute to the good work and important contribution of the granny midwives, and described the great mutual respect between lay and nurse-midwives in those days. In fact, when Hattie Hemschemeyer became the first President of the College in 1955, one of the first congratulatory letters she received was from a granny midwife in Kentucky.

But this is not 1955 and the lay-midwives of today are not granny midwives. The situation is different, especially because the lay-midwives we are hearing from are not seeking supervision from us, but are seeking parity. Their claim and demand of equivalence is where our problem and challenge lies.

I believe that the College should establish good interorganizational relationships with other groups of midwives—MANA in particular. However, we cannot merge ourselves with them.

To be "lay" specifically means to be not part of a profession. It is the exact opposite of all that we have worked for. The problem with lay-midwives for themselves, for us, and for consumers, is that they lack the structure, standards, and all of the paraphernalia of a profession. For instance, ACNM assures the public that every CNM has met certain specific published criteria of education, training, and documented competency and, thus, is qualified to provide a clearly defined range of services and care. Lay-midwives do not have these assurances behind them.

A major function of the College—perhaps our most important function—is to back up and make good our guarantee to the public that they are getting what we say they are getting when their lives and health are put into the care of a CNM. For that purpose, we have created elaborate professional machinery: accreditation of our educational programs; examination of the graduates of those programs; certification; grievance and decertification procedures; mechanisms for continuing education; research to document our practice and its outcomes; definition of our functions; standards and qualifications; and guidelines for quality assurance and peer review.

We have always had lay-midwives in America. They have provided essential services in the past and do so now in many areas. I am not against lay-midwives, and think we should help them to improve their practice where feasible. I also am not against the development in America of a cadre of limited-focus professional midwives who do not have a nursing base.

But I do not support merging ourselves with other groups of midwives at this time. I would not support any actions, which tend to confuse the public so that they cannot be sure of the standards that stand behind the initials "CNM." Therefore, I was appalled at the irresponsible act of the California legislature in seeking to confuse their own constituents by empowering the state to certify nurses as midwives, able to use the initials "CNM," although they have not met our standards.

This issue will stay open. We are not the major actors. The future depends upon the actions of other midwife groups. Because our nation is a union of states, there is the opportunity to test proposed changes at a local level before applying them nationwide. Currently, the state of Washington is experimenting with a school authorized and regulated by the state, but not by ACNM to prepare professional midwives. California, in violation of the combined spirit of the patent and copyright laws, is producing its own CNMs. (Strange, that tucked between these two states is Oregon, where ACNM certified nurse-midwives will eventually have to have a Master's degree to practice!) Nevertheless, these two state experiments are going on, and more may follow. We should watch these experiments with fair-mindedness and objectivity, and demand that they produce reliable records. We will need data to deal adequately with this issue in the future.

CONSUMERS

Another of our very important relationships is with consumers. ACNM is to be congratulated for having a Consumer Affairs Committee. Respect for the consumers of our services. open communication with consumers and sensitivity and responsiveness to consumers' needs, demands, desires, requests, and preferences have become hallmarks of nurse-midwifery care. Even our official documents assert our respect for consumers and their right to exercise choice. In particular, our new "Functions, Standards and Qualifications for Nurse-Midwifery Practice" states that we uphold the consumer's right to self-determination within the boundaries of safe care. Nevertheless, our experience with real consumers is relatively short.

Until the last decade, especially the last 5 years, nurse-midwives in the United States were essentially restricted to caring for people who did not have adequate access to physicians. People who cannot choose their care providers are "patients," but they are not "clients" or "consumers" in the sense that we now use those words. With nurse-midwifery, these people received the best possible care, but they didn't get a choice. The most exciting change in nurse-midwifery has been our evolution into a profession that now also serves an increasing number of women and families who have a choice and who have chosen us. The recent growth of nurse-midwifery in America is on the basis of consumers exercising choice.

The nurse-midwifery service at the Group Health Cooperative of Puget Sound is an example of the power which consumers can exert. Group Health is a member owned and operated health maintenance organization. It has been in operation since 1949, owns two hospitals and 13 out-patient clinics, and has one-third of the population of the Greater Seattle area as members.

In 1978, a group of women members of the Cooperative requested that the Cooperative's Board of Directors establish a nurse-midwifery service at Group Health. Although the Medical Advisory Committee did not support this idea, the consumers eventually prevailed. In 1980, a 2 year experiment in the provision of nurse-midwifery services was finally started at Group Health. This was the first and only time in its 37 years that the Cooperative's Board of Directors acted in opposition to its Medical Advisory Committee.

The nurse-midwives at Group Health have walked a rocky road. Physician opposition within your own organization is a formidable obstacle to creating a happy nurse-midwifery service. Nevertheless. an extensive evaluation of the service during its first 2 years of operation was favorable except for the persistence of physician opposition.[5] The consumers of the nurse-midwives' services rated them high. Based on that evaluation, the Group Health Board of Directors voted to continue the nurse-midwifery service and to expand it, with some concessions to the physicians. They also implemented a new personnel policy: Group Health will no longer hire an obstetrician unless he or she is willing to work with nurse-midwives. This is not a trouble-free story, but it is a good example of the power of consumers.

The issue concerning our relationship with consumers is, I realize, replete with basic questions. For instance, what kind of relationship should we strive to have with the consumers of our care?

Relationships between health-care providers and consumers are on a continuum. At one extreme, there is a highly authoritarian provider-dominated relationship in which the professional is quite sure that he or she knows best, and the consumer—the patient—has no choice but to accept the care that is offered, perhaps expressing dissatisfaction by avoiding care or other forms of what has been labeled "noncompliance." At the opposite extreme would be a provider who is open to new ideas of how to provide care and who attempts to find out what the consumer wants and then to provide what is wanted. Between these extremes is a range of interactive give-and-take relationships in which the provider combines sensitivity, openness, and responsiveness to consumer desires, with efforts to educate consumers to want (or at least to accept) that care which the provider thinks is best. Although nurse-midwives probably vary all along the middle range of this continuum, as compared with most physicians, we tend to be less authoritarian and relatively willing to adapt our care to satisfy the individual consumer's needs and preferences.

Many CNMs are now dealing, as individuals or as groups of practitioners, with the issue of this continuum between authoritarian and permissive care. It comes to the fore especially in out-of-hospital birth situations, where it is necessary, for safety, to exclude clients who do not meet low-risk criteria. How permissive or how rigid should we be?

In addition, the subject of consumers raises the issue of what Eunice Ernst calls "marketing."

Many consumers just do not know about our services. By and large, we run a starkly amateur operation when it comes to informing people about the advantages, attractions, and availability of nurse-midwifery care. We also need some marketing research. What segments of the population are we talking to and who are we listening to? If we listen to only a narrow spectrum of the population, we will not have many clients. We need to listen more carefully and analytically to more fully understand the reasons behind consumers' satisfactions, dissatisfactions, and decisions. We need more studies, like Judith Fullerton's to identify the critical elements behind consumers' choices.[6]

HEALTH CARE ECONOMISTS

We must also, now, begin to relate to a group of people who are new to us and who are very powerful and important—those individuals and groups of people who are addressing the current crisis in the financing of health-care. Currently, one out of every ten dollars spent in America is spent for health-care, and that proportion is increasing. The extraordinary cost of that care is borne, predominantly, by government and big business. Federal, state, and county governments pay the bills for Medicare and Medicaid, as well as all other forms of government-subsidized indigent care. The business community pays the premiums for the health insurance of most employed people and their families. Increasingly, the various units of government are finding that health-care costs are the fastest rising items on their budget, while many business executives are finding that their employee health insurance premiums are also their fastest rising costs. What is worse, if possible, is that they have no control over these costs. In the case of Medicare and Medicaid, they cannot even budget for these expenses because there is no way of knowing, from year to year, what the costs will be.

The leaders of government and of the business community are apparently determined to change this system. There is pending legislation in the state houses throughout the country, right now, proposing fundamental revisions in Medicaid funding, which is the biggest problem of the state.

The business round table, which is the most prestigious business group in the country and consisting entirely of chairs of large corporations, has put the issue of health-care management high on their agenda for the next 3 years. If they succeed in changing the way that health-care is paid for, that in itself will change the way health care is provided. We need to be relating to these people.

Sally Tom and our hardworking Political and Economic Affairs Committee are doing a fantastic job of working us into the existing third-party reimbursement fee-for-service system. Ruth Lubic, almost single-handedly, is explaining to the country's health-care financing futurists that we are of interest to them because we can do a better job for less.

But the rest of us have also got to help. We have done an excellent job of assuring and documenting the safety and quality of our care. Now we must do at least as well in assuring and documenting our cost efficiency. Powerful forces are influencing what may be fundamental changes in the health care system. At the same time that we continue to improve our place in the present system, we must stay abreast of these changes and help to shape them. Documented cost effectiveness will be the bottom line that determines many aspects of our future.

[1] Taylor, Montgomery, Yohalem M: Medical Practice in the 1980's: Physicians Look at their Changing Profession. Louis Harris and Associates, Inc. 1981.

[2] American College of Nurse-Midwives: Nurse-Midwifery in the United States, 1976-1977. Washington, DC, ACNM, p. 6, 1978.

[3] American College of Nurse-Midwives: Information from the Division of Examiners, 1983.

[4] Hogan: Tribute to the pioneers. Nurs-Midwif, Summer 1975.

[5] Dickstein: Evaluation of the Group Health Cooperative Demonstration Midwifery Service. Seattle: Group Health Cooperative of Puget Sound. 1983.

[6] Fullerton JDT The choice of in-hospital or alternative birth environment as related to the concept of control Nurs-Midwif 2:17ff. 1982.

THE TRAP OF LEGAL RECOGNITION[*]

Raymond G. DeVries

This book was, and remains, something of a curiosity. Reviewers of the first edition were, for the most part, bemused. They found the data interesting, accurately reported, even compelling, but they did not know what to do with my conclusions. My argument—that for midwives the cost of legal recognition would almost certainly be the end of a distinctive profession of midwifery—followed logically from the data, but many readers wanted to believe the data were anomalous. Surely, in other states at other times, midwifery would benefit from licensure.

Reviewers were left wondering if I was a friend or a foe of midwives. I often asked myself the same question. My goal, then as now, was to secure a place for a truly independent profession of midwifery. Unfortunately, my study of the most common avenue to professional independence—licensure—convinced me that it would not foster autonomous midwifery in this country. In the absence of other paths to legitimate practice, I had no choice but to recommend that midwives avoid licensure and look for new and creative ways to establish their profession (DeVries, 1986).

My discussion of "common sense" understandings of medical licensure in chapter 1 anticipated the confused response of reviewers (DeVries, 1996b). Physician reviewers, using "public common sense," assumed that licensure was an unalloyed good and recoiled at my suggestion that the public might be better served if midwives remained unlicensed (see, e.g., Russell, 1987). They failed to appreciate how licensure primarily served the interest of the dominant profession and how it removed choice, hindered communication, and diminished the quality of care[1]. Sociologists and midwives, employing their own version of common sense, could not understand my insistence that licensure would *not* benefit midwives in their competitive struggle with physicians. In their view, licensure is an effective tool in the contest between professions.

The publication of the second edition of this book gives me the welcome opportunity to revisit my analysis. Few social scientists have the luxury of testing their analyses against time, checking the relevance of their findings in a changed world. Have the events of the past ten years supported or disproved my earlier conclusions about the impact of licensure on midwifery? Have new facts come to light? Have more recent studies challenged my explanations?

In 1984, when I finished the first edition of this book, I was not optimistic about the future of licensed midwifery in the United States. Midwives here were caught in a true dilemma: legitimacy could be gained only by sacrificing the distinctiveness of their profession. Lacking the political power to shape and secure favorable legislation, midwives were at the whim of others. I suspected that all new attempts to create permissive laws would be met by organized opposition from the medical lobby. And if, over the objections of medical lobbyists, a licensing bill managed to become law, I was convinced that the details of its implementation would complicate the lives of practicing midwives and would, ironically, discourage growth of the profession.

I made these pessimistic predictions just over ten years ago. In the intervening decade our health care delivery system has changed in ways no one expected. How have American midwives fared since the mid-

---

[*] Epilogue in: Making Midwives Legal: Childbirth, Medicine and the Law (2nd edn) Columbus: Ohio State University Press. 1996

1980s? In order to answer this question we must consider the condition of midwifery on several levels: its overall health, measured in terms of its size and participation in health care and medicine; developments in licensing; the treatment of midwives in the courts; and the "changing nature" of midwifery.

HEALTH OF THE PROFESSION

There are many ways to measure the vitality of an occupational group. The most obvious is a survey of its growth: an expanding profession is a healthy profession. In the case of midwives, however, the task of counting is complicated. Widely varying definitions of midwifery make it nearly impossible to get a precise count of midwives. Does a woman certified as a nurse-midwife but practicing as a nurse "count" as a midwife? What about a traditional midwife who attends only one or two births per year? Should she be included in our census?

In spite of these definitional problems, the number of practicing midwives is periodically tallied. Because there is a standardized legal definition of certified nurse-midwifery and because CNMs have uniform training requirements, it is easier to count nurse-midwives than it is to (find and) count traditional midwives. In 1982, the American College of Nurse-Midwives estimated that 2,500 CNMs were working in the United States; ten years later that number had grown to approximately 4,000 (see ACNM, 1993; National Commission on Nurse-Midwifery Education, 1993).

When it comes to traditional midwives, the best we can do is an estimate. Given the great variation in state laws and differences of opinion about who "counts" as a traditional midwife, all tallies of traditional midwives must be viewed with skepticism. The Midwives Alliance of North America (MANA) has long recognized the need for more accurate counts of practicing midwives. In 1989 they took a step in this direction with the creation of the North American Registry of Midwives (NARM). However, the primary purpose of the NARM is not simply to provide a list of all active midwives. It is an effort to raise the credibility of midwifery, and, as such, all NARM registered midwives must pass an examination intended to establish a minimum level of competency. Hence the NARM is a subset of all practicing midwives. In 1991, two members of a task force created by the Minnesota Department of Health surveyed all 50 states and found approximately 2,000 traditional midwives in practice (Barroso & Coffey, 1991). Others claim the number may be as high as 6,000 (Korte, 1995). Because these numbers are unreliable, and because there are no earlier estimates, it is impossible to speak meaningfully about growth or decline in the number of traditional midwives.

No matter how one counts, or who one counts, the growth of midwifery has been far from explosive. Added educational programs (National Commission on Nurse-Midwifery Education, 1993) have allowed the number of nurse-midwives to expand, nearly doubling in ten years; but the total is below the expectations of the ACNM. A few years ago they coined the slogan, "10,000 (nurse-midwives) by (the year) 2000." It is unlikely that number will be achieved. We gain some perspective on the growth of midwifery by contrasting it with growth in the number of specialists in obstetrics and gynecology: in 1980 there were 26,305 obstetrician/ gynecologists in the United States; by 1992 that number had grown to 35,273 (Roback et al., 1993).

But sheer numbers is only one way to assess midwives' success. Another, perhaps better, method is to examine their contribution to the health care system or, more specifically, the number of births they attend. Here again we find the role of midwives expanding while their overall contribution remains small. In 1980 midwives attended 1.7 percent of the nation's births; by 1992 that number had grown to 4.9 percent (National Center for Health Statistics, 1994; see also DeClercq, 1992). Significant growth, yes, but midwives remain underused. Following the numbers reported above, midwives represent about 15 percent of the "obstetric workforce," and yet they attend less than 5 percent of the births.

Perhaps it is premature to expect midwives to be significant players in American health care. Before midwifery can be widely accepted, it must be proven in the crucible of research. After a heavy dose of criticism and discrediting earlier in the century (see Devitt, 1979a; Litoff, 1986), it will take some time before midwives can establish themselves as necessary members of a health care team. How is midwifery treated in the world of medical and public health research? Is the profession creating a scientific foundation for practice? Is it gaining credibility?

In the past decade, evaluations of midwife care began to appear more regularly in the pages of medical journals. A series of articles appearing in the 1980s assessed the quality of care by midwives at home births (Burnett et al., 1980; Hinds et al., 1985; Schramm et al., 1987). The conclusions of these articles were nearly identical: planned home births with trained attendants posed no special risk for mothers and babies, while unplanned home births and untrained attendants brought poor results. In a widely cited study published in the *New England Journal of Medicine,* Rooks and her colleagues (1989) verified the safety of nurse-midwife-attended births in birth centers. Further research in the 1990s supported the safety of out-of-hospital births (see, e.g., Durand, 1992; Tew, 1990). Research also emphasized the value of midwives for reducing unnecessary interventions. Both traditional midwives and nurse-midwives were credited for cutting the rate of Caesarean sections (Sakala, 1993; Butler *et al.,* 1993). Goer (1995) has collected a number of research articles that question current obstetric practices and recommend midwife care as the safest and least expensive approach to birth.

Why hasn't this small but well-placed body of scientific evidence helped midwifery prosper? The answer to this question lies in a closer look at the research itself, considering where and how it was done and the reaction it provoked. Much of the work emphasizing the value of midwives is done in health maintenance organizations (HMOs) and other managed care settings, a fact that underscores the importance of financial incentives for the future of midwifery. Midwives are popular in HMOs and government programs, environments where costs must be controlled. Because they are more often cared for in medicaid programs and HMOs, black, Hispanic, and Native American women are far more likely to have a midwife attended birth than are white women (Parker, 1994). It ought to be enough to show that midwives generate high levels of satisfaction, promote confidence in their clients, and improve outreach to underserved communities. But it is not. Midwives are allowed to flourish to the extent that they improve the bottom line.

Furthermore, supportive research is not often done by midwives themselves. We learn of the value of midwifery from epidemiologists, physicians, and social scientists. Midwifery suffers when other professions develop and expand its knowledge base. As long as the expertise of midwives is founded in knowledge developed by others, they will be a subordinate profession. In other parts of the world, where midwives have more autonomy, they claim control over a body of knowledge unique to midwifery (see DeVries & Barroso, 1996).

Finally, the response of physicians to this body of research is instructive. Their instinctive reaction is to protect the current system. In his editorial review of an article on the safety of out-of-hospital births in Missouri, the executive director of the American College of Obstetricians and Gynecologists, Warren Pearse (1987), reluctantly agrees that home birth can be safe, but he insists there is no reason to develop a system to serve the few women who choose this option. He fails to consider the documented advantages of midwives and home birth in terms of cost, accessibility, satisfaction, and the reduction of unneeded interventions. Ignoring research demonstrating how midwives save money, Pearse illogically argues that it would be *prohibitively expensive* to develop a system that licenses and regulates midwives.

Measured in terms of its growth and presence in health care, the situation of nurse-midwives is improving very gradually: their numbers are growing, educational programs are expanding, and they are attending more births. The future seems less bright for traditional midwives. Their contribution to maternity care is small and is seldom recognized. Although several states have considered midwife legislation over the past ten years and although MANA is making an effort to standardize credentialing procedures, the legal status of traditional midwives remains uneven and problematic. We turn next to a detailed review of recent legislation regulating the practices of midwives. Our focus in the following section is on the varied laws governing traditional midwifery, not on the (more or less) uniform rules for nurse-midwives.

MIDWIFERY IN THE LEGISLATURE

Among the many conclusions generated by my review of midwife legislation in the first edition, two stand out: 1) midwives themselves have little control over proposed and enacted laws; and 2) what appears to be legislation favorable to midwives often turns out to be more restrictive than the laws replaced. Over the past ten years several new pieces of legislation concerning traditional midwifery have been introduced in statehouses across the country. Do any of these differ dramatically from the laws I evaluated ten years ago?

We begin with a review of the legal status of traditional midwifery. Just after the first edition of this book was published, Wolfson (1986) reported that lay midwifery was clearly legal in 11 states, clearly illegal in 10 states, and "effectively illegal" in 12 states; the other 17 states had a variety of old and ambiguous laws. One year later, Butter and Kay surveyed a variety of state agencies and came to a slightly different conclusion:

"As of July, 1987, 10 states have prohibitory laws, five states have grandmother clauses authorizing practicing midwives under repealed statutes, five states have enabling laws which are not used, and 10 states explicitly permit lay midwives to practice. In the 21 remaining states, the legal status of midwives is unclear" (Butter & Kay, 1988: 1161).

Using yet another classification scheme, Korte (1995: 57) gave the following report of the legal status of traditional midwives in 1995: 14 states "legal by licensure, certification or registration"; 11 states "legal through judicial interpretation or statutory inference"; 7 states "not legally defined but not prohibited"; 8 states "legal by statute but licensure unavailable"; and 10 states "prohibited through statutory restriction or judicial interpretation."

Two things become evident when we compare these reports. First, traditional midwives have gained some ground in the recognition of their practice, moving from 11 (or 10) "clearly legal" states in the mid-1980s to 14 in the mid-1990s. Second, the differing totals and the different ways of counting used by the researchers reveal significant confusion over the definition of legal and illegal. This second observation should cause us to rethink our first. Have traditional midwives actually gained ground? The difficulty in distinguishing legal and illegal, permitted and unpermitted, reminds us that there is a difference between "law on the books" and "law in action." Before we celebrate the expanding role of traditional midwives, we must explore this distinction further.

The three surveys summarized above relied on reports from official agencies: departments of health, state licensing boards, and the like. They represent surveys of laws on the books, the *official* view of the legal status of midwives. Barroso and Coffey (1991) surveyed traditional midwives practicing in each of the 50 states, asking them to describe the laws governing their practices. Their report gives us a view of midwifery laws in action, the way laws are *experienced* by working midwives. They report 14 states where traditional midwifery is clearly legal, 31 "gray" states where the practice is undefined, and 16 states where traditional midwifery is clearly illegal. If you are counting, you will notice that there is something suspicious about their numbers: somehow they arrived at a total of 61 states! The reason for the inflated total is that several states were counted in both the "clearly legal" and the "clearly illegal" categories. In these states, the laws allow for licensing, but licenses are difficult or impossible to obtain, hence many midwives there choose to work illegally. In Arizona, for example, where Barroso and Coffey counted 40 traditional midwives, 25 are licensed and 15 are working without a license; of the 41 traditional midwives working in Arkansas, 20 remain unlicensed. What appears to be an advance in the recognition of traditional midwifery is not regarded as such by many practicing midwives.

The state of New York provides a recent example of "favorable" legislation that works against the interests of midwives. Korte (1995) considers New York a state where traditional midwifery is "legal by statute, but licensure unavailable." In June 1992 the New York legislature passed a bill that unifies nurse- and lay midwifery, acknowledging the legitimacy of different approaches to midwifery training. The bill established a 15-member board of midwifery charged with setting standards for education and practice.

Traditional midwives worked hard for the passage of the bill, but by early 1994 several of these same midwives felt betrayed. The midwifery board, set up in the Department of Education, included several nurse-midwives but no traditional midwives, creating doubts that less-medical, home-based practices would be protected in the new regulations. Two years after the law was passed, the mechanism to allow traditional midwives to obtain licenses was still not in place, but the prohibition on unlicensed midwifery was being enforced with a new rigor. In 1993 and 1994 several midwives were investigated by the Department of Education's Office of Professional Discipline. This heightened scrutiny caused several midwives to voluntarily stop practicing. The co-director of New York Friends of Midwives reported that four midwives in the Albany area stopped attending births for fear of being charged with practicing medicine without a license. "They are laying low," she said. After an investigation in October 1993, a midwife in eastern Long Island signed an agreement to stop attending births until she was licensed. She told a reporter, "I was working on this law day and night, I feel like I got sold out" (Karlin, 1994). Korte (1995) describes more severe actions against two upstate midwives: in 1994 Julia Kessler and Karen Pardini, with a total of 32 years' experience and 2,500 births (with no infant deaths) between them, were charged with practicing both midwifery and medicine without a license. Midwives who once practiced freely in the margins of an old law, are in clear violation of the new law.

One of the older licensing laws for traditional midwives, and one that is considered "friendly" toward midwifery, is found in the state of Washington. Passed in the early 1980s, the Washington law offers licenses to graduates of a state-accredited three-year educational program. Lay (i.e., unlicensed) midwives are allowed to practice if they do not advertise or charge for their services, a rule that allows friends or members of religious groups to assist each other at birth without fear of prosecution. How have midwives fared in this favorable environment? In 1989 two faculty members of the Seattle Midwifery School complained, "formidable barriers ... stand in the way of full practice ... for state licensed midwives: lack of (affordable) malpractice insurance, inability to obtain hospital privileges, incomplete reimbursement from third party payers and excessive restrictions on the scope of practice" (Myers & Myers-Ciecko, 1989). Three years later, Baldwin *et al.* published the results of their study of the professional relationships of Washington's midwives, concluding,

"Only certified nurse midwives have forged mutually satisfying relationships with the physician community.... Licensed midwives, despite their status as licensed birth attendants, have been dissatisfied with their consulting relationships with physicians" (1992: 262, 264).

Many midwives choose to remain outside the law. A study of unlicensed midwives in Washington state revealed that several are, in fact, practicing illegally, charging for their services (Myers *et al.*, 1990). As I noted earlier, "state certification does not ensure medical endorsement" (DeVries, 1996b: 115). Even though the state has acted in their favor, licensed midwives in Washington are limited by the unwillingness of the medical community to incorporate them fully. Situations like these in New York and Washington demonstrate the need for more uniform and more credible licensing legislation, legislation that will allow midwives to become a legitimate and recognizable part of our health system. At their best, current models of licensure allow a minimum number of midwives to survive, meeting the needs of a small group of women seeking to give birth outside the hospital. In response to uneven and confused local legislation, several state organizations of traditional midwives have initiated programs of self-certification (see DeVries, 1986; Butter & Kay, 1990), but these have done little to promote the profession or shape legislation. In whatever form, licensure as it exists today has decidedly not brought the benefits of midwifery to a larger group of women.

Several advocates of midwifery have stepped forward with plans for the promotion and regulation of midwifery:

1. Writing in a well-known alternative birth periodical, the *NAPSAC News,* Mehl Madrona and Mehl Madrona (1993) angered a number of traditional midwives when they argued that even the "good" licensing laws were inadequate, failing to advance midwifery in America. After a lengthy analysis of the current condition of midwifery in the United States and elsewhere, they insist that traditional midwives will remain marginal unless they jettison apprentice-based education in favor of rigorous formal education programs. They derive many of their suggestions for reform from their study of Dutch maternity care.

2. In 1994 the Women's Institute for Childbearing Policy (WICP) issued a position paper, "Childbearing Policy within a National Health Program," calling for a "primary maternity care system" that is centered on midwife care delivered in birth centers and homes. They suggest extending existing education and licensure programs (WICP, 1994).

3. The Midwifery Communication and Accountability Project (MCAP), founded in 1990, is seeking to make state regulation of midwifery uniform through the use of "Model State Legislation" (MCAP, n.d.).

4. As noted above, MANA established a registry exam, designed to "determine whether entry level knowledge has been achieved, and assist in fostering reciprocity between local jurisdictions" (MANA, n.d.).

5. MANA and the ACNM cooperated in the "Interorganizational Workgroup" (IWG), developing guidelines for midwifery certification in the United States. The guidelines allow for two types of midwives: the "certified midwife," credentialed through the MANA system, and the certified nurse-midwife, approved under ACNM guidelines (see WICP, 1994: 66-68; Burst, 1995; Rooks & Carr, 1995).

The number and diversity of suggestions for the regulation of midwifery coming from advocates of midwifery does not bode well for the future of the profession. Continued disagreement among midwives and their supporters—I saw the same thing in the early eighties—makes difficult the kind of coordinated and innovative effort needed to effect change. In an environment where midwifery faces persistent and strong opposition from physicians (see, e.g., Giacoia, 1991), factionalism among midwives extinguishes any hope of meaningful reform. Tjaden observes that "without state licensure, lay midwives have no true professional autonomy" (1987: 42). Unfortunately, it is also true that *with* the sort of licensure traditional midwives have experienced in the United States, created in the context of disagreements between midwives and power imbalances with the medical profession, there is no true professional autonomy either.

MIDWIVES IN THE COURTS

Where there are no clear regulations governing the practice of midwifery, an "uneasy truce" between midwives and the medical community continues: midwives are free to practice until they attract the attention of medical professionals. If a client of a midwife comes to the attention of a physician and the physician believes something improper was done, then the law is invoked as a regulatory mechanism and courts become the arena of regulation.

Over the past ten years, stories of this sort of regulation, many of them dramatic, have accumulated. Korte (1995) recounts the story of a Missouri midwife whose office was ransacked by seven law enforcement officers (wearing bullet-proof vests). They removed all her computer disks and destroyed her files and other materials. She was charged with eight felonies and several misdemeanors for practicing medicine without a license. The charges were eventually dropped in exchange for a five-year probation period. Mitford (1992: 221-40) describes similar incidents in California, and the homepage of *Midwifery Today* on the World Wide Web, a new medium for generating support for midwifery, includes an appeal for help for an Indiana midwife in legal trouble for practicing medicine without a license.

These cases and cases described by Hafner-Eaton and Pearce (1994) and DeClercq (1994) follow the pattern of legal actions against midwives reviewed in chapter 5: they are initiated by physicians; they draw media attention; courts are unwilling to levy too heavy a penalty; and the midwives involved receive support from sister midwives and clients.

A pair of recent cases, however, indicates that the character of legal actions against midwives might be changing. In late 1994 a Michigan couple whose baby died three weeks after it was born sued the two traditional midwives who attended the birth. The couple, who chose to give birth in the midwives' clinic, claimed that the supervising midwife failed to recognize an emergency and waited too long before calling the hospital. The case is remarkable because it is the *parents* (not physicians) who are bringing charges in the form of a civil (not criminal) suit for monetary damages. The father of the dead child acknowledges that "the midwife experience was beautiful," but goes on to comment, "she (the midwife) way overstepped her bounds" (Niemiec, 1994: 3a). It is worth noting that the birth took place in a clinical setting where the midwife-client relationship tends to be formalized. In the clinic the client is just that, a client, not a "co-conspirator" in the resistance to American obstetrics. When midwifery becomes established, it often adopts the form of clinical medicine, including more routinized relationships with clients. When the relationship between midwives and clients becomes more formal, legal actions like this—unheard of in the 1970s—become more common.

A second case reflects an expansion of the use of law as a tool of regulation. In this situation, described by Korte (1995: 56-57), three CNMs faced felony charges in association with an emergency breech birth (assisting at a breech birth is outside the permitted scope of practice for nurse-midwives) at a birthing center. One of the three was handcuffed and jailed. Although the charges were later dropped, the use of law to control the practices of midwives already regulated by licensing laws represents a major departure from earlier custom, and suggests a new level of scrutiny and control by physicians.

THE "CHANGING" NATURE OF MIDWIFERY

Although midwifery has not blossomed in the United States, it has been a persistent presence in American maternity care. What are the results of its proximity to medicine? The model of care represented by midwives has the power to change medical practice, but the medical setting also exerts pressure on midwifery, encouraging accommodation to the American way of birth.

There are several ways midwifery has influenced obstetric practice over the past two decades. The enormous popularity of LDRs (combined labor, delivery, and recovery rooms) can be credited to midwives and their supporters in the alternative birth movement (see Mathews & Zadak, 1991). The pioneers of parent-infant bonding research, Drs Klaus and Kennell (1976) acknowledge lay midwives and home birth as their inspiration. Although obstetricians were able to control the implementation of "bonding," they were pushed to change their practices by the presence of an alternative form of maternity care (see DeVries, 1984). More recently, Pel and Heres (1995: 95-105), studying obstetrics in the Netherlands, demonstrated the power of midwives to alter care given by individual obstetricians. Their research showed that, controlling for "risk" factors, obstetricians who work with midwives have lower rates of intervention.

But midwifery is also changed by medicine. When midwifery enters the world of obstetric technology, it runs the risk of having obstetric knowledge replace midwife knowledge. Barroso and I observed this in our survey of fetoscope use by CNMs (1996). We found that the fetoscope, a simple mechanical tool for finding fetal heart tones, is now rarely used by CNMs. The preferred tool is a "doptone", a device that uses sonar technology to make the task of finding heart tones easier. This seems an innocent development, but some midwives argue that valuable knowledge, unique to midwifery, is lost when the doptone is traded for the fetoscope. For example, a midwife using a fetoscope is able to find the point where the heart tones are the clearest and loudest, allowing the precise position of the child to be identified. With an amplified doptone, subtleties in the heartbeat are impossible to notice. Furthermore, the fetoscope brings the midwife much closer to the woman, allowing the care-giver to assess the level of relaxation, skin tone, and overall condition.

Considering that medicine is supported by both structural arrangements and cultural ideas, the "corruption" of midwifery by medicine seems much more likely than its opposite. Lacking power and authority, midwifery must adapt to succeed. An "adapted" midwifery, using the tools and techniques of medicine, has little to offer obstetrics. It is significant that the research demonstrating the potential of midwives to reduce obstetrical intervention (Pel & Heres, 1995) was done in the Netherlands. Dutch midwives remain outside of medical control and thus offer an independent perspective on maternity care. Pel and Heres (1995: 104) comment, "(because) midwives show patience and stimulate confidence, as opposed to physicians who act faster and anticipate pathologic events, the reduction in anxiety might explain the decreasing effect of the employment of midwives on the rate of obstetrical interventions."

The challenge for midwives is to find a way to practice that preserves the unique body of knowledge and method that is theirs. For some midwives this involves remaining outside the world of medicine; this is the choice made by many traditional midwives. Other midwives choose to subvert the medical setting. Nurse-midwives report a variety of techniques for getting around restrictive hospital and physicians policies: smuggling lubricants for perineal massage into "sterile" delivery rooms, removing monitors so laboring women can walk around, speeding labor with warm baths or massage rather than oxytocin, violating rules that limit food intake (DeVries & Barroso, 1996). If midwifery is to be an agent of change rather than the subject of change, this sort of resistance and subversion is necessary.

THE LAST WORD

Checking my work against empirical reality is only one way of assessing its quality. Another measure of a book's merit, one that we professional researchers sometimes find more important, is its reception by colleagues, its place in the body of recognized knowledge. For many of us "How did they like it?" becomes a more important question than "Was it true?"

Before closing this book for a second time, I must take note of the work of several other scholars who have joined the study of midwives since 1985. For the most part, their scholarship confirms and extends my research.

In their book *Labor Pains,* Sullivan and Weitz explored many of the same issues covered in *Regulating Birth.* They looked at midwifery in the United States, England, and New Zealand and came to conclusions nearly identical to mine, observing that "the rise of all modern midwifery ... (might) be a false labor" (1988: 214). Where they disagree with my analysis (109-11; 205-6), it is often the result of their oversimplification of my arguments: they ignore my emphasis on the way law interacts with other social forces, suggesting that I saw licensure as the only operative factor in midwifery's demise.

More interesting for the future of my work and the future of midwifery are studies that explore the role of culture in the decline of midwifery. Davis-Floyd's (1992) important study of birth as an American rite of passage illustrates how cultural values sustain American obstetrics. She deconstructs our American birth practices, calling attention to the need we have as a culture to affirm our values at the transitional time of birth. She reminds us that we live in a culture that values, among other things, technology, the control of nature, and patriarchy. We should expect our birthing rooms to be dominated by men and technological devices that impose their timing and regulation on the natural process of birth.

Borst's (1988, 1989, 1995) careful historical studies of Wisconsin midwives give further evidence of the cultural roots of birth practices. Her research challenges the simplistic notion that physician resistance led to the extinction of midwifery. She shows that as immigrant women assimilated, the culture that supported midwifery disappeared, and along with it the midwives: "In the end midwifery, practiced by immigrant, working class women, remained rooted in the cultural life of traditional ethnic communities. When these communities began to assimilate and adopt American ideas, there was no place for the midwife" (1989: 48).

In his study of the rise of man-midwifery in England, Wilson (1995) adds his voice to those emphasizing the role of culture in the fading fortunes of female midwives. He observes that "male practitioners were turned into midwives not by their own desire, but through the choices of women ... the making of man-midwifery was the work of women" (Wilson 1995: 192). His conclusions, which challenge conventional histories of midwifery, rest on an analysis of the role of "fashion" in shaping medical practice: "Fashion was in general the symbolic reflection of a new culture of class; in the world of women, for which childbirth was so crucial, fashion dictated the need for the man-midwife ... fashion offered a bridge by which those of intermediate or ambiguous status could symbolically climb the ranks" (Ibid.: 191).

For the most part, the first edition of this book focused on the structures that constrained midwives. If culture was part of the analysis, it was as a dependent variable: I showed how political and legal structures influenced the culture of midwifery, how the structural setting of care shaped the culture of the midwife-client relationship. But the work of Davis-Floyd, Borst, and Wilson, and my own work in the Netherlands (DeVries, 1996a) shows culture to be an important independent variable, promoting or discouraging midwifery.

"Cultural analysis" of birth is at once liberating and depressing. Liberating because it offers the knowledge we need to transform birth practices; depressing because the transformation requires changing deeply held values. Consider, in conclusion, an illustration. Martin (1987) presents a discussion of the metaphors we use to talk about birth, showing how these words—*reproduction, labor, progress*—reflect an industrial, capitalist mentality. True, and a bit disheartening when one realizes how our birth practices are tied to deeply ingrained economic ideas. But there is the hint of liberation here as well: it is freeing to learn that not all Western cultures use these same metaphors. The Dutch, for example, use different images when speaking of birth. Reproduction is *voortplanting*, literally "forward planting," an agricultural metaphor. When a Dutch woman is in labor, she is *aan het bevallen*, "in the act of birthing." Labor pains are *weeën*, the same word found in *heimwee*, homesickness, or more literally, the "aching" *(weeën)* for home. And the Dutch, you will recall, still use midwives and support birth at home.

In the preface I pointed out that twenty years ago we members of the alternative birth movement were full of hope, convinced we could change American obstetrics, convinced by the "rightness" of our quest[2]. The intervening years have been discouraging, but, oddly (naively?), I am convinced that the changes we sought are inevitable. More and more the wisdom of midwifery is confirmed by epidemiology, and, more important, social and historical research is providing new understandings of the forces that prevent the wisdom of midwifery from being realized. The re-establishment of independent midwives in the United Kingdom and Canada and the use of nurse-midwives by managed care organizations in the United States are preparing the cultural soil needed to sustain a new obstetric system, a system that is characterized by love and justice, a system that makes prudent use of our resources, a system that supports women, babies, families.

REFERENCES

ACNM (American College of Nurse-Midwives) (1993), *Facts: nurse-midwives historically key answers to maternal healthcare problem.* Washington DC: American College of Nurse-Midwives.

Baldwin, L., H.Hutchinson & R.Rosenblatt (1992), "Professional relationships between midwives and physicians: collaboration or conflict?" *American Journal of Public Health* **82**(2): 262-264.

Barroso, Rebeca & Melissa Coffey (1991), "Legal status of traditional midwives—United States". Unpublished.

Borst, Charlotte (1988), "The training and practice of midwives: a Wisconsin study." *Bulletin of the History of Medicine* **62**(4): 606-27.

Borst, Charlotte (1989), "Wisconsin's midwives as working women: immigrant midwives and the limits of a traditional occupation, 1870-1920." *Journal of American Ethnic History* **8**(2): 24-59.

Borst, Charlotte (1995), *Catching Babies: the professionalization of childbirth, 1870-1920.* Cambridge, Mass.: Harvard University Press.

Burst, H.V. (1995), "An update on the credentialing of midwives by the ACNM." *Journal of Nurse-Midwifery* **40**(3): 290-296.

Butter, J., B.Abrams, J.Parker, J.Roberts & R.Laros (1993). "Supportive nurse-midwife care is associated with a reduced incidence of Cesarean Section." *American Journal of Obstetrics & Gynecology* **168**(5): 1407-1413.

Butter, I.H. & B.J.Kay (1988), "State laws and the practice of midwifery." *American Journal of Public Health* **78**(9): 1161-1169.

Butter, I.H. & B.J.Kay (1990), "Self-certification in lay midwives' organizations: a vehicle for professional autonomy." *Social Science and Medicine* **30** (12): 1329-1339.

Davis-Floyd, R.E. (1992), *Birth as an American Rite of Passage.* Berkeley: University California Press.

DeClercq, Eugene (1992), "The transformation of American midwifery: 1975-1988." *American Journal of Public Health* **82** (5): 680-684.

DeClercq, Eugene (1994), "The trials of Hanna Porn: the campaign to abolish midwifery in Massachusetts." *American Journal of Public Health* **84** (6): 1022-1028.

Devitt, Neal (1979a), "How doctors conspire to eliminate the midwife even though the scientific data support midwifery." pp.345-370 in D.Stewart & L.Stewart, eds., *Compulsory Hospitalization: freedom of choice in childbirth?* Marble Hill, Mo.: NAPSAC (National Association of Professionals for Safe Alternatives in Childbirth).

Devitt, Neal (1979b), "The statistical case for the elimination of the midwife: fact versus prejudice, 1890-1935" (in two parts). *Women and Health* **4** (1): 81-96 and **4** (2): 169-186.

DeVries, Raymond G. (1984), "'Humanizing' childbirth: the discovery and implementation of bonding theory." *International Journal of Health Services* **14** (1): 89-104.

DeVries, Raymond G. (1984), "The contest for control: regulating new and expanding health occupations," *American Journal of Public Health* **76** (9): 1147-1151.

DeVries, Raymond G. (1996a), "The social and cultural context of birth: Lessons for health care reform from Dutch maternity care," *The Journal of Perinatal Education,* **5**(2): 25-30

DeVries, Raymond G. (1996b), *Making Midwives Legal: Childbirth, Medicine and the Law* (2nd Edn.) Columbus: Ohio State University Press

DeVries, Raymond G. & R. Barroso (1996), "Midwives among the machines: recreating midwifery in the late twentieth century." In H. Marland and A.M.Rafferty, eds., *Midwives, Society and Childbirth: debates and controversies, 1850-1995.* London: Routledge.

Durand, A.M. (1992), "The safety of home birth: the Farm Study." *American Journal of Public Health* **82** (3): 450-453.

Giacoia, George (1991), "Lay midwives in Oklahoma." *Journal of the Oklahoma State Medical Association* **84** (4): 160-2.

Goer, Henci (1995), *Obstetric Myths versus Research Realities.* Westport, Conn.: Bergin & Garvey.

Hafner-Eaton, C. & L.K. Pearce (1994), "Birth choices, the law & medicine: balancing individual freedoms & protection of the public's health." *Journal of Health Politics, Policy & Law* **19**(4): 813-35.

Hinds, M., G.Bergeisen & D.Allen (1985), "Neonatal outcome in planned vs. unplanned out-of-hospital births in Kentucky." *Journal of the American Medical Association* **253**: 1578-1582.

Karlin, Rick (1994), "Midwives stunned by law." *Albany Times Union* January 24: C1.

Klaus, Marshall & J.Kennell (1976), *Maternal-Infant Bonding.* St.Louis: Mosby.

Korte, Diana (1995), "Midwives on trial." *Mothering* **76** (Fall): 52-63.

Litoff, Judy B. (1978), *American Midwives— 1860 to the present.* Westport, Conn: Greenwood Press.

MANA (Midwives' Alliance of North America) (n.d.), *The North American Registry of Midwives.* Newton, Kans.: MANA.

Martin, Emily (1987), *The Woman in the Body: a cultural analysis of reproduction.* Boston: Beacon Press.

Mathews, J.J. & K.Zadak (1991), "The alternative birth movement in the United States: history and current status." *Women and Health* **17** (1): 39-56.

MCAP (Midwifery Communication and Accountability Project), (n.d.), "Midwifery: the heart of maternity care reform." Newton Highlands, Mass.: MCAP.

Mehl Madrona, M. & L. Mehl Madrona (1993), "The future of midwifery in the United States." *NAPSAC News* **18** (3-4): 1-32.

Mitford, Jessica (1992), *The American Way of Birth*. New York: Penguin.

Myers, S.J. & J.Myers-Ciecko (1989), "Professional midwifery." *American Journal of Public Health* **79** (4): 520.

Myers, S.J., P.St.Clair, S.Gloyd, P.Salzberg & J.Myers-Ciecko (1990), "Unlicensed midwifery practice in Washington State." *American Journal of Public Health* **80** (6): 726-728.

National Center for Health Statistics (1994), "Advance report of final natality statistics, 1992." *Monthly Vital Statistics Report* 43 (October 25): 5, supplement. Hyattsville, Md.

National Commission on Nurse-Midwifery Education (1993), *Education of Nurse Midwives: a strategy for achieving affordable, high-quality maternity care*. Washington, D.C.: American College of Nurse-Midwives.

Niemiec, Dennis (1994), "Baby's death sparks battle." *Detroit Free Press* October 3: 1A.

Parker, Jennifer (1994), "Ethnic differences in midwife-attended births." *American Journal of Public Health* **84** (7): 1137-41.

Pearse, Warren H. (1987), "Parturition: places and priorities." *American Journal of Public Health* 77 (8): 923-4.

Pel, M. & M.H.B.Heres (1995), *OBINT: a study of obstetric intervention*. The Hague: CIP-Koninklijke Bibliotheek.

Roback, Gene, L.Randolph & B.Seidman (1993), *Physician Characteristics and Distribution in the U.S., 1993 Edition*. Chicago: American Medical Society.

Rooks, J.P. & K.C.Carr (1995), "Criteria for accreditation of direct-entry midwifery education." *Journal of Nurse-Midwifery* **40** (3): 297-303.

Rooks, J.P., N.Weatherby, E.Ernst, S.Stapleton, D.Rosen & A.Rosenfeld (1989), "Outcomes of care in birth centers: the National Birth Center Study." *New England Journal of Medicine* **321**(26): 1804-11.

Russell, Keith (1987), "Midwives: a review of *Regulating Birth: midwives, medicine and the law*." *Journal of the American Medical Association* **257** (2): 252-3.

Sakala, Carol (1993), "Midwifery care and out-of-hospital birth settings: how do they reduce unnecessary Cesarean Section births?" *Social Science & Medicine* **37** (10): 1233-50.

Schramm, W.F., D.Barnes & J.Bakewell (1987), "Neonatal mortality in Missouri home births, 1978-84." *American Journal of Public Health* 77 (8): 930-5.

Sullivan, D. & R.Weitz (1988), *Labor Pains: modern midwives and home birth*. 1988. New Haven, Conn.: Yale University Press.

Tew, M., (1990), *A Safer Birth: a critical history of maternity care*. New York: Routledge.

Tjaden, Patricia (1987), "Midwifery in Colorado: a case study in the politics of professionalization." *Qualitative Sociology* **10** (1): 29-45.

WICP (Women's Institute for Childbearing Policy) (1994), *Childbearing policy within a national health program: an evolving consensus for new directions*. Boston: WICP.

Wilson, Adrian (1995), *The Making of Man-Midwifery*. Cambridge, Mass: Harvard University Press.

Wolfson, C. (1986), "Midwives and home birth: social, medical, and legal perspectives." *Hastings Law Journal* 37: 909-967.

---

[1] Russell (1987) claims the mortality rate for home birth is 50-100 times greater than for hospital birth! He fails to cite a source for this incredible statistic. See Tew (1990) for a detailed analysis of the safety of home birth.

[2] 'Preface' in: *Making Midwives Legal: Childbirth, Medicine and the Law* (DeVries 1996b: xi-xxi)

WHO CARES FOR WOMEN? SCIENCE VERSUS LOVE IN MIDWIFERY TODAY

Ann Oakley[*]

To use a fashionable phrase, midwifery today is "in crisis"[1]. In part, this is because the maternity services are themselves suffering from the cumulative effects of economic starvation, political neglect and enduring social inequalities, which serve to increase the burden of stress and ill-health carried by the health services and, of course, by society generally. The recent rise in the UK infant mortality rate may be a statistical freak, or it may signal a real effect of worsening social conditions[2]; at any rate, we cannot say that this is an era in which life for women and babies is getting demonstrably better. Recent changes in maternity leave provision, for example, mean that pregnant women in Britain have no universal, legally enforceable right to maternity leave; many of the hard-won benefits of the 1976 Employment Protection Act have been lost, and the qualifying conditions and level of payment imposed on British women are now more stringent than in any other European country[3].

Furthermore, while mothers' rights are being eroded and undermined in this and other ways, midwives themselves are having a difficult time. There are not enough of them, and the importance of their work in both hospital and community does not seem likely to be recognised by the new clinical grading structure. The dissatisfaction many midwives feel with this situation matches the lack of continuity of care about which many mothers complain; but the policy-makers appear to be incapable of adding two and two together and remedying this situation by increasing the opportunities midwives and mothers have to get to know one another.

Perhaps most sinister of all these developments, a series of legal challenges to the autonomy of particular midwives in the UK and elsewhere is effectively questioning the extent to which midwives can, in the 1980s, protect the interests of mothers and babies without being seen as meddlesome witches intent on emasculating the medical profession and damaging the moral fabric of society. Since some of the same issues are arising in these cases as were aired in the inquiry into obstetrician Wendy Savage's suspension[4], it is clear that the confrontation between the different groups of care-providers is also across gender lines (much as it was historically with the persecution of witches).

THE ART OF OBSTETRICS: GENDER (AND OTHER) DIVISIONS

In 1902 a doctor called Henry Garrigues published a book entitled *A Textbook of the Science and Art of Obstetrics*. Chapter 9 of Dr Garrigues' book is called "Midwives" and it begins:

> In the city of New York more than one-half of the parturient women are attended by this class of helpers (i.e. midwives). Most of them are Germans, Scandinavians or Italians by birth, and are employed chiefly by their

---

[*] This William Power Memorial Lecture of the Royal College of Midwives was delivered at the Royal Institute of British Architects, London, on November 21, 1988

Midwives Chronicle & Nursing Notes (July) 1989

own country women, the American and the Irish women being too intelligent and well informed to avail themselves of these ignorant and uncleanly beings.

Even in European countries, where the pupil midwives are instructed in universities by the same professors who teach the students of medicine, where they have a course extending through years and where they, after having entered on practice, are under strict government control, even there constant complaints are being uttered in the medical press in regard to the inefficiency and shortcomings of midwives.

Midwives do harm not only through their lack of obstetric knowledge, their neglect of antiseptic precautions, and their tendency to conceal undesirable features, but most of them are the most inveterate quacks. First of all they treat disturbances occurring during the puerpery, later gynaecological diseases, then diseases of children, and finally they are consulted in regard to almost everything. They never acknowledge their ignorance, and are always ready to give advice. They administer potent drugs, such as ergot and opium. Their thinly veiled advertisements in the newspapers show them to be willing abortionists; and since they have the right to give certificates of stillbirth, who knows whether or not an infant's death is due to natural causes or to criminal manipulations?

Although an evil, midwives are, however, in most countries a necessity, in view of the fact that physicians would not find time to do the work needed; this does not apply to America, where there is a superabundance of medical practitioners.

The institution of midwives is a remnant of barbaric times, a blot on our civilization which ought to be wiped out as soon as possible.'[5]

The year Dr Garrigues' book was published was the year of the Midwives' Act in Britain, which obtained for midwives here a role and position which has for long been the envy of their transatlantic colleagues. There are certain critical assumptions in this quotation.

1. Midwives are ignorant and dirty, therefore their practice is dangerous.
2. Even trained midwives are incompetent.
3. Midwives are especially unscientific because they care for women and children's health generally.
4. Men know more about obstetrics than women.
5. Doctors know more about obstetrics than anyone else.
6. Obstetrics is a science.

Actually, Garrigues wasn't quite sure whether obstetrics is a science—he referred to it as "the science and art of obstetrics," but there was no doubt in his mind that it was superior to what midwives do, and that this superiority had something to do with medical expertise. He was not alone in this, for many medical men on both sides of the Atlantic had written, and were writing, similar kinds of anti-midwifery tracts.

We have here, in these assumptions of Dr Garrigues and others, a certain polarisation of concepts—words and their opposites which sum up the terms of a continuing debate about the occupational identity and unique contribution of midwives to the care of childbearing women. Figure 1 lists these concepts: on the one hand we have midwives, women, health, normality and so forth, and on the other we have obstetricians, men, disease, abnormality, science. These oppositions represent something that goes far beyond the domains of obstetrics and midwifery: we are talking about a very deep-seated cultural divide. However my argument is that the dilemma of all the various parties involved in the maternity services today—including the midwife, the obstetrician, the paediatrician, the mother, the baby, the father and not forgetting the policy-makers—their dilemma, our dilemma, is that we are trapped within this language of opposition, which is an intensely misleading language. As a consequence we are unable to make any real progress in our understanding either of the processes involved in reproduction or of how best to help the key actors in the drama of childbirth—the mother and the baby.

Figure 1: Midwifery and Obstetrics: conceptual domains.

Midwives	- Obstetricians	Emotion	-	Reason
Women	- Men	Intuition	-	Intellect
Health	- Disease	Nature	-	Culture
Normality	- Abnormality	Feminine	-	Masculine
Art	- Science	Community	-	Institution
Social	- Medical	Family	-	Work
Subjective	- Objective	Private	-	Public
Experience	- Knowledge	Care	-	Control
Observation	- Intervention	"Soft"	-	"Hard"
Practice	- Theory			

The best way to explain this is to refer you to studies which in some way bridge this divide. One such is the work done by Richard Newton on life events—stressful occurrences—in the lives of pregnant women, and the relation between these and the risk of preterm delivery and/or low birth weight[6]. These studies found a clear association between pregnancy stress and the risk of these adverse outcomes. The point they are making is one about the social causes of an obstetric problem. Conversely, Klaus and colleagues' study[7] of the effectiveness of social support in labour makes a different, but related, point about the prevention by social means of obstetric problems. Their study demonstrates that providing social support during labour can have a powerful effect on the occurrence of problems and the need for medical intervention.

The message of studies such as Newton's and that of Klaus and colleagues is that the mind-body divide does not work as a model for explaining childbearing. The theory dominant in Western medicine, that the body is an organism and that the functioning of particular bits of it can be explained by looking at functioning elsewhere in the body, simply does not fit the facts so far as childbearing is concerned. However the "body as a machine" model produces certain well-known analogies, for example the garage analogy according to which the doctor is a mechanic and the pregnant woman is a broken down Ford (or Mercedes, depending on her social class). The garage is the hospital, providing the tools necessary to fix the malfunctioning parts. An American magazine in 1926 contained the following obstetrical dialogue:

"But is the hospital necessary at all?" demanded a young woman of her obstetrician friend. "Why not bring (have) the baby at home?"

"What would you do if your automobile broke down on a country road?" the doctor countered with another question.

"Try and fix it" said the modern chauffeuse.

"And if you couldn't?"

"Have it hauled to the nearest garage."

"Exactly. here the trained mechanics and their necessary tools are," agreed the doctor. "It's the same with the hospital. I can do my best work and the best we must have in medicine all the time—not in some cramped little apartment or private home, but where I have the proper facilities and trained helpers. If anything goes wrong, I have all known aids to meet your emergency"[8].

Proponents of "natural" childbirth have also appealed to the idea of the garage. Here is Grantly Dick-Read in 1942, talking about women's increased efficiency at motherhood:

Since when have repair shops been more important than the production plant? he asks. In the early days of motoring, garages were full of broken-down machines, but production has been improved; the weaknesses that predisposed to unreliability were discovered and in due course rectified. Today it is only the inferior makes that require the attention of mechanics. Such models have been evolved that we almost forget the relative reliability of the modern machine if it is properly cared for.

The mother is the factory, and by education and care she can be made more efficient in the art of motherhood. Her mind is of even greater importance than her physical state, for motherhood is of the mind. .
. [9]

Dick-Read has his metaphors mixed here: if motherhood is in the mind what is the mother doing in the garage? It is well-known that language embodies the interests of the user: in another medical field, Susan

Sontag[10] has written about the military metaphors used by oncologists; and male fertility specialists apparently refer to the genetic material in human sperm as "nuclear war-heads"[11].

While the mechanical model of childbearing may appeal to the mechanics amongst us, it is not a good description of how it is in reality. In reality pregnant women are not ambulant pelvises, but individuals with minds, emotions and complex personal and social lives. So where did the model come from? And why is it still around today?

SCIENCE AS OPPOSED TO LOVE

The outline of the story is familiar[12]. First of all, Dr Garrigues was right in associating the role of midwives with the more general role of women as carers of the community's health. Throughout history and in all human cultures it has been predominantly women who have cared for dependent and vulnerable individuals, including children, the old, the sick and the disabled. Female midwifery fitted easily and logically within this overall caring function. Onto this traditional fabric was then grafted the new imprint of the emergent medical profession, which laid its claim to fame not on caring—with or without continuity—but on technical expertise: science as opposed to love. Or forceps and the lying-in hospital as opposed to the purely domestic art of "catching" babies at home. Dr Garrigues and others like him needed to argue that the practice of female midwives was dangerous and unscientific and that the status of midwives in society was low. They had to do this in order to get people to accept obstetricians, and they also needed to claim that obstetricians could work the wonders that midwives were not able to do. However, these claims were unsupported by scientific evidence. In the early 1900s, for example, obstetricians said they could prevent miscarriage, preterm delivery and toxaemia. These goals have yet to be achieved today[13].

Closer examination of the evidence, therefore, reveals a profound need for obstetrical self-defence. For example in 1913, in New York City, midwives attended 40% of all births but had only 20% of maternal deaths from sepsis. Physicians, with 60% of births, had 69% of the deaths. Although midwives may have attended some less complicated cases, they were also the only attendants for poorer women who are likely to have been in the worst general health[14]. In Europe as well as North America, introduction of the forceps—the major technical advance claimed by obstetrician—is likely to have increased rather than decreased mortality"[15]. Some of the reasons for this are clear from the arguments of the early obstetricians. For example, Joseph DeLee, the American doctor who recommended the routine prophylactic use of forceps, described obstetrics in 1915 as "a major science of the same rank as surgery" and went on to assert that "even natural deliveries damage both mothers and babies, often and much. If childbearing is destructive, it is pathogenic, and if it is pathogenic it is pathologic". In short, DeLee concluded that childbearing could no longer be considered a normal function; thus, in relation to it, "the midwife would be impossible even of mention"[16].

Between 1918 and 1925 in the States, when midwifery declined nation-wide, infant deaths from birth injuries rose by 44%[17]. Perhaps fortunately, and certainly not coincidentally, when the first male midwives established instruction courses in England in the eighteenth century, the art or science of instrumental delivery was not taught to women (who paid lower fees for the course), only to men[18].

A common medical therapy in pregnancy and childbirth, for many centuries, was bloodletting, iatrogenic haemorrhage was the treatment of choice for many complaints. Some doctors even bled women into unconsciousness as a remedy for delivery pain. Bloodletting, emetics and mustard plasters (for the feet) were recommended for toxaemia of pregnancy. Routine maternity care as practised by William Goodell, Professor of the Diseases of Women at the University of Pennsylvania in 1874, is described by historians Richard and Dorothy Wertz in the following terms:

> When the patient came to the hospital, some days or weeks before delivery, she was put on a regular dosage of quinine, then a kind of all-purpose preventative. Each woman received drugs for constipation, headaches, and sleeplessness. When labor began, each received a cathartic and a bath. The staff then ruptured the amniotic sac, used forceps to expedite delivery, gave ergot when the head appeared, and hurried the expulsion of the placenta by pressing on the stomach. After cutting the cord and bathing the woman again, they gave her morphine each hour until she felt no more afterpains, and gave her quinine "until the ears rang"[19].

At the height of the anti-midwife phase, there were some medics who acknowledged the lack of scientific evidence against the midwife; some were prepared to say that women were safer in the hands of ignorant midwives than in those of "poorly educated medical men". However, according to one prominent and outspoken obstetrician in the early part of the century, "such a conclusion ... . (was) contrary to reason" and what reason dictated was that "the obstetrician should not be merely a male midwife but a scientifically trained man"[20]. In the early twentieth century, obstetricians' desire to expand the influence and increase the status of their profession seems to have been the basis of their opposition to midwives. As a group, nineteenth century doctors were not particularly affluent. Though midwifery itself was not a particularly lucrative speciality, it was guaranteed income and, more important, it opened the door on family practice[21].

MIDWIFERY AND WITCHCRAFT

The history of midwifery also tells us that there is a well-established historical connection between midwifery and witchcraft. It is worth noting a few points about this link. First of all, midwives were associated with witchcraft because not all witchcraft was bad—it was recognised that there were good witches and bad witches in medieval Europe. Another name for the good witch was wisewoman[22]. It is for this reason that the modern name for midwives in French is sage-femme . Secondly, the claim that midwives were bad witches was an important part of the Church and the State's attempt from the fifteenth century on to control both the role and the power of women, and to restrict the practice of medicine to the new university-trained male medical practitioners. This is evident in one of the earliest preserved oaths made by an English midwife applying for a Church licence in 1567. After being questioned by the Archbishop of Canterbury—no less—and eight women (presumably experienced midwives themselves), the midwife had to swear that she would "not use any kind of sorcery or incantation in the time of travail of any woman" and would baptise every infant with pure, clean water, notifying the parish curate of each baptising. It is of interest that that same oath obliges the midwife to promise "to help and aid as well, poor and rich women" and not "permit or suffer that women... shall name any other to be the father of her child"[23]. Witnessing the biological connections of kinship systems was an important social function of the midwife.

In political terms witchcraft was, of course, also the very opposite of science. In line with this argument, efficient midwives were apparently particularly likely to be branded as witches. The tale of the midwife who in the eastern counties of England reached a confinement in an impossibly short time produced the answer that a broomstick was responsible [24] (is this the origin of the modern term "flying squad"?).

SCIENCE AND THE "MASTERY" OF CHILDBIRTH

The rise of obstetrics and its eventual dominance over midwifery was thus achieved in part by the argument that those who care for childbearing women can only do so properly by viewing the female body as a machine to be supervised, controlled and interfered with by technical means, science, or reason, were given (are given) in support of this approach. Though the scientific basis of obstetrics was poor, doctors were committed to the "mastery of birth". In the absence of understanding, control and management were important—childbirth and women had to be "mastered". The masculine gender of this word is, for once, highly significant. The male role in obstetrics paralleled the male cultural role; socialised to be masters of their own fates, families and environments, it appears that the same kind of impulse possessed the men who first took over childbirth from those who traditionally cared for women—midwives.

Today the technological imperative in obstetrics remains dominant and continues to be problematic. Over the past 20 years the use of such technologies as induction of labour, electronic fetal heart rate monitoring, ultrasound, episiotomy and Caesarean section has risen; the accumulated evidence of randomised controlled trials has suggested that frequent and/or routine use of these technologies cannot be justified: nonetheless they continue to be used [25].

In part this is a problem that extends to the whole of medicine. According to a World Health Organisation report, the three most common criticisms of health care expressed today are: (1) that its benefits are distributed in a socially unequal way; (2) that it has harmful effects; and (3) that it is characterised by excessive technological intervention [26]. But the place of technology in maternity care is also a unique one, in that control and intervention versus a different attitude of watching and waiting—the prescription of normality as against the belief that childbearing is an inherently pathological process—is a division that has a unique professional representation in the form of two distinct groups of care-providers: the obstetricians and the midwives.

If technology is the obstetrician's weapon, what is the midwife's? What is a midwife anyway? According to the Oxford English Dictionary, the word midwife comes from middle English, "mid" and "wife" meaning "a woman who is with the mother at birth". More technical definitions also exist, stressing the importance of formal training and registration procedures:

> A midwife is a person who, having been regularly admitted to a midwifery educational programme, duly recognised in the country in which it is located, has successfully completed the prescribed course of studies in midwifery and has acquired the requisite qualifications to be registered and/or legally licensed to practise midwifery.

> She must be able to give the necessary supervision, care and advice to women during pregnancy, labour and postpartum period, to conduct deliveries on her own responsibility and to care for the newborn and the infant[27].

This second definition, though it stresses the need for professional qualifications, also highlights the continuity of care provided by the midwife and her proper independence in delivering the baby—that all-important phrase—"on her own responsibility".

So midwives care for women and obstetricians control and master childbirth. If obstetric technology has been shown often to rest on weak scientific foundations, its routine use being neither effective nor safe, then what evidence is there for the effectiveness and safety of caring? What is the scientific value of love, if you like?

THE VALUE OF CARING

One way this question can be addressed is by reviewing studies of midwifery care, social interventions or "social care" during pregnancy. The best of these studies (scientifically speaking) are those that have been carried out as randomised controlled trials, because only studies with this design enable one to be confident that the groups of women on whom different "treatments" are tried are otherwise as similar as possible. To criticise obstetricians (past and present) for being unscientific places a particular responsibility on the critic to establish as soundly as possible the basis of any counter argument. There have been few properly controlled trials of midwife care—which is, on its own, an important observation. One of the few studies that have been done was published some time ago by Lilian Runnerstrom in the States. This compared nurse-midwifery care with care provided by obstetric residents for 4,500 women with uncomplicated pregnancies[28]. Runnerstrom found that nurse-midwives, compared with doctors, more often used no, or only inhalational, analgesia, their care was associated with shorter labours, a much lower operative delivery rate, a somewhat lower LBW (low birth-weight) rate and fewer complications in the puerperium. A second study, also American[29], was carried out in the mid 1970s in North Carolina: this found that nurse-midwives achieved a higher spontaneous delivery rate and less use of low forceps, or rather, that mothers cared for by nurse-midwives achieved more normal labours, with the midwives' help.

The third study is French and is interesting because its findings are somewhat more complex than the others[30]. Spira and colleagues, in evaluating a programme of community midwifery care, appeared to find that it added to the risks of childbirth. However, on closer inspection the data yielded the finding that socially disadvantaged women did benefit from home care; but those with medical risks did not. Furthermore, as Judith Lumley[31] has pointed out, the high rate of obstetric complications and cervical damage among the "home" group in this study, raises the possibility that the randomisation did not work as intended, so that these women were, in fact, a higher risk group anyway.

Although not about midwifery as such, the study by Olds and colleagues[32] looked at the effect on pregnancy outcome of home visiting nurses. During their visits, the nurses provided parent education and set out to enhance "the woman's informal support systems" (something which midwives often do). A central aspect of their approach was "to emphasise the strengths of the women and their families".

Significant differences in favour of the home visited group were found for a mixed bag of outcomes including "awareness of community services" (a direct effect of the parent education, presumably), attendance at childbirth classes, discussions with family and friends of stress-related issues, paternal interaction with babies, smoking in pregnancy and the incidence of LBW—though this applied to the younger (adolescent) mothers only. Similar findings obtained in a smaller more recent study by Judy Dance in Birmingham, where a social support intervention was provided by linkworkers to pregnant Pakistani women[33]. The linkworker group experienced fewer medical problems in pregnancy, more happiness (and less unhappiness), shorter labours, less use of analgesia in labour, higher mean birth weight and fewer feeding problems.

The effectiveness of childbirth preparation in improving pregnancy outcome has never been scientifically proved, though it may of course have increased women's satisfaction, which is important. The very expectation of a pleasant delivery can affect the length of labour, as Nelson and colleagues[34] found in their Canadian study of 'Leboyer' deliveries. Another study compared the effects on labour outcomes of prenatal education versus knitting classes versus nothing at all[35]. The prenatal classes contained fairly standard information about the anatomy and physiology of labour, pain medication, relaxation techniques, hospital organisation, etc. The knitting class included instruction in basic knitting techniques and "guidance in knitting a shirt for the expected infant". Results of the study showed that birth weight in the prenatal class group was lower than in the no class group, which in turn was lower than among the knitters. Use of medication was, however, lowest among the prenatal class attenders and highest among the knitters. Such results are very likely, of course, to be mediated by women's attitudes to knitting. There is a study of the effect of music on fetal activity which demonstrates precisely this: that it is not music per se that affects the infant's prenatal activity, but whether or not the mother likes the music being played[36]. The use of Barry Manilow as a childbirth analgesic is only effective if the mother likes Barry Manilow.

SOCIAL INTERVENTIONS

Some social interventions consist of reorganising the pattern or the location of care so that it becomes more satisfying to the mother. A Scottish study[37] involved a comparison of care provided in a peripheral community, as opposed to a centralised hospital, clinic. The authors of this study found that community based care is of material and practical benefit to the mother: it costs less, and half the mothers—as opposed to none in the hospital group—are able to walk there. It is also of interest that (as all good midwives know) a community clinic facilitates conversation between midwives and mothers. A somewhat different study was carried out by Klein and colleagues comparing pregnancy outcomes in women cared for in birth[38] rooms as against more conventional hospital settings. Use of oxytocin, forceps and episiotomy was significantly lower, though the two groups of women receiving the different patterns of care had a similar level of risk.

One of the interesting messages that comes out of reviewing these social intervention studies is the relatively powerful effect even an apparently insignificant intervention can have. Carpenter's study[39] looked at the effect of one pregnancy interview with a medical student (no less), and found significant effects on pregnancy anxiety and use of pre-delivery medication. If one interview with a medical student can work such wonders, what miracles attend many prenatal conversations between mothers and midwives? The answer to this question is of course provided by the world famous study carried out by Caroline Flint[40] who was anxious to prove to the scientific world the value to women and their babies of continuous personal relationships between mothers and midwives in pregnancy. Those in the "Know Your Midwife Scheme", as opposed to those receiving standard antenatal care, felt encouraged to be more questioning antenatally, more often experienced spontaneous onset of labour, felt in control during labour, had no analgesia or Entonox only, had few episiotomies, produced slightly bigger babies that needed less resuscitation, were breast feeding at six weeks and found it easier to be a mother.

In other words, communication increases women's "mastery" of their childbirth experiences (and all these studies show that mastery is as important for women as it is for obstetricians). "Mastery" is facilitated by access to information: two randomised controlled trials of mothers holding their own case-notes as opposed to the somewhat less informative so-called "cooperation" cards[41] demonstrated increased feelings of control among women holding their own notes. Similar beneficial effects of information, though with more directly measurable health effects, were found in a trial of different ways of carrying out ultrasound examinations of pregnancy[42].

Finally, counselling and/or nonspecific social support also have the potential to influence a range of pregnancy outcomes. For example, discussing with pregnant women the likely realities of motherhood in advance will significantly reduce problems after delivery, as the Gordons showed in a now classic 1960 study of postpartum emotional problems[43]. The results of the study by Margaret Gutelius and colleagues[44] of child health supervision, which included pregnancy counselling, were quite dramatic, not only in making children whose mothers were receiving counselling sleep through the night and give up nappies earlier, but in affecting the likelihood with which husbands kept their jobs in the first three years of a child's life. A number of these studies demonstrate a serendipitous effect of social care during pregnancy on men who were not even the recipients of it, including the study I have been responsible for at the Thomas Coram Research Unit in London[45]. This study was a randomised controlled trial of social support provided by research midwives to women at risk of delivering low birth weight infants (see *Midwives Chronicle*, March 1989). We found that men living with women who received social support in pregnancy were significantly more likely than those whose partners were not supported, to help with the shopping and other children, both in pregnancy and after delivery. Equally (but not more) seriously, our study found differences between women who had social support in pregnancy and those who did not with respect to a wide range of health indices, including use of analgesia in labour, onset of labour (spontaneous or otherwise), type of delivery, infants' postnatal health care use, and mothers' health and health-care use in pregnancy and after the birth. The greatest differences were observed for antenatal hospital admissions, babies' use of neonatal care, health problems in babies after discharge from hospital, and mothers' confidence and emotional wellbeing in the early postnatal weeks.

It is important to emphasise that our "social support" midwives gave no clinical care. When asked what they had appreciated most about this type of help, the mothers put the fact that "she listened" first; 80% of them said this was important.

WHO CARES FOR WOMEN?
THE LOGIC OF INTRAPROFESSIONAL DISPUTES

In other words, love is a scientific concept and its effects on perinatal health can be quantified. Conversely, there is much in obstetrics that claims to be science but does not have this status. Behind these differences, the motives of midwives and obstetricians are also different. The whole ideology and professional training of midwives qualifies them to care for normal women, while that of obstetricians orientates them to controlling the abnormal. Though these different qualifications would seem at first sight to constitute an excellent "package" when taken together, one problem is the psychology of what has been called the 'as if' rule. By treating all pregnant women as if they are about to become abnormal, obstetricians are inclined to make them so. On the other hand, the disposition to regard pregnant women as a normal class of beings will help to facilitate this. This would seem to be one of the key processes lying behind the findings of the studies I have referred to: midwifery care encourages the normal, both directly and by enabling women, through information and greater self confidence, to take control of their own reproductive fates.

None of this is really surprising when you consider that obstetricians are doctors and thus trained in the diagnosis and management of disease. A review by Carol Sakala[46] in the United States, of midwives' and obstetricians' attitudes to pain in childbirth, highlights this particularly clearly. Looking at published information on approaches to pain as well as empirical practice, Sakala found that, in the medical domain, pharmacological approaches to pain relief were discussed almost exclusively, while midwifery practice emphasised other ways of dealing with pain, including relaxation, massage and social support. In medical practice, relief of pain was almost obligatory, while midwives recommended relying on the mothers' individual preferences. In line with this, it is significant that in Jean Walker's[47] study of how midwives and obstetricians perceive the role of the midwife, most midwives thought midwifery different from obstetrics while most doctors thought they were the same. In the Chelsea College study, four times as many doctors as midwives claimed that doctors manage normal labour[48]. But when it comes to the question of who ought to do what, the Chelsea College study found the obstetrical claim to exclusive expertise rearing its head again: doctors do not mind midwives sewing and fixing clips on, but they do not much like the idea of midwives carrying out breech or forceps deliveries or incubating infants. Partly for this reason, the number of midwives actually performing these tasks is much lower than many midwives would like.

We hear quite a lot these days about the desire of women to receive satisfying care—but one problem is that the professionals providing the care also want to be satisfied, and the job satisfaction of obstetricians relies on a desire to control and intervene in the birth process. This is clear in studies such as Ann Cartwright's survey[49] of induction of labour, in which a majority of obstetricians said that induction rates of over 40% increase their job satisfaction. Midwives also said that increased rates of induction made obstetricians happier, but had decreased their own satisfaction. This was in contrast to the view expressed by obstetricians who claimed that increased induction had made life better for midwives as well. Doctors know best; but they know best about themselves, and not about other people.

To summarise then: first, love—caring—is as important as science—technical knowledge, monitoring and intervention—in the maternity services today. Rather than being a soft option, it is a fundamental necessity. Secondly, this can be proved (for those who wish to concern themselves with scientific proof) from published studies examining the effects of social support as distinct from clinical care. Thirdly, and consequently, the goals of satisfying mothers and producing healthy babies, which are so often deemed by obstetricians to be at odds with one another, are in reality the same goal. Fourthly, the definitions of caring given by midwives on the one hand, and obstetricians on the other, have been different and opposite from the very beginnings of their uneasy collaboration in this complex, but wonderful, business of helping babies into the world. Fifthly, midwives must do everything to reclaim this concept of care (and the rest of us must do everything we can to help them), both for the sake of women and babies and for the sake of themselves.

To end, it is appropriate to quote one definition of the kind of person a midwife is, and one mother's view of the contribution good midwives are able to make to the care of women in childbirth. The definition of a midwife is offered by Soranus, who wrote the first textbook for midwives in Rome some 18 centuries ago. Soranus identified the special qualities a midwife must possess:

She must have a good memory, he wrote, be industrious and patient, moral so as to inspire confidence; be endowed with a healthy mind and have a strong constitution; and finally she must have long delicate fingers with nails cut short[50].

The mother, delivered in Cambridge in 1987, said "I think that in a perfect world every mother should have what I had—a midwife's face that said 'look, we have performed a miracle together. (And there was nothing to it!)'"[51].

[1] Hall, M. H., Crisis in the maternity services. *Br. Med. J.* 1988, **297**: pp.500-1.

[2] Macfarlane, A., Babes not out of the wood. *The Guardian*, 1988, November 9.

[3] Brannen, J., Moss, P., *New Mothers At Work*, Unwin, London, 1988.

[4] Savage, W., *A Savage Enquiry*, Fontana Books, London, 1986.

[5] Garrigues, H. E., *A Textbook of the Science and Art of Obstetrics*, pp 211-6, J.B. Lippincott, Philadelphia, 1902.

[6] Newton, R. W., Hunt, L. P., Psychosocial stress in pregnancy and its relation to low birth weight. *Br. Med. J.* 1984, **288**: pp 1191-94; Newton, R. W., Stress & premature labour, *Br. Med. J.*,1979, Vol.2: pp.1512-3.

[7] Klaus, M.H., Kennell, J.H., Robertson,S., Sosa, R., Effects of social support on maternal and infant morbidity, *Br. Med. J.*, 1986, **293**: pp.585-87.

[8] Cited in Wertz, R. W. & Wertz, D. C., *Lying-In: A History of Childbirth in America*, Free Press, New York, 1977.

[9] Dick-Read, G., *Childbirth Without Fear*, p12, Heinemann, London, 1942.

[10] Sontag, S., *Illness as Metaphor*, Farrar, Strauss & Giroux,New York, 1977.

[11]Pfeffer, N., The hidden pathology of the male reproductive system. In: H. Homans (ed), *The Sexual Politics of Reproduction*. Cower, London, 1985.

[12] Donnison, J., *Midwives and Medicine Men*, Heinemann, London, 1977.

[13] Devitt, N., The statistical case for elimination of the midwife: fact versus prejudice 1890-1935 Part II, *Women and Health*, 1979, **4**(2), pp.169-86.

[14] Devitt, N., The statistical case for elimination of the midwife: fact versus prejudice 1890-1935 Part I, *Women and Health*, 1979, **4**(1), pp.81-96.

[15] Versluysen, M. C., Midwives, medical men and 'poor women labouring of child': lying-in hospitals in the 18th century. In: H. Roberts (ed) *Women, Health & Reproduction*, Routledge & Kegan Paul, London, 1981.

[16] DeLee J. B., *Progress towards ideal obstetrics. Transactions of the American Association for the Study and Prevention of Infant Mortality*, 1915, **6**: pp.114-38.

[17] Devitt, 1979.

[18] Donegan, J. B., *Women and Men Midwives*, Greenwood Press, Westport, Conn., 1978.

[19] Cited in Wertz and Wertz, 1977, p.137.

[20] Williams, J. W., Medical education & the midwife problem in the United States, *JAMA*, 1912, **58**: pp.1-7.

[21] Versluysen, 1981.

[22] See Oakley, A., Wisewomen & Medicine Man: changes in the management of childbirth. In: Mitchell J., Oakley A. (eds) *The Rights and Wrongs of Women*, Penguin, Harmondsworth, 1976.

[23] Cited in Towler, J., and Bramall, J., *Midwives in History and Society*, p56, Croom Helm, London, 1986.

[24] Cited in Forbes, T. R., *The Midwife & the Witch*, p117, Yale University Press, New Haven, 1966.

[25] See (eds) Enkin, M., Keirse, M., Chalmers, I., *Effective Care in Pregnancy and Childbirth*, Oxford University Press, Oxford, 1989.

[26] *Health Services in Europe*, Vol.1: WHO Regional Office for Europe, Copenhagen, 1981.

[27] ICM, FIGO, and WHO.

[28] Runnerstrom, L., The effectiveness of nurse-midwifery in a supervised hospital environment, *Bull. Am. Coll. Nurse Midwives*, 1969, **14**: pp.40-52.

[29] Slome, C., Westerbee, H., Daly, M., Christenssen, K., Meglen, M., Thiede, H., Effectiveness of certified nurse-midwives. A prospective evaluation study. *Am J Obstet Gynec*, 1976, January 15, pp.177-82.

[30] Spira, N., Audras, F., Chapel, A., Debuisson, J., Jacquelin, C., Kirchhoffer, C., Lebrun, C., Prudent, C. Domiciliary care of pathological pregnancies by midwives. Comparative controlled study on 996 women. *J Gynec Obstet Biol Reprod*, 1981, **10**: pp.543-48.

[31] Lumley, J. Review article. The prevention of preterm birth: unresolved problems and work in progress. *Aust. Paediat*, 1988, **24**: pp.101-11.

[32] Olds, D. L., Henderson, C. R., Tatelbaum, R., Chamberlin, R. Improving the delivery of prenatal care and outcomes of pregnancy: a randomized trial of nurse home visitation. *Pediatrics*, 1986, **77**: pp.16-28.

[33] Dance (unpublished) *A social intervention by linkworkers to Pakistani women & pregnancy outcome*, 1987.

[34] Nelson, N.M, Enkin, M. W., Saigal, S., Bennett, K. J., Milner, R., Sackett, D. L. A randomized clinical trial of the Leboyer approach to childbirth, *New England Journal of Medicine*, 1980, **302**, pp.655-60.

[35] Timm, M. M., Prenatal education evaluation, *Nursing Research*, 1979, **28** (6): pp.338-42.

[36] Zimmer, E. Z., Divon, M. Y., Vilensky, A., Sarna, Z., Peretz, B. A., Paldi, E. Maternal exposure to music and fetal activity, *Europ. J Obstet. Gynec, reprod. Biol*, 1982, **13**: pp.209-213.

[37] Read, M. E., Gutteridge, S., McIlwaine, G.M., *A comparison of the delivery of antenatal care between a hospital and a peripheral clinic*. Report to Health Services Research Committee, Scottish Home & Health Department, 1983.

[38] Klein, M., Papageoroiou, A., Westreich, R., Spector-Dunsky, L., Elkins, V., Kramer, M.S., Gelfand, M.M. Care in the birth room versus a conventional setting: a controlled trial. *Canadian Medical Association Journal* 1984, 131, December 15, pp.1461-66.

[39] Carpenter, S., Aldrich, K., Boverman, H., The effectiveness of patient interviews. A controlled study of emotional support during pregnancy. *Arch Gen Psychiatry*, 1968, **19**: pp.110-2.

[40] Flint, C., Poulengris, P. *The 'Know Your Midwife' Scheme*. Report published by authors. London, 1987.

[41] Lovell, A., Elbourne, D., Holding the baby - and your notes, *Health Service Journal*, 1987, March 19, p.335.

[42] Reading, A. E., Campbell, S., Cox, D. N., Sledmere, C. M., Health beliefs and health care behaviour in pregnancy, *Psychol Med.*, 1982, pp.379-83.

[43] Gordon, R. E., Gordon, K. K., Social factors in prevention of postpartum emotional problems, *Obstetrics and Gynaecology*, 1960, **15**: pp.433-8.

[44] Gutelius, M. F., Kirsch, A. D., Macdonald, S., Brooks, M. R., Mcerlean, T. M., Controlled study of child health supervision: behavioural results. *Pediatrics*, 1977, **60**: pp.294-304.

[45] Oakley, A., Rasan, L. *Social Support and the Pregnancy Outcome Study*. Paper presented at Research and the Midwife Conference, 1988.

[46] Sakala, C. Content of care by independent midwives: assistance with pain in labour and birth, *Social Science and Medicine*, 1988, 26: pp.1141-58.

[47] Walker, S. F., Midwife or obstetric nurse? Some perceptions of midwives and obstetricians of the role of the midwife. *Jn of Advanced Nursing*, 1976, 1: pp 129-138.

[48] Robinson, S., Golden, S., Bradley, S., The midwife: a developing or diminishing role? *Research and the Midwife Conference*, 1980.

[49] Cartwright, A. *The Dignity of labour? A study of childbearing and induction*. Tavistock, London, 1979.

[50] Cited in Towler and Bramall, 1986, p 15.

[51] Green, J., Coupland, V., Kitzinger, J. *Great Expectations: a prospective study of women's expectations & experiences of childbirth*. Unpublished report, Childcare & Development Group, Cambridge. 1988. p 14. (Now available as book: Josephine M Green, Vanessa A Coupland & Jenny V Kitzinger (eds) *Great Expectations: a prospective study of women's expectations and experiences of childbirth* 1998, 2nd edition. Hale, Cheshire: Books for Midwives)

ELIMINATION OF THE MIDWIFE

Charles Edward Ziegler[1]

It is most gratifying to note the interest which has been awakened in the midwife problem during the past few years. The outlook is hopeful and an attempted early solution of the question may be anticipated. The danger lies in too great haste. Either we are going to settle the matter to our credit and future welfare, or we are going to make a serious and perhaps irreparable mistake. My own feeling is that the great danger lies in the possibility of attempting to educate the midwife and in licensing her to practice midwifery, giving her thereby a legal status which later cannot perhaps be altered. If she once becomes a fixed element in our social and economic system, as she now is in the British Isles and on the Continent, we may never be able to get rid of her. I agree with Dr. E. P. Davis, that she is a "menace to the health of the community, an unnecessary evil and a nuisance," and I am, therefore, unalterably and uncompromisingly opposed to any plan which seeks to give her a permanent place in the practice of medicine. In no other branch of medicine do we permit ignorant, non-medical individuals to give counsel and assistance in medical matters. Midwifery is the most poorly done of all medical work, not alone because about 50 per cent of all labors are in the hands of midwives, but largely because of the low standards of midwifery existent among physicians and laity alike. And these standards cannot be raised so long as 50 per cent of the cases are in the hands of individuals with as poor preliminary education and as little medical training as have the midwives. The argument that large numbers of physicians do as poor obstetrics as the midwives is entirely beside the question. We are quite ready to admit this, but to claim that for this reason we must retain the midwife, if we retain the physician, is absurd. Legally the midwife has as yet practically no status and, even if she had, there can be no reason why she not be subject to the same laws and requirements as those governing all other individuals practising medicine. The fact is, as I shall attempt to point out, that we can get along very nicely without the midwife, whereas all are agreed that the physician is indispensable. It thus seems that the sensible thing to do is to train the physician until he is capable of doing good obstetrics, and then make it financially possible for him to do it, by eliminating the midwife and giving him such other support as may be necessary.

I am opposed to educating and licensing midwives to practice obstetrics in this country for several reasons; first, because I believe it unnecessary, since I am convinced that a plan can be evolved and practically applied which will give to every child-bearing woman in the country competent medical attendants; and second, because I do not believe it possible to train women of the type of even the best of midwives to practice obstetrics satisfactorily.

In this country, with its great wealth and unlimited resources, it should be, and is, unnecessary that a system should exist and be supported which seeks to give to those unable to pay for competent service a service which is incompetent and unsafe and administered by untutored, non-medical individuals. We are passing through a political, social and economic revolution which is certain to result in giving to the worthy poor justice in the necessities of life, among which must be included competent medical service administered by those who are trained in medicine. They will demand it and they are going to get it. This does not necessarily mean socialism, but it does mean social justice. Talcott Williams in speaking on "Equality of Opportunity" in this country presents some astonishing facts and figures which show that the trend of modern times is toward "equality of opportunity in all that relates to economic progress." This fact, as he points out, is apparent in the marvelous growth in savings-bank deposits, industrial and regular life-insurance and in the increased ownership of houses and lands by the common people, showing that the average citizen is coming nearer and nearer to the place where he is able to secure for himself the things of life which he needs. If equality of opportunity as regards medical service is ever to come in this country, it cannot come so long as we train one class of practitioners to care for those who can pay, and another much inferior class to care for those who cannot. If this be true, then in the name of humanity and of justice let us not give to the midwife a permanent place in the practice of medicine when we know full well that she can never render anything but a service much inferior to that of the trained physicians of the future.

The practice of obstetrics carries with it much more than standing by while the natural forces of labor complete the act as best they may. Obstetrics is an important branch of medicine, and to practice it safely and successfully implies a knowledge of general medicine, as well as a knowledge and appreciation of the physiology and pathology, the normal and the abnormal, of the child-bearing process. The function of the physician in midwifery cases is to secure for the woman the best possible preparation for her labor, to accomplish her delivery safely and to leave her, so far as possible, in good physical condition; to prepare the mother for and to teach her the importance of nursing her baby, and to do everything that is possible to bring this about. A careful physical examination of the patient in each case, a thorough knowledge of her pelvis and a careful study of her previous labors may be indispensable to the successful conduct of her approaching confinement. It will perhaps never be known how many thousands of babies are sacrificed annually at birth because nothing is known of certain deformities and abnormalities until labor is well advanced. Every intelligent physician knows how important is the routine examination of the urine during pregnancy, and yet in more than 50 per cent of all the labors occurring in this country, the urine is never examined until perhaps the woman is in convulsions. Then, too, think of the thousands of women who are annually invalided as the result of unrepaired injuries to the birth-canal and from infection, to say nothing of the many who lose their lives. Those familiar with the subject believe that this appalling condition of affairs can be very largely prevented by providing skilled medical attention before, during and after childbirth. This means that pregnancy in each case must be carefully supervised, labor scientifically conducted and the mother and baby left so far as possible in good physical condition, which cannot be accomplished by untrained, non-medical individuals like the midwives.

Another very pertinent objection to the midwife is that she has charge of 50 per cent of all the obstetric material of the country without contributing anything to our knowledge of the subject. As I shall point out, a large percentage of the cases are indispensable to the proper training of physicians and nurses in this important branch of medicine. The whole country is indebted to Williams[2] for his studies on the midwife problem in this country, he has done a great and lasting service in laying bare the facts in regard to the teaching and practice of obstetrics in this country. On the other hand, Dr. Jacobi, in his inaugural address[3] at the meeting of the American Medical Association at Atlantic City in June of this year, has taken, in my opinion, a decidedly backward step as regards both the teaching and practice of obstetrics. His recommendation that 200 schools for midwives be established in the United States is as impractical as it would be impossible of accomplishment. According to Williams, but a single medical school in the country has adequate facilities for teaching obstetrics properly to medical students. A marvelous thing will have been accomplished if, during the next fifteen or twenty years, thirty institutions similar to the Sloane Hospital in New York City are established to meet the requirements of the thirty-one medical schools needed in this country, according to Flexner. To accomplish this would require the expenditure of about thirty millions of dollars and an annual budget of more than three millions of dollars to maintain them. So much is needed before we can hope to give to the students graduating from our medical schools adequate training in obstetrics, and before we can hope to compete with the German medical schools. If then, in addition, an attempt be made to establish the 200 schools recommended by Jacobi, or 170 additional ones, using the university schools also to train midwives, as in Germany, some idea may, be gained of the utter foolishness of such a recommendation.

It is, at present, impossible to secure cases sufficient for the proper training of physicians in obstetrics, since, 75 per cent of the material otherwise available for clinical purposes is utilized in providing a livelihood for, midwives. If schools for midwives were established in all the larger cities of the country, a large number of additional cases would become necessary for training the midwives and we should soon find ourselves in the anomalous position of favoring the elimination of physicians from the practice of obstetrics, by still further depriving them of clinical material for their training, in order to provide trained midwives to supplant them. If, moreover, the money which would be necessary for establishing and maintaining 200 schools for midwives, together with what would be necessary to supervise the midwives properly in their practice afterward, were used to pay physicians and nurses to care for the midwife cases, sufficient money would be available, to say nothing of the $5,000,000 which it is estimated is collected annually by midwives in this country and which should be paid to physicians and nurses for doing the work properly.

The question in my mind is not "what shall we do with the midwife?" We are totally indifferent as to what becomes of her as compared with the very vitally important question of how we shall provide competent medical service for the hundreds of thousands of the very best of our women while they are fulfilling the sacred obligations of maternity. And in this we include all classes, for we realize that obstetrics is frequently as poorly done among, those who are able to pay for competent service as among the poor who are dependent on midwives or on public charity. The answer is to be found in providing proper training and adequate compensation for physicians and nurses who alone should do the work.

It is generally recognized that obstetric teaching in this country is woefully, deficient. There has been a dearth of great obstetric teachers with proper ideals and motives, but the deficiency in obstetric institutions and in obstetric material available for teaching purposes has been even greater. It is to-day absolutely impossible to provide material enough to give to medical students before graduation anything more than the merest smattering in practical obstetrics. So far as I have been able to learn, in all but a few medical-schools in this country, the students deliver no cases in a hospital under supervision, receive but little even in the way of demonstrations on women in labor and are sent into outpatient departments to deliver at most but a half dozen cases. When we recall that abroad the midwives are required to deliver in a hospital at least twenty cases under the most careful supervision and instruction before being allowed to practice, it is evident that the training of medical students in obstetrics in this country is a farce and a disgrace to a great nation, which in other branches or medicine holds high rank. It is then perfectly plain that the midwife cases, in large part at least, are necessary for the proper training of medical students. If for no other reason, this one alone is sufficient to justify the elimination of a large number of midwives, since the standard of obstetric teaching and practice can never be raised without giving better training to physicians.

On the other hand, it is equally plain that every woman has a right, as a citizen and as a mother, to such care during and following childbirth as shall preserve her and her children in life and health. It is not difficult to prove that this cannot be accomplished by midwives, but that it can be and is being done by students of medicine under careful supervision and by recent graduates in medicine who have been trained in well-equipped and properly conducted maternity hospitals. In the Boston Lying-In Dispensary, for example, about 2,000 consecutive cases of labor have been conducted by medical students without a single maternal death and similar records are to be found all over the country where maternity dispensaries exist.

I believe that the midwife should be eliminated as rapidly as possible, but I do not believe that this can be accomplished at once or perhaps even very rapidly. Legislation will not eliminate the midwife, unless hand in hand with such legislation provision is made to take her place. While a substitute is being provided she must be supervised in her work. She should, however, not be given a license but should be given a certificate to be renewed from time to time or canceled as deemed advisable under the circumstances. Licensing her will not add to her knowledge and will not make her more efficient, but will place on the state permanent responsibility for her work. No attempt should be made to establish schools for midwives since, in my opinion, they are to be endured in ever decreasing numbers, while substitutes are being created to displace them.

Our present system of caring for the so-called "charity cases" is entirely wrong and this does not apply to midwifery cases only. Our charities are for the most part but poorly investigated and supervised and are inefficiently administered. Much of this charity is not legitimate and the cost is unjustly distributed. Physicians have been called on to do much more than their share. There is not the slightest reason why the physician should give his professional services without pay, as it is no more his business to administer without compensation to the dependent and sick poor than that of any other citizen. The fact that he is especially fitted so to serve them does not in any wise alter the situation. The poor when ill are the state's charges, just as much as when they must be fed, clothed and sheltered, and the state should minister to the needs in one case just as much as in the other. Until physicians are justly compensated for their services to the poor, the poor will not receive adequate medical attention. In the long run individuals receive just about the service to which they are entitled by the compensation provided. This is just as true in medicine as in any other field of endeavor, and so far as I can see there is not the slightest reason why it should not be. Public charities of all kinds should be placed on a strictly business basis, should be well organized, thoroughly supervised and all the workers should be justly compensated.

The placing of the burden of medical service to the poor on physicians, without compensation, has led them to seek in return excessive fees from those who can pay, with the result that much harm has been done to the cause of medicine. The practice of medicine has been thereby converted into a trade, and commercialism has destroyed much of its higher and finer side and has done untold harm in the attitude which the public should have toward the physician and the schools which educate him. And for this the leaders of the profession, the teachers of medicine, have been largely responsible. They have frequently used their professorial appointments for personal profit, prostituting the ideals of medicine to their greed for gold and "exploiting their patients at the expense of the entire profession." This does not apply to the so-called laboratory men, who have worked on modest salaries and yet have shown an unselfish devotion and enthusiasm which have astonished the whole world and who have contributed practically the only knowledge in medicine which has been worth while. Such men as Koch, Behring, Ehrlich, Flexner and a score of others are striking examples of medical men who have done a lasting service to humanity without levying a tribute on it and stand out in striking contrast, for example, to an equal number of American surgeons whose very work has been made possible only through that of the laboratory workers but who, unlike them, have demanded from their patients unreasonable and dishonest fees for no other reason than that they had the opportunity for doing so. No one questions the justice of the man of means paying in accordance with his ability toward the medical care of the dependent poor and that on this basis the burden should be equitably distributed, but it is the business of the state to collect such moneys for the purpose and not the business of private persons to levy tribute on individuals of means on the plea that they are serving the poor without pay. The state should pay the physician adequately for all his services to the poor and should collect by taxes from all the people their just share of the money necessary to care for its charges.

In medical charities economy and efficiency are all important and can best be secured when such charities are utilized for teaching purposes. Since patients in teaching institutions receive the best possible attention at the least possible cost to the state, medical education and medical service to the poor should go hand in hand. Both are matters for the state rather than for private individuals and the state should therefore see that each contributes to the other all that is possible. It is not generally appreciated that medical schools should be first of all educational institutions rather than medical institutions, that they should, moreover, be public service organizations and exist for the public good, as do other educational institutions and that the teacher of medicine should be an educator in the highest sense of the term and should stand in the closest relationship to all the problems of medical education, medical practice, eugenics and social service. He should spend his life, therefore, as a public servant and should use his calling and the innumerable possibilities and opportunities which go with it, not to enrich himself at the expense of the profession but to serve his generation in all that pertains to the public good. For all these reasons medical schools should be liberally supported by the state, as in Germany, where medical education and medical service have reached their greatest development. The number of medical schools should be limited to the actual needs of the country, and medical teachers should be put on liberal salaries and should be required to devote their entire time to teaching, research and the care of hospital and dispensary patients. Until this is done, it will not be possible to prevent many medical teachers from seeking and obtaining professorial appointments for the purpose of advancing their own personal interests.

But, you may ask, what has all this to do with the subject of my paper? This much, that men and women of influence and of means will never contribute all that is necessary in money, and in legislation to medical education and medical charities, until they have more confidence in the ideals and motives of those who administer them. And this brings up a very important matter which cannot be neglected in such a discussion as this, namely: the administration of medical charities—hospitals and dispensaries. Each supplements the work of the other and if properly coordinated they cover, without conflict, the entire field of medical service to the poor. Each is therefore indispensable and each has its legitimate field. In so far as they care for the state's charges, they should be supported by the state, the one just as much as the other. All patients applying for care either should be rigidly investigated and required to pay to the extent of their ability. To this class belong all patients who are unable to pay adequate physicians' fees, whether they can pay all, a part or none of the cost to the hospital or dispensary of caring for them. In this investigation all the facts should be taken into consideration—the size of the family, the income and cost of living, the actual legitimate earning capacity of the family; while the physical health and mental equipment must not be overlooked. If the income, whatever it be, is entirely needed for the necessities of life, it ought not to be used to pay physicians' fees. Such individuals cannot, therefore, be looked on as of any legitimate financial value to the physician, to whom their care by hospitals and dispensaries should give no cause for offense. The manifest and professed purpose of the science and art of medicine is the prevention and cure of disease. The physician exists therefore for the benefit of the patient and not the patient for the benefit of the physician; and the solution of this matter will not be reached until this fact is fully appreciated and until it governs our attitude toward providing medical service for the dependent poor. Any system, therefore, which does not provide the most economical service consistent with essential efficiency is wrong. On the other hand, physicians should not be criticized for not giving medical service gratuitously to such patients; on the contrary, they should be paid for their services to the poor, and this applies with equal force to nurses and social workers.

In Pennsylvania, the hospitals and dispensaries are paid by the state to the extent of the difference between what it costs to care for their patients and the receipts secured from them and from private gifts. This is as it should be.

Staff physicians in hospitals and dispensaries, who are given a monopoly of clinical material and therefore possess exceptional opportunity for the development of skill and the establishment of a reputation, should not be allowed to use their positions to gain a monopoly over private patients as well. This is the great evil of the present hospital system and can be prevented only by putting staff physicians and their assistants on salaries, and requiring them to devote their entire time to the work of the hospital, to research and to teaching. In the larger cities where medical schools exist, all patients for whom the state is responsible, or as many therefore as may be necessary, should be cared for in the hospitals in which the staff positions are held by the members or the medical faculties. In this way a tremendous amount of clinical material would become available for teaching purposes, and students and practitioners of medicine would be given an opportunity of securing any desired amount of training in chosen branches of medicine, while the patients themselves would receive the most efficient service at a minimum cost to the state. Nothing would be taken from the physicians in the way of income, their opportunities for advanced medical training would be much increased and the medical heads of such hospitals would become invaluable public assets as teachers, investigators and consultants. The salaries of the staff physicians and of the clinical members of the medical faculties could be provided, if necessary, by fees from the necessary number of private patients.

The vast majority of private patients should, however, be cared for in private hospitals supported by private and corporate capital. No one objects to any physician making all the money to which his skill and reputation entitle him, but he has no right to do so on the investments of public moneys.

From what has been said it would appear that the elimination of the midwife is to be brought about in time through the establishment of obstetric charities consisting of maternity hospitals and maternity dispensaries with all that goes with them in the form of social service, visiting nurses, prenatal work, relief work, etc. The hospital is to care for all who, for one reason or another, cannot secure proper attention at home, and the dispensary for those who are delivered at home. The majority of women will always be cared for at home, and it is desirable that they should be when conditions permit it. A mother with a number of children cannot usually leave them to advantage, and while it is true that physically she cannot and should not care for them, her presence in the home is necessary to order and discipline. Then, too, the cost of caring for patients in hospitals is much greater than in their own homes. Dispensary patients, moreover, are more likely to do for themselves all that they are able to do and thus be not so entirely dependent on help. Both the hospital and dispensary should be in charge of one head in the form of a medical director and, in medical canters, both institutions should be a part of, or closely affiliated with, a medical school.

In cities of the first and second class, especially where medical schools exist, the midwife can in time be entirely eliminated through the establishment and extension of obstetric charities—hospitals and dispensaries. The vast majority of patients who are unable to pay physicians can be cared for by medical students, provided the requirements for graduation are increased so as to give students the necessary training, in obstetrics.

My own feeling is that before going into private practice each student should be required to deliver personally not less than fifty cases under careful supervision, and should also be taught to do on the living subject all the obstetric operations which the granting of his diploma gives him license to perform, as I hold that, it is little less than criminal to permit practitioners of medicine to jeopardize the life and health of human beings by performing on them operations which they had not done and perhaps had never seen performed in their student days. The average practitioner who gains his experience in obstetrics by operating solely on his own responsibility rarely, if ever, learns to do it safely, and therefore always remains a menace to his patients, and should he eventually become an accomplished operator, his knowledge has been gained at the cost of much invalidism and of a number of deaths. My argument, therefore, is that if he must acquire the knowledge, it is much better that he should do so under careful supervision and instruction. The public should learn that it is the duty of every citizen, if for no other reason than that of the safety of his own family, to insist that students of medicine be not only supplied with clinical material, but that they be required to utilize it in acquiring the knowledge which is indispensable to efficiency in the practice of obstetrics. If the midwife cases and such others as are dependent on public charity were used for teaching purposes, not only would the patients themselves receive excellent care but also sufficient clinical material would be available to give every graduate in medicine such obstetric training as would make him a safe and efficient practitioner.

In the larger cities, therefore, maternity hospitals and maternity dispensaries, properly, co-ordinated, well equipped and efficiently, conducted, offer the sane and logical solution of the midwife problem. In the smaller cities and towns the problem is somewhat more difficult, but even there it can be very largely handled by utilizing as maternity dispensary stations the many small hospitals, which are being established so rapidly all over the country. By increasing the annual hospital budget to include such dispensary service, all patients unable to pay physicians, including also the vast majority of midwife cases, could be provided for at a very reasonable cost per patient. In this way the pupil nurses in such hospitals could be given the training in obstetric nursing which is now so generally required for the registration of graduate nurses, while the medical service could be very largely supplied by recent graduates in medicine serving as interns in such hospitals, and thereby acquiring, under proper supervision, invaluable experience in operative obstetrics. In the rural and other districts where there are no hospitals and where there will always exist a lack of medical practitioners, the midwife must continue her work, "doubly dangerous" because of the scarcity of physicians, unless the state places a higher value than heretofore on human life and health and comes to the rescue. On this point, I am in entire agreement with Professor Pritchett of the Carnegie Foundation in saying that "a sanitary service, subsidized by the state, will alone render efficient relief in backward districts without demoralizing the profession."

In attempting to secure certain data with regard to midwives in several of the large cities, I have been much disappointed. In Boston, for example, with 18,000 births reported last year, it is not known how many midwives there are or how many cases are delivered by them, although birth registration is compulsory. As Boston has a much smaller percentage of foreign-born population than Pittsburgh, it would seem fair, on the basis of Pittsburgh statistics, to estimate that the number of cases cared for in Boston by midwives and dispensaries combined would not exceed 30 per cent. As the dispensaries care for about 19 per cent, the midwives probably deliver not over 11 per cent or 1,980 cases.

In New York City, according to Dr. Baker, 51.996 births, or 40 per cent of the total number in 1911, were in the hands of about 1.300 midwives. In Philadelphia, in 1911, the estimated number of births was 44,000 and the actual number registered was 40,066, of which latter number, 21.09 per cent or 8,450, were delivered by 194 midwives. In Baltimore, in 1911, there were but 9,283 reported births, showing very incomplete returns. On the basis of the United States Census Reports, the annual birth-rate for Baltimore should be about 17,000 and if the midwives deliver 50 per cent of this number they care for about 8,500 cases. The number of registered midwives in Baltimore is 162.

There were 15,422 reported births in Pittsburgh in 1911, of which 4,864, or 31.53 per cent, were delivered by 150 midwives. Of 12,839 births reported in Cleveland from July 1, 1911, to July 1, 1912, 5,127, or 40 per cent., were in the hands of 266 midwives.

In Chicago, registration is not compulsory so that complete statistics are not available. Dr. Henry G. Ohls, who has gone over the records of all births reported between Jan. 1 and July 1, 1912, gives the first reliable birth statistics, as far as they go. He finds in the total of 19,939 births reported during the six months that 43.55 per cent, or 8,445, were in the hands of an unknown number of midwives. Dr. Ohls estimates the number of births in Chicago for 1912 to be 57,438. On the basis of his statistics, 50 per cent, or 28,719, ought to be a fair estimate of the number of cases delivered by midwives.

On the basis of the number of students graduating annually (1911-12) from the combined medical schools in Boston, New York, Philadelphia, Baltimore, Pittsburgh, Cleveland and Chicago, it is interesting to see to what extent the midwife cases in these cities could be handled by students alone.

In the data given, it would appear that in some instances, at least, not all of the cases credited to undergraduate students were actually delivered by them, since many of the deliveries were most probably demonstration cases, observed collectively by a number of students, while the actual delivery was being conducted by one of their number under supervision. Then, too, in certain cities, large numbers of cases are delivered by graduate physicians doing postgraduate work and their cases are also included among those credited to undergraduate students. These facts doubtless account, to some extent at least, for the great difference in the number of cases reported as delivered by students in the different cities, and must be taken into consideration in interpreting the following figures. In this study it is estimated that, if midwives did not exist, at least 25 per cent of the patients now under their care could afford to and would employ physicians.

1. Boston: Number of students, 190; cases delivered by students in outpatient departments, 3,500 (19 per cent.); midwife cases, 1,980 (11 per cent.). Cases credited to each student, 18, and 10 additional to handle the midwife cases, or a total of 28 cases per student.
2. Philadelphia: Number of students, 437; cases delivered by students in outpatient departments, 2,566; midwife cases (less 25 per cent.), 6,318. Cases credited to each student, 6, and 15 additional to handle the midwife cases, or a total of 21 cases per student.
3. Baltimore: Number of students, 334; cases delivered by students in outpatient departments, 1,746; midwife cases (less 25 per cent.), 6,375. Cases credited to each student, 5, and 19 additional to handle the midwife cases, or a total of 24 cases per student.
4. Pittsburgh: Number of students, 66; cases delivered by students in the hospital and dispensary 264; midwife cases (less 25 per cent.), 3,648. Cases credited to each student, 4, and 55 additional to care for the midwife cases, or a total of 59 cases per student.
5. Cleveland: Number of students, 66; cases delivered by students in outpatient departments, 605; midwife cases (less 25 per cent.), 3,845. Cases credited to each student, 9, and 58 additional to care for the midwife cases, or a total of 67 cases per student.
6. Chicago: Number of students, 608; cases delivered by students in outpatient departments, 1,927; midwife cases (less 25 per cent.), 21,540. Cases credited to each student, 3, and 35 additional to handle the midwife cases, or a total of 38 cases per student.
7. New York City: Number of students, 325; cases delivered by students, 3,780; midwife cases (less 25 per cent.), 38,997. Cases credited to each student, 12, and 120 additional to handle the midwife cases, or a total of 132 cases per strident. If the students delivered 50 cases each or a total of 16,250, there would still remain 26,527 cases to be cared for, so that in New York City at least, it would seem that the midwives must do a large part of the work for some time to come, unless the city or state does a considerable part of the work through dispensaries employing physicians and nurses on salaries. At the same time this would not be so much of an undertaking as it at first appears, since fully 50 per cent of the 38,997 midwife cases could pay to dispensaries, as they now pay to midwives, $10 each and the remainder could pay at least $5 each, the minimum mid-wife fee in New York City. If the midwives were eliminated in New York City, all their cases could be handled through maternity dispensaries for an additional expenditure of not over $100,000 a year, provided such dispensaries received as much in fees as the midwives now do.

I shall conclude my paper with the plan which we have adopted for the solution of the midwife question in Pittsburgh.

It will perhaps he best appreciated what the Pittsburgh plan is when I say that it is, in its development, the concrete expression of the views set forth in this paper. If the recommendations which have been made appear visionary and impracticable, it must be remembered that a number of them are already in operation in Pittsburgh and are working out beautifully and that we fully expect to carry out the entire scheme within the next half dozen years.

About three and a half millions of dollars are available for the building, equipment and endowment of a woman's hospital to be built in Pittsburgh during the coming year; and the sum of $50,000 has already been subscribed, from an entirely different source, for the maintenance of a maternity dispensary which was opened about six months ago.

The hospital, which is the first of its kind to be established in this country, has been modeled largely after the well-known *Frauenkliniker* of Germany and will therefore care for both obstetric and gynecologic cases. Abraham Flexner, in his "Medical Education in Europe," expresses exactly the point of view which we have taken for years and which now finds its expression in the new Magee Hospital. He says, in speaking of the German clinics for women, that "the women's clinic combines obstetric and gynecologic wards. Separation into two specialties tends to make a midwife of the obstetrician and an abdominal surgeon of the gynecologist, to the neglect of the fundamental pathologic and physiologic problems in both cases. Consolidation avoids the necessity of drawing arbitrary lines by way of making two specialties where Nature has made but one: for obstetrics and gynecology have a single physiologic and anatomic point of departure, namely the child-bearing function."

The new hospital will have accommodations for 125 adult patients in the wards and twenty-five private rooms. It is peculiarly well adapted for teaching purposes, having an operating and teaching amphitheatre, a number of examining rooms, delivery rooms and recovery rooms, research laboratories, a medical library, museum and the necessary offices and other rooms for the medical director and his assistants. There are also rooms for photography, x-ray and hydrotherapeutic departments and an isolation department for infected cases, with the necessary operating and sterilizing rooms. In the private pavilion there is a private gynecologic operating room, several private delivery and recovery rooms, a cystoscopy room, etc. The institution will be erected in the center of a ten-acre plot of ground and will be surrounded by a number of separated and isolated gardens for private patients, ward patients, nurses, physicians, etc.

The medical director of the hospital is also professor of obstetrics in the University of Pittsburgh. He resides with his family on the hospital grounds, is paid a salary sufficiently large to make him independent of private practice and to enable him to devote all his time to the work of the hospital, to research and teaching. All fees received from private patients go into the hospital treasury.

The Pittsburgh Maternity Dispensary, within two blocks of the Magee Hospital, is closely affiliated with the hospital, having the same directing head. It is located in two large houses of twelve rooms each and has dormitory accommodations for a dozen physicians and students, as many nurses and social workers, in addition to the dispensary rooms proper. The present staff of workers consists of a social worker, two graduate physicians, and three graduate nurses, all on salaries and devoting their entire time to the work of the dispensary; also a number of medical students. The number of workers will be increased as the growth of the work demands it.

The present hospital, housed in temporary quarters, will care for about 350 cases of labor during the present year and we expect to care for as many more cases in the dispensary during the first year of its existence, or a total of 700 cases, all available for teaching purposes. Our senior medical students, forty-five in number, will during the present year witness at least fifteen deliveries each, of which number each student will personally deliver six cases under constant supervision and instruction, three in the hospital and three in the dispensary.

The work in Pittsburgh is young, but the outlook is most promising and we feel that we have in the combination of hospital and dispensary, both teaching institutions, the solution of the midwife problem. And what can be done in Pittsburgh can be done in every other large city in the country. The creation of obstetric charities, such as I have attempted to describe, and the education of the people will, in time, make the midwife unnecessary and her elimination inevitable.

Forbes and Halket Streets.

[1] Professor of Obstetrics in the University of Pittsburgh and Medical, Director of the Elizabeth Steel Magee Hospital, Pittsburgh. Read before the American Association for Study & Prevention of Infant Mortality at the Annual Meeting in Cleveland, October, 1912.
   Journal of the American Medical Association, **60** (1913): 32-38
[2] Williams, J. Whitridge: Medical Education and the Midwife Problem in the US *J.A.M.A.*, Jan. 6, 1912, p.1.
[3] Jacobi, A.: The Best means of Combating Infant Mortality, *J.A.M.A.*, June 8, 1912, p.1735.

THE EUROPEAN MIDWIFE

Irvine Loudon[*]

If we put ourselves in the position of a perceptive traveller with an interest in midwifery who toured through north-west Europe and Britain in the 1820s, we would have found that everywhere there were medical practitioners, whether they called themselves men-midwives, accoucheurs, or obstetricians, who regularly attended normal as well as abnormal deliveries. Obstetrics was still a relatively new medical discipline which was awarded an honourable position by the medical profession in some countries and denigrated in others. We would also have found lying-in hospitals, some as separate institutions, others as departments of general hospitals. In England, but probably nowhere else, we would have noted a number of thriving out-patient lying-in charities[1]. But the most striking difference would have been that between British and the Continental midwives.

Almost everywhere on the Continent we would have noted that midwives were licensed by the state or local government. Licensing was still concerned with recruiting the 'right' sort of woman. But there was greater emphasis on training and regulation than there had been in the eighteenth century. Midwifery in the limited sense of the practice of midwives had become a profession, or at the very least a skilled and respected craft or trade.

Nevertheless, the traditional untrained midwife—the *Jordgumma* of Sweden and the handywoman of England—still existed. As far as I know, no European country had succeeded in outlawing the traditional midwife who was often preferred because she was cheaper, or more familiar (she might be one of a long line of mothers and daughters well known for delivering babies), or because she was not too grand to help with menial tasks and the housework after the baby was born (which in most normal home confinements was always the prime consideration for lying-in women), and sometimes simply because women disliked being 'bossed-about' in their own home by someone in a position of authority. All of these were important practical points.

Nevertheless, over a long period of time the traditional midwife on the Continent was replaced by the trained midwife. Because it was a prolonged process, I suspect—but do not really know—that it was a relatively painless one. It is not too fanciful to say that on the Continent the licensed midwife and licensed obstetrician grew up together from infancy to adulthood. In the 1820s there were still many traditional midwives in rural areas, working beside and competing with, the trained and licensed midwives. But in large cities there would have been a larger proportion of trained midwives—the *sage femmes première classe* of Paris for instance—who were influential, powerful, responsible, and formidable women.

Touring through England we would have found a very different state of affairs. Normal deliveries had to a large extent become the province of medical practitioners, especially the surgeon-apothecaries who were now becoming known as the general practitioners[2]. The midwives of England had no formal training and no licensing, not even by the church, let alone the state or local government[3]. Almost to a man, English medical practitioners would have told us that the majority of midwives were dirty, ignorant, and incompetent and confined in their practice to patients too poor to pay a doctor's fee. The minority of better-class midwives were either employed by doctors as maternity nurses when they were strictly confined to

* Death in Childbirth: An International Study of Maternal Care & Maternal Mortality 1800-1950 Section from chapter 23, pages 423-7

nursing care, or they found employment in the hospitals or lying-in charities where they usually received some sort of training.

Why did Britain in the early nineteenth century fail to license and regulate midwives along the lines of the Continent? Were there any opportunities for doing so? There were, and the most important was in 1812 when the Association of Apothecaries and Surgeon-Apothecaries drew up a plan to regulate the medical profession which became a Parliamentary bill. At the insistence of the Colleges of Physicians and Surgeons, the bill was subjected to radical revision and finally reached the statute book as the Apothecaries Act of 1815[4].

One of the items in the original bill was the licensing of midwives. Here, however, the motive was self-interest. The emphasis was not on training but on the outlawing and prosecution of untrained midwives so that there would be a small number of licensed midwives firmly under the thumbs of the doctors. This plan, which was linked to a proposal to outlaw the quacks or irregular practitioners with whom the midwives were bracketed, was dropped at an early stage. It was impossible to outlaw quacks, and impossible to outlaw midwives at a time when they were delivering at least half the mothers in the kingdom.

In Britain, the absence of any plans to train and license midwives until the late nineteenth century was due to the indifference of the medical establishment and the opposition of general practitioners. The control of medical practice in Britain was mediated through bodies such as the General Medical Council. The Council was dominated by the medical corporations, and the corporations were dominated by physicians and surgeons who were for the most part indifferent or hostile to obstetrics, and much more concerned with the quality of nurses than midwives. The main opposition came from the general practitioners who, with a contrariness which has marked the politics of general practitioners to the present day, had changed their ground between 1812 and the end of the century. Once the licensing of midwives became a genuine possibility, they took fright and opposed the plans on the grounds that the trained midwife would be a much more dangerous form of opposition than the untrained; as indeed proved to be the case.

When, after a long uphill struggle, the Midwives Act of 1902 was introduced, it was unable to produce overnight a system such as that which had developed in the Netherlands, Sweden, and Denmark over a period of many years. For pragmatic reasons England was forced to license untrained women already in practice, the 'bona fides'[5]. Moreover, midwifery was seen as a branch of nursing rather than a profession *sui generis*. Many who sat for the certificate of midwifery did so to further their careers as nurses and never practised as midwives[6].

It might be argued that the nurse-midwife was a better article than the plain midwife. Mary Breckinridge[7] believed as much and it was probably true in rural areas. On the other hand, the subordination of midwifery to nursing (the exact opposite to the Netherlands and Denmark), the lateness of introducing state licensing, and the millstone round the neck in the form of the bona fides from 1902 to the late 1920s, prevented the British from developing a profession of midwives comparable in quality to that seen on the Continent until the 1930s; and by that time in most Western countries the move from home to hospital deliveries was already well under way.

I think my argument that there were much greater differences between Britain and the United States on the one hand and European countries on the other in the development of midwives than there were in the development of care provided by medical practitioners and lying-in hospitals is probably true. If it is, the crucial question is whether trained midwives made for better and safer childbirth. It may seem silly to ask such a question for which an affirmative answer seems self-evident. After all, systems of training and licensing midwives were introduced to provide a better system of maternal care. But that was not their only purpose. To many practitioners licensing was a means of keeping the midwife in a subordinate position and limiting her activities. The Swedish midwife was allowed to use instruments: but when she did she had to write a report justifying their use: Swedish doctors did not. Relationships between doctors and midwives in countries like Denmark may have been cordial, but it was a relationship which was based on medical dominance.

To return to the question of the effectiveness, of if you like, the safety of the trained midwife. We have already seen favourable evidence in this chapter in the case of Swedish midwives in the mid-nineteenth century. And in previous chapters there was the further evidence such as the Kentucky Frontier Nursing Service, the Queen's Institute nurse-midwives in Britain, and the out-patient lying-in charities which depended largely on the midwives trained by those institutions. In fact, throughout the years I have spent on this study, I have found—and it was not a finding I expected—that wherever a city, a county, a region, or a nation, had developed a system of maternal care which was firmly based on a body of trained, licensed, regulated, and respected midwives (especially when the midwives worked in close and cordial co-operation with doctors and lying-in hospitals) the standard of maternal care was at its highest and maternal mortality was at its lowest. I cannot think of an exception to that rule. Whether as a consequence the record of maternal care on the Continent of Europe was better than it was in Britain or America is a conclusion which must follow consideration of deliveries by European doctors and European lying-in hospitals.

[1] Léon le Fort undertook such a tour in the mid-19th century in order to write his memorable work Des maternités (Paris, 1866), and remarked that out-patient maternity charities were a peculiarity of British maternal care.

[2] Loudon, Medical Care and the General Practitioner: 1750-1850 (Oxford, 1986).

[3] Except in the very limited sense that some midwives and nurses were employed by the poor law authorities and their being chosen was a sort of official recognition.

[4] Loudon, Medical Care and the General Practitioner, 152-70.

[5] Loudon, Death in Childbirth: An International Study of Maternal Care & Maternal Mortality 1800-1950 (Oxford, 1992), chapter 13.

[6] R. Dingwall, A.M. Rafferty, & C. Webster, An Introduction to the Social History of Nursing (London, 1988), 169.

[7] Loudon, Death in Childbirth, chapter 18.

INTERVIEW WITH PROFESSOR GERRIT-JAN KLOOSTERMAN

Rineke van Daalen & Reinie van Goor [†]

Gerrit-Jan Kloosterman has an almost legendary reputation, not only in the Netherlands, but also in international circles of obstetricians. He is an obstetrician himself, but he also ardently defends the Dutch obstetric system, with its division between normal deliveries at home attended by midwives and pathological deliveries in hospitals attended by obstetricians. This point of view makes Kloosterman a lonely figure among specialist colleagues abroad and, to a much lesser degree, in the Netherlands, where almost 90 percent of the obstetricians accept his view that healthy women must have a free choice between hospital and home delivery. His advocacy of home birth causes him to be reviled by champions of advanced technology, but makes him a favorite among those who want to improve primary care and preserve home birth and autonomous midwives.

Kloosterman was born in 1915 and completed his medical studies in 1947. In that year, he came to Amsterdam, where he was appointed director of the School for Midwives. Ten years later, he became professor in obstetrics and gynecology at the University of Amsterdam, a position he held until 1983. In the last few years of his professorship, he became increasingly concerned with the Dutch obstetric system, especially in preserving home birth. His concern for good prenatal care to improve ways of screening for low- and high-risk pregnancies is thus quite understandable. His ideas have not only influenced obstetricians and gynecologists in Amsterdam and in the Netherlands in general, but they have also been attended to in other countries. He became Fellow and *ad eundem* of the Royal College of Obstetricians and Gynaecologists and Honorary Fellow of the American College of Obstetricians and Gynecologists.

His views are based on trust in nature and respect for the preferences of the woman. The first part, the trust in nature, is allied with great curiosity for the physiology of pregnancy and birth and with a reserved, critical attitude towards new medical inventions and interventions. Respect for the woman's preferences is reflected in Kloosterman's interest in the psycho-social aspects of his profession. This interest manifested itself in attention to the psychosomatic aspects of pain during birth. It has led him to be active in supporting a woman's right to have an abortion since 1967.

BECOMING AN OBSTETRICIAN

I was born in a humanistically oriented family in Arnhem, a town in the eastern part of the Netherlands. I started to study medicine because I was interested in people, the most fascinating and

---

[†] In: Eva Abraham-Van der Mark (ed.), *Successful Home Birth & Midwifery: The Dutch Model*, Bergin & Garvey: Westport, Connecticut, 1993.

incomprehensible part of Creation. I felt less attracted by studies that dealt only with dead nature. My interest in people had both physical and spiritual aspects. A human being must be perceived as a totality.

Originally I wanted to become a generalist, a general practitioner somewhere in the countryside. That work would give me the opportunity to practice all the different aspects of the study of medicine. Attending at deliveries was at that time an important part of a general practitioner's work. He must be well prepared to give obstetric assistance in rural districts. After completion of my medical study in Utrecht, I decided to spend one year at the university clinic for obstetrics and gynecology (with Professor K. de Snoo). Soon I became so absorbed in that specialty and its scientific aspects that I stayed seven years and became a gynecologist. I wrote my thesis in that field, on the subject of the rhesus factor and polylethality.

IN SUPPORT OF THE MIDWIFE

I came to the School for Midwives not because I loved the midwife, but because I loved the profession. It was my scientific interest that led my teacher to encourage me to apply for the function of Director of the Amsterdam School for Midwives. In those days that position represented a move in the direction of a scientific career. Directors of schools for midwives were "sub-professors," who not only practiced what they had learned at the university, but tried to advance the profession further. I was especially attracted by that combination.

The School for Midwives in Amsterdam was one of the three institutes for the education and training for midwives. These institutes were obstetrical and gynecological hospitals, responsible for more than a thousand deliveries a year and a large number of gynecological operations. Fifty pupil midwives worked for three years as interns in that hospital and attended twenty hours of weekly theoretical and practical instruction in the delivery room, the wards, and the incubator room.

The midwife schools were relatively isolated from obstetric science and had little affiliation with developments in the medical world. I was afraid that this isolation would make them second-rate institutions. In 1956, I suggested to the Amsterdam Municipality that the School for Midwives should be integrated in a well-equipped municipal hospital, but it took twenty years before this integration was finally arranged. Now the schools for midwives in Heerlen and Rotterdam have also been integrated in hospitals. In my opinion, this association with hospitals was their salvation. It is only possible to work at a top level when there are laboratories at your disposal, and when you cooperate with surgeons, specialists for internal diseases, pediatricians, and bacteriologists.

Dutch midwives have kept their relatively strong position because they are legally qualified to practice obstetrics autonomously since the Health Law of 1865. They were never classified as nurses or as paramedical personnel as they are in neighboring countries. At their examination, the Dutch midwives' oath to practice obstetrics to the best of their knowledge and ability is a more restricted version of the one physicians take in medicine, surgery, and obstetrics. The medical world in 1865 was of the opinion that the midwife should not be subordinate to doctors, but should work at their side. She could and can see part of the profession of medicine as her own.

But as prosperity rose and the number of doctors increased, doctors began to take over the work of midwives. They pretended they could do that work better. Some physicians wanted to keep rich patients for themselves and sent the needy ones to the midwife, who became the doctor for the poor. This situation changed in the second half of the twentieth century, at least in the Netherlands. Although it amazed some people, I referred women with a normal pregnancy to a midwife. The wealthy husband of a client whom I referred to a midwife in the 1950s was highly indignant about my advice and cried: "How can I explain to my friends that I send my wife to a midwife? They will think that I try to economize at her expense". Since then I have always stressed the fact that the midwife is not meant as a help to the poor, but as a protector to the healthy.

There have always been people who saw the potential of the midwife, but only in the Netherlands has the potential been realized. We have continually updated the knowledge and experience of the midwife. As far as preventive measures are concerned, we enable midwives to use the most recent advances in obstetric science.

Until the end of the nineteenth century, midwives, like doctors, only attended during the birth. When the importance of prenatal care became clear, midwives also received the right to care for a pregnant woman, first from the twenty-sixth week, later from the start of the pregnancy. Only if there is pathology must a midwife refer clients to an obstetrician.

When I was director of the School for Midwives, I was instrumental in getting the law passed permitting midwives to repair a tear in the perineum. When syphilis tests, blood tests, and rhesus factor tests became part of pre-natal care, some people said: "You cannot leave that to midwives." I said: "I do not know any reason why midwives could not perform such tests. Doctors do not test the blood themselves; they, too, send it to a laboratory. It does not make any difference if the sample has been taken by a physician or by a midwife". Actually, there are no scientific or rational arguments for a doctor's monopoly in these respects. In my view, that is only an artificial way of relegating the midwife to a subordinate role. Finally the law was altered in 1955, and some time later, midwives were allowed to give local anesthesia. Whenever advances in knowledge and technology threatened to leave the midwife behind, we adjusted her qualifications so that she had access to all methods of preventive medicine, including ultrasound.

TRUST IN NATURE

Respect for nature, that is characteristic for Dutch obstetrics. The old ideas of Hippocrates about natural healing power are often practiced in the Netherlands, even in obstetrics. "Masterly expectancy" was a typically English catchword, which was very important at a delivery. There were always warnings against impatience. A well-known nineteenth-century German professor, Ahlfelt, recommended to his pupils to leave their forceps at home. If they needed them, they could go home and get them; in the meantime the baby was often born. While his recommendation was given in many nineteenth-century textbooks, in the Netherlands it was really practiced. This trust in nature when dealing with medical issues is an important feature of the Dutch culture.

After World War II this mentality changed, especially under the influence of Western obstetricians who are impressive when handling pathology but sometimes abuse their possibilities. In many highly developed countries, 25 percent of the pregnant women deliver with a Caesarean section, and once a Caesarean section has been done, it often means Caesarean sections for later births. In the Netherlands, this is not necessarily the case. If there is no indication for a Caesarean section in the next pregnancy, the woman will have her baby in the normal way. It can be said that there is a Dutch obstetric tradition in the sense that practicing technology is not that pivotal. An ordinary healthy woman with a normal pregnancy is essentially able to look after herself. We take this as our basic assumption.

In the United States, in Sweden, and in England much effort is devoted to arranging a painless birth. Lately, a group of English members of Parliament visited one of the academic hospitals in Amsterdam. To my great surprise, they suggested that the fact that so many Dutch women had their babies spontaneously, without any anesthesia, was related to our Calvinism. The Calvinist view is to give birth to children in sorrow. The Dutch would keep anesthesia from women in labor because of the Old Testament. That idea never occurred to me before. It is an interesting viewpoint, but it is not mine. It is obvious that we try to make childbirth as pleasant and painless as possible.

I blame many obstetricians who prevent those women willing to accept some hardship to bring forth their children without anesthesia from doing so. When women became aware of the dangers inherent in childbirth as they came to realize that some children were born with a handicap, that stillbirths could happen, and that some women died in childbed, birth became sorrowful, more an emotional than a physical burden. This is also what the Bible says—it does not say that birth became painful: "In sorrow wilt thou bring forth thy children". Other languages use the same word: in German the word is *Beschwer*. I am not a scripturalist, but the image is apt.

Physical pain at childbirth is above all caused by emotions; for that reason a physical approach in fighting pain is not adequate. It is obvious that it is the mission of physicians to lessen pain, but what is the best way to do that during labor? You can make a woman senseless, or you can paralyze her by giving her injections, but these are somatic methods to allay the pain. Once I heard an American midwife say: "Our obstetrics is perineum-centered". That was a good description. Many obstetricians do not look beyond that small part of the body, but many problems in pregnancy, especially during birth, take place in the cerebrum and must be treated there: by helping women in psychic distress, by attending them carefully during pregnancy, and by reassuring them during birth.

THE WOMAN'S WISHES

The wishes of the woman are the only valid argument in obstetrics. Her will must be decisive: if she wants to have birth without any intervention, without anesthesia, without having an episiotomy, if she wants to give birth at home and in the presence of her husband, and if she wants to hold her baby right after birth and to put it to her breast, if there are no medical contraindications, she must be allowed to do so. She also must be free to choose the place of delivery. Financial arguments should not be the main ones in making this choice.

Coercion is wrong under any circumstances. That holds even for abortion. The mother-to-be is the protector of the unborn life, not the physician. If she does not want the baby, it makes no sense to force her. My ideas changed a lot in that respect. I hesitated for a long time, but now I can see abortion as a kind of assistance. At present, I consider my original view, that doctors should protect the unborn life, an overestimation of our own importance, as a masculine attitude that does not do justice to the pregnant woman.

THE NORMAL AND THE PATHOLOGICAL

In our obstetric system, in which patience is so important, midwives are indispensable. Obstetricians who have studied for twelve years at the university are not the right ones to sit next to a woman, hold her hand, and wipe her forehead. A doctor can do that a couple of times, but if that is all he does, he will start to ask himself: "Why did I study?" There is the possibility he will become impatient and irritated, and will think, "The devil, the baby still isn't there.... I'll get it." In any case, he uses technology and is admired because of that. "Clever doctor, beautiful forceps, the head of the baby doesn't even show any signs that it was used," or "these Caesarean section babies always have such beautiful round heads. That is nice for these children; they will be clever pupils."

People like to hear what technology can do, and that is the way medicine developed in many countries in the Western world, but medical knowledge has been overrated in the twentieth century. Edward Shorter's *A History of Women's Bodies* demonstrates this overestimation; he sees obstetricians and gynecologists as the liberators of women who were permanently anemic, afflicted with complaints of menstruation, and many dying in childbed. Their feeble constitution made them subordinate to men until gynecologists released them from the vexations of their body. This is such terrible nonsense. At the end of the nineteenth century, during the first wave of feminist emancipation, gynecologists were almost powerless.

After World War II, obstetricians came to have an ever stronger hold on the obstetric system. Up to the 1950s, they were still willing to visit a laboring woman at home, while country doctors were semi-obstetricians. The general practitioner dealt with much pathology until the 1960s, but after that time, obstetricians only attended to women in a hospital. During the 1970s, even general practitioners did fewer deliveries. Their experience with home birth was not sufficient anymore because of the declining birth rate. Besides, they did not like to wake up in the middle of the night for a normal birth.

Because of this, health insurance companies were in need of unequivocal directives to help with screening between normal and pathological pregnancies and birth. The costs of hospital birth were only paid when there were medical indications, but some of the conditions for these indications were ambiguous or idiotic. Psychological indications were lacking for cases of panic when nothing medical was wrong. In 1958 the advisers of the insurance companies invited me to give a lecture about indications for hospital deliveries, and they asked me to make a record of this speech. They started to use what I'd said as a checklist for medical indications. Years later I heard that this list was called the "Kloostermanlist." Obstetricians regularly wrote me about their concerns: They would complain about an indication being omitted, or that they had a problem but could not give a referral since it was not mentioned on my list. So the list was growing and growing, and questionable indications were added to it. Besides, it was also used in another way than originally intended. In many cases, the list gave only recommendations, which guaranteed the right to a paid hospital stay, but some obstetricians were making the list obligatory: if an indication for specialist help appeared on it, the woman had to be sent to a hospital.

For these reasons, the list had to be revised. A committee was set up, which cleared the whole list, but the obstetricians did not want to accept the new list. The old one had only two categories, "yes" and "no."

The new one had three: "yes," "no," and "consultation." In the third instance, midwives had final say. Some obstetricians objected to this because they considered themselves the experts, and they did not want to comply if the midwife said, "I disagree with you." I myself do not see any justification for their fears; midwives will listen to good arguments; it is in their own interest to do so.

There is always a conflict between natal and prenatal care. In Sweden, the emphasis is on natal care, which concentrated in bastions of technology, while in the Netherlands, special attention is given to prenatal care. We must admit that the Dutch organization of obstetrical care created a problem that does not exist in many other countries. There all deliveries are supposed to take place in a hospital. We try to determine during pregnancy, that is during prenatal care, which women must go to hospital and which women may choose between a home or hospital confinement. This choice became an important feature of our prenatal care.

In retrospect, it can be said that 95 percent of all pregnant women could have been confined without any assistance, but before the birth, during pregnancy, we have to be more careful and advise up to 30 percent to have their deliveries in a hospital. Dutch professors and directors of the schools for midwives have always taken that position. After good prenatal care, 70 or 80 percent of all women's pregnancies are normal: one child, good placement, the head presents, no disproportion between head and pelvis. One can say to these women: "Everything is going well." I admit that you must say to the other 20 or 30 percent: "This will become a breech birth; the head does not present. It may be better to have your baby in the hospital."

The screening between the normal and the pathological has become more and more stringent. Twenty-five years ago I expected a decrease in the number of women from the 5 percent who then had to go to a hospital during labor. That prediction did not come true. At present, almost 20 percent of the women who wanted to have their first baby at home will be sent to hospital during labor. That increase is owing to an increased fear of risk. The number of unexpected risks decreased, however, which made the emergency cases decrease as well.

In short, the basis of our health system is that primary caretakers do the referrals: midwives are for normal deliveries, and obstetricians are for pathological births. In my opinion, that is an excellent system, but it is terribly important that there be mutually good relations between midwives and obstetricians. In the surrounding countries, obstetricians have a kind but condescending attitude towards midwives, even though they save the doctors much time. When the baby is ready to be born, midwives must call for the doctor. Afterwards, the doctor takes the credit and sends his bill. In the Netherlands, the autonomous independent midwife can rely on the sympathy and the respect of the obstetricians who work in the hospital. Some women of the 30 percent who want to have their babies at home assisted by a midwife are handed over to obstetricians just before, or even during, birth. In these instances, the woman is welcome in the hospital. Abroad, a woman will often be reproached: "How could you be so stupid as to want to have your baby at home?" Women are afraid of that kind of confrontation, and that may be a reason for some of them to stay at home too long.

Delaying the transfer to hospital causes risks that could have been avoided at an earlier moment. Such risks give obstetricians the opportunity to warn against home birth. Throughout the industrial world, home birth has thus been made to appear dangerous. That is something I reproach the obstetricians for. I see this as result of a struggle for power between a dominating masculine world and a female world. If the two camps of midwives and obstetricians face off against one another, the midwife will get the worst of it. Midwives must be careful; they must be willing and able to argue with individual obstetricians, but they should not antagonize the world of obstetricians or their professional association. I am opposed to polarization. Some people blame me for exaggerating the qualities of midwives, and that may be right, but I hope that those with less power, the women, in the long run will win.

THE FUTURE OF HOME BIRTH

In the 1950s, a delegation from the Soviet Union visiting the Netherlands asked why we still had training courses for midwives. At that time, they still had midwives, but they were very proud that soon they would be able to offer the services of obstetricians to the whole population. They thought that was the best care anyone could get. I did not agree with them. Ten years later, they still had midwives, but then home birth was forbidden. At a conference in Moscow organized by the World Health Organization, I spoke in defense of home birth. The Russians were particularly set against it, "because it was forbidden and because hospitals were better for the people". In my opinion, the reasons against home birth were: bad social conditions, poor housing, and above all an ideology that suited hospital births: "everyone is a child of the state, isn't he?"

And ever since, home births have decreased throughout the Western world. Sweden has been a pioneer in that respect. In the beginning of the 1960s, almost 100 percent of Swedish women had their babies in a hospital, preferably in large hospitals with more than 3,000 deliveries a year. Although technically this is defensible, from a psychological or a sociological perspective, the issue is more difficult. In the Western world, obstetricians have systematically obstructed home birth, and recently, the German obstetric association wrote a letter to all the Ministries of Health of the *Bundesländer* that contained the slogan *Schlusz mit der Hausgeburt* (stop home birth). The association set themselves up as protectors of German children, acting against the romantic ideas of some parents.

The Dutch obstetric system has become an anomaly, causing more and more amazement in surrounding countries. I defended home birth at a London congress on obstetric organization in the 1980s, which was visited by mothers-to-be, midwives, pediatricians, and obstetricians. Many obstetricians left the meeting because of lack of interest and to protest. Their actions demonstrate the emotional character of the issue. The obstetricians' criticism is becoming louder and louder. My viewpoint in favor of midwives and home birth is supported mainly by psychologists, psychiatrists, pediatricians, and sociologists. Sometimes objections to home birth in the Netherlands refer to the relatively slow decrease in perinatal mortality in the last decennia. But throughout the Western world, differences in perinatal mortality have diminished; our present-day slower decline in perinatal mortality may be explained by our earlier low perinatal mortality level.

The place of delivery is not an important factor influencing perinatal mortality. Within the Netherlands, there appears to be no correlation between regional percentages of home birth and regional perinatal mortality rates.

In 1978, I was afraid that the number of home births was diminishing beyond a critical level, but during the last fifteen years, the number of home births did not decline, while perinatal mortality continued to diminish, from 12.5 to 9.1 per thousand. Nevertheless, there is increasing pressure to give up home birth, and the impending unification of Europe may even reinforce this tendency. Besides, changing social conditions threaten the Dutch obstetric system. Some of these are high-rise buildings with twenty stories, traffic jams. These circumstances make home birth more hazardous. Another threat to the Dutch obstetric system lies in what will happen to the profession of midwife. The midwives' position may weaken with the disappearance of the old-fashioned dedication. The lifelong devotion of earlier midwives hardly exists anymore.

But I hope that home birth will endure, because there will always be some women who want to have their babies at home. They like to be self-reliant, they feel "I can work it out myself," and they prefer the intimacy of the home. My wife is one of those women, and when I asked her why she preferred to stay at home, she said that she didn't like all those strangers at her bed. All over the world, groups of this kind of woman are advocating home birth. For these people, our system may serve as an example. So, the minister of health for Ontario came here to see for himself. When he went back to Canada, he set up an experiment with lying-in clinics, good prenatal care, a good selection system, and legally recognized midwives. For implementing the Dutch system, a good infrastructure like that is necessary, with well-trained midwives who have learned to work autonomously and who are not subservient, but complementary to obstetricians.

We can only maintain our obstetric system if the international community of obstetricians becomes more tolerant towards our way of working, and women with a normal pregnancy dare to have their babies at home, while those who are at risk go to a hospital. There is some risk that the wrong people will stay at home, people who will take unacceptable risks. I want to warn against romanticism, but if we succeed in lighting the fire for home birth, our system will survive.

A CROSS-NATIONAL ANALYSIS OF MIDWIFERY POLITICS: SIX LESSONS FOR MIDWIVES

Eugene R. Declercq [1]

ABSTRACT

Research based on interviews and analysis of documentary sources on the politics of midwifery in Canada, Denmark, the Netherlands, the UK and the US, suggests six political lessons for midwives and the organisations that represent them. The lessons are: general health reforms represent both an opportunity and a threat to midwives' status, and midwives must learn to communicate in ways policy makers understand; research matters; coalition building is essential; the media cares (a little); it is much easier to defend the status quo than create new policy; it is essential to clarify who is to be considered a midwife. A constant grass roots awareness of and involvement in a country's political and policy making process is seen as a necessity if midwives are to prosper as a profession.

INTRODUCTION

Developments in the legal, financial and political context in which midwives practise have come more rapidly in recent years (Kitzinger, 1988) as has interest in overall health system reform (Blendon *et al.*, 1990). These changes range from the reintroduction of midwifery in Canada to a challenge to midwives' autonomy in the Netherlands, to a series of governmental reports supporting expanded midwifery in the UK (DoH, 1993) to midwives in some US states being prosecuted (Sullivan & Weitz, 1988), while other states are providing more support for midwife services (Bidgood-Wilson *et al.*, 1992).

Reported in this paper is part of the author's larger study, of comparative maternal and child health policy which is based on an analysis of government documents, published research and over 100 interviews with midwives, health officials, legislators and researchers in five countries: Canada, Denmark, the Netherlands, the UK and the USA. The interviews were unstructured, elite interviews (Dexter, 1970) conducted primarily during the summers of 1991, 1992 and 1993.

Midwives interviewed were of two general types. Officials in midwifery organisations in the respective countries were interviewed and they were asked about any recent reforms in maternal and child health policies in their country, the likely impact of these changes on midwives' practice and the role their organisation may have played in initiating or implementing the reforms. A non-representative sample of practising midwives were also interviewed to develop a sense of their awareness of the organisational efforts and the impact of reforms on their individual practice. The paper draws on this research base to develop six political lessons hopefully applicable to midwives in a variety of settings.

Lessons: General health reforms represent both an opportunity and a threat to midwives' status. Midwives must learn to communicate in ways policy makers understand.

A number of countries are involved in serious discussion of potential changes to their health delivery systems, most notably at present, the USA. These changes may be based on outside interventions, such as the Safe Motherhood Initiative, be part of a cyclical process of review as in the UK, or be put on the political agenda by a new leader as in the USA and the Netherlands. In all of these cases concerns about midwifery did not initiate the reform efforts but midwives' status could be substantially influenced by the results of these actions. The health reforms focus primarily on cutting overall costs, occasionally on improving access to care and, in a few cases, improving the quality of care.

If midwives can make a policy relevant argument for the expansion of their services, then they can use the reform for their benefit. What is a "policy relevant argument"? Policy makers, being politicians and bureaucrats, usually focus on the two commodities that define their power: money and votes. Midwives must begin to document the costs as well as the outcomes associated with their care more carefully in order to convince those in authority that health care costs can be reduced without sacrificing, and probably improving, quality. There is remarkably little data on the costs of midwifery care and while it is easy to assume it costs less than physician-based care, the empirical case has to be made to those in a position to change policy.

In democracies is their any electoral advantage to be gained from supporting midwifery? In most cases, there will be too few midwives in a country to form a serious voting bloc and midwives are unlikely to have sufficient financial resources to enable them to compete politically with physicians. There are, however, important resources available to midwives. First they can try to shape public opinion. The very limited systematic research on public opinion of midwives suggests that midwives have a positive, if somewhat nebulous, image in the public mind (Declercq, 1982). Creating a positive image through a more concerted public relations effort, such as that initiated in the late 1980s by the Royal College of Midwives (RCM) in the UK can place midwives on the 'side of the angels' in these debates. This approach has been used by physicians for decades to reach the level of professional sovereignty they possess in many systems (Starr, 1982).

Secondly, midwives can form coalitions with other relevant groups, such as nurses, health attendants, antenatal educators and most of all parents (see lesson 3). In the current USA health reform debates, the American College of Nurse-Midwives has joined with a variety of 'mid-level providers', such as nurse-practitioners, physician assistants and chiropractors in an attempt to ensure inclusion in a basic package of benefits provided to all Americans. Finally, midwives can help an elected official to appeal to crucial voting blocs. Politicians are constantly trying to characterise their concern for a particular group (mothers) or concept (motherhood) quickly and midwifery can symbolise politically powerful issues such as: empowering women, healthy babies, reducing society's reliance on technology, providing individuals with greater freedom of choice and cutting government spending. Most of these issues are part of health reform debates and while politicians may forget some promises once elected, they will be hard pressed to completely ignore the symbols they invoked for health reform.

It is essential that midwives remember that while health reform may influence them, they are rarely, if ever, the focus of the debate and they constantly run the danger of being victims of unintended consequences. In the Netherlands, for example, an effort to introduce more competition into health services led to an attempt by general practitioners to eliminate "primat", the rule that protects the financial autonomy of midwives. Midwives in the Netherlands fought the change, and ultimately their efforts were rewarded when their actions led to delays in the implementation of any changes. When the overall reform effort failed, midwives maintained the status quo, which in this case was in their favour. Midwives' actions were important, but the initial threat and the ultimate victories of midwives were driven by forces that cared little about the future of midwifery. These reforms are merely one of dozens of health issues (and hundreds of general issues) policy makers face and the greatest difficulty is often simply getting their attention (Kingdon, 1984).

The ultimate goal for midwives may be a form of self regulation, such as that maintained by physicians in the USA. However, physicians, with all their resources and a tradition of self regulation in the USA, are likely to lose much of their remaining autonomy in the forthcoming reforms, so the likelihood that any group will attain such power in the future is slim. Midwives' organisations must be constantly involved in political activity and aware of political changes. In this way they can anticipate changes that are proposed and respond to them quickly and effectively.

RESEARCH MATTERS

The existence of data that documents the outcomes and costs of midwifery care is essential. As national midwifery organisations in a number of countries begin more systematic data collection efforts, there is a need for co-operation among practising midwives and constant communication of findings back to those same midwives.

Policy makers respond to systematic research if for no other reason than to provide formal backing for decisions they were inclined to make anyway. Most importantly, however, the research that has been undertaken suggests that midwives have a powerful case to make. They must simply broaden the database, address some questions that might be of greater interest to policy makers than midwives (e.g. how much money is saved by using midwives?) and communicate the findings in a manner that the public can understand.

One of the factors that influenced the direction of the UK's proposed reforms in maternal and child health provision was the work undertaken by the National Perinatal Epidemiology Unit in Oxford, which was cited at a number of places in testimony before the House of Commons Health Committee (1992) and by MPs themselves. In the dynamic situation generated from health reforms or in more narrow cases, such as in the USA when a single state commission may want to prevent physicians who back up midwives at home births from receiving malpractice insurance, there is a crucial need for systematic research to address the question. Research can seldom be produced on demand, but must be part of an ongoing effort. The fact that a variety of current physician practices are not research based (Chalmers et al., 1989) does not justify midwives delaying any longer in the collection of their own data.

COALITION BUILDING IS ESSENTIAL

As noted above, one of the keys to building political power is the development of coalitions with other related groups. The demise of midwifery in the USA was abetted by the isolation of midwives from each other, let alone potential allies (Declercq, 1994). Midwives and potential supporters can spend a great deal of time fighting each other when their primary campaign should be against those who wish to limit midwifery. The USA debate between nurse-midwives and direct entry midwives has consumed resources that would be better applied to the growth of American midwifery in general. Direct-entry midwives were notably absent from the coalition of 'mid-level' providers seeking to be included in the Clinton health reforms. Midwives often complain about the lack of respect they receive from physicians, but potential midwife supporters, such as parent educators and nurses, may raise the same issues concerning midwives.

The establishment of the Midwives' Alliance of North America (MANA) is a reflection of this mutual concern and a sign of growing political maturity. MANA was formed in 1982 by direct-entry and nurse-midwives in the USA interested in identifying common ground and enhancing communication between all midwives in the USA (Sullivan & Weitz, 1988). Through a newsletter, conferences and informal meetings, members seek to keep lines of communication open between all midwives in the USA. Likewise, the decison of the RCM to keep communications open with the Association of Radical Midwives (ARM) allowed for a number of the reforms proposed by ARM to be eventually implemented. The same strategy of inclusion of dissidents has historically been used with great success by the American Medical Association (AMA) (Wilsford, 1991). As Wilsford has noted "Internal strains have been a feature of the AMA's organizational life from its inception ... But, precisely, conflict within the AMA has almost always remained within".

In general, the usefulness of coalition building will vary according to the culture and politics of a society, but midwives need to be sensitive to which groups might be allies and develop lines of communication to them *before* a crisis develops. This must be done without sacrificing either group's autonomy. This is best accomplished by identifying areas of common interest, uniting around those issues while merely communicating on other issues where interests are unrelated or may even conflict.

THE MEDIA CARES (A LITTLE AND FOR A SHORT TIME)

The nature of midwifery practice, involving such culturally important symbols as motherhood and babies, lends itself to media coverage. Certainly the demise of midwifery in some countries was hastened by a media campaign that misled the public concerning the nature of midwifery (Litoff, 1978). Like political involvement, media relations is a long-term effort where persistence and sensibility to reporters' and editors' needs will eventually yield great dividends in building support for a profession not well known by the public.

What does the media want from midwives? Access is one critical need. When reporters call midwifery organisations for comment, they usually need an immediate response to meet some dead-line and if one is not forthcoming, they simply look elsewhere. They also want information provided at a level the public understands, such as with the research discussed above. A common scenario is for a reporter simply to seek reactions from various organisations to the publication of research findings, and in maternal and child health care midwives are a natural source. If no midwife spokesperson is available, reporters merely call the next person on their list. There is also the possibility of development of 'midwife/pundits' who, because of their media skills, are called upon for comment on a wide array of issues and become celebrities in their own right. While this can cause friction in and between groups, at this point it might be a worthwhile trade-off for midwife organisations to focus attention on (or elect to leadership roles) individuals with media 'savvy'.

Midwives must be in a position to respond to what Kingdon (1984) terms 'focussing events'. These are often unplanned events, which serve to draw public attention to an issue and can be used by advocates to advance a cause. For example, media coverage of a celebrity home birth attended by a midwife will usually be accompanied by an additional story, termed a sidebar, about home birth or midwifery in general, and this is a rare opportunity to inform an otherwise uninterested public. While the public may initially be drawn to the story of their favourite actress's decision to have a home birth, they may well read the accompanying story that describes research on home birth.

A common alternative is to personalise a government or research report, by focusing on the experiences of 'real people'. The day after the publication of a UK governmental report entitled 'Changing Childbirth' (DoH, 1993) *The Daily Telegraph* published a series of stories under the headline 'Would You Have Your Baby at Home?' (Daily Telegraph, 1993). As the RCM illustrated by hiring a public relations advisor who was also experienced in politics, there is potential to develop positive long-term relations with the press that can support midwives' policy initiatives as well. As with policy makers, however, midwifery is only one of the many issues reporters deal with, and their attention spans are often the length of time it takes to publish or broadcast the next edition.

IT IS MUCH EASIER TO DEFEND THE STATUS QUO THAN CREATE NEW POLICY

In most countries policy initiatives of any kind face a wide array of obstacles, not the least of which is inertia. Comprehensive, integrated reforms of policies are valued in theory, but in practice they would alter so many existing relationships that interest groups can easily defeat them, resulting in an incremental approach to policy making. This reality has two important consequences for midwives. First, midwives must defend with vigour those cases where the system favours them and they will likely retain those powers. The example of Dutch midwives, discussed above, is a case in point. Likewise, proposed reforms that might have limited midwives' involvement in antenatal and postpartum care in Denmark ran counter to well established, government sanctioned protocols and were not implemented (Declerq, 1991).

The second implication for midwives is the need for patience and persistence in trying to implement even the smallest change. Bureaucrats and elected officials plan to be around long into the future, and are in no hurry to take risks that might jeopardise that future. Therefore, delay is a natural and attractive policy option available to them. Midwives should not expect major shifts in power, even in the context of larger reforms. If midwives want to increase their autonomy, for example, it may have to involve a series of small steps (e.g. a new reimbursement scheme, a regulatory change and a slight expansion of defined responsibilities may be combined into a significant increase in power) rather than a single sweeping reform.

IT IS ESSENTIAL TO CLARIFY WHO IS TO BE CONSIDERED A MIDWIFE

Is midwifery a profession or a calling? This debate goes beyond this paper and is central to midwives' success and failure in policy making. The respect and affection midwives garner from women and families can be offset by the tendency of policy makers to underestimate their value as health providers. The desire to serve women and babies is not a prohibition to political activity and policy sophistication, but midwives can waste limited resources on debates over who is a 'real midwife', rather than valuing the importance of diversity in any organised human activity. This problem rises at a number of levels. It can be a demeaning attitude toward a traditional birth attendant or a direct-entry midwife, combined with a failure to recognise the important roles they play in their communities. Condescension toward midwives in other (any 'other' will do) countries is of course self-defeating. A growing problem is the failure of midwives to recognise the contribution of their colleagues not currently in clinical practice.

In a sense, midwives are victims of their own success. As they have grown in importance, they, like other organised groups, have experienced division of labour and some midwives are now in teaching, administrative and research positions. As much as midwives may choose their career path for reasons other than policy making, they must invest in the future of their profession/ calling and support those midwives who are involved in related careers. Midwives in clinical practice regularly dismissed the contribution of midwives who had moved into administrative, research or teaching roles. The phrase, which I heard in virtually every country and setting I studied, 'She's a (politician/researcher/bureaucrat) now and not really a midwife any more', is ultimately, self defeating and creates divisions where coalitions are essential.

CONCLUSION

There is no simple answer to the political challenges midwives face, but there is one constant: a recognition of the importance of political awareness and activity if midwifery is to survive and prosper. This activity cannot be limited to a select few midwives in national or provincial offices, but must be seen as at least part of every midwife's commitment to the future of her/his profession. Enhancing political awareness and activity as part of midwifery education helps all midwives become invested in the future of their profession and hopefully will expand the relatively small corps of midwives currently responsible for political activity. Midwives' roles were diminished over the last century not because of their failure as caregivers, but because of their failure to respond to the political challenges they faced. There are many understandable reasons for this behaviour in the past, but to repeat it would be folly.

ACKNOWLEDGEMENTS

This research was supported by grants from the Nuffield Foundation, the British Council and the Merrimack College Faculty Development Committee.

REFERENCES

Bidgood-Wilson M, Barickman C, Ackley, S 1992 Nurse-midwifery today: a legislative update, part 1. *Journal of Nurse-Midwifery*, **37**: 96-140

Blendon R, Leitman I, Donelan K 1990 Satisfaction with the health care systems. In Ten Nations. *Health Affairs* **9**: 185-192

Charmers I, Enkin M, Keirse MJN C 1989 *Effective care in pregnancy and childbirth*. Oxford University Press, Oxford

Daily Telegraph 1993 Would you have your baby at home? In You and your family (Aug 6): 4-5

Declercq E 1982 Public opinion toward midwifery and home birth: an exploratory analysis. *Journal of Nurse Midwifery* **28**: 19-22

Declercq E 1991 Expanding midwives' roles in the delivery of perinatal care: a cross-national analysis. Paper presented at the annual meeting of the American Public Health Association, Atlanta, Georgia

Declercq E 1994 The Trials of Hanna Porn. *American Journal of Public Health* **84**: 1022-1028

Department of Health (DoH) 1993 *Changing Childbirth, Report of the Expert Maternity Group*. HMSO, London

Dexter L 1970 *Elite and specialized interviewing*. Evanston, Ill. Northwestern University Press

House of Commons Health Committee 1992 *Second report: Maternity Services*. HMSO, London

Kingdon J 1984 *Agendas, alternatives and public policies*. Little Brown, Boston
Kitzinger S (ed) 1988 *The midwife challenge*. Pandora Press, London
Litoff J 1978 *American midwives: 1860 to the present*. Greenwood Press, Westport, Conn.
Starr P 1982 *The social transformation of American medicine*. Basic Books, New York
Sullivan D, Weitz R 1988 *Labor pains*. Yale University Press, New Haven
Wilsford D 1991 *Doctors and the State*. Duke University Press, Durham

[1] E.R Declercq, Professor of Political Science, Merrimack College, North Andover, MA 01845, USA. This work was first presented at the 23rd International Congress of the International Confederation of Midwives in Vancouver, Canada, May 1993.
Midwifery (1994) **10**, 232-37, Reprinted with permission of Harcourt Publishing Company.

CHOICE, CONTINUITY AND CONTROL: CHANGING MIDWIFERY TOWARDS A SOCIOLOGICAL PERSPECTIVE

Jane Sandall [†]

ABSTRACT

In this paper sociological theories of the professions and the organisation of work are drawn on to explain current developments in the organisation of maternity care. Utilising the literature on the sociology of the professions and general trends in health policy and labour markets, possible reasons for the current renaissance in midwifery and some implications for midwives are discussed. Thus, whilst some women and midwives may be building a paradigm of 'woman-centred' practice based on an equal partnership, for other midwives, the result may be a divided workforce consisting of an elite core and casualised periphery based on the ability to give a full-time flexible commitment to work. The implications of excluding those midwives who are unable to combine full-time work with their own domestic commitments are discussed.

INTRODUCTION

In this paper some implications of recent changes in maternity policy in the UK are examined. The aim of the paper is to draw on sociological theories of the professions and the organisation of work to understand current developments in the organisation of midwifery work.

Current changes in midwifery are interesting when viewed from a sociological perspective as there is an increasing amount of literature examining the professionalisation of female-dominated occupations (Witz 1990; 1992; Walby *et al.* 1994; Davies 1995). A current study of maternity care reveals firstly, the extent to which the traditional boundaries of midwifery and medical practice are being challenged and negotiated, secondly, that constraints from state policy are crucial in deciding whether women's and midwives' demands are realised, and thirdly, that these changes may either result in a feminist-inspired paradigm of partnership with women and/or the creation of a new midwifery elite with the associated casualisation of employment for those midwives on the periphery.

POLICY CHANGES

One of the most commonly expressed wishes of expectant women is that they have continuity of carer, i.e. that they be attended during their pregnancy, labour and postnatal period by a midwife with whom they have established a relationship (Department of Health 1993: 14). This has been the key theme in two recent reports on maternity care (House of Commons 1992; Department of Health 1993). These reports differed from past reports (Social Services Committee 1980) in that they have critically reassessed the roles of

---

[†] *Midwifery*, **11**, (1995):201-9, Reprinted with permission of Harcourt Publishing Company.

health professionals and for the first time taken into account the views and experiences of women and consumer organisations who had always been active and vocal before making policy recommendations.

The reports also contain similarities in that both the *Short Report* (Social Services Committee 1980) and *Changing Childbirth* (Department of Health 1993) have acknowledged the evidence but not taken any action concerning the wider socio-economic context of childbirth. For example, the *Short Report* recognised the association between poverty and an increased perinatal mortality rate (Social Services Committee 1980) and assumed that obstetric intervention could compensate for adverse social circumstances (Russell 1982). Similarly, although the Winterton Committee expressed concern about the financial needs of parents living in poverty and made recommendations about benefit levels (House of Commons 1992), the *Cumberlege Report* (Department of Health 1993) has no remit outside National Health Service (NHS) care and contains an assumption that social support and increased choice and control on the part of women may partly compensate for poverty (Streetly 1994).

This is in spite of evidence documenting the widening gap of socio-economic differentials in health in the 1980s (Davey Smith & Egger 1993), the continued association between poverty and higher perinatal mortality rates (OPCS 1993, Tables 7a; 7 & 8) and the fact that by 1993, 30% of children were born into families on means tested benefits (Maternity Alliance 1993).

Changing Childbirth (Department of Health 1993) has been welcomed by the National Association of Health Authorities and Trusts (NAHAT 1993) and all regions, districts and trusts in England have been instructed to review their maternity services in 1994/1995 (National Health Service Management Service Executive 1994) and develop a strategy to implement the ten key indicators of success within five years.

POLICY BACKGROUND

Since the early 1980s, there has been an increasing emphasis on cost effectiveness of medical care (National Audit Office 1990). Economic assessments in this country (Mugford 1990), but also in the USA (Annandale 1989) and Canada (Romalis 1985), were beginning to show that centralisation of maternity units was not based on good evidence about the cost-effectiveness of the policy. Furthermore, research found that the outcome for women in terms of satisfaction and infant and maternal morbidity appeared to be no worse in midwife run schemes than obstetric schemes and might even be improved (Flint *et al.* 1989). Also, reviews of the evidence on place of birth suggested that planned home birth for women at low obstetric risk had similar (Campbell & Macfarlane 1987) or even better outcomes (Tew 1985, 1990) than those of a woman at equally low obstetric risk delivered in an obstetric unit.

Accompanying the concern with escalating costs were doubts about the contribution high technology scientific medicine was making to health. For example, a report from the World Health Organisation described the adverse impact of increasing medicalisation of childbirth on perinatal and maternal morbidity (WHO 1986). Furthermore, the first systematic meta-analysis of research in the fields of reproductive medicine and maternity care was published in 1989 (Chalmers *et al.* 1989). This provided further evidence that for many interventions there was no proven benefit and others caused harm.

The 'cultural critique' of medicine informed by the writings of McKeown (1976), and the more radical claims of medical iatrogenesis of Illich (1977) and feminist attacks on medicine as sustaining patriarchy (Ehrenreich & English 1973) challenged the legitimacy of the professional's authority which coincided with the neo-liberal view concerned about restricting consumer choice (Green 1988). These critiques were sustained by empirical evidence and comment from medical sociologists (Comoroff 1977; Macintyre 1977; Cartwright 1979; Oakley 1980; Graham & Oakley 1981). But it has been consumer organisations such as local Community Health Councils (Robinson 1974), the National Childbirth Trust and the Association for Improvements in Maternity Services which have also played a key role in this debate around childbirth (Durward & Evans 1990; Kitzinger 1990).

All this created a climate where it was valid for politicians, the public and the media to question the effectiveness and efficiency of medical care, particularly in an area such as maternity where consumer voices had been particularly vocal and litigious about its shortcomings (Ennif 1991). It was also occurring in a context of a government that sought to challenge unacceptable professional power (Department of Health & Social Security 1983), shift acute services into the community (Department of Health 1989b) and emphasise the rhetoric of consumer choice (Department of Health 1989a. Department of Health 1991; Department of Health 1992). These themes can all be seen in the key themes of Changing Childbirth report (Box 1) Department of Health 1993).

> **Box 1 Key themes of *Changing Childbirth* report**
> Consumer-led care responsive to local needs
> Accessible and appropriate care
> Efficient and effective care
> Shift to community-based care
> Provides value for money

CONTINUITY OF CARER

Why is continuity of carer so important? It has been recognised that the social aspects of the professional-client/patient relationship can play a vital role in client/patient satisfaction and this has been directly associated with improved health status (Fitzpatrick *et al.* 1983). For example, continuity of care was found to have beneficial effects for patients and providers in the specialty of paediatrics (Becker *et al.* 1974). Furthermore, research of social support in pregnancy (Oakley *et al.* 1990), and more particularly birth (Hodnett 1993), suggest that supported women feel less anxious, more in control and more satisfied with their care and that this translates into better physical and psychological outcomes for mother and baby.

WHAT DOES CONTINUITY OF CARER MEAN IN PRACTICE?

The concept of continuity of care has been very poorly defined (Murphy-Black 1992). Team midwifery developed as a way of organising care to increase continuity of carer and the current pattern of maternity care has been mapped by the Institute of Manpower Studies (Wraight *et al.* 1993). This national survey of all maternity units in England and Wales listed five key indicators for the 14 'genuine' teams which were defined as:

1. No more than six midwives in a team;
2. Defined caseload;
3. Total continuity from 'booking' to postnatal period;
4. Midwives working in hospital and community depending on the woman's needs;
5. At least 50% of women delivered by a known midwife.

'Known' midwife is not defined in the report. Furthermore, one of the arguments for community-based midwifery care is that women at high obstetric risk (as deemed in the medical sense) benefit as much, if not more, from continuity of midwifery care (Middlemiss *et al.* 1989; Oakley *et al.* 1990). This has been the rationale behind community-based teams of midwives who provide care to all women in a geographical area regardless of 'risk' status, either on their own responsibility or in association with an obstetrician (House of Commons 1992).

Apart from the difficulties in implementing new ways of working in the way that was intended, there is limited evidence as to what continuity of care actually means in practice to midwives and women (Lee 1994) and some evidence that continuity does not automatically equate with good quality care (Reid *et al.* 1983).

A woman's experience of team continuity may vary significantly from 'getting care from known caregivers at crucial times' (Garcia 1995: 96). Garcia's (1995) review of the evidence concerning women's views of continuity indicate that, although continuity of care matters to most women, it depends how the question is asked and that to focus on continuity may neglect other aspects of care that are equally important. If there has been limited evidence supporting complete continuity of care, why has it become so important for midwives?

A SOCIOLOGICAL PERSPECTIVE

Many midwives, women and consumer groups have welcomed these recommendations (Page 1993) which represent a radical shift in policy from the past. Implicit in this enthusiasm for the ideology of continuity of care are the following assumptions which may explain why current changes in maternity care can be seen as a process of professionalisation within midwifery:

1. That midwives who provide continuity of care will regain the professional autonomy that has been lost by working in a hierarchical setting dominated by medicine, and that job satisfaction will increase correspondingly;

2. That a female dominated occupation such as midwifery will provide more nurturant 'woman-centred' care than has been the case in the past;

3. That greater choice and control for women is contingent upon midwives also having greater occupational autonomy over their practice and organisation of work.

These assumptions all need to be critically examined and one of the advantages of a sociological perspective is that it can provide a historical understanding which may throw light on the present and also provide a critical understanding when we examine social change. The sociology of professions has often used medicine as a paradigm for the analysis of the role of professions in society (Parsons 1954). Using historical sources writers have explained that professional power and status have been achieved through a process of professionalisation, for example either by a Weberian process of occupational monopoly and closure (Larkin 1983; Freidson 1970) or a Marxist notion of a privileged position in the class structure (Johnson 1972; Larson 1977). This could be defined as the struggle for occupational advancement at the expense of related occupations and everyone else (Walby *et al*. 1994).

These analyses have been criticised from a feminist perspective for establishing a paradigm of the professions as the study of male dominated occupations and therefore inappropriate to explain the position and professionalisation of female-dominated occupations. Furthermore, until recently they have ignored the role that gender and patriarchy have played in divisions of labour within health care (Crompton & Sanderson 1990) and have rendered female occupations in health care either invisible or inaccurately represented (Carpenter 1993). The concept of patriarchy is now used by contemporary feminist scholars to refer to gender relations in which men are dominant and women subordinate. It thus describes a societal wide system of social relations of male dominance (Witz 1992: 3).

Witz (1992) extends Parkin's model of exclusionary closure (Parkin 1979) to explain the various professionalisation strategies adopted by dominant and subordinate occupations. Because of their lack of access to privileges and power that male dominated occupations were able to draw upon, the strategies used by midwives at the turn of the century in the UK were described as those of dual closure, i.e. usurping traditional boundaries set by medical men and excluding other non-accredited women from their sphere of practice. For midwives, this was achieved by a process of licensing and credentialism, the culmination of which was the Midwives' Act of 1902 (Donnison 1988).

MIDWIVES' NEW PROFESSIONAL PROJECT

Dingwall *et al*. (1988) also argued that midwifery emerged in the 20th century within the context of specific social and economic conditions, which united the provision of a cheap service to the poor with the desire of some middle-class women to establish female control over childbirth. They suggest this alliance kept the ideology of a midwife as an independent practitioner alive during the 20th century, whilst in practice its economic and clinical sphere of practice was being eroded (see Fox 1993).

Midwives have always suffered demarcationary closure from medical men and this increased during the 20th century as boundaries between normal and abnormal pregnancy and birth were redefined. There has also been continuing concern expressed by midwives that their traditional remit has been eroded by an increasing medical dominance of birth since the 1960s (Robinson 1990). Partly in response to these events, but also influenced by feminism and an altruistic empathy with consumer unhappiness about their experience of childbirth (Weitz 1987), midwives began to develop their new 'professional project' (Sandall 1991).

The Association of Radical Midwives (ARM) was formed in 1976 expressing a concern for the erosion of the midwives' role and the resulting poor quality of care offered. Originally started as a study and support group for student midwives, ARM has evolved into a political action group, both in alliance with organisations in the maternity rights movement and within midwifery.

ARM proposed a radical change in the division of labour, arguing for greater autonomy for midwifery practice and increased choice and autonomy for women (this volume pp.000-000). In 1986, ARM published *The Vision* (ARM 1986), a draft proposal for the future of maternity services, proposing that 70% of midwives would work in community based group practices, giving continuity of care in conjunction with teams attached to consultants. By 1989, in a response to *Working for Patients* (Department of Health 1989a), ARM were proposing that the group practices would contract for services with the new purchaser health authorities, emphasising the cost effectiveness of midwifery care.

By 1992, these principles can be seen as having influenced mainstream policy (House of Commons 1992, Department of Health 1993), as in 1902, as midwives were tightly constrained by three sets of power relations: the managerial relations of control within the NHS, the inter-occupational ones between doctors and midwives, and intra-occupational relations of control within midwifery. The others are between the professionalisers and the rank and file midwife who will live and work with the implications of the policy change. For example, the new proposals for maternity care issued three challenges to existing occupational boundaries:

1. By proposing that midwives become self employed and set up in their own group practices and contract their labour to the new health purchasing authorities they challenged the managerial and medical domination within the NHS;
2. By reclaiming their role in providing continuity of care for all women and providing care without a general practitioner referral, they claim a primacy of a 'special' relationship with women over the doctor's;
3. By providing continuity of care to all women in a geographically defined area regardless of risk categorisation and having admission rights to midwifery beds in hospital they challenge the traditional demarcationary boundaries of the medical profession.

These claims contain usurpatory dimensions and the ideology of continuity of care schemes reasserts control over the heart (in a metaphorical sense too) of the practice of midwifery. Thus, midwives are claiming a discrete sphere of knowledge and expertise, legitimated by a desire for a more equal partnership with women in an area where medical care has been criticised.

IMPLICATIONS FOR MIDWIVES

Historical evidence suggests that one result of a professionalisation process in midwifery (Heagerty 1990; Leap & Hunter 1993) and nursing (Abel Smith 1960) has been an increase in divisions of labour along the lines of ethnicity (King Edward's Hospital; Fund for Nursing 1990), class (Robinson 1992; Carpenter 1993) and domestic commitments (Robinson 1993).

Robinson (1992) and Salvage (1988) have both argued that a division into a core and peripheral workforce may be occurring in primary nursing and Walby *et al.* (1994) suggest such changes may reflect a general trend in the NHS and labour markets in general, although this may be too simplistic (see Gilbert *et al.* 1992). Walby *et al.*'s (1994) study of inter-professional relations between doctors and nurses in an acute hospital setting suggests that the organisation of work in the NHS contains examples of both a traditional Fordist labour process, i.e. one that subdivides tasks to less skilled workers who are paid efficiency (Aglietta 1979) and a post-Fordist labour process, i.e. highly trained, consumer focused, committed and autonomous workers whose jobs are loosely defined and flexible (Piore & Sabel 1984).

One drawback of this post-Fordist flexibility has been the development of a two-tier workforce where the skilled committed core workforce is differentiated from the peripheral workforce who are employed on short-term and temporary contracts and part-time work (Atkinson & Meager 1986; Bagguley *et al.*1990). The working practices required to implement Changing Childbirth suggest that the new midwife will fit the post-Fordist model, i.e. creative, committed, flexible and focused on the consumer. But will there also be the corollary, the elite core workforce and the casual periphery, and who will be in these two groups?

Providing continuity of care requires a radical change in the way that many midwives work at the moment in terms of increased flexibility and the impact of regular on-call work on midwives' personal lives (Jackson 1995) and research in progress should provide evidence as to sustainability and implementation of policy into practice, one possibility is that the rhetoric has changed but the reality stays the same (National Perinatal Epidemiology Unit 1995; Sandall 1994).

Fifty three per cent of midwives are estimated to have dependent children (Buchan & Stock 1990) and the number of midwives who work part-time has been increasing in the last five years to approximately 40% (English National Board 1993). Thus, this issue is of particular importance to an occupation where midwives who have experienced birth and childrearing themselves could potentially have much to bring to their work. Robinson's longitudinal study of midwives' careers (Robinson 1993; Robinson & Owen 1994) has suggested the possibility that midwives with domestic responsibilities will be excluded from this potentially higher status and higher paid work, particularly since antipathy towards women who cannot pursue full-time work has always operated within midwifery. For example, discrimination against women with children attempting to train as midwives (Braun 1990), downgrading of midwives returning to work part-time and a reluctance to implement job sharing (McDowall 1990).

Furthermore, recent national surveys of midwifery found inconsistencies in the grading of salary scales and the development of two tiers of midwives, those who could work flexibly and those who were limited to shifts and part-time work (Stock & Wraight 1993; Lewis 1995).

In general, the emphasis on the single woman's career path has disadvantaged those women who could not pursue a full-time career (Davies 1990). The exclusion of women with domestic commitments has been legitimated by the perception that such women have a less than full-time commitment to their work (Lorber 1985) and replicates findings from other studies of women in the NHS (Davies & Rosser 1986; Mackay 1989; Equal Opportunities Commission 1991).

This notion of gendered jobs and gendered organisations has been explored by Acker (1990) who argues that 'the concept of a job assumes a particular gendered organisation of domestic life and social production'. Thus, the gendered notion of a job is modelled on the full-time male career pathway and female career pathways that require career breaks and part-time work are a nuisance and disadvantage (Davies 1995) and the associated benefits rarely recognised (Warwick 1995).

AUTONOMY VERSUS STRESS

There is a suggestion that providing continuity of care results in increased autonomy which improves job satisfaction (Shoham-Yakubovich *et al.* 1989) but there is also evidence of increased stress in midwifery generally (Carlisle *et al.* 1994). Stock and Wraight (1993) found that midwives were trading off increased autonomy and job satisfaction with greater intrusion into their personal lives and increased demands for flexible working hours. Some evaluations of team midwifery have confirmed that some midwives felt 'burnt out' by the stressful on-calls, poor sick cover and interprofessional conflict (Watson 1990). Some of these midwives shared the characteristics identified in a survey of US midwives suffering 'burn out' (Beaver *et al.* 1986) in that they were young, qualified in the last five years and worked alone sometimes without adequate support. Furthermore, evidence from the Netherlands suggests that Dutch midwives face similar problems combining a private life with a job that requires total dedication and continuous availability (Benoit 1991). Indeed, midwifery could be characterised as a 'greedy profession', i.e. where great commitment, loyalty, time and energy are required (Coser 1974; Segal 1986) but where the rewards are great.

IMPLICATIONS FOR WOMEN

It has been assumed that because midwifery is a female-dominated occupation, midwives will guard the rights and interests of women and give a more holistic, empathetic and egalitarian style of care, which will ensure choice and control for women (House of Commons 1992; Page 1993). But this assumption needs to be critically examined as there is little evidence to support this view. Lorber (1985) found that external structural factors influence professional behaviour regardless of gender and others have highlighted how organisational factors can curtail or enhance the giving of woman-centred care (Green *et al*. 1986; Annandale 1987; Kirkham 1987).

The issue of whose interests are served is explored further by Oakley (1986) and Salvage (1988) who both suggest that the struggle by nurses to achieve professional status (in terms of a male-dominated paradigm as a professional model) may reproduce the unequal power relationship that already exists between the medical profession and many patients. Oakley suggests that a feminist inspired model of partnership with users of services is the way forward and both Stacey (1992) and Davies (1995) elaborate on what a client-centred paradigm of professional partnership and practice may look like. What needs to be remembered is that neither midwives nor women are homogenous groups about whom generalisations can be made.

CONCLUSION

The ideology of continuity of care reasserts control over the heart (in a metaphorical sense too) of the practice of midwifery. Thus, midwives are claiming a discrete sphere of knowledge and expertise, legitimated by a desire for a more equal partnership with women in an area where medical care has been criticised. It has a powerful appeal to all the interest groups within midwifery, to the generalists by emphasising the primacy of the midwife/woman relationship, to the academic professionaliser by offering increased autonomy, and lastly, to government and managers (whose support is vital to implement change) by providing cost effective care (although economic data to support this assertion is scanty).

Witz (1990) describes the strategy pursued by midwives in the 19th century as a 'female professional project' using a strategy of dual closure. Since 1902, the midwifery elite has pursued this same strategy at the expense of those midwives who did not fit the model to create an occupational structure suitable for 'educated refined gentlewomen' (Witz 1990). The midwifery elite also used gendered exclusion until the 1973 Sex Discrimination Act made such tactics illegal (Donnison 1988).

Midwives have always suffered demarcationary closure from medical men and this had been increasing over the 20th century as boundaries between normal and abnormal were redefined. Partly in response to these events, but also informed by feminism and altruistic empathy with consumer unhappiness about the organisation of maternity care, some midwives began to develop their new 'professional project'.

This new strategy of dual closure contains usurpationary dimensions, as midwives reclaim their role in providing continuity of care for all women. Now, as in 1902, midwives are tightly constrained by the three sets of power relations, the managerial relations of control within the NHS, the inter-occupational ones between doctors and midwives, and intra-occupational relations of control within midwifery between the 'elite' professionalisers and the rank and file and increasing consumer pressure to be partners in care.

Current attempts to develop professional status are dependent on state mandate, funding and political expedience (White 1985). The interest shown by the UK Government in the cost effectiveness of midwife care and the alliance that has been forged with consumers may well mean that this female professional project may be successful but at the cost of dividing the midwifery workforce. A sociological perspective suggests that midwifery as a female-dominated occupation may either be developing a new feminist paradigm of a profession in partnership with women, or once again, as in the beginning of the 20th century, a strategy of dual closure may exclude the rank and file midwife who may be expected to pay the price for the professionalising elite.

ACKNOWLEDGEMENTS

Jane Sandall was a Doctoral Research Scholar, Research Training Scheme, NHS Executive R & D Division, University of Surrey, UK. Address at time of publication of this reader: J. Sansdall, Reader in Midwifery, Department of Midwifery, City University, Philpot Street, London, E1 2EA, UK.

REFERENCES

Acker J 1990 Hierarchies, jobs, bodies: a theory of gendered organisations. *Gender and Society* **4** (2): 139-158

Aglietta M 1979 *A theory of capitalist regulation: the US experience.* Verso Press, London

Abel Smith B 1960 *A history of the nursing profession.* Heinemann, London

Annandale E C 1987 Dimensions of patient control in a free standing birth centre. *Social Science and Medicine* **25** (11): 1235-48

Annandale E C 1989 The malpractice crisis & the doctor-patient relationship. *Sociology of Health & Illness* **11**(1): 1-23

Association of Radical Midwives 1986 *The Vision—proposals for the future of the maternity services.* Association of Radical Midwives, Ormskirk

Atkinson J. Meager N 1986 *Changing work patterns: how companies achieve flexibility to meet new needs.* NEDO, London

Bagguley P, Mark-Lawson J. Shapiro D *et al.*1990, *Restructuring: place, class and gender.* Sage, London

Becker M H, Drachman R H, Kirscht J P 1974 A field experiment to evaluate various outcomes of continuity of physician care. *American Journal of Public Health* **64**: 1062-1070

Beaver R C, Sharp E S, Cotsonis G A 1986 Burn-out experienced by nurse midwives. *Journal of Nurse-Midwifery* **31** (1): 3-15

Benoit C 1991 *Midwives in passage: a case study of occupational change.* ISER Press, St. John's, Newfoundland

Braun J 1990 Sex discrimination against student midwives. *MIDIRS*, No.15

Buchan J. Stock J 1990 *Midwives' careers and grading.* IMS Report 201 Institute of Manpower Studies, University of Sussex

Campbell R, Macfarlane A 1987 *Where to be born? The debate and the evidence*, National Perinatal Epidemiology Unit, Oxford

Carlisle C, Baker G, Riley *et al.*1994 Stress in midwifery: a comparison of midwives and nurses using the work environment scale. *International Journal of Nursing* **31** (1): 13-22.

Carpenter M 1993 The subordination of nurses in health care: towards a social divisions approach. In Riska E, Wegar K. Eds. *Gender work and medicine; women and the medical division of labour.* Sage, London

Cartwright A 1979 *The dignity of labour? A study of childbearing and induction.* Institute for Social Studies in Medical Care. Tavistock, London

Chalmers I, Enkin M. Keirse M J N C 1989 *Effective care in pregnancy & childbirth.* Oxford Univ. Press, Oxford

Comoroff J 1977 Conflicting paradigms of pregnancy: managing ambiguity in antenatal encounters In Davis A., Horobin G, eds. *Medical encounters: the experience of illness and treatment.* Croon Helm, London

Coser L 1974 *Greedy institutions: patterns of undivided commitment.* Free Press, New York

Crompton R, Sanderson K 1990 *Gendered jobs and social change*, Unwin Hyman, London

Davies C 1995 *Gender and the professional predicament in nursing.* OUP, Buckingham

Davies C Rosser J 1986 Gendered jobs in the health service: a problem for labour process analysis. In Knights D, Willmott H, eds. *Gender and the labour process.* Gower, Aldershot.

Davies C 1990 *The collapse of the conventional career.* English National Board Project Paper 3. English National Board for Nursing, Midwifery and Health Visiting, London

Davey Smith G, Egger M 1993 Socio-economic differentials in wealth & health. *Brit. Med. Journal* **307**: 1085-6

Department of Health and Social Security 1983 *NHS Management Inquiry, DA, (83) 38* (Chairman R. Griffiths). Department of Health 1989a Working for Patients, CM 555, HMSO, London

Department of Health 1989b *Caring for People: community care in the next decade & beyond*, Cm 849, HMSO, London

Department of Health 1991 *The Patient's Charter.* HMSO, London

Department of Health 1992 *Maternity Services, Government response to the second report from the Health Committee, session 1991-2*, Cm 2018. HMSO, London

Department of Health 1993 *Changing Childbirth, Report of the Expert Maternity Group*, HMSO, London

Dingwall R Rafferty, A Webster C 1988 *An introduction to the social history of nursing*. Routledge, London

Donnison J 1988 *Midwives and medical men: a history of inter-professional rivalries and women's rights*. Heinemann, London.

Durward L, Evans R 1990 Pressure groups and maternity care. In Garcia J Kilpatrick R, Richards M. eds. *The politics of maternity care: services for childbearing women in 20th century Britain*. Clarendon Press, Oxford

Ehrenreich B, English D 1973 *Witches, midwives and nurses: a history of women healers*, Glass Mountain Pamphlet No 1, Compendium, Writers and Readers Publishing Co-operative, London

English National Board 1993 *Annual Report 1992/3*. English National Board for Nursing, Midwifery and Health Visiting, London

Ennif M 1991 Change in obstetric practice in response to fears of litigation in the British Isles. *Lancet* **338** (8767): 616-618

Equal Opportunities Commission 1991 *Equality management: women's employment in the NHS*. EOC, Manchester

Fitzpatrick R, Hopkins A P, Harvard-Watts O 1983 Social dimensions of healing: a longitudinal study of outcomes of medical management of headaches. *Social Science and Medicine* **17**(8): 501-510

Flint C, Poulengeris, P, Grant A 1989 The 'Know Your Midwife's scheme—a randomised controlled trial of continuity of care by a team of midwives. *Midwifery* **5**: 11-16

Fox E 1993 An honourable calling or a despised occupation: licensed midwifery and its relation to district nursing in England and Wales before 1948. *Social History Medicine* **6**(2): 237-259

Freidson E 1970 *The Profession of Medicine*. Dodd, Mead & Co. New York

Garcia J 1995 Continuity of carer in context: what matters to women? In Page L, ed. *Effective group practice in midwifery*, Blackwell, Oxford

Gilbert N Burrows, R Pollert A 1992 *Fordism and flexibility, divisions and social change*. Macmillan, Basingstoke.

Graham H. Oakley A 1981 Competing ideologies of reproduction: medical and maternal perspectives on pregnancy. In Roberts H. (ed.) *Women, health and reproduction*. Routledge and Kegan Paul, London

Green D 1988 *Everyone a private patient*. Institute of Economic Affairs, London

Green V A Kitzinger J V, Coupland J M 1986 *The division of labour: implications for staffing structure for doctors and midwives on the labour ward*. Child Care and Development Group, University of Cambridge

Heagerty B V 1990 *Class, gender and professionalization: the struggle for British midwifery, 1900-36*. Unpublished D.Phil, Michigan State University

Hodnett E D 1993 Support from caregivers during childbirth. In Enkin M W. Keirse M J N C, Renfrew M J *et al.*, eds. *Pregnancy and childbirth module 'Cochrane database of systematic reviews'*: Review no.03871, 12 May 1993, 'Cochrane updates on disc'. Disc issue 2, Update Software, Oxford

House of Commons 1992 *The Health Committee Second Report: Maternity Services*, **1** (Chair N. Winterton), HMSO, London

Illich I 1977 *Disabling professions*. Marion Boyars, London

Jackson K 1995 Changing childbirth: encouraging debate. *British Journal Midwifery* **3** (3): 137-138

Jackson K 1994 Knowing your midwife: how easy is it? *British Journal Midwifery* **2** (10): 507-508

Johnson T J 1992 *Professions and power*. Macmillan, London

King Edward's Hospital Fund for London 1990 *Racial equality: the nursing profession. Equal Opportunities Taskforce*. Occasional Paper No.6. King Edward's Hospital Fund for London, London

Kirkham M 1987 *Basic supportive care in labour: interaction with and around labouring women*. Unpublished PhD thesis, University of Manchester, Manchester

Kitzinger J 1990 Strategies of the early childbirth movement: a case study of the National Childbirth Trust. In Garcia J. Kilpatrick R. Richards M, eds. *The politics of maternity care: services for childbearing women in twentieth century Britain*. Clarendon Press, Oxford

Larkin G 1983 *Occupational monopoly and modern medicine*, Tavistock, London

Larson M 1977 *The rise of professionalism*. University of California, Berkeley

Leap N. Hunter B 1993 *The midwives' tale: an oral history from handywoman to professional midwife*. Scarlet Press, London

Lee G 1994 A reassuring familiar face? *Nursing Times* **90** (17): 66-67

Lewis P 1995 Standing up for midwives: introducing the RCM's Employment Affairs Committee. *Midwives* **198** (1,285):54

Lorber J 1985 More women physicians: will it mean more humane healthcare? *Social Policy* **16**(1): 50-54

Macintyre S 1977 The management of childbirth: a review of the sociological research issues. *Social Science & Medicine* **11**: 477-484

Mackay L 1989 *Nursing a problem.* Open University Press, Milton Keynes

Maternity Alliance 1993 Editorial, born in poverty. *Maternity Action* (61):9

McDowall J 1990 Working in tandem. *Nursing Times* **86**(28): 72-73.

McKeown T 1976 *The role of medicine: dream, mirage or nemesis.* Nuffield Provincial Hospitals Trust. London

Middlemiss C. Dawson A, Gough N *et al.*1989 A randomised study of a domiciliary antenatal care scheme: maternal psychological effects. *Midwifery* **5**: 69-74

Mugford M 1990 Economics of scale & low risk maternity care: what is the evidence? *Maternity Action* **46**: 100-2

Murphy Black T 1992 Systems of midwifery care in use in Scotland. *Midwifery* **8**: 113-124

National Association of Health Authorities and Trusts 1993 *NAHAT's response to Changing Childbirth. The report of the Expert Maternity Group.* NAHAT. London

National Audit Office 1990 *The Maternity Services: Report by the Comptroller & Auditor General.* No.297, HMSO. London

National Health Service Management Executive 1991 *Junior doctors: the new deal.* HMSO: London

National Health Service Management Executive 1994 *Woman-centred maternity services.* Department of Health. Leeds

National Perinatal Epidemiology Unit 1995 *Evaluation of new midwifery practices, ongoing research.* NPEU, Oxford

Oakley A 1980 *Women confined: towards a sociology of childbirth*, Martin Robertson, Oxford

Oakley A 1986 The importance of being a nurse. In: Oakley A (ed). *Telling the truth about Jerusalem.* Blackwell Scientific, Oxford

Oakley A. Rajan L. Grant A 1990 Social support and pregnancy outcome. *British Journal Obstetrics and Gynaecology* **997**: 155-162

OPCS 1993 *Mortality statistics, perinatal and infant.* HMSO. London

Page L 1993 Changing Childbirth. *MIDIRS Midwifery Digest* **3**:4

Parkin F 1979 *Marxism and class theory: a bourgeois critique*, Tavistock, London

Parsons T 1954 The professions and social structure. In: Parsons T. (ed.) *Essays in sociological theory.* Free Press. New York

Piore M, Sabel C 1984 *The second industrial divide.* Basic Books, New York

Reid M. Gutteridge S. McIlwaine G M 1983 *A comparison of the delivery of care between a hospital and a peripheral clinic. Report submitted to the Scottish Home & Health Department.* Social Paediatric and Obstetric Research Unit, University of Glasgow

Robinson J 1974 Active management of childbirth reduces hazards and anxiety. *The Times*, 12/8/84, Page 6

Robinson K 1992 The nursing workforce: aspects of inequality. In Robinson J, Gray A, Elkan R, (eds.) *Policy issues in nursing.* Open University Press, Milton Keynes

Robinson S 1990 Maintaining the independence of the midwifery profession: a continuing struggle. In: Garcia J, Kilpatrick R, Richards M (eds.) *The politics of maternity care: services for childbearing women in twentieth century Britain.* Clarendon Press, Oxford

Robinson S 1993 Combining work with caring for children: findings from a longitudinal study of midwives' careers. *Midwifery* **9** (4): 183-196

Robinson S, Owen H 1994 Retention in midwifery: findings from a longitudinal study of midwives' careers. In: Robinson S, Thomson A M (eds.) *Midwives' Research and Childbirth*, Vol **3**. Chapman and Hall, London

Romalis S 1985 Struggle between providers and recipients: the case of birth practices. In Lewin E, Oleson V. (eds.) *Women, Health and Healing*, Tavistock, London

Russell J 1982 Perinatal mortality: the current debate. *Sociology of Health & Illness* **4**(3): 302-319

Salvage J 1988 Professionalization—or struggle for survival? A consideration of current proposals for the reform of nursing in the United Kingdom. *Journal of Advanced Nursing* **13**: 515-519

Sandall J 1991 *Recent developments in maternity care in Britain: towards a sociological perspective.* Unpublished MSc, Royal Holloway and Bedford New College, University of London

Sandall J 1994 Research abstract 272, *MIRIAD.* Books for Midwives Press, Cheshire

Segal M 1986 The military and the family as greedy institutions, *Armed Forces and Society* 13:1

Shoham-Yakubovich I, Carmel S. Zwanger L *et al.*1989 Autonomy, job satisfaction and professional self image among nurses in the context of a physicians strike. *Social Science and Medicine* 28 (12): 1315-20

Social Services Committee, 1980 *Perinatal and Neonatal Mortality Second report 1979-1980* (Chairman R. Short), HMSO, London

Stacey M 1992 *Regulating British medicine: the General Medical Council*, Wiley, Chichester

Stock J. Wraight A 1993 *Developing continuity of care in maternity services: the implications for midwives.* Institute of Manpower Studies, University of Sussex

Streetly A 1994 Maternity care in the 1990s. *Health for all 2000 News* 26: 14-15

Tew M 1985 Place of birth and perinatal mortality. *Journal of College of General Practitioners* 35: 390-394

Tew M 1990 *Safer childbirth? A critical history of maternity care.* Chapman and Hall, London

Walby S. Greenwell J. Mackay L, *et al.*1994 *Medicine and nursing, professions in a changing health service.* Sage, London

Warwick C 1995 Midwives and maternity leave. *Maternity Action* 67: 6-7.

Watson P 1990 *Report on the Kidlington midwifery scheme.* Institute of Nursing, Radcliffe Infirmary, Oxford

Weitz R 1987 English midwives and the Association of Radical Midwives. *Women and Health* 12 (1); 79-89

White R 1985 Political regulators in British nursing. In: White R (ed.) *Political issues in nursing*, Vol 1, John Wiley, Chichester

Witz A 1990 Patriarchy and professions: the gendered politics of occupational closure. *Sociology* 24 (4): 675-690

Witz A 1992 *Professions and patriarchy.* Routledge. London

WHO 1986 *Having a baby in Europe.* WHO, Geneva

Wraight A, Ball, Seccombe I *et al.*1993 *Mapping Team Midwifery.* IMS Report Series 242. Institute of Manpower Studies, University of Sussex.

WHITHER MIDWIFERY: THE FUTURE OF MIDWIFERY

Edwin R. van Teijlingen

The way we see the future is determined by the way we see the past. We are "inevitably affected by our past" (Kirkham 1996: 191). It is difficult to make statements about the future, especially since any longer-term predictions are more likely to be 'wrong' than 'right'. We 'predict' and 'forecast' on the basis of how we see the past and present, what we know, and our judgement of what has gone before and what is going on now. In that sense, as Swann (1962: 259) reminded us: "Prophecies are really just extrapolations..." When predicting what could or should happen to midwifery many authors 'simply' extrapolate from the past; consequently some papers on the 'future' of midwifery read as if they could have easily been included in the history section of this reader. Following the approach of extrapolating the future from the past may simply lead to copying or continuing the past into the future. "The very knowledge that gives us the feeling that we understand what the past was all about may prevent us from learning anything about it" (Fischhoff 1980).

Although the future cannot generally be predicted with great accuracy, "futures can be invented" (Gabor 1964: 161). Through social engineering, political decision-making (legislation and regulation), lobbying, media publicity, and other human interventions we can help to shape our future. This is equally true for the future of midwifery as it is for any other socially constructed activity. In fact Giddens (1989: 21) pointed out that "our possibilities for the future" are a major element of the *sociological imagination* in the eyes of C. Wright Mills (1970) who coined the phrase originally. "Sociology helps us not only to analyse existing patterns of social life, but to see some of the 'possible futures' open to us. The imaginative pursuit of sociological work can show us not just what *is the case*, but what *could become the case* should we seek to make it so" (Giddens 1989: 21).

There seems to be very little material written on the future of midwifery, which was, of course, to be expected. When researching and analyzing it is far more difficult to 'predict' the future than it is to explain the past. Analyzing the past has the major advantage that one knows the present-day end result of historical developments. For that reason we can look back at some older papers recommending the most likely future for their time.

DIFFERENT FUTURES FOR MIDWIFERY?

There are different views in the literature on what the future holds for midwifery, depending on who is predicting, where they are and what their reasons are for making the prediction. At least three possible paths for midwifery have been predicted (Table 1).

First, the future of midwifery could lie in a return to more traditional midwifery, whereby pregnant women receive one-to-one care during home births or in low-technology birth centers. Secondly, the future of midwifery could bring further development of the high-technology obstetric hospital approach. Thirdly, the midwife could become more professionalized through increased academic education resulting in midwives occupying positions in more powerful and influential jobs with higher status. It is of course possible that overlap occurs between some of these pathways. For example, it is not inconceivable that academic midwifery education provides midwives with the confidence to argue in favor of and provide more community-based midwifery. Nor it is impossible that academic midwifery education leads to midwives developing skills to use certain obstetric technology currently the prerogative of medical practitioners.

Table 1 Three different future for midwifery

Type of midwifery	Some characteristics
Traditional midwifery	▪ Focus low-tech birth ▪ Stress psycho-social aspects ▪ Home, birth centre, short-stay hospital deliveries
Specialist obstetric nurse	▪ Post nursing specialty ▪ Increase use of (medical) technology ▪ Focus on hospital birth
Academic midwifery	▪ Increased use of evidence-based practice ▪ University-based education ▪ Midwifery part of hospital/academic hierarchy

BACK TO THE FUTURE

In the first option midwifery will return to its roots of 'low-tech birth' with an emphasis on providing psychosocial support rather than obstetric care in a setting where people are seen to be more important than the technical equipment and hospital routines. This trend can be seen in many industrialized countries, often in reaction to the medicalization of childbirth. For example, Johnston (1995:13) argued that in Australia: "Continuity of caregiver has been shown to reduce the mother's need for obstetric intervention.... The inappropriate use of obstetric technology carries a cost to the mother, the child, and society." In some areas of Britain, for example Glasgow and Aberdeen, experiments are taking place with semi-independent midwifery units within the obstetric hospital. In a Midwifery Development Unit based at the major teaching hospital in Glasgow "each pregnant woman had a named midwife whom she met at the first antenatal visit and who aimed to provide the majority of planned episodes of care from booking to discharge..." (Turnbull *et al.* 1996: 213). Thus midwives aim to provide total care for each woman throughout the pregnancy and labour and the postnatal period (Turnbull *et al.* 1995). This view can also be found in *The Vision'* (in this volume), a publication of a British organization called The Association of Radical Midwives (ARM 1986). Also Jenkins (1992 and this volume) urges the British midwifery profession "to focus all its energies into changing practice" towards a more women-centred midwifery model. In addition, Donley (1986) argues for the upgrading of the role and status of the New Zealand midwife in order that "she could again be autonomous and operate according to the WHO definition." A different factor determining the future of midwifery might be the decrease in interest in obstetrics as a specialty amongst doctors. North American doctors are less likely to choose to go into obstetrics due to the high cost of malpractice insurance (Davis-Floyd 1992: 300). Thus leaving a gap in the market that can be filled by midwives.

DeVries (1993: 141) raised the question: "Can midwives survive in the modern world without sacrificing their tradition, their identity and their unique body of knowledge?" His thesis is that professional groups can gain power by 'creating' risk—that is by *emphasizing* risk, by redefining life events as 'risky'. In his view "midwives are bound to lose status as birth became less risky and as 'better' practitioners appeared who could help manage this uncertain time" (DeVries 1993: 143). He concluded that the attempt by some midwives to seek a niche in the modern medical environment by claiming to be experts in 'low-risk' birth threatens their credibility as a professional group. "Midwives seem to face an unusual predicament: to enhance their status it seems they must renounce their tradition. They can earn their niche in the system only if they cease to be recognizable as midwives" (DeVries 1993: 144).

In non-western societies this trend is often apparent in a call for recognizing the contribution made by TBAs (Traditional Birth Attendants) and incorporating them in the official health care structure. For example, Lecky-Thompson (1994) explores the reasons why Australian traditional midwives need to be recognized. In developing countries we might also find a growing understanding and appreciation of the TBA. Betts (1996:114), for example, stresses the role of the professional midwife in training and supervising TBAs at village level and in the 1980s pilot training courses were begun to upgrade the skills of the Zimbabwean TBAs, to familiarize them with the rural clinics, and to encourage them to make appropriate referrals to the clinics (see Sparks in this volume). Although Jordan (1989:925) warns us that "in spite of decades of experience, training programs for TBAs have not been particularly successful", a view echoed by many (see for example, Jeffery & Jeffery 1989; MacCormack 1989). The reasons for this failure, according to Jordan (1989) lie partly in the ethnocentric approach of the instructors when the teaching TBAs, partly in the reliance on the biomedical model for teaching content, and partly in the reliance on formal instructional teaching methods, rather than the more informal apprenticeship training. Of course, one should not overromanticize the use of apprenticeships in specialized learning in traditional societies (Browner 1989: 938).

THE SPECIALIST OBSTETRIC NURSE

As a second alternative, the future of midwifery could lie in a further development of the high-technology obstetric hospital approach. Following this approach midwives would conduct more antenatal tests, use more sophisticated monitoring equipment in a hospital setting, and perhaps offer a little more psychosocial support. This possible future development is reflected in Crawford's advocacy for sub-specialties within midwifery (this volume). She lists a number of areas that "are ripe to become areas of midwifery sub-specializing", for example, obstetric operating theatre and recovery room; intensive care of the seriously ill mother; and antenatal and postnatal clinics. Crawford mentions both the biomedical sub-specialty, e.g. the "midwife interventionist" in the realm of intensive care, monitoring and supervision, and low psycho-social sub-specialty, e.g. the outpatient clinic which requires "special skills and a special temperament from midwives." Kargar (1992: 22) commenting on developments in Britain in the past decades pointed to the "gradual emergence in Britain of the obstetric nurse who goes under the title of midwife." Under this scenario the specialist midwife is at risk of becoming more engulfed by a nursing framework. Burrows (1991 and this volume) argues that if midwives allow themselves "to be treated as obstetric nurses, we deserve all we get. We are practitioners in our own right, able to care totally for the mother during normal pregnancy, labour and the puerperium". The midwife as specialist obstetric nurse will be outnumbered by other (specialist) nurses in both the workplace and professional bodies. A situation already a thorn in the flesh for many British midwives, whose central professional body, the UKCC (United Kingdom Central Council), is shared with and dominated by the nursing profession. Frame and North (1990:7) argued that over the past decade midwives have expended a lot of energy to retain their status and separate identity and that nurses have not expressed solidarity on issues related to midwives' pay and working conditions.

Tymstra (1993:136) argues that "Medical-technological developments form a strong threat to the Dutch midwifery system, which always placed the natural character of pregnancy at the fore". Faulkner (1985:106) argues that "The greater dependence of women on the expertise and technology of doctors may be explained partly by the medicalization of all matters relating to our ability to bear children."

In non-western societies this trend includes the stamping out of an "obsolete and old-fashioned tradition", and a take over of the provision of maternity care by modern western medicine. Thus TBAs are replaced by midwives/nurses trained according to a western model. This view is not confined to the developing world, Hardin presented a paper at the Southern Medical Association in New Orleans in which he argued that "...it seems that what is most needed in this country is the better training of physicians in obstetrics, and not an attempt to educate the midwives to the extent of the European midwives", furthermore, since midwifery "cannot be eradicated, the danger to the public can be minimized by some provision of proper regulation, supervision and control of the midwife by the state" (Hardin 1925: 348). One of the replies to Hardin's paper addressed the question: "Why do we have midwives?" "Because the public does not demand any better .... I do not believe we ought to try to educate midwives. It cannot be done. We should educate the public and when people demand better things, they will get them" (Marlette 1925: 350).

THE ACADEMIC MIDWIFE

In the third possible scenario midwifery follows the path of the professionalising nursing profession, in other words the midwife becomes more like the doctor. The midwife would become more professional, based on her now academic education and position in the hospital/medical hierarchy. Many recognize that midwifery education is important for the profession. Thus midwifery education in the UK is now regarded as "the bedrock upon which the profession is built" (Robinson 1991: 302), and it has been argued that the midwifery curriculum should generate autonomy and professionalism (Thomson & Hall 1994: 34). "Enhancing political awareness and activity as part of midwifery education helps all midwives become invested in the future of their profession and hopefully will expand the relatively small corps of midwives currently responsible for political activity" (Declerq 1994: 236). Legal requirements can act as push factor in the direction of academic training in midwifery, e.g. Rooks (1983, and in this volume) pointed out that the state of Oregon introduced a law, which stated that all nurse-midwives should have Masters degrees in nursing (sic.).

Porter suggests in this volume that midwives who have followed a more academic midwifery education, an increasingly popular option in the UK as in the USA, may find it easier to accept the call for evidence-based practice than do those who have trained, mainly in clinical areas, with minimal education in health service research methods. Being able to evaluate the research evidence will enable academically trained midwives to question the strengths and weaknesses of clinical practice in obstetrics. There is a growing literature on the subject of evidence-based maternity care (especially Chalmers 1988; Chalmers *et al* 1989), that is available, not just to medical practitioners, but also to midwives and consumers of maternity services. Kirkham (1996: 182) points out that, on the one hand, "a body of knowledge is beginning to be built from midwifery research" although, on the other hand, "Midwifery research is very new. Few aspects of midwifery have yet been researched." In addition the growth in the number of midwife-researchers in Western Europe and elsewhere[1] might provide the midwifery profession with its academically trained advocates in the debates surrounding pregnancy and childbirth.

Furthermore, the establishment in the UK of the *Midwives Information and Resource Centre* (MIDIRS) in 1986, the work of the Midwifery Research Database (MIRIAD) in 1989 (Midwifery Research Initiative 1991; Simms *et al.* 1994) and developments based on information technology such as the establishment of the Computers in Teaching Initiative at the Centre for Nursing and Midwifery at the University of Sheffield (UK) in 1995 (Proctor & Hible 1995: 2) are signs of the growing professionalisation of midwifery.

For those involved in midwifery and those who care about its development one can see reasons for optimism as well as pessimism. One of the consequences of the recent incorporation of midwifery education in the university education in Britain is the questioning of the academic credibility of midwifery teachers who were themselves trained in the old style midwifery colleges (Clarke 1994: 252). Also noteworthy is the suggested backlash against evidence-based care from midwives "moving into higher education who confuse anything with the word 'sciences' or 'evidence' in the title with the medical model, and who avoid like the plague anything that might seem 'reductionist'" (Page 1996: 191).

Professionalising developments in midwifery can also be observed in some developing countries, where midwives are trained to perform what were traditionally obstetric interventions, such as emergency caesarian sections, repair ruptured uteri and perform hysterectomies (Duale 1992; Betts 1996: 116).

FINAL CONSIDERATIONS

It is, of course, likely that a number of future scenarios develop in different places and at different times. It is possible that midwifery develops in other ways, very differently from the three scenarios mentioned above. Moreover, some of the three scenarios will happen at the same time and place. For example, Britain in the 1980 and 1990s saw the establishment of independent community midwives as well as postgraduate courses in midwifery. Whereas in the Netherlands, the length of midwifery education was increased from three to four years in 1994, the emphasis is still very much on community-based midwifery. In many developing countries traditional midwifery co-exists with western-style nurse-midwifery. Perhaps all we "can be sure about is change", as highlighted by Kroll (1996: xi) in the 'Preface' of her book *Midwifery Care for the Future: Meeting the Challenge.*

REFERENCES

ARM, 1986, *The Vision. Proposal for the future of the maternity services*, Ormskirk: Association of Radical Midwives

Betts, G.A., 1996, Midwifery education for the future–The needs of 'Developing' Countries, In: *Midwives and Safer Motherhood*, Murray, S.F. (ed.), London: Mosby

Browner, C.H., 1989, Comments, *Social Science and Medicine*, **28**:937-8

Burrows, P., 1991, Midwifery: profession with a future, *Midwife, Health Visitor & Community Nurse*, **27**: 143.

Chalmers, I., 1988, *Oxford Database of Perinatal Trials*, Oxford: Oxford University Press

Chalmers, I., Enkin, M., Keirse, M.J.N.C., 1989, *Effective Care in Pregnancy and Childbirth*, Oxford: Oxford University Press

Clarke, R.A., 1994, Future imperfect for midwife teachers?, *Midwives Chronicle & Nursing Notes* **107**: 252

Davis-Floyd, R.E., 1992, *Birth as an American Rite of Passage*, Berkeley: University of California Press

Declerq, E.R., 1994, A cross-national analysis of midwifery politics: six lessons for midwives, *Midwifery*, **10**, 232-7 and in this volume.

DeVries, R. G. (1993), 'A cross national view of the status of midwives,' 131-146 in *Gender, Work and Medicine: women and the medical division of labor*, Riska, E. & Wegar, K. (Eds), London, Sage Publications.

Donley, J., 1986, *Save the Midwife*, Auckland: New Women's Press

Duale, S., 1992, Delegation of responsibility in maternity care in Karawa rural health zone, Zaire, *International Journal of Gynaecology & Obstetrics*, **38** (Suppl.):33-5

Faulkner, W., 1985, 'Medical technology and the right to heal', In. *Smothered by Invention: Technology in Women's Lives*, Faulkner, W, E. Arnold (eds.), London: Pluto

Fischhoff, B., 1980, For those condemned to study the past: heuristics and biases in hindsight, In: *Judgement under Uncertainty: Heuristics and Biases*, Kahneman, D., Slovic, O., Tversky, A. (eds.), Cambridge: Cambridge University Press

Frame, S., North, J., 1990, Will history repeat itself?, *Midwifery Matters* No.44: 6-7

Gabor, D., 1964, *Inventing the future*, Harmondsworth: Penguin Books

Giddens, A., 1989, *Sociology*, Cambridge: Polity Press

Hardin, E.R., 1925, The midwife problem, *Southern Medical Journal*, **18**:347-9

Jeffery, R., P.M. Jeffery, 1989, Comments, *Social Science & Medicine*, **28**:939

Jenkins, R., 1992, Midwifery: which way forward? *Professional Care of Mother & Child*: 164-67

Johnston, J., 1995, Issues in private practice: midwife care—the future *Australian College of Midwives*. **8**:13-6

Jordan, B., 1989, Cosmopolitical obstetrics: some insights from the training of traditional midwives, *Social Science & Medicine*, **28**:925-37

Kargar, I, 1992, Last chance for midwives, *Nursing Times*, **88**:22

Kirkham, M., 1996, Professionalization past and present: with women or with the powers that be?, In: *Midwifery Care for the Future: Meeting the Challenge*, Kroll, D. (ed.), London: Baillière Tindall

Kroll, D. (ed.), 1996, *Midwifery Care for the Future: Meeting the Challenge*, London: Baillière Tindall

Lecky-Thompson M., 1994, The recognition of traditional midwives, *Australian College of Midwives*. **7**:7-8

Marlette, G.C., 1925, Discussion (Abstract), *Southern Medical Journal*, **18**:349

MacCormack, C.P., 1989, Comments, *Social Science & Medicine*, **28**:941-3

Midwifery Research Initiative, 1991, *MIRIAD: Midwifery Research Database*, Oxford: National Perinatal Epidemiology Unit

Mills, C. Wright, 1970, *The Sociological Imagination*, Harmondsworth: Penguin

Page, L., 1996, The backlash against evidence-based care, *Birth*, **23**: 191-2

Proctor, P.M., Hible, G., 1995, Editorial, *The CTI Centre for Nursing and Midwifery at the University of Sheffield Newsletter*, **1**:2-3

Robinson, S., 1991, Preparation for practice: the educational experiences and career intentions of newly qualified midwives, In: *Midwives, Research & Childbirth* Vol **2**, Robinson, S. & Thomson, A.M. (eds.). London: Chapman & Hall

Rooks, J.P, 1983, The Context of Nurse—Midwifery in the 1980s: Our Relationships with Medicine, Nursing, Lay-Midwives, Consumers & Health Care Economist, *Journal of Nurse-Midwifery*, **28**: 3-8

Simms, C, McHaffie, H., Renfrew, M.J., Ashurst, H. (eds.), 1994, The Midwifery Research Database MIRIAD, a sourcebook of information about research in midwifery, Hale: Books for Midwives Press

Swann, M., 1962, What of the future?, In: *What the Human Race is up to*, Mitchison, N. (ed.), London: Victor Gollancz Ltd

Thomson, V., Hall, D., 1994, Case study: a credit scheme for nurses and midwives, In: Humphreys, J., Quinn, F.M. (eds.), *Health Care Education: The challenge of the market*, London: Chapman & Hall

Turnbull D., Reid M., McGinley M., Sheilds N.R., 1995, Changes in midwives' attitudes to their professional role following implementation of the midwifery development unit, *Midwifery* **11**:110-9

Turnbull D., Holmes, A., Sheilds, R., Cheyne, H., Twaddle, S., Harper Gilmour, W., McGinley M., Reid M., Johnstone, I., Geer, I., McIlwaine, G., Burnett Lunan, C., 1996, Randomized, controlled trial of efficacy of midwife-managed care, *The Lancet*, **348**:213-8

Tymstra, T., 1993, 'The impact of medical-technological developments on midwifery in the Netherlands', In. *Successful Home Birth and Midwifery: The Dutch Model*, E. Abraham-Van der Mark (ed.), Westport, Connecticut: Bergin & Garvey

[1] For example, to name but a few the McMaster Midwifery Education Program in Canada, see web page: **http://www-fhs.mcmaster.ca/midwifery/student/index2.htm**; the Nurse-Midwifery program at Georgetown University, Washington D.C., the oldest Catholic university in the USA, highlights that upon completion of degree requirements, students are eligible to take the certification examination of the American College of Nurse-Midwives Certification Council, see web page: **http://www.dml.georgetown.edu/schnurs/midwife1. html**; Boston University also offers a nurse-midwifery education program which was established in 1991 see web page: **http://med-sph.bu.edu/depts/mch/nmep.htm**; since 1991, a World Health Organization Collaborating Center for Nursing and Midwifery Development was designated in the George Mason University College of Nursing and Health Science (Fairfax, Virginia, USA).see web page: **http://www.ido.gmu.edu/ centers/whocc/;** there is also a graduate program in nurse-midwifery at the University of Pennsylvania, Philadelphia, see web page: **http://www.upenn.edu/nursing/courses/midwifery/midwiferyhome.html**. In addition Rooks (1983, and in this volume) mentioned the Midwifery School in Seattle.

MIDWIFERY: WHICH WAY FORWARD?

Rosemary Jenkins [*]

The Nurses, Midwives and Health Visitors Act came into force almost 13 years ago, with scenes reminiscent of this year's dissolution of Parliament. Along with a number of other Bills in their final stages it was "nodded through" in the final hours of the Callaghan government. With what, to many, seemed undue haste at the end, the Central Midwives Boards were swept away and replaced by multidisciplinary bodies, i.e. the United Kingdom Central Council (UKCC) and the National Boards.

From the start the Act had its detractors in the midwifery profession who saw the statutory change as yet another blow to the independence of the profession. Their fears would seem to have been justified when the English National Board accepted, against the strongly worded advice of its Midwifery Committee, the changed role of its education officers to a generic rather than a specialist role. The possible weakness of the Act, in requiring consultation with the Midwifery Committee with no obligation on the UKCC to act on any advice, and with the difficult-to-interpret phrase "all things relating to midwifery", proved too much for some midwives who set up the Midwifery Legislation Group and have since campaigned for new legislation.

But how necessary is a legislative framework for the protection of midwifery, and should legislation be used for this purpose? Or, as with previous legislation, should the prime aim be the protection of the public? DeVries has suggested that dynamic and autonomous midwifery practice is only truly to be found where there is an absence of licensure and that once legislation is introduced there is a tendency for midwives to adopt medical models for their care. Looking at the development or regression of midwifery in the United Kingdom and the statutory framework, it is very hard to see that one in any way influences the other.

Midwifery saw its period of most rapid decline during the 1970s. There were just 13 years from the Peel Report, which advocated provision for 100% hospital confinement, through to the research of Chelsea College in the role and responsibility of the midwife, which showed a clear decline in the autonomy of the midwife. The Peel Report's recommendation of 100% consultant-influenced hospital confinement was achieved. General practitioners in "shared care" programmes moved en masse to provide antenatal care.

Midwives became marginalised into parentcraft teaching and post-natal care, still delivering babies, but under strictly-worded medical protocols. The autonomous route to training, the then Direct-Entry Course, also almost disappeared. Yet during these years midwifery had its own statutory bodies—the Central Midwives Boards. And during this period of greatest decline the Board finally achieved apparent professional independence. For the first time it had, as its chairman, a midwife.

Since 1979 the profession has been steadily clawing back what it almost lost. There are now 18 programmes of pre-registration training, funded in part with Department of Health assistance. And now the House of Commons Health Committee has recommended what amounts to an open-ended charter for the return of autonomous midwifery practice. Yet, during all this time, the profession has been governed by the multidisciplinary UKCC and National Boards.

[*] Secretary of the RCM Welsh Board, Dyfed
Professional Care of Mother & Child June (1992): 164-7

There is unlikely to be any proven causal relationship, albeit in an inverse direction, between the existing statutory bodies and the ebb and flow of midwifery practice. The greater likelihood is that the return to independent practitioner status will depend far more on the actions of midwives rather than the actions of a remote statutory body.

The profession is presented with its greatest challenge for decades by the recent Health Committee Report on the Maternity Services chaired by Nicholas Winterton. This recommends midwives to hold their own caseloads; to be recognised as the primary carer for many women; to have midwife-led units; to have admitting rights to hospitals. Yet the Health Committee got it right when, in its report, it said that changes in maternity services to meet the needs of women will not come about by wishing. They will need a concerted effort.

Midwifery is a small profession with about 35,000 in active practice. It is a woman's profession, serving women, and therefore is at a gender disadvantage. It will need to focus all its energies into changing practice to the model suggested in the Winterton report. And it is in this direction, rather than towards achieving possibly irrelevant statutory independence, that the profession should go. Protection of the professional identity can only really be achieved if every practitioner undertakes willingly to meet the needs and choices of her clients. Let's leave the role of statute to where it really belongs—not ring-fencing us, but protecting the mothers and babies we serve.

[1] DeVries R G. Midwifery and the Problem of Licensure. Greenwich Conn.: JAI Press Inc, 1982.
[2] Midwifery Advisory Committee. Sir John Peel (Chairman). Domiciliary Midwifery and Maternity Bed Needs. London: HMSO 1970
[3] Robinson S, Golden J. Bradley S. A Study of the Role and Responsibilities of the Midwife. Nursing Education Research Unit, Chelsea College, University of London 1983
[4] House of Commons Health Committee (Chair: Winterton) 2nd Report, Vol 1.1991-2, London: HMSO

MIDWIFERY: PROFESSION WITH A FUTURE

Pamela Burrows[*]

In contrast to some of my colleagues, I am optimistic for the future of midwifery. Why do I feel this optimism? Look around, do you not see the enthusiasm of the student midwives eager for responsibility, autonomy and demonstrating real empathy for those under their care? And the majority of practising midwives who support women throughout their pregnancy, labour and puerperium with dedication despite the pressure under which they work? Most midwives are juggling their lives at work with responsibility for families and children, and yet fulfil their role professionally and enthusiastically.

DON'T LET DOCTORS TAKE THE CREDIT

We are aware that we are a minority profession, and the need for vigilance must be stressed to ensure that midwifery flourishes and that mothers and families of the future can expect the ultimate in care. The medical profession cannot take all the credit for the reduction in mortality and morbidity in childbirth. More than 75% of deliveries are performed by midwives, together with the majority of intrapartum care, and any emergency action in the event of abnormality occurring is initiated by midwives. Referrals made to GPs and obstetricians when problems are diagnosed during the pregnancy and puerperium are also initiated by midwives.

Let us not underestimate the value of the care we give to the mothers and babies. Perhaps we should not be so modest. In future, let us make everyone more aware of our role as midwives. We have many opportunities for spreading the word, e.g. when booking expectant mothers, during relaxation and parentcraft classes, to friends and relatives, medical students, senior house officers and, dare I say it, obstetricians.

STRENGTHEN SUPERVISION

To enable midwives to perform their role effectively, the supervision of midwives' needs to be strengthened and this is in the pipeline. Midwifery teachers and midwifery managers must give more support for the principle of greater autonomy for midwives, and ensure that the midwife's role is not eroded. This is a factor of key importance.

The Midwifery Committee of the English National Board argued strenuously for the retention of the specialist midwifery education officer and despite being overruled on this matter, and the introduction of the new generic education officers, we did ensure specialist midwifery input for validation of training institutions. We also negotiated for the situation to be evaluated after a period of one year.

[*] Midwifery Sister on the Midwifery Unit at the District General Hospital, Stafford, working on the Delivery Suite under an internal rotation system. Pamela Burrows is also elected midwife member of the English National Board for Nurses, Midwives & Health Visitors

We cannot, however, rely upon the Midwifery Committee at the Board to fight for everything in midwifery. As individuals we must look at our practice and ensure that our skills are being utilised effectively. What is the point in duplication of care? If we allow ourselves to be treated as obstetric nurses, we deserve all we get. We are practitioners in our own right, able to care totally for the mother during normal pregnancy, labour and the puerperium.

ACKNOWLEDGE ACCOUNTABILITY

How much of your role as a midwife is limited by local policies? Policies are not tablets of stone and can be changed by discussion and negotiation. Try it, if you feel frustrated by them. You may be pleasantly surprised by how much you can achieve.

We can fulfil our important job in whatever sphere of practice we operate. Just because many of us work in a hospital, this need not erode our future role. We always support and advise, and our role in hospital can be enhanced, as at Hinchingbrook Hospital where the midwife's role is truly recognised in the "working without Registrars" situation. We must acknowledge our accountability and be prepared to make decisions about the care we provide for the mothers and babies.

CHERISH THE STUDENTS

To ensure we continue to have a future supply of good midwives we must create a supportive, caring environment for student midwives. There will be a reduced supply of young people in the near future to meet the demand, and clinical grading in midwifery will need to be addressed. However, we can look to the more mature entrant into midwifery: the mother who has children less dependent upon her, and people who wish to change direction in their career. These recruits will provide an abundance of knowledge from their past experience which should be looked upon as an asset to midwifery. We will need to be flexible in our approach to working hours to accommodate these students. We should look upon this as an advantage to us all in the future, should our own family situation change.

Support and consideration for our colleagues should be high on our order of priorities, to ensure midwives stay in the profession. This must be nurtured from management downwards. Crisis within a profession concentrates the mind on these matters, and I trust we may all benefit.

We have a fantastic job—*long live midwifery*—and it's up to us to be assertive and keep it going. We don't have to wave banners, but you can if you must. Strive for more autonomy at a local level, and if enough of us do then the future of midwifery will be secure.

THE VISION: PROPOSALS FOR THE FUTURE OF THE MATERNITY SERVICES

Association of Radical Midwives[*]

INTRODUCTION

There has been a growing awareness that all is not well with the present organization of the maternity services. In 1982, mothers and fathers were sufficiently angered by what they saw as the routine use of inappropriate obstetric technology that 5,000 of them demonstrated outside the Royal Free Hospital in London[1]. Many midwives are 'dissatisfied with the present conveyor-belt system of midwifery care'[2]. The report *The Role and Responsibilities of the Midwife*[3] extensively documents underuse of the midwife's skills and conflict resulting from overlap of her role with that of the doctor. The Maternity Services Advisory Committee was aware of the "numerous consumer complaints about the so-called impersonal nature of care in hospitals, where maternity services are now concentrated"[4]. They recommended effective use of midwives' skills (4a) and stated that continuity of care is important to enable the woman to build a relationship with the staff (4b). The Royal College of Obstetricians and Gynaecologists report that a common complaint is that a pregnant woman may see many different doctors[5], and acknowledge that delivery by the same midwife as seen antenatally is ideal (5a). Midwives and mothers want a safe, sensitive service that sees childbirth as a part of life, not as a disease.

We have set out in A.R.M. to propose a new "Vision" for the maternity services in 10 years time. We recognize and applaud the strides our profession has made particularly in the last 10 years, but feel the crisis is far from over. Many midwives feel frustrated with the present segmented pattern of care[6,7] and find themselves feeling far from "practitioners in their own right"[8].

Childbearing women, too, have much to tell us about horizons to be reached which will provide increased flexibility and satisfaction for both midwives and mothers[9]. The combined efforts of users of the service and professionals will be needed to effect real improvements (4c). Research into established practice has shown some procedures to be unnecessary and others to be of no clear benefit[10,11,12]. Further research is urgently needed to evaluate the obstetric interventions that users and midwives are increasingly unhappy with[13,14]. In addition, there is the wasteful duplication of services, principally by medical practitioners and midwives[15], but also by hospital medical staff and General Practitioners[16]. In this day of severe financial restraints upon health resources, we feel it is time for this structure to be re-examined[17,18].

We fully support the ideals of the National Health Service and are committed to the implementation of the "Vision" within the N.H.S.

Research has demonstrated that the role of the midwife is still not as recognized or as highly respected as it should be among our medical and nursing colleagues as well as the general public[3]. The following definition of a Midwife was adopted by the International Confederation of Midwives and International Federation of Gynaecologists and Obstetricians, after amendment of the definition formulated by the World Health Organisation:

---

[*] The Association of Radical Midwives, 62, Greetby Hill, Ormskirk, Lancs. L39 2DT, UK Reprinted with permission.

"A midwife is a person who, having been regularly admitted to a midwifery educational programme, duly recognised in the country in which it is located, has successfully completed the prescribed course of studies in midwifery and has acquired the requisite qualifications to be registered and/or legally licensed to practise midwifery."

She must be able to give the necessary supervision, care and advice to women during pregnancy, labour and the postpartum period, to conduct deliveries on her own responsibility and to care for the newborn and the infant. This care includes preventative measures, the detection of abnormal conditions in mother and child, the procurement of medical assistance and the execution of emergency measures in the absence of medical help. She has an important task in health counselling and education, not only for the patients, but also within the family and the community. The work should involve antenatal education and preparation for parenthood and extends to certain areas of gynaecology, family planning and childcare. She may practise in hospitals, clinics, health units, domiciliary conditions or in any other service"[19].

Throughout this draft proposal the midwife is referred to as 'she'. The term 'mother' or 'woman' should be taken to include her partner and children where appropriate. No offence is implied to male midwives, fathers, and children. This is purely for convenience.

BASIC PRINCIPLES

The basic principles from which this proposal evolves are:

- The relationship between mother and midwife is fundamental to good midwifery care[20].
- The mother is the central person in the process of care[21].
- Informed choice in childbirth for women[22].
- Full utilization of midwives' skills[23,24].
- Continuity of care for all childbearing women [24a,25,26].
- Community based care[6,15a,20].
- Accountability of services to those receiving them[4].
- Care should do no harm to mother and baby.

1. The Overview

1. 1.

In 10 years time, 60-70% of midwives will work in community based group practices of 2-5 midwives[15c]. These midwives will work from a variety of places depending on local need[15d] . These midwives will be responsible for the care of the vast majority of women. It is generally accepted that 85% of women having a baby in Europe do not have complications[6,27].

1.2.

30-40% of midwives will be hospital based, and organized in teams. These teams, working with a consultant obstetrician, will be responsible for the antenatal, intranatal, and postnatal care of the 15% of women who present with complications at booking or who develop them during pregnancy. A higher ratio of midwives to mothers will be needed to provide the more intensive care required. The hospital-based teams will continue to work shifts, and those in the community will work a flexible rota including being "on call". We recognize that not all midwives can work full-time and we envisage job sharing as one alternative.

1.3.

Midwives will be the recognised point of entry into care for all pregnant women[28,7]. Their services will be publicized widely and information will be available for women to choose the team or group practice that they prefer. Group practices will encourage antenatal discussion groups, postnatal support groups, breastfeeding groups etc., as well as conducting 'education for parenthood' classes. Hospital teams would encourage similar groups such as twins and caesarean support groups. The aim will be to help all women take an active role in their pregnancies and experiences of childbirth and parenting. Pregnancy tests will be available at the group practices and at hospital. Midwives will be seen as the professionals to consult in all matters relating to childbirth[29] (see above: Definition of a Midwife).

1.4.

The rest of this document deals with various aspects of the overview in more detail. Your comments would be most appreciated. Indeed, if the maternity services are to be radically changed to meet the needs of families in the future, we NEED your ideas and comments.

This is your chance to change the maternity services, your chance to influence the type of midwifery care given in the future.

2. Group Practices

2.1.

Flexibility will be the keynote in these practices of 2-5 midwives to allow for the variations of local needs around the country and the preferences of individual midwives. Premises will vary according to the local situation. The midwife will not wear a uniform and will be known in the community from her visits to schools as well as from her work directly with childbearing women.

2.2.

Her role is seen to be that of the expert in matters relating to pregnancy, childbirth and the puerperium, the educator in this field, the facilitator in encouraging women to define and fulfil their own needs, the care-giver at a time when women may be at their most vulnerable, the sympathetic and trusted friend[19,22].

2.3.

Women may come to these practices seeking pre-conceptual advice or may come requesting a pregnancy test. They may come for an introductory chat or for a full booking visit. All women would be given a comprehensive list of group practices in the district as well as the telephone number of the local Supervisor of Midwives with the advice that any problems would be dealt with by her in strict confidence.

2.4.

Midwives in group practices would have direct access to laboratory and other services (e.g. scans) which may be required for normal pregnant women. They would have direct access to consultant obstetricians to request an opinion on any case in doubt[30,31], though any decision to transfer the woman to consultant care would be shared between the consultant, the midwife, and the woman as partners in care[22].

2.5.

Midwives in group practices would deliver women in hospital and at home[32], according to individual circumstances and individual choice[23,24b]. Length of postnatal stays in hospital would vary depending on the mother's condition and personal preferences. Practice midwives would visit regularly to provide the principal care and advice.

2.6.

Postnatal care would continue at home for 10-14 days as at present with responsibility up until 28 days at the discretion of the midwife[33]. Full use would be made of this time based on the foundation of trust established to assist in the establishment of satisfactory feeding and in the adjustment of the family to its new member.

2.7.

Group practices would be composed of midwives with varying lengths of experience. Newly qualified midwives would be required to work on an apprentice basis for one year before being fully responsible members, and would be self-selected and group approved prior to joining a practice as a full member[15e].

2.8.

Each practice would have one representative who would attend regular local meetings with their peers and supervisor to discuss any relevant information that could be usefully shared (e.g. research findings, specific case studies). It would be a source of support and communication between practices and an opportunity to formulate needs and policies. There would also be great benefits derived from the participation of hospital team midwives in such regular meetings to ensure that channels of communication are open and midwives have the opportunity to see each other as equals.

3. Hospital Teams

3.1.

Continuity of care will be an essential component of care for the women who are diagnosed as having complications at booking or during their pregnancy[17,31,7]. Their care will be managed by a small team of midwives working in close co-operation with a consultant obstetrician[2]. Senior House Officers (S.H.O.s) and medical students will participate as learners only. The care will be managed by joint decisions made between midwives, their consultant, and the mother.

3.2.

The hospital team will conduct antenatal, intranatal, and postnatal care including home visits (unless geographically prohibitive) for all the women they book. Each team will most likely be based from a hospital ward which will include antenatal and postnatal beds and consulting rooms for clinic appointments. It is to be remembered that the bulk of the present hospital population will be the responsibility of the community group practices, and will be returning to their homes after relatively short postnatal stays if they have been delivered in hospital. Therefore the ratio of midwives to high dependency patients should be high and the care received of a superior quality to the present stretched resources found in most hospitals.

3.3.

There would remain sufficient flexibility in the service to allow the care of women with complications to be shared between a community group practice and a hospital team if this seemed the most desirable alternative. Indeed, for a woman who is transferred late in pregnancy, it would seem most likely that her postnatal care would return to the community group practice. It is expected that community group practice midwives will maintain some social relationship with women who have been transferred to hospital teams.

3.4.

Hospital team midwives could choose to organize themselves into fixed rota shifts or variable shifts depending on their individual requirements. In any case, with a ratio of approximately 7 midwives to one consultant, the mother would have an opportunity to become familiar with the entire team during the course of her care[34].

3.5.

As mentioned earlier, hospital team midwives would be educators in every sense as are their colleagues in the community. They could facilitate additional discussion and support groups for women having special needs e.g. caesarian support, twins, premature baby groups etc. They would conduct all normal deliveries for women under team care and assist in the complicated deliveries as familiar and skilled care givers[2].

3.6.

As in the community group practices, newly qualified midwives would be required to fulfil an apprentice year before becoming a full member of a team, and subject to the approval of other members of the team. Team midwives would be responsible to the Supervisor of Midwives as well as to the team consultant. As in the community, women on referral to a hospital team would receive a complete list of other teams in the area with the name, address and telephone number of the Supervisor of Midwives.

3.7.

The Special Care Baby Unit or Neonatal Intensive Care Unit would be retained as a specialized area within the hospital, maintaining its own staff with specialist training and experience[29a].

4. The Role of the Doctor

4.1.

There will be, as now, General Practitioner Obstetricians (G.P.O.s) and hospital-based Consultant Obstetricians supported by Registrars. S.H.O.s will become learners in both the hospital team practices and the community based group practices.

4.2.

Much of the obstetric care given by G.P.s at the moment results in either duplication of or failure to make full use of midwives' skills[28]. We recognize that the G. P. has a long-term commitment to the family and could be the source of much valuable background information in some cases. We support this contribution and foresee midwives routinely informing the woman's G.P. when care was undertaken.

4.3.

The G.P. will continue to provide medical care when the woman is ill but the midwife will be recognized as the expert in the field of normal childbirth[19]. The midwife will be able to initiate all emergency treatment, and have the backup of an efficient 'flying squad' to help with an obstetric or paediatric emergency.

4.4.

In order for women to have a real and wider choice in maternity care, it would be possible for a G.P. to provide total antenatal, intranatal, and postnatal care. Presently in the Netherlands women choose to book with a midwife, with a G. P. who provides maternity care, or with an obstetrician[30]. This may be a little used option but would provide an alternative method of care for the woman who particularly wants continuity of care from her G.P.

4.5.

The hospital based Consultant Obstetrician would be recognised, as now, as being the expert in the abnormal. The Consultant would be supported by a Registrar and would share much responsibility for care with a trusted team of midwives. The total caseload would be greatly reduced from current levels, enabling care to be given in a more total and humane manner[31]. The pregnant woman and her partner would have sufficient time at appointments for all aspects of care to be discussed so that the most suitable management could be agreed upon. Outcomes are likely to improve where advice is understood and tailored to individual needs[31].

4.6.

The team midwives will meet regularly with the Consultant and Registrar to discuss relevant research and initiate any changes in care considered useful. The professionals will share responsibility and decision making with the woman[35]. Other doctors, medical students, and student midwives would participate as learners within the team.

4.7.

The Consultant Obstetrician would also be available to give an opinion on any aspect of a woman's care that gave cause for concern directly to a community based group practice midwife[36]. Any decision to transfer part or total care to the hospital-based team would involve the woman, the midwife, and the consultant. As stated earlier, a flexible approach to the sharing of care could be maintained to suit individual circumstances. Midwifery and medical staff will each recognize the special skills of the other and come to decisions with the full participation of the women and their partners to the satisfaction of all concerned.

5. Financial Implications

5.1.

We fully support the ideals of the National Health Service that:

- The provision of care should be free to the user at the point of uptake.
- Midwifery care should be equally available to all users.

5.2.

At present, midwives are grossly undervalued and underpaid. The 'Short Report' recommended that midwives be paid at the same salary scale as Health Visitors[24c]. The Royal College of Midwives suggests a salary equivalent to Registrars, and say: "Salary levels for midwives are presently linked to nurses' pay scales. It is the view of the College that these pay scales do not reflect the role and responsibilities of the midwife or the value to society of the provision of an effective comprehensive 24 hour midwifery service"[37].

5.3.

We propose a salary of £11,000-£15,000 p.a. at present day values, with increments for each year of experience and for additional relevant qualifications e.g. the Advanced Diploma in Midwifery. Apprentice year midwives would be paid an interim figure between final year student pay and practicing midwives' starting salary. An administrative allowance would be paid to cover practice running costs, which would allow for the provision of a non-midwife practice manager. This manager might be shared between 2 or more group practices and would do the accounting, secretarial, and administrative work. These allowances may have to be weighted to allow for North/South and Urban/Rural disparity.

5.4.

Midwives will still be able to work privately, maintaining this area of choice for women and midwives. It is envisaged that there will be less demand for private care once midwifery is organized on the principles outlined in this paper.

6. Supervision

6.1.

The Supervisor of Midwives will be retained in a valuable and enhanced role. She has a vital part to play in the protection of the public by supporting the midwives in her locality and maintaining a high standard of practice[38].

6.2.

She will initiate regular and frequent meetings with representatives from all group practices and consultant teams in order to stimulate the exchange of ideas and experience. She will provide information on opportunities for further education including refresher courses, study days, and in-service training. She will be responsible for recommending for disciplinary action any midwife whose practice is not safe or competent. The Supervisor of Midwives will be the spokesperson for midwives in her locality. She will convey their suggestions and needs to regional and national bodies.

6.3.

She will be appointed for a 3-year term by the Local Supervising Authority in accordance with an election by the midwives she will supervise. During her term as Supervisor, she will maintain some clinical commitment. She may have previously held a senior post, e.g. Senior Tutor, or could equally be drawn from the ranks as an experienced, wise midwife. Her role as support person to midwives in her locality would allow her to fulfil a much needed and valued service.

7. Education

7.1.

Midwifery training will be primarily by a 3-year Direct Entry course[40]. There will continue to be a post registration course for qualified nurses who wish to become midwives. We will see a broadening and deepening of present educational goals[41,42].

7.2.

Selection will not depend so much on "O" levels[43] as on the combination of application form, interview, and group discussion. As midwifery will no longer be 'an additional qualification', there will undoubtedly be less wastage through training people who have little intention to practise[44]. However, selection procedures will seek out candidates with an aptitude for professional responsibility and self-motivation[45]. Applicants for midwifery training would have had some "life experience", and those under 21 and over 50 would be discouraged from training[46].

7.3.

Midwifery training will be a 3-year course, probably grant based for the first 2 years and salaried for the third. Students will be supernumerary to the work force[42]. Subjects covered will include communication skills and counselling[22], psychology, sociology, anatomy and physiology, health and disease, research methods, epidemiology, philosophy of science, political awareness, management skills, assertiveness training, and rights and disciplinary procedures as well as current course content[29b]. Student midwives would be expected to have conducted 60 deliveries by the end of their training and to be competent at suturing and emergency procedures such as intubation and putting up I.V.I.s. Clinical tutors would regularly teach in community group practices as well as hospital teams.

7.4.

Post-qualification education will be encouraged[17]. As previously stated, one of the duties of the Supervisor of Midwives will be to ensure in-service training for midwives in her locality. It will be expected that all midwives would attend at least one 2 day course per year. Refresher courses will be obligatory every 5 years[39a].

7.5.

There is a need for a course between the level of the refresher course and the Advanced Diploma in Midwifery. Any midwife with special responsibility for teaching students in hospital or community should have taken such an interim course[47]. Within each Region, Districts will apportion a proportion of 1-2 midwives' salaries in order for there to be regionally appointed Research Midwives. A sabbatical period of 6 months-one year should be allowed for all midwives at regular intervals (e.g. after every 7-10 years of full time practice) for the pursuance of research or further study.

8. The Role of the U.K.C.C. & the National Boards

8.1.

The U.K.C.C. and National Boards, being statutory bodies, will undoubtedly remain structurally similar to today. However, we would envisage far more midwife clinicians as elected members to the National Boards. This grounding in the daily realities of midwifery is seen as essential to accurate decisions on a policy-making level. We would foresee that elected midwife Board Members will be involved in the appointment of midwifery education officers.

8.2.

It is also felt that midwives involved at a senior level in the professional organizations or trade union should not hold senior positions in the U.K.C.C. or National Boards as the resultant concentration of power in the hands of a few could lead to a loss of representation for practising midwives.

9. Management

9.1.

The present hierarchical structure of management in maternity care needs to be reassessed. One of the main problems is the lack of a career progression that encourages or maintains clinical commitment. Good caring midwives move away from the 'hands-on' situation and may lose touch with what is happening at grass roots level. This estrangement leads to lack of support for clinical midwives and consequent lack of support by practising midwives for their managers, who, struggling within the present constraints make incomprehensible decisions. Midwives working within this proposed 'Vision' would be paid a suitable salary so they would not look to management jobs to enhance their pay.

9.2.

Essential to this proposed management structure are:

- The maintenance of some clinical commitment by midwifery managers.
- The involvement of midwives in the appointment of managers.
- That the status of clinical midwives and midwife managers remains equal.

9.3.

There will be a midwife manager at regional level (Regional Midwife Manager, R.M.M.), responsible for regional funding and resource allocation. She will participate in discussions with government representatives, multidisciplinary health professionals and representatives of user groups[1,48], to plan for the health needs of the future. She will be responsible for the collection of statistics on maternity and neonatal care in her region.

9.4.

At district level there will be a District Midwife Manager (D.M.M.) with similar responsibilities for funding resources and statistics. She will actively facilitate projects to deal with local weaknesses or needs in maternity care, e.g. poor uptake of parentcraft classes by teenage mothers or language barriers to receivers of care.

9.5.

There will be a District Midwifery Planning Committee (D.M.P.C.) with a membership of 21 or less. Membership will consist of delegates from the group practices and from the hospital teams, representatives from user groups (in the ratio of 1:4 users to midwives), a Supervisor of Midwives, the D.M.M., and possibly a midwifery tutor.

9.6.

A Midwife Co-ordinator may be needed in some places, especially where there is more than one unit giving maternity care in a district. She will fulfil the role of Unit Midwife Manager (U.M.M.) and be elected by the midwives she represents and is responsible for. She will also continue to have her own clinical commitments.

9.7.

Midwives and users would be involved in the appointment of the District Midwife Manager. The District Midwifery Planning Committee would nominate midwives for the post of Regional Midwife Manager.

9.8.

As mentioned previously, community-based group practices would have practice managers. These managers would be non-midwives who would be responsible for ordering supplies, accounting, administrative, and secretarial work. A practice manager might be shared between two or more practices depending on local circumstances.

10. Conclusion

10.1

We have attempted to produce our vision for the maternity services in 10 years time. We wish to change the perception of the general public about midwives so that we can practise the profession for which we have been trained[27]. Midwives are unique in their combination of skill, sensitivity, and training, to be 'with woman' through one of life's landmark experiences which has long term effects on the individual, the family, and society as a whole[49]. We must generate a new feeling in midwifery. We owe it to ourselves and to those we serve.

[1] Beech, B. 1985. *The role of consumer advocacy in birth care.* Paper presented at W.H.O. International Conference on Appropriate Technology for Birth, Brazil. Available from: Health Rights, 157 Waterloo Road, London SE1 8XF.

[2] Hooton, P. 1984. Patterns of care: the team approach to midwifery care. *Midwives Chronicle & Nursing Notes.* Oct. Suppl., pp. v-vi.

[3] Robinson, S. *et al.* 1984. *The role and responsibilities of the midwife. Nursing Education Research Unit Report.* Chelsea College. University of London.

[4] Munro, A. 1982. *Maternity Care in Action, Part l-Antenatal Care.* First Report of the Maternity Services Advisory Committee. HMSO p.v. 4a) 1, 10; 4b) 5, 9; 4c) vi.

[5] RCOG 1982. *The report of the working party of the Royal College of Obstetricians & Gynaecologists on antenatal & intrapartum care.* Published by the RCOG Sec.11,8 5a) Sec.6,10.

[6] Walker, J. 1985. Meeting midwives midway. *Nursing Times.* Oct.23., pp. 48-50.

[7] Thomson, A. 1980. Planned or unplanned? Are midwives ready for the 1980's? *Midwives Chronicle & Nursing Notes.* March., pp. 68-72.

[8] UKCC. 1983. Notices Concerning a Midwife's Code of Practice for Midwives practising in England & Wales. July *Limits of Practice.* Section 2, p.3.

[9] Beech, B. 1985. *Maternity care in Britain.* Community Rights Project, 157 Waterloo Road, London SE1 8XF.

[10] Romney, M. 1980. Pre-delivery shaving: an unjustified assault? *Journal of Obstetrics & Gynaecology.* No. 1, pp. 33-35.

[11] Romney, M. & Gordon, J. 1981. Is your enema really necessary? *British Medical Journal.* 282: 1269.

[12] Sleep, J. *et al.* 1984. West Berkshire Perineal Management Trial. *British Medical Journal.* 289: 587-590.

[13] Inch, S. 1985. Management of the third stage of labour-another cascade of intervention. *Midwifery* 1(1): 14-22.

[14] NCT 1983. *Tests and Technology in Obstetrics, A Consumer Guide.* Published by the *National Childbirth Trust,* 9, Queensborough Terrace, London.

[15] DHSS 1971. *The Organization of group practices.* Report of the Sub-Committee of Standing Medical Advisory Committee. Recommendation No.74; 15a) No.74; 15b) No.4, 83, 84; 15c) No. 13; 15d) No.49; 15e) No.61.

[16] Robinson, S. 1985. Responsibilities of midwives and medical staff-findings from a national survey. *Midwives Chronicle & Nursing Notes.* 98. March: pp. 64-71.

[17] Newson, K. 1984. What sort of midwifery service do we want? in *Pregnancy Care for the 1980's* edited by Zander, L. & Chamberlain, G. The Royal Society of Medicine. pp. 258-262.

[18] BMJ 1986. The benefits of midwife care. *British Medical Journal.* 292.April 12.: 1019.

[19] UKCC 1986. *A Midwife's Code of Practice for Midwives Practising in the U.K.* HMSO: 1.

[20] Humphrey, C. 1985. The community midwife in maternity care. *Midwife Health Visitor & Community Nurse.* 21: pp. 349-55.

[21] Field, P., 1985. Parents' reactions to maternity care. *Midwifery.* 1(1): pp.37-46.

[22] WHO, 1985. Appropriate technology for birth. *Lancet.* 2.: pp.436-7.

[23] Klein, M. *et al.* 1983. A comparison of low risk pregnant women booked for delivery in two systems of care: shared care (consultant) & integrated general practice unit: II Labour & delivery management & neonatal outcome. *British Journal of Obstetrics & Gynaecology.* 90: pp. 123-8.

[24] Short, R. 1980. *Perinatal and neonatal mortality. Second Report from the Social Services Committee.* Vol. 1. Recommendation No.67; 24a) No.103; 24b) No.87; 24c) No.89.

[25] Peel, J. 1970. *Domiciliary midwifery & maternity bed needs.* Report of the Sub-committee of the Standing Maternity & Midwifery Advisory Committee. Recommendation No.a) iii,p.61.

[26] Hale, C. 1985. Mothers on the assembly line. *Nursing Mirror.* 161. Aug.7.: pp.24-26.

[27] WHO 1986. *Having a Baby in Europe.* HMSO

[28] Robinson, S. 1985. Providing maternity care in the community. *Midwife Health Visitor & Community Nurse.* 21.Aug.: pp.274-279.

[29] Court, S. 1976. *Fit for the future. Report of the Committee on Child Health Services.* Vol. 1. Ch.8. Postscript No. 1, 2, p.370; 29a) No.7, 8; 29b) No. 10.

[30] Jeffs, J. 1980. A new look at childbirth in the Netherlands. *Midwives Chronicle & Nursing Notes.* Dec.: pp.431-433.

[31] McKee, I.A. 1980. Community antenatal care-the way forward? available from Sighthill Health Centre, Calder Rd, Edinburgh.

[32] Campbell, R. *et al.* 1984. Homebirths in England and Wales, 1979: perinatal mortality according to intended place of delivery. *British Medical Journal.* **289.**: pp.721-24.

[33] UKCC 1983. *Handbook of Midwives Rules.* Sec.27,, HMSO: p.5

[34] Shuter, M. 1985. The familiar round. *Nursing Mirror.* **161.**Nov.6.: pp.34-37.

[35] Phaff, J.M.L., *et al.* 1975. *Midwives in Europe.* Council of Europe. European Public Health Committee.

[36] Flint, C. 1985. Labour of Love. *Nursing Times.* Jan.30: pp. 16-18.

[37] RCM 1985. *Evidence to the Pay Review Body for Nursing Staff, Midwives, Health Visitors and Professions Allied to Medicine.* Published by Royal College of Midwives.

[38] Hughes, D. 1985. Supervisors of midwives. *Midwives Chronicle & Nursing Notes.* **98**, Nov.: pp.299-300.

[39] UKCC 1986. *Handbook of Midwives' Rules.* HMSO p.17, Sec. 44; 39a)p. 13, Sec.37.

[40] Newson, K. 1981. Direct entry method of training midwives in three countries: 1 the Netherlands. *Midwives Chronicle & Nursing Notes.* Feb.: pp.39-43.

[41] ENB 1985. *Strategy for Future Education/Training Courses.* London.

[42] UKCC, 1985. *Project 2000.* London.

[43] Stewart, B. 1981. In need of tender loving care. *Nursing Mirror.* **152**, March 12: pp.35-37.

[44] Robinson, S. 1986. Career intentions of newly qualified midwives. *Midwifery* 2(1): pp.25-36

[45] Tiran, D. 1986. More career advice for midwives. *Midwives Chronicle & Nursing Notes.* Jan. p.8.

[46] 1986. Direct entry training. *Association of Radical Midwives Newsletter* No.28: pp.48-9

[47] Bolton, A. 1985. Personal communication on 'Developments in Midwifery Care Course'. St Mary's Hospital, Manchester.

[48] Huntingford, P. 1978. Obstetric practice: past, present, and future, in *The Place of Birth*, edited by Kitzinger, S. & Davis, J. Oxford University Press: pp.229-50.

[49] Flint, C. 1986. *Sensitive Midwifery.* Heinemann Press.

THE FUTURE OF MIDWIFERY PRACTICE: A PERSONAL VIEW

J. Selwyn Crawford[*]

It appears to me that as we approach the end of the century the midwifery profession has lost its way in a morass of self-doubt, loss of confidence and a desperate search for a secure sense of identity. I am convinced, although many others will not agree, that in part this is a resultant of the submergence of the specialists in midwifery within the general corpus of the nursing profession. I thought when this coalescence was first mooted that it augured ill for midwives, but the profession's leaders agreed to it and now they are stuck with it. However, an opportunity has manifested for midwives to retrieve their dignity of independent identity, and thereby to regain the aura which will attract aspirants of the highest rank of competence and dedication to their ranks.

The floundering which I have observed within the body of midwives during the past decade or more is the direct resultant of the changes in obstetric practice and the diminishing incidence of severe maternal and perinatal disease. As the incidences of perinatal mortality and morbidity, and those of maternal mortality and near-death, fall, due to rising standards of public health, antenatal care and labour ward practice, so the direct involvement of the "general midwife" has become disseminated into each of several areas, leading to confusion and to lack of confidence of the individual midwife in her ability to apply special skills in each of those areas.

In stark terms my advocacy is that the midwifery profession should recognise that there are sub-specialties within that profession, and should organise its structure accordingly.

There is nothing unusual in this. After centuries of "general surgeons", the surgical profession diverged into a multitude of sub-specialties, as did the "general physicians" more recently, we have seen the emergence of anaesthetists who superimpose upon their general competence specific talents within the spheres of neuro-anaesthesia, transplant surgery, pain clinics, obstetrics and the like. Even the obstetrician/gynaecologists are now recognising a degree of fragmentation of their general discipline: "pure obstetricians", experts in the problems of infertility, gynaecological oncology etc.

The midwifery profession has, for some time, included some "sub-specialties", most notably community midwifery, administration and teaching. It appears to be unusual for either the administrators or the midwifery tutors to engage in clinical practice (just as it is within the general nursing profession, for reasons which—especially among the tutors—I have never fully understood), so there would be nothing new in identifying midwives with special interests which they pursue, to the exclusion of many others, and thus gain and provide a higher degree of proficiency in those areas.

[*] Consultant Anaesthetist, Birmingham Maternity Hospital, UK
Midwives Chronicle & Nursing Notes 101 June 1988: 169-70

AREAS OF MIDWIFERY SUB-SPECIALISING

I suggest the following are ripe to become areas of midwifery sub-specialising: labour ward care (including neonatal resuscitation); obstetric operating theatre and recovery room; intensive care of the seriously ill mother; antenatal and postnatal clinics; antenatal and postnatal wards (including day-stay wards for repetitive assessment of fetal status and maternal health).

With the increasing—and welcome—tendency to integrate small obstetric hospitals into larger, yet easily manageable, units, and the concurrent move to identify regional centres for the intensive care of actually and potentially seriously ill mothers and babies, the demands upon the midwives in these larger units are increasing in number and each is increasing in intensity. There is still a need for midwives to fulfil their classical role as informed supporters of the healthy pregnant woman, the mother during labour and delivery, and the mother and her baby during the first days after birth. Understanding of involvement in these activities will always remain the bedrock of midwifery training and, possibly, the initial phase of post-graduate midwifery practice. However, just as in all other professions, some doctors, after initial supervised post-graduate training in the acceptance of responsibility, pursue their career in general practice, and others develop a specific interest in a narrower field, so should midwives be encouraged to confine their activities to areas which particularly attract them.

Understandably, most of the "sub-specialist" midwives will be congregated within the larger DGHs and teaching hospitals. The increasing sophistication of monitoring the condition of mother and fetus during labour, the niceties of managing effective and safe pain relief during labour, and the frequency with which informed and adept resuscitation is available for the depressed neonate, starkly identity the need for a cohort of midwives who are highly trained in labour ward "management", and are nor doing their three- or six-month day or night stint in the delivery suite as part of their rotation through the hospital. The ever-increasing incidence of caesarean sections, both elective and emergency, plus the other operative procedures which come within the span of obstetric care (cervical cerclage, removal of retained placenta, evacuation of retained products of conception, repair of perineal or abdominal wounds, and the like) mean that the obstetric theatre is occupied for more time per week than are most general surgical theatres. Midwives should be in control of these theatres, collaborating with the obstetricians and the anaesthetists, as well as staffing the recovery ward. With their basic understanding of the needs and ills of the pregnant woman, the midwife is much better equipped to care for such patients than is the general theatre nurse.

"MIDWIFE INTENSIVISTS"

Advances in the monitoring and treatment of the seriously ill obstetric patient—outstandingly the one with moderate or severe pre-eclampsia—are placing increasingly heavier demands upon the facilities to be provided by an obstetric unit. In the most recently published *Confidential Enquiries into Maternal Deaths in England and Wales* (1979-81, HMSO, London, 1986), attention is drawn to the fact that pregnancy induced and pregnancy associated hypertension are now the major contributors to maternal deaths. The authors of the report suggest that an important reason for this is that the incidence of the more severe forms of these diseases has fallen nationally, resulting in a diminution of the ability and understanding of how to treat them promptly and effectively when they do on occasion present. The authors of the report make a strong recommendation that mothers who develop moderate or severe pre-eclampsia be referred to designated regional centres for appropriately intensive care. Advances in non-obstetric care, such as for cardiac disease (congenital or acquired), cystic fibrosis, various blood diseases and so forth, have meant that women who, in previous decades, would have either not survived to the age of child-bearing or would have been denied the opportunity of pregnancy, are now appearing in increasing numbers in our obstetric units. All of these mothers require more intensive supervision than is normally provided during labour, at delivery and for a variable time postnatally. This should be afforded within the obstetric unit, in specifically equipped intensive care rooms staffed by midwives who have a special interest and expertise in the care of the seriously ill. It is, in my opinion, a derogation of the dignity and professionalism of midwives and obstetric medical personnel (specifically obstetricians and obstetric anaesthetists) for such mothers to be transferred to a general ITU, staffed by doctors and nurses who are really not conversant with the particular attributes of the pregnant (and immediate postpartum) state. There should be a sub-specialty of "midwife intensivists" who elect to receive further training in the realm of intensive care monitoring and supervision.

The outpatient clinic is another area which requires special skills and a special temperament from midwives who would run it with informed interest, sympathy and efficiency. The designation of this activity as a sub-specialty of midwifery would surely add to the dignity and self-assurance of those who made it their career.

Equally, the care of mothers in an antenatal ward—whether long stay or for day-stay review—and of mothers and their babies in a postnatal ward, require specialised skills and interests from the midwifery staff, and should receive appropriate recognition.

I appreciate that in many obstetric units, large and some small, there is already a considerable degree of specialist activity among the more senior of the midwifery staff. However, I believe that there remains a considerable tendency to "shuffle the pack" every now and again, based upon the philosophy that midwives should remain "generalists", able to turn their hand to any and all aspects of care of the pregnant woman and her infant. The result of this "Jill of all trades" approach is the logical one that many intelligent and competent midwives feel themselves to be mistress of none. Specifically they feel great unease when called upon to engage in one or other of the sub-specialist areas which I have defined, if they have not maintained a committed interest in it. One resultant has been a diminution of self-assurance within the midwifery profession as a whole, which has possibly contributed to the steady decrease in numbers both by resignations and a failure to recruit.

A NOBLE ACTIVITY

I believe that by identifying specific roles among qualified midwives and providing designated titles appropriate to those roles, which will serve to demonstrate that the practitioners have skills additional to their basic midwifery accomplishments, the decline in morale and self-confidence which many of us sense currently permeates the profession will be reversed, and pride in the performance of a noble activity restored.

No doubt such developments as I have suggested will be looked upon with disfavour by many of the more elderly in the profession, and especially by those who, whilst walking its corridors of centrally based power, have tended to lose an understanding of affairs as they now exist at shopfloor level. Perhaps it is time for a gentle revolution from below to allow midwifery rationally to meet the challenges of the late 20th century.

INDEX

D

E

F

G

H

I